The Matrix Eigenvalue Problem

Second Edition

John Lund
Montana State University

Kendall Hunt
publishing company

www.kendallhunt.com
Send all inquiries to:
4050 Westmark Drive
Dubuque, IA 52004-1840

Printed in the United States of America
10 9 8 7 6 5 4 3 2

Thanks to my better Angels:
Nancy, Carissa and Gunnar.

John Lund

Contents

Preface

There are many interesting results available for inclusion in an introductory matrix class. In the design of a one-semester course there is a struggle between what to include and what to leave out. There needs to be an economy of topic selection. This book will focus on what here is termed the Big Two. The first of the Big Two is the orthogonal subspace decomposition of $\mathcal{R}^n$ into the row space, R_A, and the null space, $\mathcal{N}(A)$, of the $m \times n$ matrix A (Theorem(4.28)). These special subspaces (combinations of the rows or columns of A) are studied and developed in Chapter Four. The second of the Big Two is the orthogonal diagonalization of symmetric matrices (Theorem(5.28)). Diagonalization refers to a transformation of the matrix A to a diagonal matrix. This categorization as first and second is a sequential rather than a hierarchal rating. As a consequence, Theorem(4.28) is the focal point of Chapter Four and Theorem(5.28) is the focal point of Chapter Five. To assemble the ideas and tools necessary to provide a reason to believe the validity of the Big Two, several definitions and results are needed. Many of these ancillary results, besides being an aid in the progression towards the Big Two, also possess independent interest. As a case in point, it is somewhat surprising that the dimension of the row space R_A is related to the dimension of the column space $\mathcal{C}_A$ of a matrix A but the actual dimensional equality dim $\mathcal{C}_A$ = dim R_A is amazing. This is Theorem(4.20). It is fundamental in establishing the orthogonal subspace decomposition of $\mathcal{R}^n$, the first of the Big Two. A second case is taken from Chapter Five. In every example in the chapter, the geometric multiplicity of an eigenvalue is less than or equal to its algebraic multiplicity. This result can be established using Schur's lemma, an item from Chapter Five which seems not to have received the attention it deserves. This result guarantees that an arbitrary $n \times n$ matrix A is orthogonally similar to an upper triangular matrix. The lemma is the catalyst which leads to the orthogonal diagonalization of the symmetric matrix A, the second of the Big Two.

The main idea of Chapter One is contained in the definition of the dot or scalar product in Definition(1.8). The formula leads to an analytic condition for vectors to be orthogonal (perpendicular). Linear systems are reviewed in Chapter Two so as to get everyone on the same page and provide a familiar backdrop against which matrix operations can be introduced. The inconspicuous Theorem(2.13) advertises the null space of a matrix A. Once matrix multiplication is defined in Chapter Three, it is seen that among all $n \times n$ matrices, the diagonal matrices are the simplest with which to work. In both Chapters Four and Five the machinery is being built to find all matrices that, in the sense of similarity, behave like diagonal matrices. Along the way, the important Theorem(3.28) reveals the equivalence of zero determinants, matrix non-invertibility and nontrivial homogeneous solutions. The latter part of this equivalence is a special case of Theorem(2.13). This continues the forecast for the definition of the null space $\mathcal{N}(A)$ in Chapter Four. The zero determinant portion of the equivalence gives the tool needed to calculate eigenvalues in Chapter Five.

There are 74 exercises (not counting parts) in the text. It is recommended that the student do or read every one. Most of the exercises are computational. They are designed to illustrate and reinforce the ideas from the text. Some exercises are used to illustrate named matrices: the orthogonal matrices in Exercise(3.18), or projection matrices in Exercise(5.19). There are a few exercises that are closer to discussions than exercises. These exercises illustrate the application of results of the text to problems which are interesting in their own right. One illustration here is the Least Squares solution in Exercise(4.17). In another illustration, the reader is led through, by way of example, a problem on rank in Exercise(5.15). This is the exercise that gives a reason to believe the result that the geometric multiplicity of an eigenvalue is less than or equal to its algebraic multiplicity. Lastly, leading up to the diagonalization of symmetric matrices is the diagonalization of a non-symmetric matrix. Exercise(5.3) and Exercise(5.4) use this idea to solve an arbitrary second-order difference equation. Exercise(5.5) includes the famous Fibonacci formula.

The numbering in the book is called the gutter(left-hand)-thumb(right-hand) numbering system. On the gutter side of the page are found the enumeration of definitions, theorems and examples in consecutive order. For instance, Theorem(4.28) falls between Definition(4.27) and Example(4.29). Theorem(4.19) will occur prior to Definition(4.27) and Example(4.31) will occur after Example(4.29). On the thumb side of the page the displayed equations, which are used for "near-by" reference, are independently numbered. Equation(4.42), (4.43) and (4.44) occur consecutively within Example(4.29).

This text has been completed in a one-semester class (forty-five days) as follows: Chapters One and Two are done in eight lectures. Chapter Three is done in seven lectures. This is one third of the semester. The remaining two thirds of the semester can be split between ten and twenty lectures for Chapters Four and Five, respectively. At the end of Chapters One and Two there are sample quizzes which the author has used as twenty five minute exams. At the end Chapters Three, Four and Five there are sample tests which the author has used as hour exams.

Chapter 1

Vectors

The central idea of this chapter is contained in the definition of the dot or scalar product formula in Definition(1.8). This is for two reasons. From this formula an analytic development for orthogonal (perpendicular) vectors is given (Theorem(1.10)). As a consequence of this development a formula is obtained for the projection of one vector onto another. This simple formula has far-reaching consequences, which are manifest in the Gram-Schmidt process and the projection of a vector onto a subspace in Exercise(4.16). Another reason for the importance of the dot product is that the product provides the basis for the definition of matrix multiplication. Indeed, the matrix multiplication is an organized collection of dot products. The generalization of the dot product arising from the introduction of the complex numbers (Definition (5.17)) in Chapter Five is the catalyst that leads to one of the Big Two: the orthogonal diagonalization of symmetric matrices.

1.1   Vectors with Two Components

A point in the x_1-x_2 plane, $\mathcal{R}^2$, is an ordered pair denoted by (v_1, v_2). This is found by designated the point $(0,0)$ as a reference point called the origin and moving v_1 units in the horizontal direction (the right if $v_1 > 0$ and to the left if $v_1 < 0$) and moving v_2 units in the vertical direction (up if $v_2 > 0$ and down if $v_2 < 0$). There are times when the pair of points and the pair's location are more important than are the individual points of the pair.

Definition 1.1 Vector, Components, Standard Position, Length, the Zero vector and non-Standard Position: A **vector** in the plane is denoted by $\vec{v} = \begin{bmatrix} v_1 \\ v_2 \end{bmatrix}$ where v_1 (v_2) is called the first (second) component of $\vec{v}$. The vector can be viewed as a directed line segment beginning at the point $(0,0)$ and ending at the point (v_1, v_2). The point $\begin{bmatrix} 0 \\ 0 \end{bmatrix}$ is called the initial point of the vector and the point $\begin{bmatrix} v_1 \\ v_2 \end{bmatrix}$ is called the terminal point of the vector. The vector $\vec{v}$ in Figure 1.1 with initial point $\begin{bmatrix} 0 \\ 0 \end{bmatrix}$ and terminal point $\begin{bmatrix} v_1 \\ v_2 \end{bmatrix}$ is said to be in **standard position**. Another idea taken from geometry is the notion of the **length** of the vector $\begin{bmatrix} v_1 \\ v_2 \end{bmatrix}$. This is the standard Euclidean distance from the point $(0,0)$ to (v_1, v_2), that is,

$$||\vec{v}|| \equiv \sqrt{v_1^2 + v_2^2}.$$

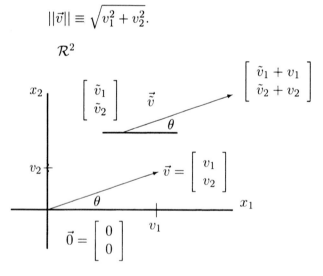

Figure 1.1

It is convenient to regard the origin $\vec{0} = \begin{bmatrix} 0 \\ 0 \end{bmatrix}$ as a vector. It is called the **zero vector** and has zero length. A vector is said to be in a **non-standard position** if the initial point of the vector is not located at $\begin{bmatrix} 0 \\ 0 \end{bmatrix}$.

Example 1.2 A vector in non-standard position is obtained by defining the vector $\vec{\tilde{v}}$ with initial point $(\tilde{v}_1, \tilde{v}_2)$ and terminal point $(\tilde{v}_1 + v_1, \tilde{v}_2 + v_2)$. This vector $\vec{\tilde{v}}$ is shown in Figure 1.1. The slopes of the line segments, that is $\dfrac{v_2}{v_1}$, along $\vec{v}$ and $\vec{\tilde{v}}$ are the same. In addition, the length of $\vec{\tilde{v}}$ is given by

$$||\vec{\tilde{v}}|| = \sqrt{(\tilde{v}_1 + v_1 - \tilde{v}_1)^2 + (\tilde{v}_2 + v_2 - \tilde{v}_2)^2} = \sqrt{v_1^2 + v_2^2} = ||\vec{v}||.$$

An example with the specific components $v_1 = 3$ and $v_2 = 1$ is provided by $\vec{v} = \begin{bmatrix} 3 \\ 1 \end{bmatrix}$.

The length of $\vec{v}$ is given by $||\vec{v}|| = \sqrt{3^2 + 1^2} = \sqrt{10}$. If the initial point of the vector $\vec{\tilde{v}}$ is $\begin{bmatrix} \tilde{v}_1 \\ \tilde{v}_2 \end{bmatrix} = \begin{bmatrix} 2 \\ 2 \end{bmatrix}$ and the terminal point is $\begin{bmatrix} v_1 + \tilde{v}_1 \\ v_2 + \tilde{v}_2 \end{bmatrix} = \begin{bmatrix} 5 \\ 3 \end{bmatrix}$ then

$$||\vec{\tilde{v}}|| = \sqrt{(5-2)^2 + (3-2)^2} = \sqrt{10}.$$

The slope of the line segment along $\vec{v}$ and the slope along $\vec{\tilde{v}}$ are both $\dfrac{3-2}{5-2} = \dfrac{1}{3}$.

Definition 1.3 Equality, Sum, Scalar Multiple, and Parallel: If two vectors $\vec{v}$ and $\vec{\tilde{v}}$ have the same direction and have the same length they are called **equal**. For the vectors $\vec{v}$ and $\vec{\tilde{v}}$ in Figure 1.1, $\vec{v} = \vec{\tilde{v}}$. One vector is simply located at a different position in space than is the other vector. *With only a few exceptions, vectors will always be assumed to be in standard position.* If the two vectors $\vec{v} = \begin{bmatrix} v_1 \\ v_2 \end{bmatrix}$ and $\vec{u} = \begin{bmatrix} u_1 \\ u_2 \end{bmatrix}$ are in standard position, then the two vectors are called **equal** if $v_1 = u_1$ and $v_2 = u_2$. The **sum** is defined by

$$\vec{v} + \vec{u} = \begin{bmatrix} v_1 \\ v_2 \end{bmatrix} + \begin{bmatrix} u_1 \\ u_2 \end{bmatrix} = \begin{bmatrix} v_1 + u_1 \\ v_2 + u_2 \end{bmatrix}.$$

Let α be a real number. The vector defined by

$$\alpha\vec{v} = \alpha \begin{bmatrix} v_1 \\ v_2 \end{bmatrix} = \begin{bmatrix} \alpha v_1 \\ \alpha v_2 \end{bmatrix}$$

is called a **scalar multiple** of $\vec{v}$. The length of $\alpha\vec{v}$ is found from the calculation

$$\begin{aligned} ||\alpha\vec{v}|| &= \sqrt{(\alpha v_1)^2 + (\alpha v_2)^2} = \sqrt{\alpha^2 \left(v_1^2 + v_2^2\right)} \\ &= |\alpha|\sqrt{\left(v_1^2 + v_2^2\right)} = |\alpha| \, ||\vec{v}|| \, . \end{aligned}$$

Given two vectors $\vec{v}$ and $\vec{z}$ in standard position, if there is a non-zero scalar α such that $\vec{z} = \alpha\vec{v}$, then the two vectors are called **parallel**.

Example 1.4 If $\alpha = -1$ then $\alpha \vec{u} = (-1)\vec{u} = \begin{bmatrix} -u_1 \\ -u_2 \end{bmatrix}$ is a vector with the same length as the vector $\vec{u}$ but is pointed in the opposite direction as $\vec{u}$ (see Figure 1.2). More generally, the scalar multiple $\alpha \vec{v}$ is a vector in the direction of $\vec{v}$ if $\alpha > 0$ and is shorter (or longer) than $\vec{v}$ depending, on whether $0 < \alpha < 1$ ($\alpha > 1$). In Figure 1.1 the vector $\vec{\tilde{v}}$ is parallel to $\vec{v}$. To see this and apply the definition of parallel in this paragraph, one first needs to put $\vec{\tilde{v}}$ in standard position. The geometric representation of the sum and difference of two vectors is shown in the Figure 1.2. If $\vec{v}$ ($\vec{u}$) is placed at the terminal point of $\vec{u}$ ($\vec{v}$) to form a parallelogram, then $\vec{v} \pm \vec{u}$ are the two diagonals of the resulting parallelogram.

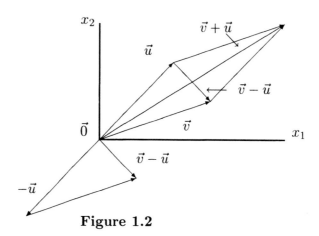

Figure 1.2

This is called the **the parallelogram rule of addition**. The diagonal $\vec{v} - \vec{u}$ can be regarded as a sum since the vector $\vec{v} - \vec{u} = \vec{v} + (-1)\vec{u}$ is found by adding $-\vec{u}$ to the vector $\vec{v}$. Now locate this vector as the second diagonal in the parallelogram. This is one of those few occasions when it is handy to place a vector out of standard position. In Figure 1.2 assume $\vec{v} = \begin{bmatrix} 3 \\ 1 \end{bmatrix}$ and $\vec{u} = \begin{bmatrix} 2 \\ 2 \end{bmatrix}$. Put the initial point of $\vec{v}$ ($\vec{u}$) at the terminal point of $\vec{u}$ ($\vec{v}$) to form the parallelogram in the figure. Now the vector

$$\vec{v} + \vec{u} = \begin{bmatrix} 3 \\ 1 \end{bmatrix} + \begin{bmatrix} 2 \\ 2 \end{bmatrix} = \begin{bmatrix} 5 \\ 3 \end{bmatrix}$$

is one of the diagonals of the parallelogram, and the vector

$$\vec{v} - \vec{u} = \begin{bmatrix} 3 \\ 1 \end{bmatrix} - \begin{bmatrix} 2 \\ 2 \end{bmatrix} = \begin{bmatrix} 1 \\ -1 \end{bmatrix},$$

when moved out of standard position, is the other diagonal of the parallelogram. The vector $\vec{u} - \vec{v} = (-1)(\vec{v} - \vec{u})$ is also the latter diagonal, except it points in the opposite direction.

1.2 Rules for the Arithmetic of Vectors

Theorem 1.5 The Laws of Vector Addition and Scalar Multiplication: If $\vec{v}$, $\vec{u}$, and $\vec{w}$ are 2-vectors and α and β are scalars, then the following arithmetic of vectors are satisfied:

1. $\vec{v} + \vec{u} = \vec{u} + \vec{v}$
                5. $\alpha(\vec{v} + \vec{w}) = \alpha\vec{v} + \alpha\vec{w}$

2. $(\vec{v} + \vec{u}) + \vec{w} = \vec{v} + (\vec{u} + \vec{w})$
    6. $\alpha(\beta(\vec{v})) = (\alpha\beta)\vec{v}$

3. $\vec{v} + \vec{0} = \vec{v}$
                     7. $(\alpha + \beta)\vec{v} = \alpha\vec{v} + \beta\vec{v}$

4. $\vec{v} + (-\vec{v}) = \vec{0}$
             8. $1\vec{v} = \vec{v}$.

The laws of vector addition and scalar multiplication follow from Definition (1.3) and the corresponding property of the real numbers. The commutative law of vector addition,

$$\vec{v} + \vec{u} = \begin{bmatrix} v_1 \\ v_2 \end{bmatrix} + \begin{bmatrix} u_1 \\ u_2 \end{bmatrix} = \begin{bmatrix} v_1 + u_1 \\ v_2 + u_2 \end{bmatrix} = \begin{bmatrix} u_1 + v_1 \\ u_1 + v_2 \end{bmatrix} = \begin{bmatrix} u_1 \\ u_1 \end{bmatrix} + \begin{bmatrix} v_1 \\ v_2 \end{bmatrix} = \vec{u} + \vec{v},$$

follows from Definition (1.3) (the second and fourth equalities) and the fact that the real numbers are commutative (the middle equality).

Definition 1.6 Linear Combination, Unit Vectors, and Canonical Unit Vectors: A **linear combination** of the vectors $\vec{v}$ and $\vec{u}$ is the vector defined by

$$\alpha\vec{v} + \beta\vec{u} = \alpha \begin{bmatrix} v_1 \\ v_2 \end{bmatrix} + \beta \begin{bmatrix} u_1 \\ u_2 \end{bmatrix} = \begin{bmatrix} \alpha v_1 + \beta u_1 \\ \alpha v_2 + \beta u_2 \end{bmatrix}.$$

The scalars α and β are called the coefficients of the linear combination. If $\alpha > 1$ and $\beta > 1$ then the two vectors $\alpha\vec{v}$ and $\beta\vec{u}$ are vectors which are longer than are the vectors $\vec{v}$ and $\vec{u}$. By the parallelogram rule, the linear combination $\alpha\vec{v} + \beta\vec{u}$ is the diagonal in the parallelogram with sides $\alpha\vec{v}$ and $\beta\vec{u}$ in Figure 1.3. If $\vec{v} = \begin{bmatrix} v_1 \\ v_2 \end{bmatrix}$ is non-zero, the vector

$$\vec{u} = \frac{\vec{v}}{||\vec{v}||} = \frac{1}{||\vec{v}||} \begin{bmatrix} v_1 \\ v_2 \end{bmatrix} = \begin{bmatrix} \dfrac{v_1}{||\vec{v}||} \\ \dfrac{v_2}{||\vec{v}||} \end{bmatrix}$$

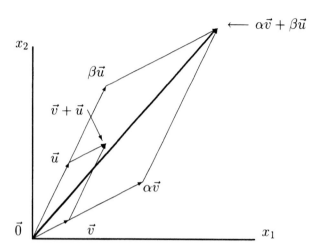

Figure 1.3

is called a **unit vector** since it has length one

$$||\vec{u}|| = \sqrt{\left(\frac{v_1}{||\vec{v}||}\right)^2 + \left(\frac{v_2}{||\vec{v}||}\right)^2} = \sqrt{\frac{(v_1)^2 + (v_2)^2}{||\vec{v}||^2}} = \sqrt{\frac{||\vec{v}||^2}{||\vec{v}||^2}} = 1.$$

The unit vector $\vec{u}$ is parallel to $\vec{v}$ with the scalar in Definition (1.3) given by $\alpha = \frac{1}{||\vec{v}||}$. The **canonical unit vectors**

$$\vec{e_1} = \begin{bmatrix} 1 \\ 0 \end{bmatrix} \quad \text{and} \quad \vec{e_2} = \begin{bmatrix} 0 \\ 1 \end{bmatrix}$$

are frequently denoted by $\vec{i} = \vec{e_1}$ and $\vec{j} = \vec{e_2}$.

Example 1.7 Let $\vec{v} = \begin{bmatrix} v_1 \\ v_2 \end{bmatrix}$ be a vector in $\mathcal{R}^2$. The vector $\vec{v}$ is the linear combination

$$\vec{v} = \begin{bmatrix} v_1 \\ v_2 \end{bmatrix} = \begin{bmatrix} v_1 \\ 0 \end{bmatrix} + \begin{bmatrix} 0 \\ v_2 \end{bmatrix} = v_1 \vec{e_1} + v_2 \vec{e_2}.$$

Any vector $\vec{v} \in \mathcal{R}^2$ is a linear combination of the canonical vectors $\vec{e_1}$ and $\vec{e_2}$, and the coefficients in the linear combination are simply the components of the given vector. It is also the case that any vector in $\mathcal{R}^2$ can be written as a linear combination of the vectors

$\begin{bmatrix} 1 \\ 1 \end{bmatrix}$ and $\begin{bmatrix} -1 \\ 1 \end{bmatrix}$. To find α and β so that

$$\vec{v} = \begin{bmatrix} 3 \\ 1 \end{bmatrix} = \alpha \begin{bmatrix} 1 \\ 1 \end{bmatrix} + \beta \begin{bmatrix} -1 \\ 1 \end{bmatrix} = \begin{bmatrix} \alpha - \beta \\ \alpha + \beta \end{bmatrix}$$

requires $\alpha - \beta = 3$ and $\alpha + \beta = 1$. Adding the two equations gives $2\alpha = 4$ so that $\alpha = 2$. Putting $\alpha = 2$ in $\beta = \alpha - 3$ gives $\beta = -1$. It can also be shown that

$$\vec{v} = \begin{bmatrix} -3 \\ 5 \end{bmatrix} = (1) \begin{bmatrix} 1 \\ 1 \end{bmatrix} + (4) \begin{bmatrix} -1 \\ 1 \end{bmatrix}$$

or, more generally,

$$\vec{v} = \begin{bmatrix} v_1 \\ v_2 \end{bmatrix} = \left(\frac{v_1 + v_2}{2} \right) \begin{bmatrix} 1 \\ 1 \end{bmatrix} + \left(\frac{v_2 - v_1}{2} \right) \begin{bmatrix} -1 \\ 1 \end{bmatrix}.$$

Obtaining the latter is the subject of Chapter Two.

1.3 The Dot or Scalar Product

Definition 1.8 Dot or Scalar Product and Transpose: Given $\vec{v}$ and $\vec{u}$ the **dot product** of these vectors is the scalar quantity defined by

$$\vec{v} \cdot \vec{u} = v_1 u_1 + v_2 u_2 \ .$$

It is convenient to also have the notion of a row vector. If $\vec{v} = \begin{bmatrix} v_1 \\ v_2 \end{bmatrix}$ then the **transpose** of $\vec{v}$ is defined by $\vec{v}^{\,T} = [v_1 \ v_2]$ which is simply the vector $\vec{v}$ written horizontally. With this notation the dot product can be written

$$\vec{v} \cdot \vec{u} = \vec{v}^{\,T} \vec{u} = [v_1 \ v_2] \begin{bmatrix} u_1 \\ u_2 \end{bmatrix} \equiv v_1 u_1 + v_2 u_2. \tag{1.1}$$

Definition 1.9 Orthogonal (Perpendicular) Vectors and Perp: The vector $\vec{v}$ is **orthogonal (perpendicular)** to the vector $\vec{u}$ if the angle between them is $\theta = \dfrac{\pi}{2}$. The notation for a vector $\vec{v}$ being orthogonal to $\vec{u}$ is $\vec{v} \perp \vec{u}$ which is read $\vec{v}$ **perp** $\vec{u}$ (**perp** from **perp**endicular). The zero vector is declared orthogonal to every vector. The reason for this declaration will be clarified in the following theorem.

Theorem 1.10 The dot product satisfies the following identities:

1. $\vec{v} \cdot \vec{u} = \vec{v}^{\,T} \vec{u} = \vec{u}^{\,T} \vec{v} = \vec{u} \cdot \vec{v}$;

2. $\vec{v} \cdot \vec{v} = ||\vec{v}||^2$;

3. $(\vec{v} + \vec{u}) \cdot \vec{w} = \vec{v} \cdot \vec{w} + \vec{u} \cdot \vec{w};$

4. $\alpha \vec{v} \cdot \vec{u} = \alpha(\vec{v} \cdot \vec{u});$

5. $\vec{v} \cdot \vec{u} = v_1 u_1 + v_2 u_2 = ||\vec{v}|| \, ||\vec{u}|| \cos(\theta), \quad 0 \le \theta \le \pi;$

6. and the vector $\vec{v}$ is orthogonal to $\vec{u}$ if and only if $\vec{v} \cdot \vec{u} = 0.$

Parts 1, 2, 3, and 4 follow directly from the definition of the dot product. To see part 1 write

$$
\begin{aligned}
\vec{v} \cdot \vec{u} &= \vec{v}^T \vec{u} = [v_1 \; v_2] \begin{bmatrix} u_1 \\ u_2 \end{bmatrix} \equiv v_1 u_1 + v_2 u_2 \\
&= u_1 v_1 + u_2 v_2 = [u_1 \; u_2] \begin{bmatrix} v_1 \\ v_2 \end{bmatrix} \\
&= \vec{u}^T \vec{v} = \vec{u} \cdot \vec{v}
\end{aligned}
$$

so that the dot product commutes. If $\vec{v} = \vec{u}$ in the previous display, then

$$
\vec{v}^T \vec{v} = [v_1 \; v_2] \begin{bmatrix} v_1 \\ v_2 \end{bmatrix} \equiv \vec{v} \cdot \vec{v} = v_1^2 + v_2^2 = ||\vec{v}||^2,
$$

which is part 2. Each of parts 3 and 4 are also shown by writing out the quantity in terms of the components of the vectors involved. Part 5 is a little more involved. Denote the angle between the vectors $\vec{v}$ and $\vec{u}$ by θ which is depicted in Figure 1.4. The law of cosines relates the squares of the lengths of the three sides of the triangle by the identity

$$
||\vec{v} - \vec{u}||^2 = ||\vec{v}||^2 + ||\vec{u}||^2 - 2||\vec{v}|| \, ||\vec{u}|| \cos(\theta) . \tag{1.2}
$$

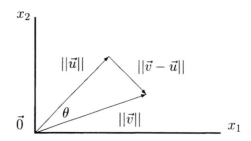

Figure 1.4

Using part 2 of Theorem(1.10) with $\vec{v}$ replaced by $\vec{v} - \vec{u}$ calculate the length

$$
\begin{aligned}
||\vec{v} - \vec{u}||^2 &= (\vec{v} - \vec{u})^{\,T} (\vec{v} - \vec{u}) = \left(\vec{v}^{\,T} - \vec{u}^{\,T}\right)(\vec{v} - \vec{u}) \\
&= \vec{v}^{\,T}\vec{v} - \vec{v}^{\,T}\vec{u} - \vec{u}^{\,T}\vec{v} + \vec{u}^{\,T}\vec{u} = ||\vec{v}||^2 - 2\vec{v}^{\,T}\vec{u} + ||\vec{u}||^2 \qquad (1.3) \\
&= ||\vec{v}||^2 - 2\vec{v} \cdot \vec{u} + ||\vec{u}||^2.
\end{aligned}
$$

The last two equalities use $\vec{v} \cdot \vec{u} = \vec{v}^{\,T}\vec{u} = \vec{u}^{\,T}\vec{v}$ from part 1. Equating the right-hand sides of (1.2) and (1.3) gives, after canceling $||\vec{v}||^2$ and $||\vec{u}||^2$, the important identity

$$
\vec{v} \cdot \vec{u} = v_1 u_1 + v_2 u_2 = ||\vec{v}||\,||\vec{u}|| \cos(\theta).
$$

This completes part 5 of the theorem. Part 6 requires showing two things. If $\vec{v} \perp \vec{u}$ then by Definition(1.9) the angle between $\vec{v}$ and $\vec{u}$ is $\theta = \dfrac{\pi}{2}$ so that $\vec{v} \cdot \vec{u} = 0$ by Part 5. This shows that if $\vec{v} \perp \vec{u}$ then $\vec{v} \cdot \vec{u} = 0$. To see the converse statement, assume that $\vec{v} \cdot \vec{u} = 0$. By part 5 it follows that $||\vec{v}||\,||\vec{u}|| \cos(\theta) = 0$ which can happen if $||\vec{v}||$ (or $||\vec{u}|| = 0$) or $\theta = \dfrac{\pi}{2}$. If $\theta = \dfrac{\pi}{2}$ then $\vec{v} \perp \vec{u}$. If $||\vec{v}|| = 0$ then $\vec{v} = \vec{0}$ so, with the zero vector declared orthogonal to every vector, it follows that $\vec{v}$ is orthogonal to $\vec{u}$. Hence, if $\vec{v} \cdot \vec{u} = 0$ then $\vec{v} \perp \vec{u}$ which completes part 6.

Definition 1.11 Projection of $\vec{u}$ along $\vec{v}$: Given the two non-zero vectors $\vec{v} = \begin{bmatrix} v_1 \\ v_2 \end{bmatrix}$ and $\vec{u} = \begin{bmatrix} u_1 \\ u_2 \end{bmatrix}$ define a vector parallel to $\vec{v}$ by

$$
\vec{w} = \left(\frac{\vec{v} \cdot \vec{u}}{||\vec{v}||^2}\right) \vec{v} \equiv \operatorname{proj}_{\vec{v}}(\vec{u}). \qquad (1.4)
$$

The vector $\vec{w}$ is called the **projection of $\vec{u}$ onto $\vec{v}$**. Geometrically, it appears in Figure 1.5 that $\vec{e} = \vec{u} - \vec{w} = \vec{u} - \operatorname{proj}_{\vec{v}}(\vec{u})$ is orthogonal to $\vec{v}$. This is another case when putting a vector in non-standard position is geometrically suggestive. To verify that the vector $\vec{e}$ is orthogonal to the vector $\vec{v}$ check the dot product

$$
\begin{aligned}
\vec{v} \cdot \vec{e} = \vec{v} \cdot (\vec{u} - \vec{w}) &= \vec{v} \cdot \vec{u} - \vec{v} \cdot \vec{w} = \vec{v} \cdot \vec{u} - \vec{v} \cdot \left(\frac{\vec{v} \cdot \vec{u}}{||\vec{v}||^2} \vec{v}\right) \\
&= \vec{v} \cdot \vec{u} - \left(\frac{\vec{v} \cdot \vec{u}}{||\vec{v}||^2} \vec{v} \cdot \vec{v}\right) = \vec{v} \cdot \vec{u} - \vec{v} \cdot \vec{u} = 0
\end{aligned}
$$

where $\vec{v} \cdot \vec{v} = ||\vec{v}||^2$ was used in the third equality. By Theorem(1.10) $\vec{e} \perp \vec{v}$. Since $\vec{w}$ is parallel to $\vec{v}$ the vector $\vec{e}$ is also orthogonal to $\vec{w}$. More is true. Every vector $\vec{u} \in \mathcal{R}^2$ can be decomposed in the form

$$
\vec{u} = \vec{w} + (\vec{u} - \vec{w}) = \left(\frac{\vec{v} \cdot \vec{u}}{||\vec{v}||^2}\right) \vec{v} + \left(\vec{u} - \left(\frac{\vec{v} \cdot \vec{u}}{||\vec{v}||^2}\right) \vec{v}\right) = \operatorname{proj}_{\vec{v}}(\vec{u}) + \left(\vec{u} - \operatorname{proj}_{\vec{v}}(\vec{u})\right)
$$

where the two components, by the previous calculation, are orthogonal.

Example 1.12 If $\vec{v} = \begin{bmatrix} 3 \\ 1 \end{bmatrix}$ and $\vec{u} = \begin{bmatrix} 2 \\ 2 \end{bmatrix}$ The vector $\vec{w}$ is

$$\vec{w} = \text{proj}_{\vec{v}}(\vec{u}) = \frac{\vec{v} \cdot \vec{u}}{||\vec{v}||^2}\vec{v} = \frac{(6+2)}{(\sqrt{10})^2}\begin{bmatrix} 3 \\ 1 \end{bmatrix} = \frac{4}{5}\begin{bmatrix} 3 \\ 1 \end{bmatrix}$$

so that the vector $\vec{e}$ is $\vec{e} = \vec{u} - \vec{w} = \begin{bmatrix} 2 \\ 2 \end{bmatrix} - \frac{4}{5}\begin{bmatrix} 3 \\ 1 \end{bmatrix} = \frac{1}{5}\begin{bmatrix} -2 \\ 6 \end{bmatrix}$.

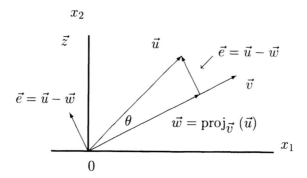

Figure 1.5

The dot product

$$\vec{e} \cdot \vec{v} = \frac{1}{5}\begin{bmatrix} -2 \\ 6 \end{bmatrix} \cdot \begin{bmatrix} 3 \\ 1 \end{bmatrix} = \left(\frac{-2}{5}\right)(3) + \left(\frac{6}{5}\right)(1) = 0$$

verifies that the vector $\vec{e}$ is orthogonal to $\vec{v}$. Further, the calculation

$$\begin{aligned} ||\vec{w}||^2 + ||\vec{e}||^2 &= ||[\, 12/5 \;\; 4/5\,]\,||^2 + ||\,[-2/5 \;\; 6/5]\,||^2 \\[2mm] &= \frac{144 + 16}{25} + \frac{4 + 36}{25} = \frac{160 + 40}{25} = \frac{200}{25} \\[2mm] &= 8 = \left(\sqrt{2^2 + 2^2}\right)^2 = ||\vec{u}||^2, \end{aligned}$$

shows that the triangle with sides $\vec{w}$, $\vec{e}$ and $\vec{u}$ is a right triangle. The orthogonal decomposition of the vector $\vec{u}$ mentioned in Definition(1.11) takes the form

$$\vec{u} = \vec{w} + (\vec{u} - \vec{w}) = \begin{bmatrix} 2 \\ 2 \end{bmatrix} = \frac{4}{5}\begin{bmatrix} 3 \\ 1 \end{bmatrix} + \frac{2}{5}\begin{bmatrix} -1 \\ 3 \end{bmatrix}.$$

1.4   Vector Equalities and Inequalities

Theorem 1.13 The Cauchy-Schwartz Inequality, the Triangle Inequality and the Parallelogram Theorem: Given the vectors $\vec{v}$ and $\vec{u}$ the **Cauchy-Schwartz Inequality** reads

$$|\vec{v} \cdot \vec{u}| \leq ||\vec{v}|| \, ||\vec{u}|| \, . \tag{1.5}$$

The **triangle inequality** is

$$||\vec{v} + \vec{u}|| \leq ||\vec{v}|| + ||\vec{u}|| \tag{1.6}$$

and the **Parallelogram theorem** states

$$||\vec{v} + \vec{u}||^2 + ||\vec{v} - \vec{u}||^2 = 2||\vec{v}|| + 2||\vec{u}||^2. \tag{1.7}$$

If neither $\vec{v}$ or $\vec{u}$ are the zero vector then the equality in part 5 of Theorem(1.10) can be written

$$\cos(\theta) = \frac{\vec{v} \cdot \vec{u}}{||\vec{v}|| \, ||\vec{u}||} \, . \tag{1.8}$$

Since $-1 \leq \cos(\theta) \leq 1$ the identity in (1.8) gives the inequality $-1 \leq \dfrac{\vec{v} \cdot \vec{u}}{||\vec{v}|| \, ||\vec{u}||} \leq 1$. This inequality is the same as $-||\vec{v}|| \, ||\vec{u}|| \leq \vec{v} \cdot \vec{u} \leq ||\vec{v}|| \, ||\vec{u}||$ which when written in terms of an absolute value is (1.5) for non-zero $\vec{v}$ or $\vec{u}$. The Cauchy-Schwartz inequality is trivially true if $\vec{v}$ or $\vec{u}$ is the zero vector so (1.5) is valid for all vectors. Replacing $\vec{u}$ by $-\vec{u}$ in (1.3) followed by the Schwartz inequality gives

$$\begin{aligned}
||\vec{v} + \vec{u}||^2 &= (\vec{v} + \vec{u})^T (\vec{v} + \vec{u}) = ||\vec{v}||^2 + 2\vec{v} \cdot \vec{u} + ||\vec{u}||^2 \\
&\leq ||\vec{v}||^2 + 2||\vec{v}|| \, ||\vec{u}|| + ||\vec{u}||^2 \quad \text{Schwartz Inequality} \\
&= \left(||\vec{v}|| + ||\vec{u}|| \right)^2 .
\end{aligned} \tag{1.9}$$

Taking the square root gives the triangle inequality (1.6). Finally, use the equality statements in (1.3) and (1.9) to find

$$\begin{aligned}
||\vec{v} + \vec{u}||^2 + ||\vec{v} - \vec{u}||^2 &= ||\vec{v}||^2 + 2\vec{v} \cdot \vec{u} + ||\vec{u}||^2 + \left(||\vec{v}||^2 - 2\vec{v} \cdot \vec{u} + ||\vec{u}||^2 \right) \\
&= 2||\vec{v}||^2 + 2||\vec{u}||^2
\end{aligned} \tag{1.10}$$

which establishes the Parallelogram theorem.

Example 1.14 Let $\vec{v} = \begin{bmatrix} 3 \\ 1 \end{bmatrix}$ and $\vec{u} = \begin{bmatrix} 2 \\ 2 \end{bmatrix}$ so that the dot product

$$\vec{v} \cdot \vec{u} = \vec{v}^T \vec{u} = [3 \ 1] \begin{bmatrix} 2 \\ 2 \end{bmatrix} = 3(2) + 1(2) = 8$$

which when compared with the product of the lengths of $\vec{v}$ and $\vec{u}$

$$\vec{v} \cdot \vec{u} = 8 = \sqrt{64} < \sqrt{80} = \sqrt{10}\sqrt{8} = ||\vec{v}|| \, ||\vec{u}||$$

illustrates the Cauchy-Schwartz inequality. Recall from Example (1.12) that the projection of $\vec{u}$ onto $\vec{v}$ is given by $\vec{w} = \dfrac{4}{5} \begin{bmatrix} 3 \\ 1 \end{bmatrix}$ and

$$\vec{v} \cdot \vec{w} = 8 = \frac{40}{5} = \sqrt{10}\sqrt{\frac{(16)(10)}{25}} = ||\vec{v}||\,||\vec{w}||$$

which shows that equality can occur in the Cauchy-Schwartz inequality. See Exercise(1.5). Since $\vec{v} + \vec{u} = \begin{bmatrix} 5 \\ 3 \end{bmatrix}$ the calculation

$$
\begin{aligned}
||\vec{v} + \vec{u}||^2 &= (\sqrt{34})^2 = 34 < (||\vec{v}|| + ||\vec{u}||)^2 \\
&= \left(\sqrt{10} + \sqrt{8}\right)^2 = 10 + 8 + 2\sqrt{10}\sqrt{8} = 18 + 8\sqrt{5}
\end{aligned}
$$

where the inequality follows from $34 - 18 = 16 = 8 \cdot 2 < 8\sqrt{5}$ since $2 < \sqrt{5}$. This inequality also illustrates the triangle inequality which reads

$$||\vec{v} + \vec{u}|| = \sqrt{34} < ||\vec{v}|| + ||\vec{u}|| = \sqrt{10} + \sqrt{8}.$$

Define $\vec{w} = \dfrac{4}{5}\vec{v}$ so the sum can be written $\vec{v} + \vec{w} = \left(1 + \dfrac{4}{5}\right)\vec{v}$ and satisfies

$$||\vec{v} + \vec{w}|| = \left(1 + \frac{4}{5}\right)||\vec{v}|| = ||\vec{v}|| + ||\vec{w}||,$$

so that equality can occur in the triangle inequality. See Exercise(1.5). Comparing the two calculations

$$||\vec{v}|| = \sqrt{3^2 + 1^2} = \sqrt{10} \quad \text{and} \quad ||\vec{u}|| = \sqrt{2^2 + 2^2} = \sqrt{8}$$

with the lengths of the two diagonals

$$||\vec{v} + \vec{u}|| = \sqrt{5^2 + 3^2} = \sqrt{34} \quad \text{and} \quad ||\vec{v} - \vec{u}|| = \sqrt{2}$$

illustrates the Parallelogram theorem

$$||\vec{v} + \vec{u}||^2 + ||\vec{v} - \vec{u}||^2 = (\sqrt{34})^2 + (\sqrt{2})^2 = 36 = 2(10) + 2(8) = 2||\vec{v}||^2 + 2||\vec{u}||^2.$$

1.5   Vectors with n Components

Very little changes in passing from $2-$vectors to $n-$vectors. The two vectors $\vec{v}$ and $\vec{u}$ in $\mathcal{R}^n$ are defined by

$$\vec{v} = \begin{bmatrix} v_1 \\ v_2 \\ \vdots \\ v_n \end{bmatrix} \quad \text{and} \quad \vec{u} = \begin{bmatrix} u_1 \\ u_2 \\ \vdots \\ u_n \end{bmatrix}.$$

Each of these are points in $n-$dimensional space. If the coordinate axis are labeled x_i, $i = 1, 2, \ldots, n$ then v_i is v_i units on the x_i-axis. The definitions of scalar multiplication and vector addition read

$$\alpha \vec{v} = \begin{bmatrix} \alpha v_1 \\ \alpha v_2 \\ \vdots \\ \alpha v_n \end{bmatrix} \quad \text{and} \quad \vec{v} + \vec{u} = \begin{bmatrix} v_1 + u_1 \\ v_2 + u_2 \\ \vdots \\ v_n + u_n \end{bmatrix}$$

which are the $n-$dimensional analogues of Definition(1.3). Each of the eight properties listed for vector addition and scalar multiplication listed in Theorem (1.5) remain valid. The **transpose** of the $n-$vector $\vec{v}$ is the row vector $\vec{v}^{\,T} = [v_1 \; v_2 \; \cdots \; v_n]$ and the **dot or scalar product** has the same definition

$$\vec{v}^{\,T}\vec{u} \equiv \vec{v} \cdot \vec{u} = v_1 u_1 + v_2 u_2 \cdots + v_n u_n.$$

If $\vec{u} = \vec{v}$ the dot product gives the **length** of $\vec{v}$

$$\vec{v} \cdot \vec{v} \equiv \vec{v}^{\,T}\vec{v} = v_1{}^2 + v_2{}^2 \cdots + v_n{}^2 \equiv ||\vec{v}||^2 .$$

If the angle between $\vec{v}$ and $\vec{u}$ is θ then the formula

$$\vec{v} \cdot \vec{u} = ||\vec{v}|| \, ||\vec{u}|| \cos(\theta)$$

remains valid. If $\vec{v}$ is **orthogonal** to the vector $\vec{u}$ then $\vec{v} \cdot \vec{u} = 0$. As in the case of vectors of length two, if the zero vector is declared orthogonal to every vector then $\vec{v}$ is orthogonal to $\vec{u}$ if and only if $\vec{v} \cdot \vec{u} = 0$. This is again denoted by $\vec{v} \perp \vec{u}$ and read $\vec{v}$ **perp** $\vec{u}$. The **Cauchy-Schwartz** and **triangle inequalities** read

$$|\vec{v} \cdot \vec{u}| \le ||\vec{v}|| \, ||\vec{u}|| \quad \text{and} \quad ||\vec{v} + \vec{u}|| \le ||\vec{v}|| + ||\vec{u}||,$$

respectively. The **Parallelogram theorem**

$$||\vec{v} + \vec{u}||^2 + ||\vec{v} - \vec{u}||^2 = 2||\vec{v}||^2 + 2||\vec{u}||^2$$

remains valid. The proof in Theorem (1.13) can be repeated verbatim.

Example 1.15 Given the vectors $\vec{v} = \begin{bmatrix} 1 \\ 1 \\ 2 \end{bmatrix}$ and $\vec{u} = \begin{bmatrix} -1 \\ 2 \\ 1 \end{bmatrix}$ the calculation

$$\vec{v} \cdot \vec{u} = 1(-1) + (1)2 + (2)1 = 3 < ||\vec{v}|| \, ||\vec{u}|| = \sqrt{6}\sqrt{6} = 6$$

illustrates the Schwartz inequality. Using $\vec{v} + \vec{u} = \begin{bmatrix} 1 \\ 1 \\ 2 \end{bmatrix} + \begin{bmatrix} -1 \\ 2 \\ 1 \end{bmatrix} = \begin{bmatrix} 0 \\ 3 \\ 3 \end{bmatrix}$ the triangle inequality reads

$$||\vec{v} + \vec{u}|| = \sqrt{18} = \sqrt{3 \cdot 6} = \sqrt{3}\sqrt{6} < ||\vec{v}|| + ||\vec{u}|| = \sqrt{6} + \sqrt{6} = 2\sqrt{6}$$

since $\sqrt{3} < 2$. The length of the other diagonal is $||\vec{v} - \vec{u}|| = \sqrt{2^2 + (-1)^2 + 1^2} = \sqrt{6}$ so that the parallelogram theorem reads

$$||\vec{v} + \vec{u}||^2 + ||\vec{v} - \vec{u}||^2 = 18 + 6 = 24 = 2(6) + 2(6) = 2||\vec{v}||^2 + 2||\vec{u}||^2.$$

As in Definition(1.11), the vector $\vec{w}$ defined by

$$\vec{w} = \frac{\vec{v} \cdot \vec{u}}{||\vec{v}||^2} \vec{v} = \text{proj}_{\vec{v}}\, \vec{u} = \frac{[(1)(-1) + 1(2) + 2(1)]}{(\sqrt{1^2 + 1^2 + 2^2})^2} \begin{bmatrix} 1 \\ 1 \\ 2 \end{bmatrix} = \frac{1}{2} \begin{bmatrix} 1 \\ 1 \\ 2 \end{bmatrix} \tag{1.11}$$

is called the **projection of $\vec{u}$ along $\vec{v}$**. The error vector is

$$\vec{e} = \vec{u} - \vec{w} = \vec{u} - \text{proj}_{\vec{v}}\, \vec{u} = \begin{bmatrix} -1 \\ 2 \\ 1 \end{bmatrix} - \frac{1}{2} \begin{bmatrix} 1 \\ 1 \\ 2 \end{bmatrix} = \frac{3}{2} \begin{bmatrix} -1 \\ 1 \\ 0 \end{bmatrix}. \tag{1.12}$$

The calculation

$$\begin{aligned} \vec{e} \cdot \vec{v} &= (\vec{u} - \vec{w}) \cdot \vec{v} = \frac{3}{2} \begin{bmatrix} -1 \\ 1 \\ 0 \end{bmatrix} \cdot \begin{bmatrix} 1 \\ 1 \\ 2 \end{bmatrix} \\ &= \left(\frac{3}{2}\right) [(-1)(1) + (1)(1) + (0)(2)] = 0 \end{aligned}$$

verifies that $\vec{e} \perp \vec{v}$. The triangle with sides $\vec{w}$, $\vec{e}$ and $\vec{u}$ is a right triangle so

$$||\vec{w}||^2 + ||\vec{e}||^2 = \frac{1}{4}\left(1^2 + 1^2 + 2^2\right) + \frac{9}{4}\left((-1)^2 + 1^2 + 0^2\right) = \frac{6}{4} + \frac{18}{4} = 6 = ||\vec{u}||^2.$$

As in Example(1.12) the vector $\vec{u}$ can be decomposed

$$\vec{u} = \begin{bmatrix} -1 \\ 2 \\ 1 \end{bmatrix} = \vec{w} + (\vec{u} - \vec{w}) = \frac{1}{2} \begin{bmatrix} 1 \\ 1 \\ 2 \end{bmatrix} + \frac{3}{2} \begin{bmatrix} -1 \\ 1 \\ 0 \end{bmatrix}.$$

Given any two vectors $\vec{v}$ and $\vec{u}$, if $\vec{w}$ is defined by the first equality in (1.11) and $\vec{e}$ by the first equality in (1.12), then $\vec{v}$ is orthogonal to $\vec{e}$ and the decomposition of the vector $\vec{u}$ defined in Definition(1.11) applies here.

A **linear combination** of the vectors $\vec{v}$ and $\vec{u}$ is given by the vector

$$\alpha\vec{v} + \beta\vec{u} = \alpha \begin{bmatrix} v_1 \\ v_2 \\ \vdots \\ v_n \end{bmatrix} + \beta \begin{bmatrix} u_1 \\ u_2 \\ \vdots \\ u_n \end{bmatrix} = \begin{bmatrix} \alpha v_1 + \beta u_1 \\ \alpha v_2 + \beta u_2 \\ \vdots \\ \alpha v_n + \beta u_n \end{bmatrix}$$

where the α and β are real numbers. The **canonical unit vectors** are defined by the vectors

$$\vec{e}_1 = \begin{bmatrix} 1 \\ 0 \\ \vdots \\ 0 \end{bmatrix}, \ \vec{e}_2 = \begin{bmatrix} 0 \\ 1 \\ \vdots \\ 0 \end{bmatrix}, \ \cdots, \ \vec{e}_n = \begin{bmatrix} 0 \\ 0 \\ \vdots \\ 1 \end{bmatrix}$$

so that for any vector $\vec{v} \in \mathcal{R}^n$

$$\vec{v} = \begin{bmatrix} v_1 \\ v_2 \\ \vdots \\ v_n \end{bmatrix} = v_1 \vec{e}_1 + v_2 \vec{e}_2 \cdots + v_n \vec{e}_n \ .$$

Example 1.16 In $\mathcal{R}^3$ the canonical vectors are

$$\vec{e}_1 = \begin{bmatrix} 1 \\ 0 \\ 0 \end{bmatrix}, \ \vec{e}_2 = \begin{bmatrix} 0 \\ 1 \\ 0 \end{bmatrix} \text{ and } \vec{e}_3 = \begin{bmatrix} 0 \\ 0 \\ 1 \end{bmatrix} \ .$$

Similar to the note in Definition(1.6) the vectors are frequently denoted by $\vec{e}_1 = \vec{i}$, $\vec{e}_2 = \vec{j}$, and $\vec{e}_3 = \vec{k}$. An arbitrary vector $\vec{v}$ can be written as the simple linear combination

$$\vec{v} = \begin{bmatrix} v_1 \\ v_2 \\ v_3 \end{bmatrix} = (v_1)\vec{e}_1 + (v_2)\vec{e}_2 + (v_3)\vec{e}_3.$$

A specific example here is given by

$$\vec{v} = \begin{bmatrix} 4 \\ 5 \\ -2 \end{bmatrix} = (4)\vec{e}_1 + (5)\vec{e}_2 + (-2)\vec{e}_3 = (4)\begin{bmatrix} 1 \\ 0 \\ 0 \end{bmatrix} + (5)\begin{bmatrix} 0 \\ 1 \\ 0 \end{bmatrix} + (-2)\begin{bmatrix} 0 \\ 0 \\ 1 \end{bmatrix} \ .$$

It is also the case, but perhaps not so transparent, that the vector $\vec{v}$ can be written as a linear combination of the three vectors $\vec{u}_1 = \begin{bmatrix} 1 \\ 0 \\ 1 \end{bmatrix}$, $\vec{u}_2 = \begin{bmatrix} 1 \\ 1 \\ 1 \end{bmatrix}$ and $\vec{u}_3 = \begin{bmatrix} 1 \\ 1 \\ -1 \end{bmatrix}$. One can check that the linear combination

$$\vec{v} = \begin{bmatrix} 4 \\ 5 \\ -2 \end{bmatrix} = (-1)\begin{bmatrix} 1 \\ 0 \\ 1 \end{bmatrix} + (2)\begin{bmatrix} 1 \\ 1 \\ 1 \end{bmatrix} + (3)\begin{bmatrix} 1 \\ 1 \\ -1 \end{bmatrix} \tag{1.13}$$

is valid. If the vector $\vec{u}_1$ is changed to $\vec{\hat{u}} = \begin{bmatrix} 1 \\ 1 \\ 0 \end{bmatrix}$, then it is impossible to write the vector $\vec{v}$ as a linear combination of $\vec{\hat{u}}$, $\vec{u}_2$ and $\vec{u}_3$. This means that there are no scalars α, β and γ

so that

$$\vec{v} = \begin{bmatrix} 4 \\ 5 \\ -2 \end{bmatrix} = (\alpha) \begin{bmatrix} 1 \\ 1 \\ 0 \end{bmatrix} + (\beta) \begin{bmatrix} 1 \\ 1 \\ 1 \end{bmatrix} + (\gamma) \begin{bmatrix} 1 \\ 1 \\ -1 \end{bmatrix}. \qquad (1.14)$$

How to find the coefficients in the expansion in (1.13), or the impossibility of finding such numbers as in (1.14), is the subject of Chapter Two. For the present see Exercise(1.7) .

Example 1.17 So far nothing has been said about the sum of, for example, the vectors

$$\vec{v} = \begin{bmatrix} 1 \\ 2 \end{bmatrix} \quad \text{and} \quad \vec{u} = \begin{bmatrix} 0 \\ 2 \\ -1 \end{bmatrix}.$$

Here is the reason. For these two vectors one definition of a sum might be $\vec{v} + \vec{u} = \begin{bmatrix} 3 \\ 1 \end{bmatrix}$ since $\vec{u}$ has a zero in its first component and that doesn't count because zero is nothing! But mathematics is a subject where zero and nothing are different. Another attempt to define the sum of these two vectors is

$$\vec{v} + \vec{u} = \begin{bmatrix} 1 \\ 4 \\ -1 \end{bmatrix} \quad \text{or} \quad \vec{v} + \vec{u} = \begin{bmatrix} 0 \\ 3 \\ 1 \end{bmatrix}.$$

The first definition may be regarded as add $\vec{v}$ to the "top" part of $\vec{u}$ and the second as add $\vec{v}$ to the "bottom" part of $\vec{u}$. This lack of definiteness is why the sum of vectors with a different number of components is left undefined. Using the same "top" and "bottom" thinking one might be inclined to define

$$\vec{v}^T \vec{u} = \vec{v} \cdot \vec{u} = 1(0) + 2(2) = 4 \quad \text{or} \quad \vec{v}^T \vec{u} = \vec{v} \cdot \vec{u} = 1(2) + 2(-1) = 0$$

where the first equality used the "top" part of $\vec{u}$ and the latter used the "bottom" part of $\vec{u}$. It is troublesome that one equality (the second) implies that $\vec{v} \perp \vec{u}$ and the other does not. As in sums, it is best to leave the dot product of vectors with a different number of components undefined.

1.6 Exercise Set

Exercise 1.1 Let $\vec{v} = \begin{bmatrix} 2 \\ 1 \end{bmatrix}$, $\vec{u} = \begin{bmatrix} -1 \\ 3 \end{bmatrix}$, $\vec{w} = \begin{bmatrix} 3 \\ -1 \end{bmatrix}$, $\vec{x} = \begin{bmatrix} 1 \\ 2 \\ 0 \end{bmatrix}$, $\vec{y} = \begin{bmatrix} 1 \\ 0 \\ -1 \end{bmatrix}$ and

$\vec{z} = \begin{bmatrix} 2 \\ 0 \\ 2 \end{bmatrix}$. Find each of the following quantities or state that the quantity is undefined.

(i)	$\|\vec{v}\|$	(iv)	$\vec{v} \cdot \vec{u}$	(vii)	$\vec{v} + \vec{u}$	(x)	$\vec{v} \cdot \vec{y}$
(ii)	$\|\vec{u}\|$	(v)	$\vec{w} \cdot \vec{u}$	(viii)	$\vec{u} + \vec{y}$	(xi)	$\vec{x} \cdot \vec{y}$
(iii)	$\|\vec{x}\|$	(vi)	$\vec{u} \cdot \vec{y}$	(ix)	$\vec{y} + \vec{z}$	(xii)	$\vec{y} \cdot \vec{z}$

Exercise 1.2 If $\vec{v} = \begin{bmatrix} 2 \\ 1 \end{bmatrix}$, $\vec{w} = \begin{bmatrix} -1 \\ 2 \end{bmatrix}$, and $\vec{u} = \begin{bmatrix} -1 \\ 3 \end{bmatrix}$ show that

(i)	$\|\vec{v} + \vec{w}\|^2 = \|\vec{v}\|^2 + \|\vec{w}\|^2$	(vi)	$\|\vec{v} + \vec{u}\| < \|\vec{v}\| + \|\vec{u}\|$
(ii)	$\|\vec{v} - \vec{w}\|^2 = \|\vec{v}\|^2 + \|\vec{w}\|^2$	(vii)	$\|\vec{v} - \vec{u}\| < \|\vec{v}\| + \|\vec{u}\|$
(iii)	Find $\vec{v} \cdot \vec{w}$	(viii)	Find $\vec{v} \cdot \vec{u}$
(iv)	Find $\text{proj}_{\vec{v}}(\vec{w})$	(ix)	Find $\text{proj}_{\vec{v}}(\vec{u})$
(v)	Find $\text{proj}_{\vec{w}}(\vec{u})$	(x)	Find $\text{proj}_{\vec{u}}(\vec{v})$

Exercise 1.3 Repeat Exercise(1.2) for $\vec{v} = \begin{bmatrix} 2 \\ 1 \\ 0 \end{bmatrix}$, $\vec{w} = \begin{bmatrix} -1 \\ 2 \\ 1 \end{bmatrix}$, and $\vec{u} = \begin{bmatrix} 1 \\ 1 \\ 1 \end{bmatrix}$.

Exercise 1.4 Sometimes the projection of a vector along another is not as it appears in Figure 1.5. This is illustrated with the vectors $\vec{v} = \begin{bmatrix} -3 \\ 1 \end{bmatrix}$ and $\vec{u} = \begin{bmatrix} 2 \\ 2 \end{bmatrix}$.

1. Find the vectors

$$\vec{w} = \text{proj}_{\vec{v}}(\vec{u}) = \left(\frac{\vec{v} \cdot \vec{u}}{\|\vec{v}\|^2} \right) \vec{v} \quad \text{and} \quad \vec{e} = \vec{u} - \vec{w}.$$

On a graph, as in Figure 1.5, draw the vectors $\vec{v}$, $\vec{u}$, $\vec{e}$ and $\text{proj}_{\vec{v}}(\vec{u})$. For the latter, it helps to put the vector $-\vec{v}$ on your graph.

2. Change the vector $\vec{w}$ to $\vec{w} = \text{proj}_{\vec{u}}(\vec{v}) = \left(\frac{\vec{v} \cdot \vec{u}}{\|\vec{u}\|^2} \right) \vec{u}$ and repeat part 1. For this part, it helps to put the vector $-\vec{u}$ on your graph.

Exercise 1.5 Given the vectors $\vec{v} = \begin{bmatrix} 6 \\ -4 \\ 2 \end{bmatrix}$ and $\vec{u} = \begin{bmatrix} 3 \\ -2 \\ 1 \end{bmatrix}$. Show by calculating the stated quantities each of the following

(i) $\vec{v} \cdot \vec{u} = ||\vec{v}||\,||\vec{u}||$ and   (ii) $||\vec{v} + \vec{u}|| = ||\vec{v}|| + ||\vec{u}||$ note $\vec{v} = 2\vec{u}$

The identities (i) and (ii) are true in general for parallel vectors. Here is a way to see this. If $\vec{v}$ or $\vec{u}$ is the zero vector then (i) and (ii) are true. Assume $\vec{v}$ and $\vec{u}$ are non-zero $n-$tuples. Here is an outline to see that $\vec{v} \cdot \vec{u} = ||\vec{v}||\,||\vec{u}||$ if and only if $\vec{v} = \alpha\vec{u}$ for some scalar $\alpha > 0$. If $\vec{v} \cdot \vec{u} = ||\vec{v}||\,||\vec{u}||$ then, from $\vec{v} \cdot \vec{u} = ||\vec{v}||\,||\vec{u}||\cos(\theta)$, it follows that $\cos(\theta) = 1$ or $\theta = 0$. By Definition(1.3) $\vec{v}$ and $\vec{u}$ are parallel which means there is an $\alpha > 0$ so that $\vec{v} = \alpha\vec{u}$. Conversely, if $\vec{v} = \alpha\vec{u}$ for $\alpha > 0$ then the angle, θ between the vectors is zero so that $\vec{v} \cdot \vec{u} = ||\vec{v}||\,||\vec{u}||\cos(\theta) = ||\vec{v}||\,||\vec{u}||$. To see that (ii) is true in general for parallel vectors, begin with equation(1.9) to write

$$\begin{aligned} ||\vec{v} + \vec{u}||^2 &= ||\vec{v}||^2 + 2\vec{v} \cdot \vec{u} + ||\vec{u}||^2 \\ &= ||\vec{v}||^2 + 2||\vec{v}||\,||\vec{u}|| + ||\vec{u}||^2 \quad \text{from part (i) for } \vec{u} = \alpha\vec{v} \\ &= (||\vec{v}|| + ||\vec{u}||)^2 \,. \end{aligned}$$

Take square roots to find part (ii).

Exercise 1.6 Given the vectors $\vec{v} = \begin{bmatrix} -1 \\ 2 \end{bmatrix}$ and $\vec{u} = \begin{bmatrix} 2 \\ 1 \end{bmatrix}$ show by calculating the stated quantities that

(i) $||\vec{v} \pm \vec{u}||^2 = ||\vec{v}||^2 + ||\vec{u}||^2$ and   (ii) $\vec{v} \cdot \vec{u} = 0$.

Illustrate with a graph as in Figure 1.4. Repeat for the vectors $\vec{v} = \begin{bmatrix} -1 \\ 2 \\ 1 \end{bmatrix}$ and $\vec{u} = \begin{bmatrix} 1 \\ 1 \\ -1 \end{bmatrix}$.

The identity (i) is true in general for orthogonal vectors. Here is a way to see this. More generally, let $\vec{v}$ and $\vec{u}$ be non-zero $n-$tuples. The first equality in the identity

$$||\vec{v} \pm \vec{u}||^2 = ||\vec{v}||^2 + \pm 2\vec{v} \cdot \vec{u} + ||\vec{u}||^2 = ||\vec{v}||^2 + ||\vec{u}||^2$$

is from equations (1.3) and (1.9). The last equality follows if and only if $\vec{v} \cdot \vec{u} = 0$, or $\vec{v}$ and $\vec{u}$ are orthogonal.

Exercise 1.7 Show that if it were the case that

$$\vec{v} = \begin{bmatrix} 4 \\ 5 \\ -2 \end{bmatrix} = (\alpha)\begin{bmatrix} 1 \\ 1 \\ 0 \end{bmatrix} + (\beta)\begin{bmatrix} 1 \\ 1 \\ 1 \end{bmatrix} + (\gamma)\begin{bmatrix} 1 \\ 1 \\ -1 \end{bmatrix} = \alpha\vec{u} + \beta\vec{u}_2 + \gamma\vec{u}_3 \,.$$

then the first and second components read $\alpha + \beta + \gamma = 4$ and $\alpha + \beta + \gamma = 5$. Subtract the first of these from the second to see that it is impossible to write $\vec{v}$ as a linear combination of the vectors $\{\vec{u}, \vec{u}_2, \vec{u}_3\}$ (see equation (1.14)). Notice that $2\vec{u} = \vec{u}_2 + \vec{u}_3$ and this combination of the set of vectors, as will be seen in Chapter 2, is the reason $\vec{v}$ can not be written in terms of the set $\{\vec{u}, \vec{u}_2, \vec{u}_3\}$.

Exercise 1.8 This problem shows that the vector dot product can lead to interesting geometric formulas. Here is one for the area of a parallelogram. Let $\vec{v} = \begin{bmatrix} v_1 \\ v_2 \end{bmatrix}$ and $\vec{u} = \begin{bmatrix} u_1 \\ u_2 \end{bmatrix}$ be the legs of the parallelogram shown in Figure 1.7. The area of a parallelogram A_p is given by

$$A_p = ||\vec{v}||\,||\vec{e}|| \quad \text{where} \quad \vec{e} = \vec{u} - \vec{w} = \vec{u} - \text{proj}_{\vec{v}}(\vec{u})$$

Let θ be the angle between $\vec{v}$ and $\vec{u}$. Define the reflected vector $\vec{u}_r = \begin{bmatrix} u_2 \\ -u_1 \end{bmatrix}$ so that $\vec{u} \cdot \vec{u}_r = 0$ and the two vectors are orthogonal. Hence, the angle between $\vec{u}_r$ and $\vec{w}$ is $(90^o - \theta)$. From part 5 of Theorem(1.10)

$$\vec{v} \cdot \vec{u}_r = u_2 v_1 - u_1 v_2 = ||\vec{v}||\,||\vec{u}_r|| \cos(90^o - \theta).$$

From Figure 1.6 $\sin(\theta) = \dfrac{||\vec{e}||}{||\vec{u}||} = \dfrac{||\vec{e}||}{||\vec{u}_r||} = |\cos(90^o - \theta)|$. Why are there absolute values? Hence, $||\vec{e}|| = ||\vec{u}_r|||\cos(90^o - \theta)|$. It follows from the previous display that

$$A_p = ||\vec{v}||\,||\vec{e}|| = ||\vec{v}||\,||\vec{u}_r|||\cos(90^o - \theta)| = |u_2 v_1 - u_1 v_2|\,.$$

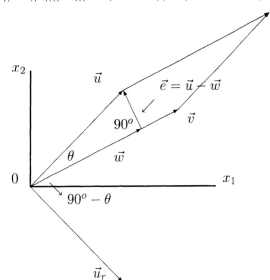

Figure 1.6

1. In Example(1.12) for the vectors $\vec{v} = \begin{bmatrix} 3 \\ 1 \end{bmatrix}$ and $\vec{u} = \begin{bmatrix} 2 \\ 2 \end{bmatrix}$, $\vec{e} = \dfrac{1}{5} \begin{bmatrix} -2 \\ 6 \end{bmatrix}$. Compare the calculation of $A_p = ||\vec{v}||\,||\vec{e}||$ versus $A_p = |u_2 v_1 - u_1 v_2|$ to show that $A_p = 4$.

2. Change the vector $\vec{v}$ to $\vec{v} = \begin{bmatrix} -3 \\ 1 \end{bmatrix}$ and leave $\vec{u} = \begin{bmatrix} 2 \\ 2 \end{bmatrix}$. Find the area A_p. This illustrates a reason for the absolute value in the formula.

1.7   Sample Quizzes

1.7.1   Sample Quiz 1

Name_____   Date_____

1. Let $\vec{v} = \begin{bmatrix} -1 \\ 3 \end{bmatrix}$, $\vec{u} = \begin{bmatrix} 3 \\ 1 \end{bmatrix}$, $\vec{0} = \begin{bmatrix} 0 \\ 0 \end{bmatrix}$, and $\vec{z} = \begin{bmatrix} 2 \\ 1 \\ 1 \end{bmatrix}$. Find each of the following or state that the expression is undefined.

(a) $\vec{0} \cdot \vec{v} =$

(b) $\vec{v} + \begin{bmatrix} 1 \\ -3 \\ 0 \end{bmatrix}$

(c) $\vec{v} \cdot \vec{u} =$

(d) $\text{proj}_{\vec{v}}(\vec{u})$

(e) $||\vec{v}||$

(f) $||\vec{z}||$

(g) $||\vec{v} + \vec{u}||^2$

(h) $||\vec{v}||^2 + ||\vec{u}||^2$

(i) $\vec{0} \cdot \begin{bmatrix} 1 \\ -3 \\ 0 \end{bmatrix}$

(j) $\text{proj}_{\vec{u}}(\vec{v})$

(k)   If $\vec{w} = \begin{bmatrix} 1 \\ -3 \\ 0 \end{bmatrix}$ then $\text{proj}_{\vec{z}}(\vec{w}) =$

2. Find $\vec{x} = \begin{bmatrix} x_1 \\ x_2 \end{bmatrix}$ so that $\vec{x}$ is **perpendicular to both** $\vec{v} = \begin{bmatrix} -1 \\ 3 \end{bmatrix}$ and to $\vec{u} = \begin{bmatrix} 3 \\ 1 \end{bmatrix}$.

3. Draw each of $\vec{u} = \begin{bmatrix} 2 \\ 1 \end{bmatrix}$ and $\vec{v} = \begin{bmatrix} 4 \\ -3 \end{bmatrix}$ on the graph in **Figure 1**. Determine each of the following:

   (a) $||\vec{u}|| =$ (b) $||\vec{v}|| =$

   (c) the dot product $\vec{u} \cdot \vec{v} =$

   (d) $\text{proj}_{\vec{u}}(\vec{v}) =$

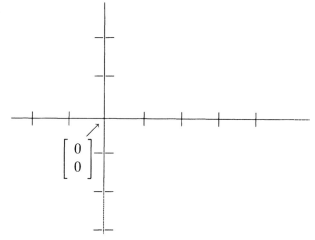

Figure 1

   (e) Find the angle between the vectors $\vec{u}$ and $\vec{u} - \vec{v}$.

   (f) Draw $\text{proj}_{\vec{v}}(\vec{u})$ on the graph in **Figure 1**.

1.7.2   Sample Quiz 2

Name_____   Date_____

1. Define the vectors $\vec{u} = \begin{bmatrix} 3 \\ 3 \end{bmatrix}$ and $\vec{v} = \begin{bmatrix} 4 \\ 2 \end{bmatrix}$.

   (a) In the figure draw each of $\vec{u} - \vec{v}$. and $\vec{u} + \vec{v}$.

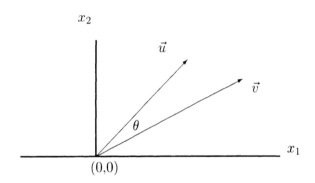

   (b) Find the cosine of the angle θ between the vectors $\vec{u}$ and $\vec{v}$.

   (c) Find a number α so that the vector $\vec{e} = \vec{u} - \alpha\vec{v}$ is perpendicular to $\vec{v}$. Draw the vector $\vec{e}$ in the figure.

2. Let $\vec{v} = \begin{bmatrix} -1 \\ 2 \end{bmatrix}$, $\vec{u} = \begin{bmatrix} 2 \\ 1 \end{bmatrix}$ and $\vec{0} = \begin{bmatrix} 0 \\ 0 \end{bmatrix}$. Short answer, calculate the given quantity.

(a) $\vec{0} + \vec{v} =$

(b) $\vec{v} + \begin{bmatrix} 1 \\ -3 \\ 0 \end{bmatrix}$

(c) $\vec{v} \cdot \vec{v} =$

(d) $||\vec{v}||^2 =$

(e) $||\vec{u}||^2 =$

(f) $||\vec{v} + \vec{u}||^2 =$

(g) $||\vec{v}||^2 + ||\vec{u}||^2 =$

(h) $||\vec{v} - \vec{u}||^2 = \ .$

(i) $\text{proj}_{\vec{u}}(\vec{v}) =$

(j) $\vec{v} \cdot \begin{bmatrix} 1 \\ -3 \\ 0 \end{bmatrix} =$

(k) If $\vec{w} = \begin{bmatrix} 2 \\ 2 \end{bmatrix}$ then $\text{proj}_{\vec{w}}(\vec{v}) =$

(l) If $\vec{w} = \begin{bmatrix} 2 \\ 2 \end{bmatrix}$ then $\text{proj}_{\vec{w}}(\vec{u}) =$

3. Let $\vec{x} = \begin{bmatrix} 5 \\ \alpha \\ \alpha \end{bmatrix}$ and $\vec{z} = \begin{bmatrix} -2 \\ 3 \\ 2 \end{bmatrix}$. Find α so that $\vec{x}$ is orthogonal to $\vec{z}$.

Chapter 2

Linear Systems

Linear systems provide a familiar backdrop against which matrix manipulations can be introduced. This close association of the the linear system with a corresponding matrix system puts in context the familiar operations done on linear systems with the corresponding operations performed on matrix systems. This is the main point of this chapter and is housed in Section 2.7 in the discussion of row echelon forms. These forms, found in Definition(2.10), introduce pivots. The numerical count of pivots resurfaces in the important idea of rank in Chapter Four. The unobtrusive Theorem(2.13) has uses throughout the remainder of the text. It advertises the idea of a null space, which is one of the subspaces mentioned in the first of the Big Two. Exercises(2.1) through (2.8) are offshoots of worked examples in the chapter. They are designed to give a facility in manipulating row operations and a familiarity with the nature of the solutions of linear systems. Exercise(2.9) is an advertisement for the matrix inverses in Chapter Three.

2.1   Two Equations in Two Unknowns

An example of a linear equation in the two unknowns x_1 and x_2 is given by

$$2x_1 - 2x_2 = 3. \tag{2.1}$$

Geometrically, linear means that the graph of the equation is a straight line. A solution to the equation is an ordered pair that satisfies the equation. The pair $x_1 = 2$ and $x_2 = 1/2$, represented by the vector $\begin{bmatrix} 2 \\ 1/2 \end{bmatrix}$, is a solution since $2 \cdot 2 - 2\left(\dfrac{1}{2}\right) = 4 - 1 = 3$. A different linear equation is defined by

$$x_1 + \frac{1}{2}x_2 = \frac{3}{4}. \tag{2.2}$$

The ordered pair $\begin{bmatrix} 1 \\ -1/2 \end{bmatrix}$ is a solution to (2.2) since $1 + \dfrac{1}{2}\left(\dfrac{-1}{2}\right) = 1 - \dfrac{1}{4} = \dfrac{3}{4}$. In addition, since $2 \cdot 1 - 2\left(\dfrac{-1}{2}\right) = 2 + 1 = 3$, the ordered pair $\begin{bmatrix} 1 \\ -1/2 \end{bmatrix}$ is also a solution to (2.1). Hence, this ordered pair simultaneously satisfies both (2.1) and (2.2). Geometrically, this is represented by the intersection of the two lines with $\alpha = 1$ and $\beta = -1/2$ in Figure 2.1. If the equation in (2.2) is replaced by the equation

$$x_1 - x_2 = \frac{3}{2} \tag{2.3}$$

then this equation is parallel to the equation in (2.1). The x_2−intercept (obtained by putting $x_1 = 0$) of both (2.1) and (2.3) is given by $x_2 = \dfrac{-3}{2}$. Hence the equation in (2.3) represents the same line as the line in (2.1). Indeed, equation (2.3) is simply one half the equation in (2.1). Geometrically, the line defined by (2.3) is the same as the line in (2.1). Finally, if the last equation is replaced by the equation

$$x_1 - x_2 = -4 \tag{2.4}$$

then this equation has no solutions in common with the first equation. This equation is parallel to the first equation and has a different x_2 intercept. The slope of each line is one and the intercepts are $x_2 = -3/2$ and $x_2 = 4$, respectively. This is represented by the two parallel lines (rising to the right) in Figure 2.1

In each of the above three cases, equation (2.1) combined with (2.2), (2.3) or (2.4), respectively, there are two linear equations in the two unknowns x_1 and x_2. As illustrated, there are three possible outcomes: a unique solution ((2.1) combined with (2.2)), infinitely many solutions ((2.1) combined with (2.3)) and no solution ((2.1) combined with (2.4)). This illustrative example represents all that can occur in any linear system. This is the subject of this chapter.

In general, a linear equation in the two unknowns x_1 and x_2 has the algebraic form

$$a_{11}x_1 + a_{12}x_2 = b_1$$

where a_{11} and a_{12} are called the coefficients of the equation. Define the two vectors

$$\vec{a}_1 = \begin{bmatrix} a_{11} \\ a_{12} \end{bmatrix} \quad \text{and} \quad \vec{x} = \begin{bmatrix} x_1 \\ x_2 \end{bmatrix}$$

and, using the dot product notation from Chapter One, rewrite the linear equation

$$\vec{a}_1 \cdot \vec{x} = \begin{bmatrix} a_{11} \\ a_{12} \end{bmatrix} \cdot \begin{bmatrix} x_1 \\ x_2 \end{bmatrix} = [a_{11} \ a_{12}]^T \begin{bmatrix} x_1 \\ x_2 \end{bmatrix} = a_{11}x_1 + a_{12}x_2 = b_1 \ .$$

If $a_{12} \neq 0$ the equation is the straight line with the slope $m = \dfrac{-a_{11}}{a_{12}}$. If $a_{12} = 0$ the equation is a vertical line parallel to the x_2−axis and has the equation $x_1 = \dfrac{b_1}{a_{11}}$. This is illustrated in Figure 2.1.

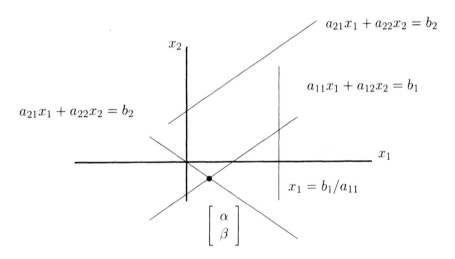

Figure 2.1

A second equation in the unknowns x_1 and x_2 defines another straight line

$$a_{21}x_1 + a_{22}x_2 = b_2 \ .$$

Define the vector $\vec{a}_2 = \begin{bmatrix} a_{11} \\ a_{12} \end{bmatrix}$ and write this equation in the form

$$\vec{a}_2 \cdot \vec{x} \equiv \begin{bmatrix} a_{21} \\ a_{22} \end{bmatrix} \cdot \begin{bmatrix} x_1 \\ x_2 \end{bmatrix} = [a_{21} \ a_{22}]^T \begin{bmatrix} x_1 \\ x_2 \end{bmatrix} = a_{21}x_1 + a_{22}x_2 = b_2 \ .$$

This chapter studies solving the system of two equations in two unknowns

$$\begin{cases} a_{11}x_1 + a_{12}x_2 = b_1 \\ a_{21}x_1 + a_{22}x_2 = b_2 \end{cases} \tag{2.5}$$

and in the process shows how to associate a matrix equation with (2.5). A first step in the latter direction consists of defining the 2×2 array $A = \begin{bmatrix} a_{11} & a_{12} \\ a_{21} & a_{22} \end{bmatrix}$ and then writing the system (2.6) in the compact form

$$A\vec{x} \equiv \begin{bmatrix} a_{11} & a_{12} \\ a_{21} & a_{22} \end{bmatrix} \begin{bmatrix} x_1 \\ x_2 \end{bmatrix} \equiv \begin{bmatrix} \vec{a}_1^T \vec{x} \\ \vec{a}_2^T \vec{x} \end{bmatrix} = \begin{bmatrix} b_1 \\ b_2 \end{bmatrix} \equiv \vec{b}. \qquad (2.6)$$

The second equivalence ($\equiv$) is the definition of the product of the 2×2 array A with the vector $\vec{x}$. The possibilities for the solution of (2.6) are all contained in the following definition.

Definition 2.1 Consistent and Inconsistent 2×2 systems, Coefficient and Augmented Matrices: The solution (or lack of solution) of the system in (2.6) fall into one of the three cases.

1. The two equations have a unique solution. This unique solution is an ordered pair

$$\begin{bmatrix} x_1 \\ x_2 \end{bmatrix} = \begin{bmatrix} \alpha \\ \beta \end{bmatrix}$$

   marked by a dot in the Figure 2.1. The coordinates of this point satisfy both

$$a_{11}\alpha + a_{12}\beta = b_1 \quad \text{and} \quad a_{21}\alpha + a_{22}\beta = b_2.$$

   The pair of equations in this instance is called a **consistent** system of equations. In the case of equations (2.1) and (2.2) this is the point given by $\begin{bmatrix} \alpha \\ \beta \end{bmatrix} = \begin{bmatrix} 1 \\ \dfrac{-1}{2} \end{bmatrix}$

2. The two equations have infinitely many solutions. This means one equation is a multiple of the other equation: there is a scalar c so that

$$c\left[a_{11}x_1 + a_{12}x_2 - b_1 \right] = a_{21}x_1 + a_{22}x_2 - b_2.$$

   Geometrically, the two equations represent the same line. If $a_{11} \neq 0$ then the variable x_1 can be solved for in terms of the variable x_2

$$x_1 = -\frac{a_{12}}{a_{11}}x_2 + \frac{b_1}{a_{11}},$$

   and the variable x_2 can be assigned any value. For this reason the variable x_2 is called a **free variable** . In (2.1), $a_{11} = 2, a_{12} = -2$ and $b_1 = 3$ so that $x_1 = x_2 + \dfrac{3}{2}$ and for (2.3), $a_{21} = 1, a_{22} = -1$ and $b_2 = \dfrac{3}{2}$ so that $x_1 = x_2 + \dfrac{3}{2}$. If $a_{11} = 0$ then $a_{21} = 0$ (the equations are multiples) and the two lines are parallel to the x_1-axis with x_2 intercept $\dfrac{b_1}{a_{12}} = \dfrac{b_2}{a_{22}}$. The pair of equations are again called a **consistent** system of equations.

3. The two equations have no solution. This case is represented by parallel but distinct lines. The two lines are parallel if $\dfrac{a_{11}}{a_{12}} = \dfrac{a_{21}}{a_{22}}$ and are distinct if $a_{12}b_2 \neq a_{22}b_1$.

In (2.1), $a_{11} = 2, a_{12} = -2$ and $b_1 = 3$ and for (2.4), $a_{21} = 1, a_{22} = -1$ and $b_2 = -4$ so that $\dfrac{a_{11}}{a_{12}} = \dfrac{2}{-2} = 1 = \dfrac{1}{-1} = \dfrac{a_{21}}{a_{22}}$ and $a_{12}b_2 = (-2)(-4) = 8 \neq (-1)(3) = a_{22}b_1$. In the event that $a_{11} = 0$ then $a_{21} = 0$ (the equations are multiples) and the two distinct lines are parallel to the x_1-axis with x_2 intercepts $\dfrac{b_1}{a_{12}} \neq \dfrac{b_2}{a_{22}}$. The pair of equations is called an **inconsistent** system of equations.

In any of the three cases the 2×2 array of numbers $\begin{bmatrix} a_{11} & a_{12} \\ a_{21} & a_{22} \end{bmatrix}$ is called the 2×2 **coefficient matrix** of the system and the 2×3 array $\left[\begin{array}{cc|c} a_{11} & a_{12} & b_1 \\ a_{21} & a_{22} & b_2 \end{array} \right]$ is called the **augmented matrix** of the system. Suppose that

$$\begin{cases} \hat{a}_{11}x_1 + \hat{a}_{12}x_2 = \hat{b}_1 \\ \hat{a}_{21}x_1 + \hat{a}_{22}x_2 = \hat{b}_2 \end{cases}$$

is a second set of two equations in two unknowns. If solutions of this system are also solutions of the system in (2.2) then the two systems are called **equivalent**. The associated augmented matrices

$$\left[\begin{array}{cc|c} a_{11} & a_{12} & b_1 \\ a_{21} & a_{22} & b_2 \end{array} \right] \quad \text{and} \quad \left[\begin{array}{cc|c} \hat{a}_{11} & \hat{a}_{12} & \hat{b}_1 \\ \hat{a}_{21} & \hat{a}_{22} & \hat{b}_2 \end{array} \right]$$

are also called equivalent. If neither of the systems have solutions then the two systems, as well as their augmented matrices, are also called **equivalent**.

Example 2.2 This example illustrates all of the cases mentioned above. Find a solution, if possible, for the system

$$\begin{cases} 2x_1 - 2x_2 = 3 \\ x_1 + a_{22}x_2 = b_2 \end{cases} \tag{2.7}$$

where a_{22} is arbitrary. Notice that the first equation is the equation in (2.1). By allowing the coefficient a_{22} and the term b_2 to be arbitrary at the outset allows the discussion of all of the cases occurring in the discussion around equations (2.2) to (2.4). These parameters will be given specific values as this example develops. The augmented matrix for this system is

$$\left[\begin{array}{cc|c} 2 & -2 & 3 \\ 1 & a_{22} & b_2 \end{array} \right].$$

Multiply the equation $2x_1 - 2x_2 = 3$ by $-1/2$ and add the result to the second equation to find $(1 + a_{22})x_2 = b_2 - 3/2$. The result is the new system

$$\begin{cases} 2x_1 - 2x_2 = 3 \\ \qquad (1 + a_{22})x_2 = \dfrac{2b_2 - 3}{2}. \end{cases} \tag{2.8}$$

This system, although different from (2.7), is equivalent to the original system. The advantage in the second system is that it has a simpler form (the second equation has the single unknown x_2). The augmented matrix for the simpler and equivalent system is

$$\left[\begin{array}{cc|c} 2 & -2 & 3 \\ 0 & (1 + a_{22}) & \dfrac{2b_2 - 3}{2} \end{array} \right].$$

If $a_{22} \neq -1$, the solution to the second equation in (2.8) is given by

$$x_2 = \frac{2b_2 - 3}{2(a_{22} + 1)}.$$

Substitute this quantity in the first equation in (2.8) and solve for x_1 to find

$$\begin{aligned}
x_1 = x_2 + \frac{3}{2} & = \frac{2b_2 - 3}{2(a_{22} + 1)} + \frac{3}{2} \\
& = \frac{2b_2 - 3}{2(a_{22} + 1)} + \frac{3(a_{22} + 1)}{2(a_{22} + 1)} \\
& = \frac{2b_2 - 3 + 3a_{22} + 3}{2(a_{22} + 1)} = \frac{3a_{22} + 2b_2}{2(a_{22} + 1)}.
\end{aligned}$$

Collecting these two quantities in vector form gives the unique solution to the system

$$\vec{x} = \left[\begin{array}{c} x_1 \\ x_2 \end{array} \right] = \left[\begin{array}{c} \dfrac{3a_{22} + 2b_2}{2(a_{22} + 1)} \\[2ex] \dfrac{-3 + 2b_2}{2(a_{22} + 1)} \end{array} \right] \quad \text{if } a_{22} \neq -1. \tag{2.9}$$

The system is consistent with the unique solution in (2.8) illustrating part 1 in Definition(2.1). Referring to equation (2.2) from the opening example, $a_{22} = \dfrac{1}{2}$ and $b_2 = \dfrac{3}{4}$, so the vector in (2.9) reads

$$\begin{aligned}
\vec{x} = \left[\begin{array}{c} x_1 \\ x_2 \end{array} \right] & = \left[\begin{array}{c} \dfrac{3\left(\dfrac{1}{2}\right) + 2\left(\dfrac{3}{4}\right)}{2(1/2 + 1)} \\[3ex] \dfrac{-3 + 2\left(\dfrac{3}{4}\right)}{2(1/2 + 1)} \end{array} \right] \\[4ex]
& = \left[\begin{array}{c} \dfrac{(3/2) + (3/2)}{2(1/2 + 1)} \\[3ex] \dfrac{-3 + 2\,(3/4)}{2(1/2 + 1)} \end{array} \right] = \left[\begin{array}{c} \dfrac{3}{3} \\[2ex] \dfrac{-3/2}{3} \end{array} \right] = \left[\begin{array}{c} 1 \\[1ex] -\dfrac{1}{2} \end{array} \right]
\end{aligned}$$

which is what was found in the lines following (2.2).

If $a_{22} = -1$ then the second equation in (2.8) takes the form $0x_2 = b_2 - 3/2$, which admits two possibilities.

1. If $b_2 = 3/2$ the first equation in the original system (2.7) is two times the second equation so there are infinitely many solutions. Solve the first equation for x_1, so that $x_1 = \dfrac{3 + 2x_2}{2} = \dfrac{2x_2 + 3}{2}$ and x_2 can take on any value. This situation was also illustrated in the opening paragraph when equations (2.1) and (2.3) were combined into a system. As in Definition(2.1) the variable x_2 is called a **free variable**. In vector form

$$\vec{x} = \begin{bmatrix} x_1 \\ x_2 \end{bmatrix} = \begin{bmatrix} \dfrac{2x_2 + 3}{2} \\ x_2 \end{bmatrix} = x_2 \begin{bmatrix} 1 \\ 1 \end{bmatrix} + \begin{bmatrix} 3/2 \\ 0 \end{bmatrix} \equiv \vec{x}_h + \vec{x}_p.$$

It is okay to let x_1 be the free variable (solve the first equation for $x_2 = \dfrac{2x_1 - 3}{2}$) and then an equivalent form of the solution is

$$\vec{x} = \begin{bmatrix} x_1 \\ x_2 \end{bmatrix} = \begin{bmatrix} x_1 \\ \dfrac{2x_1 - 3}{2} \end{bmatrix} = x_1 \begin{bmatrix} 1 \\ 1 \end{bmatrix} + \begin{bmatrix} 0 \\ -3/2 \end{bmatrix} \equiv \vec{x}_h + \vec{x}_p$$

where the connection between the two forms of the solutions is $x_1 = x_2 + 3/2$. Replace x_1 by $x_2 + 3/2$ in the latter to obtain the former. It is immaterial whether one declares x_1 or x_2 the free variable. For either of the above forms the part of the solution $\vec{x}_h$ is called the **homogeneous** solution and $\vec{x}_p$ is called a **particular** solution. It is the case that $\vec{\tilde{x}}_p = \begin{bmatrix} 2 \\ 1/2 \end{bmatrix}$ is also a particular solution to the problem. Substitute $x_1 = 2$ in the last displayed line. There are infinitely many particular solutions, all of which are obtained by adding a multiple of the homogeneous solution to a particular solution. This is why $\vec{x}_p$ or $\vec{\tilde{x}}_p$ is called **a particular** solution and not **the particular** solution. Any particular solution can be used in the general solution. If the components of $\vec{x}_h$ are substituted into each of the equations in the system (2.7) then each equation gives zero. If the components of $\vec{x}_p$ are substituted into each equation in (2.7) then equation one gives 3 and equation two gives 3/2. The sum $\vec{x} \equiv \vec{x}_h + \vec{x}_p$ is called the **general** solution to the linear system. The unique solution in (2.9) can be written in the form $\vec{x}_h + \vec{x}_p$ by regarding $\vec{x}_h = \vec{0}$. This is still called the **homogeneous** solution but is usually not written. The **particular** solution is the unique solution listed in (2.9).

2. If $b_2 \neq 3/2$, (in the opening example, equation (2.4)), $b_2 = -4$), then the second equation in (2.7) reads

$$0x_2 = \frac{2b_2 - 3}{2} \neq 0$$

and there is no value of x_2 satisfying this equation. Geometrically, the two lines are parallel and distinct so there are no solutions. This is the case of inconsistency mentioned in part 3 of Definition(2.1).

The process of passing from one linear system to a simpler equivalent linear system is called *Gauss Elimination*. This procedure will be formally defined after a few examples of its use. Before turning to these examples, a brief review of the geometry of planes will help in Example(2.3) and Example(2.4).

2.2   Planes and Normals

The geometry used in Figure 2.1 to illustrate the solutions (or lack of solutions) of equations in two unknowns can be extended to equations in three unknowns. A portion of the graph (the triangular region) of the plane defined by the equation

$$x_1 + 2x_2 + 3x_3 = \vec{N_1} \cdot \vec{x} = \begin{bmatrix} 1 \\ 2 \\ 3 \end{bmatrix} \cdot \begin{bmatrix} x_1 \\ x_2 \\ x_3 \end{bmatrix} = 6 \qquad (2.10)$$

is shown in Figure 2.2. Notice for example, if $x_2 = 0$, then the graph of the equation reads $2x_1 + 4x_3 = 12$ which is the straight line passing through the two vertexes $\begin{bmatrix} 6 \\ 0 \\ 0 \end{bmatrix}$ and $\begin{bmatrix} 0 \\ 0 \\ 3 \end{bmatrix}$.

The equation of the lines through the other two legs of the triangle are obtained by setting $x_1 = 0$ $(3x_2 + 4x_3 = 12)$ and $x_3 = 0$ $(2x_1 + 3x_2 = 12)$, respectively. The vector $\vec{N_1} = \begin{bmatrix} 2 \\ 3 \\ 4 \end{bmatrix}$

is called a normal to the plane. It is orthogonal to every vector in the plane. This will be shown for arbitrary planes.

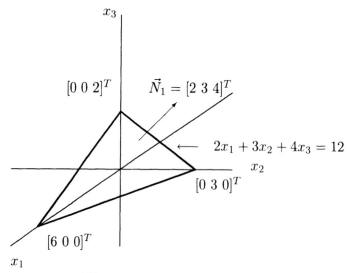

Figure 2.2

To see that the equation $a_{11}x_1 + a_{12}x_2 + a_{13}x_3 = b_1$ represents a plane assume that $\begin{bmatrix} x_1 \\ x_2 \\ x_3 \end{bmatrix}$

is an arbitrary point on the plane and the point $P = \begin{bmatrix} a \\ b \\ c \end{bmatrix}$ a fixed point on the plane. The

vector $\vec{p} = \begin{bmatrix} x_1 - a \\ x_2 - b \\ x_3 - c \end{bmatrix}$ lies in the plane. Define the vector of coefficients $\vec{N}_1 = \begin{bmatrix} a_{11} \\ a_{12} \\ a_{13} \end{bmatrix}$

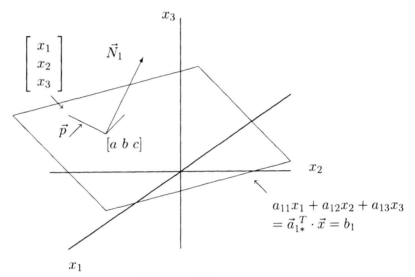

Figure 2.3

and calculate the dot product

$$\vec{N}_1 \cdot \vec{p} = \begin{bmatrix} a_{11} \\ a_{12} \\ a_{13} \end{bmatrix} \cdot \begin{bmatrix} x_1 - a \\ x_2 - b \\ x_3 - c \end{bmatrix} = a_{11}(x_1 - a) + a_{12}(x_2 - b) + a_{13}(x_3 - c)$$

$$= a_{11}x_1 + a_{12}x_2 + a_{13}x_3 - (a_{11}a + a_{12}b + a_{13}c)$$

$$= a_{11}x_1 + a_{12}x_2 + a_{13}x_3 - b_1 = 0$$

where the second to last equality follows from the assumption that the point $\begin{bmatrix} a \\ b \\ c \end{bmatrix}$ lies on

the plane, that is $a_{11}a + a_{12}b + a_{13}c = b_1$ and the last equality from the assumption that

the point $\begin{bmatrix} x_1 \\ x_2 \\ x_3 \end{bmatrix}$ lies on the plane. Hence as the $\begin{bmatrix} x_1 \\ x_2 \\ x_3 \end{bmatrix}$ varies the locus of points defined

by the equation $a_{11}x_1 + a_{12}x_2 + a_{13}x_3 = b_1$ is a plane. From part 6 of Theorem(1.10) the vector $\vec{N}_1$ is perpendicular to any vector $\vec{p}$ in the plane and therefore it is perpendicular to the plane. This vector is called the **normal** to the plane. See Figure 2.3.

Consider the equation of a second plane

$$2x_1 + 5x_2 + 4x_3 = \vec{N}_2 \cdot \vec{x} = \begin{bmatrix} 2 \\ 5 \\ 4 \end{bmatrix} \cdot \begin{bmatrix} x_1 \\ x_2 \\ x_3 \end{bmatrix} = 4 \qquad (2.11)$$

Notice that the normal, $\vec{N}_2$, for the plane in (2.11) is not a constant multiple of the normal $\vec{N}_1$ for the plane in (2.10). This means that these normals are not parallel Recall from Definition(1.3) that parallel vectors are constant multiples of each other. In turn, this implies that the two planes represented by equations (2.10) and (2.11) are not parallel. Stated affirmatively, the two planes must intersect. See Figure 2.4.

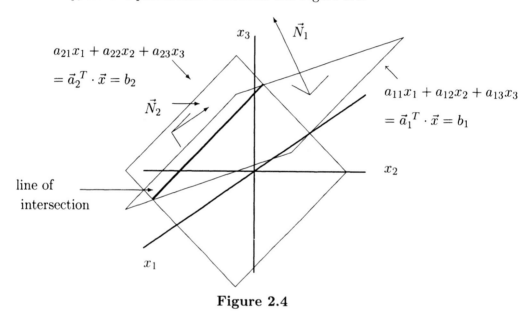

Figure 2.4

2.3   Two Equations in Three Unknowns

Example 2.3 Discuss solving the system

$$\begin{array}{rcl} x_1 + 2x_2 + 3x_3 &=& 6 \\ 2x_1 + 5x_2 + 4x_3 &=& 4 \end{array} \qquad (2.12)$$

To obtain the matrix equation for (2.12) define the vectors

$$\vec{a}_1 = \begin{bmatrix} 1 \\ 2 \\ 3 \end{bmatrix}, \ \vec{a}_2 = \begin{bmatrix} 2 \\ 5 \\ 4 \end{bmatrix}, \ \text{and} \ \vec{x} = \begin{bmatrix} x_1 \\ x_2 \\ x_3 \end{bmatrix}.$$

The transpose of the first two are the rows of the coefficient matrix A for (2.12) so the linear system can be written as

$$A\vec{x} \equiv \begin{bmatrix} 1 & 2 & 3 \\ 2 & 5 & 4 \end{bmatrix} \begin{bmatrix} x_1 \\ x_2 \\ x_3 \end{bmatrix} = \begin{bmatrix} \vec{a}_1^T \vec{x} \\ \vec{a}_2^T \vec{x} \end{bmatrix} = \begin{bmatrix} 6 \\ 4 \end{bmatrix}. \tag{2.13}$$

The matrix equation in (2.17) houses the two dot products, $\vec{a}_i^T \vec{x} = b_i$, $i = 1, 2$, which are the two equations in (2.12). The augmented matrix for the system reads

$$[A \mid \vec{b}] = \begin{bmatrix} 1 & 2 & 3 & 6 \\ 2 & 5 & 4 & 4 \end{bmatrix}.$$

In light of the close of the previous section, solving this system is equivalent to finding the line of intersection of these two planes. This line is marked in Figure 2.4.

If the first equation in (2.12) is multiplied by (-2) and the result added to the second equation, then the equivalent system is

$$\begin{cases} x_1 + 2x_2 + 3x_3 &= 6 \\ 0x_1 + x_2 - 2x_3 &= -8 \end{cases} \tag{2.14}$$

whose augmented matrix is

$$\begin{bmatrix} 1 & 2 & 3 & 6 \\ 0 & 1 & -2 & -8 \end{bmatrix}.$$

Solve the second equation in (2.13) for x_2

$$x_2 = 2x_3 - 8$$

so that x_3 is the free variable. Alternatively, solving the second equation in (2.13) for x_3 yields

$$x_3 = \frac{1}{2}x_2 + 4$$

in which case x_2 is the free variable. It does not matter which variable is chosen as the free variable (see Exercise(2.6)). For reasons that will emerge, x_3 is the choice made for the free variable. Solve the first equation in (2.13) for x_1 and substitute the expression just found for x_2 to see that

$$x_1 = -2x_2 - 3x_3 + 6 = -2(2x_3 - 8) - 3x_3 + 6 = -7x_3 + 16 + 6 = -7x_3 + 22.$$

A vector form defining the infinitely many solutions is given by

$$\begin{bmatrix} x_1 \\ x_2 \\ x_3 \end{bmatrix} = \begin{bmatrix} -7x_3 + 22 \\ 2x_3 - 8 \\ x_3 \end{bmatrix} = x_3 \begin{bmatrix} -7 \\ 2 \\ 1 \end{bmatrix} + \begin{bmatrix} 22 \\ -8 \\ 0 \end{bmatrix} = \vec{x}_h + \vec{x}_p. \tag{2.15}$$

Geometrically, this particular solution $\vec{x}_p$ is a vector from the origin to the point $\begin{bmatrix} 22 \\ -8 \\ 0 \end{bmatrix}$

which lies on the line of intersection of the two planes. The homogeneous solution, with say

$x_2 = 1$, reads $\vec{x}_h = \begin{bmatrix} -7 \\ 2 \\ 1 \end{bmatrix}$ which give what are called the direction numbers for the line.

As in Example(2.2), another particular solution is given by $\vec{\tilde{x}} = \begin{bmatrix} 1 \\ -2 \\ 3 \end{bmatrix}$ which is obtained

by selecting $x_3 = 3$ in (2.15).

It is not always the case that the variable with the largest subscript is the free variable. Change the number 5 in the second equation in (2.12) to the number 4 and solve the system

$$\begin{cases} x_1 + 2x_2 + 3x_3 & = 6 \\ 2x_1 + 4x_2 + 4x_3 & = 4 \end{cases}.$$

As in the previous case multiply the first equation by (-2) and add to the second equation to find

$$\begin{cases} x_1 + 2x_2 + 3x_3 & = 6 \\ 0x_1 + 0x_2 - 2x_3 & = -8 \end{cases}$$

whose augmented matrix is

$$\left[\begin{array}{ccc|c} 1 & 2 & 3 & 6 \\ 0 & 0 & -2 & -8 \end{array} \right].$$

Solving the second equation, $-2x_3 = -8$, for x_3 gives $x_3 = 4$. Solve the first equation for x_1 and substitute $x_3 = 4$ to find

$$x_1 = -2x_2 - 3x_3 + 6 = -2x_2 - 3(4) + 6 = -2x_2 - 6$$

In this case it is impossible for x_3 to be the free variable. The solution takes the form

$$\begin{bmatrix} x_1 \\ x_2 \\ x_3 \end{bmatrix} = \begin{bmatrix} -2x_2 - 6 \\ x_2 \\ 4 \end{bmatrix} = x_2 \begin{bmatrix} -2 \\ 1 \\ 0 \end{bmatrix} + \begin{bmatrix} -6 \\ 0 \\ 4 \end{bmatrix} = \vec{x}_h + \vec{x}_p.$$

Both forms of the solution are written as a sum of the homogeneous and particular solutions, $\vec{x}_h + \vec{x}_p$, as it was in equation (2.12). This will be formalized in Definition(2.12).

Finally, change the second equation in the last system to $2x_1 + 4x_2 + 6x_3 = 4$ so that

$$\begin{cases} x_1 + 2x_2 + 3x_3 & = 6 \\ 2x_1 + 4x_2 + 6x_3 & = 4 \end{cases}.$$

Once again multiply the first equation by (-2) and add to the second equation to

$$\begin{cases} x_1 + 2x_2 + 3x_3 &= 6 \\ 0x_1 + 0x_2 + 0x_3 &= -8 \end{cases}$$

so that whose augmented matrix reads

$$\left[\begin{array}{ccc|c} 1 & 2 & 3 & 6 \\ 0 & 0 & 0 & -8 \end{array}\right]. \tag{2.16}$$

The last equation $0x_1 + 0x_2 + 0x_3 = -8$ cannot be satisfied for any point $\begin{bmatrix} x_1 \\ x_2 \\ x_3 \end{bmatrix}$ so the system is inconsistent. Geometrically, this inconsistency could have been predicted. Notice that a normal for the first and second plane are $\begin{bmatrix} 1 \\ 2 \\ 3 \end{bmatrix}$ and $\begin{bmatrix} 2 \\ 4 \\ 6 \end{bmatrix}$, respectively. Since the normal to the planes are parallel the planes are parallel. Moreover, the planes have different x_1-intercepts so they do not intersect.

2.4 Three Equations in Three Unknowns

Adding the equation $x_1 + 3x_2 + a_{33}x_3 = b_3$ where a_{33} and b_3 are parameters to the system in (2.12) leads to the following system of three equations in three unknowns.

Example 2.4 Discuss the solutions, if any, for the linear system

$$\begin{aligned} x_1 + 2x_2 + 3x_3 &= 6 \\ 2x_1 + 5x_2 + 4x_3 &= 4 \\ x_1 + 3x_2 + a_{33}x_3 &= b_3 . \end{aligned} \tag{2.17}$$

Each one of these equations represents a plane in three space. The addition of the third equation in (2.16) allows for the three possibilities: a unique solution (the third plane crosses the line of intersection in Figure 2.4 in exactly one point), infinitely many solutions (the third plane contains the line of intersection) and no solution (the third plane misses the line of intersection). As in Example(2.2) allowing the new equation to have the parameters a_{33} and b_3 allows the illustration of all of these cases. The matrix equation representing the system in (2.17) is given by

$$A\vec{x} \equiv \begin{bmatrix} 1 & 2 & 3 \\ 2 & 5 & 4 \\ 1 & 3 & 2 \end{bmatrix} \begin{bmatrix} x_1 \\ x_2 \\ x_3 \end{bmatrix} = \begin{bmatrix} 6 \\ 4 \\ b_3 \end{bmatrix} \quad \text{so that } [A \mid \vec{b}\,] = \left[\begin{array}{ccc|c} 1 & 2 & 3 & 6 \\ 2 & 5 & 4 & 4 \\ 1 & 3 & a_{33} & b_3 \end{array}\right]. \tag{2.18}$$

is the augmented matrix for the system. An example of a solution of the linear system is given by specifying an a_{33} and b_3, say if $a_{33} = 2$ and $b_3 = 1$ then $\vec{x} = \begin{bmatrix} 1 \\ -2 \\ 3 \end{bmatrix}$. This can be checked by substituting $x_1 = 1$, $x_2 = -2$ and $,x_3 = 3$ into each equation of the system in (2.17) or, what is equivalent, multiplying A times $\vec{x}$ as follows

$$A\vec{x} \equiv \begin{bmatrix} 1 & 2 & 3 \\ 2 & 5 & 4 \\ 1 & 3 & 2 \end{bmatrix} \begin{bmatrix} 1 \\ -2 \\ 3 \end{bmatrix} = \begin{bmatrix} 1(1) + 2(-2) + 3(3) \\ 2(1) + 5(-2) + 4(3) \\ 1(1) + 3(-2) + 2(3) \end{bmatrix} = \begin{bmatrix} 6 \\ 4 \\ 1 \end{bmatrix}.$$

If $a_{33} = 1$ and $\vec{b} = \begin{bmatrix} 6 \\ 4 \\ -2 \end{bmatrix}$ then the vector $\vec{x} = \begin{bmatrix} 8 \\ -4 \\ 2 \end{bmatrix}$ is a solution of (2.17). However,

if $a_{33} = 1$ and $\vec{b} = \begin{bmatrix} 6 \\ 4 \\ 1 \end{bmatrix}$, then there are no solutions to (2.17). This is not the least bit

transparent from looking at the system (2.17). To see how to find the solution of (2.17) and also to lend some clarity to the last statement about the system having no solution, consider the two columns;

Equations with the variables   Augmented Matrix

$$\begin{array}{rrrcl}
x_1+ & 2x_2+ & 3x_3 & = & 6 \\
2x_1+ & 5x_2+ & 4x_3 & = & 4 \\
x_1+ & 3x_2+ & a_{33}x_3 & = & b_3
\end{array}
\qquad \text{Step 1} \qquad
\begin{bmatrix} 1 & 2 & 3 & | & 6 \\ 2 & 5 & 4 & | & 4 \\ 1 & 3 & a_{33} & | & b_3 \end{bmatrix}$$

$$\begin{array}{rrrcl}
x_1+ & 2x_2+ & 3x_3 & = & 6 \\
 & x_2- & 2x_3 & = & -8 \\
x_1+ & 3x_2+ & a_{33}x_3 & = & b_3
\end{array}
\qquad \begin{array}{c}\text{Step 2} \\ (-2)\text{Eq1} + \text{Eq2}\end{array} \qquad
\begin{bmatrix} 1 & 2 & 3 & | & 6 \\ 0 & 1 & -2 & | & -8 \\ 1 & 3 & a_{33} & | & b_3 \end{bmatrix}$$

(2.19)

$$\begin{array}{rrrcl}
x_1+ & 2x_2+ & 3x_3 & = & 6 \\
 & x_2- & 2x_3 & = & -8 \\
 & x_2+ & \alpha x_3 & = & b_3 - 6
\end{array}
\qquad \begin{array}{c}\text{Step 3} \\ (-1)\text{Eq1} + \text{Eq3} \\ \alpha = a_{33} - 3\end{array} \qquad
\begin{bmatrix} 1 & 2 & 3 & | & 6 \\ 0 & 1 & -2 & | & -8 \\ 0 & 1 & \alpha & | & b_3 - 6 \end{bmatrix}$$

$$\begin{array}{rrrcl}
x_1+ & 2x_2+ & 3x_3 & = & 6 \\
 & x_2- & 2x_3 & = & -8 \\
 & & \beta x_3 & = & b_3 + 2
\end{array}
\qquad \begin{array}{c}\text{Step 4} \\ (-1)\text{Eq2} + \text{Eq3} \\ \beta = a_{33} - 1\end{array} \qquad
\begin{bmatrix} 1 & 2 & 3 & | & 6 \\ 0 & 1 & -2 & | & -8 \\ 0 & 0 & \beta & | & b_3 + 2 \end{bmatrix}.$$

The column on the left is related to the column on the right by putting the equations in the equivalent augmented matrix representation. Step 1 is just the association of the set of equations in (2.17) to the matrix equation in (2.18). In the second step the first equation is multiplied by (-2) and added to the second equation, $[(-2)\text{Eq1} + \text{Eq2}]$, which yields a new second equation. This is why the second equation in step 2 has no x_1 term, so the matrix representation in row two has a 0 in the x_1 position. To proceed from Step 2 to Step 3 multiply the first equation in Step 1 by (-1) and add this result to the third equation $[(-1)\text{Eq1} + \text{Eq3}]$. The result is that the third equation in step 3 has no x_1 term so the augmented matrix representation has a 0 in row three in the first position. Finally, to obtain the result in Step 4, the second equation in Step 3 is multiplied by (-1) and then added to the third equation $[(-1)\text{Eq2} + \text{Eq3}]$. This is why the third equation in Step 4 has no x_2. The augmented matrix representation in row three has a 0 in the x_2 position. Although the system of equations in each step is a different set of equations, the systems are equivalent because the solution (or lack of a solution) to any one of the systems is a solution to any of the other systems. *For this reason, for example,* Eq2 *is the notation for the second equation in each step.* This convention will be kept throughout the remainder of this text.

One advantage of the system in Step 4 is that it is simpler than any of the preceding systems. The third equation has only one unknown and the last equation in Step 4 reads

$$\beta x_3 = (a_{33} - 1)x_3 = b_3 + 2. \tag{2.20}$$

so that, for any value of $a_{33} \neq 1$ and any value b_3 the unique solution of equation (2.20) is

$$x_3 = \frac{b_3 + 2}{a_{33} - 1}.$$

Using this value of x_3 in the second equation in Step 4 gives

$$x_2 = -8 + 2x_3 = -8 + \frac{2b_3 + 4}{a_{33} - 1} = \frac{2b_3 + 4}{a_{33} - 1} - 8$$

and finally, using the first equation from Step 4, gives

$$\begin{aligned} x_1 &= 6 - 2x_2 - 3x_3 = 6 - 2\left[\frac{2b_3 + 4}{a_{33} - 1} - 8\right] - 3\left[\frac{b_3 + 2}{a_{33} - 1}\right] \\ &= 22 + \frac{(-7b_3 - 14)}{a_{33} - 1} = \frac{(-7b_3 - 14)}{a_{33} - 1} + 22. \end{aligned}$$

This process of obtaining the solution in reverse order, relative to the index of the variable, is called back substitution. Instead of listing the components of the solution individually, it is useful to house the three previous equations as the vector identity

$$\vec{x} = \begin{bmatrix} x_1 \\ x_2 \\ x_3 \end{bmatrix} = \begin{bmatrix} \dfrac{(-7b_3 - 14)}{a_{33} - 1} + 22 \\ \dfrac{2b_3 + 4}{a_{33} - 1} - 8 \\ \dfrac{b_3 + 2}{a_{33} - 1} \end{bmatrix}, \qquad a_{33} \neq 1. \tag{2.21}$$

As in Example(2.2), the homogeneous solution $\vec{x}_h = \vec{0}$ is not written, and $\vec{x} = \vec{x}_p$ in (2.21) is the unique (particular) solution. Substituting $a_{33} = 2$ and $b_3 = 1$ into (2.21)

$$\vec{x} = \begin{bmatrix} \dfrac{(-7 - 14)}{2 - 1} + 22 \\ \dfrac{2 + 4}{2 - 1} - 8 \\ \dfrac{1 + 2}{2 - 1} \end{bmatrix} = \begin{bmatrix} -21 + 22 \\ 6 - 8 \\ 3 \end{bmatrix} = \begin{bmatrix} 1 \\ -2 \\ 3 \end{bmatrix}$$

which is the solution found in the discussion following equation (2.18).

If $a_{33} = 1$ in (2.20), then there are two possible outcomes.

1. First assume $b_3 = -2$ in conjunction with $a_{33} = 1$ in (2.20) so that equation reads

$$0x_3 = b_3 + 2 = 0$$

or $0 = 0$ which is true for any value of x_3. However, it reveals no information on the dependence of the unknowns: x_1, x_2 and x_3. One of the variables, say x_3, is a free variable (it can take on arbitrary values). The two other rows of the reduced form of the matrix in (2.19) reads

$$
\begin{array}{rcr}
x_1 + 2x_2 + 3x_3 &=& 6 \\
x_2 - 2x_3 &=& -8 \\
\beta x_3 &=& b_3 + 2
\end{array}
\qquad
\begin{array}{l}
\beta = a_{33} - 1 = 0 \\
b_3 = -2
\end{array}
\qquad
\left[
\begin{array}{ccc|c}
1 & 2 & 3 & 6 \\
0 & 1 & -2 & -8 \\
0 & 0 & \beta & b_3 + 2
\end{array}
\right]
$$

$$
\begin{array}{rcr}
x_1 + 2x_2 + 3x_3 &=& 6 \\
x_2 - 2x_3 &=& -8 \\
0x_3 &=& 0
\end{array}
\qquad
\left[
\begin{array}{ccc|c}
1 & 2 & 3 & 6 \\
0 & 1 & -2 & -8 \\
0 & 0 & 0 & 0
\end{array}
\right] . \quad (2.22)
$$

The second line in (2.22) can be solved for x_2 to find

$$x_2 = -8 + 2x_3 = 2x_3 - 8$$

so that x_3 is the free variable. See Exercise(2.5) for the form of the solution if the variable x_2 is chosen as the free variable. Returning to (2.22), solve the first equation for x_1 and substitute x_2 from the last display in the expression for x_1 to find

$$x_1 = 6 - 2x_2 - 3x_3 = 6 - 2(2x_3 - 8) - 3x_3 = 22 - 7x_3. = -7x_3 + 22.$$

The vector form of the solution reads

$$
\left[
\begin{array}{c}
x_1 \\
x_2 \\
x_3
\end{array}
\right]
=
\left[
\begin{array}{c}
-7x_3 + 22 \\
2x_3 - 8 \\
x_3
\end{array}
\right]
$$

$$
=
x_3
\left[
\begin{array}{c}
-7 \\
2 \\
1
\end{array}
\right]
+
\left[
\begin{array}{c}
22 \\
-8 \\
0
\end{array}
\right]
\equiv \vec{x}_h + \vec{x}_p
\qquad (2.23)
$$

so there are infinitely many solutions. As in Example(2.2), $\vec{x}_h$ is called the **homogeneous** part of the solution and $\vec{x}_p$ is called a **particular** solution. As a reminder, if the components of $\vec{x}_h$ are substituted into each of the equations in the system (2.16) then each equation gives zero. If the components of $\vec{x}_p$ are substituted into each of the equations in the system (2.16) equation one gives 6, equation two gives 4 and equation three gives $b_3 = -2$. The sum $\vec{x} \equiv \vec{x}_h + \vec{x}_p$ is the **general** solution to the linear system and, as in Example(2.2), the portion of the solution corresponding to the free variable is the homogeneous solution. In the lines following (2.18) it was

mentioned that if $a_{33} = 1$ and $b_3 = -2$ then $\vec{x} = \begin{bmatrix} 8 \\ -4 \\ 2 \end{bmatrix}$ is a solution to (2.16). This

follows from (2.23) with $x_3 = 2$.

2. If $a_{33} = 1$ and $b_3 \neq -2$ then the equation (2.20) cannot be satisfied for any value of x_3. The last matrix in Step 4 of the (2.18) takes the form

$$\begin{bmatrix} 1 & 2 & 3 & 6 \\ 0 & 1 & -2 & -8 \\ 0 & 0 & 0 & b_3 + 2 \neq 0 \end{bmatrix} \tag{2.24}$$

A specific case of inconsistency is illustrated by taking $\vec{b} = \begin{bmatrix} 6 \\ 4 \\ 1 \end{bmatrix}$. Notice that The

vector $\vec{x} = \begin{bmatrix} 8 \\ -4 \\ 2 \end{bmatrix}$ satisfies the first two equations in (2.24) but when substituted

into the third equation, $x_1 + 3x_2 + x_3 = 8 + 3(-4) + 1 = -3 \neq -2$. Hence, the system is inconsistent.

2.5 Three Equations in Two Unknowns

As a final example, here is a system with fewer unknowns than equations.

Example 2.5 Let a_{32} and b_3 be parameters in the system

$$\begin{cases} x_1 & + & x_2 & = & 2 & : & \text{Eq 1} \\ x_1 & + & 2x_2 & = & 1 & : & \text{Eq 2} \\ 2x_1 & + & a_{32}x_2 & = & b_3 & : & \text{Eq 3} \end{cases} \tag{2.25}$$

where the labeling of the three equations facilitates the discussion. If Eq 1 in (2.25) is multiplied by (-1) [then (-2)] and added to Eq 2 (Eq 3) then the equivalent system is

$$\begin{cases} x_1 & + & x_2 & = 2 \\ & & x_2 & = -1 \\ & & \alpha x_2 & = b_3 - 4 \quad \text{where} \quad \alpha = a_{32} - 2 \end{cases} \tag{2.26}$$

Now a solution of the entire system (2.25) must satisfy each equation of the system. In particular, consider the two equations in two unknowns

$$\begin{cases} x_1 + x_2 & = & 2 \\ x_2 & = & -1 \end{cases} \tag{2.27}$$

obtained from the first two equations in the system (2.26). It is straightforward to show that the unique solution to the system in (2.27) is

$$\begin{bmatrix} x_1 \\ x_2 \end{bmatrix} = \begin{bmatrix} 3 \\ -1 \end{bmatrix}. \tag{2.28}$$

In Figure 2.5 this point is the intersection of the lines represented by Eq 1 and Eq 2 in the original system (2.25). Whether the point in (2.28) is a solution of the original system (2.18) depends on whether the line represented by Eq 3 passes through the point of intersection in Figure 2.5. This is a statement about the behavior of the parameters a_{32} and b_3. The last equation in (2.25) must pass through $x_1 = 3$ and $x_2 = -1$. This means

$$2x_1 + a_{32}x_2 = 2(3) + a_{32}(-1) = 6 - a_{32} = b_3. \tag{2.29}$$

So if (2.29) is not satisfied then the system in (2.25) is inconsistent. For example, if $a_{32} = 4$ and $b_3 \neq 2$, say $b_3 = 1$ then the system (2.25) with Eq 3 given by $2x_1 + 4x_2 = 1$ is inconsistent. There are three different ways that the system in (2.25) can be consistent.

1. If $a_{32} = 4$ then $b_3 = 6 - a_{32} = 2$ and Eq 3 reads $2x_1 + 4x_2 = 6$ which is twice Eq 2. In Figure 2.5 the graph of the second and third lines are the same.

2. If $a_{32} = 2$ then $b_3 = 6 - a_{32} = 4$ and Eq 3 reads $2x_1 + 2x_2 = 4$ which is twice Eq 1. In Figure 2.5 the graph of the first and third lines are the same.

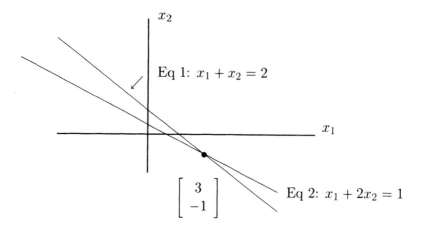

Figure 2.5

3. Suppose the parameter a_{32} in Eq 3 is chosen so that the slope of Eq 3 is not -1 (the slope of Eq 1) nor $\dfrac{-1}{2}$ (the slope of Eq 2). Since the slope of Eq 3 is given by $\dfrac{-2}{a_{32}}$ this selection is accomplished by taking $a_{32} = 3$ and then $b_3 = 6 - a_{32} = 3$ and Eq 3 reads $2x_1 + 3x_2 = 3$. This is depicted in Figure 2.6.

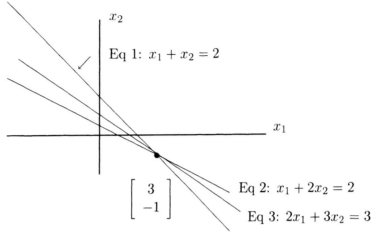

Eq 1: $x_1 + x_2 = 2$

$\begin{bmatrix} 3 \\ -1 \end{bmatrix}$

Eq 2: $x_1 + 2x_2 = 2$

Eq 3: $2x_1 + 3x_2 = 3$

Figure 2.6

2.6 Equivalent Systems and Matrices

Definition 2.6 Consistent and Inconsistent Systems: The previous examples are all included in the linear system defined by the m-linear equations in n-unknowns x_j:

$$
\begin{aligned}
a_{11}x_1 + a_{12}x_2 + \cdots + a_{1j}x_j + \cdots + a_{1n}x_n &= b_1 \\
a_{21}x_1 + a_{22}x_2 + \cdots + a_{2j}x_j + \cdots + a_{2n}x_n &= b_2 \\
&\vdots \\
a_{i1}x_1 + a_{i2}x_2 + \cdots + a_{ij}x_j + \cdots + a_{in}x_n &= b_i \qquad (2.30) \\
&\vdots \\
a_{m1}x_1 + a_{m2}x_2 + \cdots + a_{mj}x_j + \cdots + a_{mn}x_n &= b_m \; .
\end{aligned}
$$

A vector $\vec{x} = [x_1 \; x_2 \; \ldots \; x_n]^T$ is called a **solution** of (2.30) if, when $\vec{x}$ is substituted in each of the m-equations, then each equation is a true statement. If such a solution exists, the system is called **consistent** and if not the system is called **inconsistent**. This is the same language that was introduced for the $m = n = 2$ case in Definition(2.1).

In the preceding examples there have been rearrangements of the original system that facilitate finding the solution of the system or illustrate that no solution exists. In Definition (2.1) these rearrangements defined what are called equivalent systems. Equivalent means that the solution (or lack of a solution) for one system is the same for an equivalent system. These notions for the system in (2.30) are formalized in the following definition.

Definition 2.7 Equivalent Systems: There are three rearrangements of the system in (2.30) that are important. If the scalar multiple of the ith equation

$$\alpha a_{i1}x_1 + \alpha a_{i2}x_2 + \cdots + \alpha a_{ij}x_j + \cdots + \alpha a_{in}x_n = \alpha b_i$$

is added to the qth equation and the qth equation in (2.30) is replaced by

$$(\alpha a_{i1} + a_{q1})x_1 + (\alpha a_{i2} + a_{q2})x_2 + \cdots + (\alpha a_{ij} + a_{qj})x_j + \cdots + (\alpha a_{in} + a_{qn})x_n = \alpha b_i + b_q$$

then the new system,

$$
\begin{aligned}
a_{11}x_1 + \cdots + a_{1j}x_j + \cdots + a_{1n}x_n &= b_1 \\
&\vdots \\
a_{i1}x_1 + \cdots + a_{ij}x_j + \cdots + a_{in}x_n &= b_i \\
&\vdots \\
(\alpha a_{i1} + a_{q1})x_1 + \cdots + (\alpha a_{ij} + a_{qj})x_j + \cdots + (\alpha a_{in} + a_{qn})x_n &= \alpha b_i + b_q \\
&\vdots \\
a_{m1}x_1 + \cdots + a_{mj}x_j + \cdots + a_{mn}x_n &= b_m ,
\end{aligned}
\tag{2.31}
$$

is said to be **equivalent** to the original system. If $\alpha \neq 0$ and the ith equation

$$a_{i1}x_1 + a_{i2}x_2 + \cdots + a_{in}x_n = b_i , \quad i = 1, 2, \ldots m$$

is replaced with

$$\alpha a_{i1}x_1 + \alpha a_{i2}x_2 + \cdots + \alpha a_{in}x_n = \alpha b_i,$$

then the resulting system is called **equivalent** to the original system in (2.30). Finally if the ith and q^{th} equation are interchanged the new system is called **equivalent** to the original system. This means that if the vector $\vec{x}$ is a solution of (2.30) then $\vec{x}$ is also a solution of (2.31). If the two systems, for example (2.30) and (2.31), do not have solutions, then the systems are also called **equivalent**.

For each of the m equations in (2.30) define the n-vector $\vec{a_{i*}}^T = [a_{i1}\ a_{i2} \cdots a_{ij} \cdots a_{in}]$ and set $\vec{x} = [x_1\ x_2\ \cdots\ x_i\ \cdots\ x_j \cdots\ x_n]^T$. If the equations in (2.30) are interpreted as dot products then the linear set of equations can be written in the compact form

$$
A\vec{x} =
\begin{bmatrix}
a_{11} & a_{12} & \cdots & \cdots & a_{1j} & \cdots & a_{1n} \\
a_{21} & a_{22} & \cdots & \cdots & a_{2j} & \cdots & a_{2n} \\
\vdots & \vdots & \ddots & \cdots & \vdots & \vdots & \vdots \\
a_{i1} & a_{i2} & \cdots & \cdots & a_{ij} & \cdots & a_{in} \\
\vdots & \vdots & \ddots & \cdots & \cdots & \ddots & \vdots \\
\vdots & \vdots & \cdots & \cdots & \vdots & \vdots & \vdots \\
a_{m1} & a_{m2} & \cdots & \cdots & a_{mj} & \cdots & a_{mn}
\end{bmatrix}
\begin{bmatrix}
x_1 \\ x_2 \\ \vdots \\ x_i \\ \vdots \\ x_j \\ \vdots \\ x_n
\end{bmatrix}
=
\begin{bmatrix}
\vec{a_{1*}}^T \vec{x} \\
\vec{a_{2*}}^T \vec{x} \\
\vdots \\
\vec{a_{i*}}^T \vec{x} \\
\vdots \\
\vec{a_{m*}}^T \vec{x}
\end{bmatrix}
=
\begin{bmatrix}
b_1 \\ b_2 \\ \vdots \\ b_i \\ \vdots \\ b_m
\end{bmatrix}.
\tag{2.32}
$$

The definition of an $m \times n$ array multiplying an $n \times 1$ vector is given by the second equality in (2.32). In words, the product is the $m \times 1$ vector whose i^{th} entry is the dot product of the ith row of A with the vector $\vec{x}$.

Definition 2.8 Coefficient and Augmented Matrices: The $m \times n$ array

$$A \equiv [a_{ij}]_{mn} = \begin{bmatrix} a_{11} & a_{12} & \cdots & \cdots & a_{1j} & \cdots & a_{1n} \\ a_{21} & a_{22} & \cdots & \cdots & a_{2j} & \cdots & a_{2n} \\ \vdots & \vdots & \ddots & \cdots & \vdots & \vdots & \vdots \\ a_{i1} & a_{i2} & \cdots & \cdots & a_{ij} & \cdots & a_{in} \\ \vdots & \vdots & \cdots & \cdots & \vdots & \vdots & \vdots \\ a_{m1} & a_{m2} & \cdots & \cdots & a_{mj} & \cdots & a_{mn} \end{bmatrix} \qquad (2.33)$$

is called the **coefficient matrix** of the linear system in (2.30). Also associated with the linear system (2.30) is the $m \times (n+1)$ **augmented matrix**

$$[A \mid \vec{b}\,] \equiv \begin{bmatrix} a_{11} & a_{12} & \cdots & \cdots & a_{1j} & \cdots & a_{1n} & \vline & b_1 \\ a_{21} & a_{22} & \cdots & \cdots & a_{2j} & \cdots & a_{2n} & \vline & b_2 \\ \vdots & \vdots & \ddots & \cdots & \vdots & \vdots & \vdots & \vline & \vdots \\ a_{i1} & a_{i2} & \cdots & \cdots & a_{ij} & \cdots & a_{in} & \vline & b_i \\ \vdots & \vdots & \cdots & \cdots & \vdots & \vdots & \vdots & \vline & \vdots \\ a_{m1} & a_{m2} & \cdots & \cdots & a_{mj} & \cdots & a_{mn} & \vline & b_m \end{bmatrix}. \qquad (2.34)$$

The linear system (2.31) has the $m \times (n+1)$ augmented matrix

$$[\tilde{A} \mid \vec{b}\,] \equiv \begin{bmatrix} a_{11} & \cdots & \cdots & a_{1j} & \cdots & a_{1n} & \vline & b_1 \\ a_{21} & \cdots & \cdots & a_{2j} & \cdots & a_{2n} & \vline & b_2 \\ \vdots & \ddots & \cdots & \vdots & \vdots & \vdots & \vline & \vdots \\ a_{i1} & \cdots & \cdots & a_{ij} & \cdots & a_{in} & \vline & b_i \\ \vdots & \vdots & \cdots & \vdots & \vdots & \vdots & \vline & \vdots \\ (\alpha a_{i1} + a_{q1}) & \cdots & \cdots & (\alpha a_{ij} + a_{qj}) & \cdots & (\alpha a_{in} + a_{qn}) & \vline & \alpha b_i + b_q \\ \vdots & \vdots & \cdots & \vdots & \vdots & \vdots & \vline & \vdots \\ a_{m1} & \cdots & \cdots & a_{mj} & \cdots & a_{mn} & \vline & b_m \end{bmatrix}. \qquad (2.35)$$

In light of the Definition(2.7) on equivalent systems, the following definition for row equivalent matrices is natural.

Definition 2.9 Row Equivalent Matrices and Elementary Row Operations: The matrix A is said to be **row equivalent** to the matrix B if A and B are the same size and B is obtained from A by one or more of the following operations:

1. Multiply a row of A by a scalar and add this result to another row of A;

2. Multiply a row of A by a non-zero scalar;

3. Interchange two rows of A.

Each operation is called an **elementary row operation**. The notation for A is equivalent to B is $A \sim B$. The two matrices in (2.34) and (2.35) are equivalent and $[A \mid \vec{b}\,] \sim [\tilde{A} \mid \vec{b}\,]$ where $\vec{b}$ is the $(n+1)^{st}$ column in (2.35).

The method of solving the linear system in (2.32) proceeds in the same fashion as was illustrated in the four examples opening this chapter. That is: apply elementary row operations to the augmented system in (2.34) with the goal of obtaining a simpler system. This simpler system is defined as follows.

2.7   Row and Reduced Row Echelon Form

Definition 2.10 Row Echelon Form and Gauss Elimination: Any $m \times (n+1)$ non-zero matrix $[A \mid \vec{b}\,]$ can be transformed to **row echelon form**, $[U \mid \vec{b}\,]$, which is an $m \times (n+1)$ equivalent matrix satisfying each of the following conditions:

1. The zero row(s), if any, are below the non-zero row(s);

2. For each non-zero row, the leading non-zero entry (reading from the left) is called the **pivot**. Each pivot in a lower number row is to the right of the pivot in a higher numbered row;

3. All entries in a column below the pivot are zero.

The process of transforming $[A \mid \vec{b}\,]$ to the row echelon form $[U \mid \vec{b}\,]$ is called **Gauss Elimination**. Two cases can occur. Since $[A \mid \vec{b}\,] \sim [U \mid \vec{b}\,]$ it is also the case that $A \sim U$. Assume that U has r pivots. If the vector $\vec{b}$ has a non-zero $(r+1)^{st}$ component then the problem $A\vec{x} = \vec{b}$ has no solution. This is because the $(r+1)^{st}$ row, after restoring the variables, reads

$$0x_1 + 0x_2 + \cdots + 0x_n = \tilde{b}_{r+1}$$

where $\tilde{b}_{r+1}$ is the $(r+1)^{st}$ **non-zero** component of $\vec{b}$. This is impossible to satisfy, so the system is inconsistent. See (2.16) in part 2 of Example(2.3) and (2.24) in part 2 of Example(2.4). If $[U \mid \vec{b}\,]$ also has r pivots then the system is consistent. The process of obtaining the solution to $A\vec{x} = \vec{b}$ from $U\vec{x} = \vec{b}$ is called **back substitution**. The components $x_i, i = 1, 2 \ldots, x_n$ of the solution $\vec{x}$ are determined, based on their index, backwards (higher indexed components determined before lower indexed components). Here is an example illustrating all of these definitions.

Example 2.11 The calculation in (2.19) resulted in

$$\left[A \mid \vec{b}\right] = \begin{bmatrix} 1 & 2 & 3 & 6 \\ 2 & 5 & 4 & 4 \\ 1 & 3 & a_{33} & b_3 \end{bmatrix} \sim \begin{bmatrix} 1 & 2 & 3 & 6 \\ 0 & 1 & -2 & -8 \\ 0 & 0 & \beta & b_3 + 2 \end{bmatrix} \equiv \left[U \mid \vec{b}\right],$$

where $\beta = a_{33} - 1$, so that the matrices $\left[A \mid \vec{b} \right]$ and $\left[U \mid \vec{b} \right]$ are row equivalent. The matrix $\left[U \mid \vec{b} \right]$ is in row echelon form. The pivots are $u_{11} = u_{22} = 1$ and $u_{33} = \beta = a_{33} - 1 \neq 0$ if $a_{33} \neq 1$. The process of obtaining the solution from the set of equivalent equations

$$
\begin{array}{rrrcl}
x_1 + & 2x_2 + & 3x_3 & = & 6 \\
 & x_2 - & 2x_3 & = & -8 \\
 & & \beta x_3 & = & b_3 + 2
\end{array}
$$

was illustrated in the lines following (2.20) to obtain (2.21). This is the back substitution method. The component x_3 is found, then x_2 and lastly x_1. If $a_{33} = 1$ and $b_3 + 2 = 0$ then using (2.36)

$$
\left[A \mid \vec{b} \right] = \left[\begin{array}{ccc|c} 1 & 2 & 3 & 6 \\ 2 & 5 & 4 & 4 \\ 1 & 3 & a_{33} & b_3 \end{array} \right]
$$

$$
\sim \left[\begin{array}{ccc|c} 1 & 2 & 3 & 6 \\ 0 & 1 & -2 & -8 \\ 0 & 0 & 0 & 0 \end{array} \right] \equiv \left[U \mid \vec{b} \right],
$$

so that $\left[A \mid \vec{b} \right]$ and $\left[U \mid \vec{b} \right]$ are equivalent matrices. There are two pivots, $u_{11} = u_{22} = 1$. The solution is obtained from

$$
\begin{array}{rcl}
x_1 + 2x_2 + 3x_3 & = & 6 \\
-x_2 - 2x_3 & = & -8.
\end{array}
$$

In the second equation, one can regard either x_2 or x_3 as the free variable. For reasons that will emerge in the Example(2.14) take x_3 as the free variable. Note that x_3 corresponds to the column in the augmented matrix in equation(2.36), which is not a pivot position. This gives the solution found in (2.23). See also Exercise(2.5).

Definition 2.12 Reduced Row Echelon Form, Free Variables, the Homogeneous, the Particular and the General Solution: Any $m \times (n+1)$ non-zero matrix $[A \mid \vec{b}]$ can be transformed to **reduced row echelon form** using elementary row operations, which is an equivalent matrix satisfying each of the following:

1. The zero row(s), if any, are below the non-zero row(s);

2. For each non-zero row, the leading non-zero entry (reading from the left) is the number 1 (these are the pivot positions and, for convenience here, will be referred to as pivots). Each pivot is to the right of the pivot above it;

3. All entries above and below the pivot position 1's are zero.

Assume the system $A\vec{x} = \vec{b}$ is consistent and that $[\,\mathcal{E}\mid\vec{b}\,]$ is the reduced row echelon form of $[\,A\mid\vec{b}\,]$. Assume that $[\,\mathcal{E}\mid\vec{b}\,]$ has r pivots. The number of **free variables** is $n - r$ and the free variable(s) index corresponds to the non-pivot elements column position. The **general** solution has the form

$$\vec{x} = \vec{x}_h + \vec{x}_p.$$

The **homogeneous** part of the solution, $\vec{x}_h$, contains the $n - r$ **free** variables. If the components of $\vec{x}_h$ are substituted into each of the equations in the original system then each equation gives zero. If the components of the **particular** part of the solution $\vec{x}_p$ are substituted into each of the equations in the original system, then the ith equation yields the given quantity b_i, $i = 1, 2, \ldots, m$.

Theorem 2.13 Assume that the $m \times n$ matrix A has r pivots. The **homogeneous problem** $A\vec{x} = \vec{b} = \vec{0}$ is always consistent. If $r = n$ the unique solution to $A\vec{x} = \vec{0}$ is $\vec{x} = \vec{0}$. The homogeneous problem has non-zero solutions if and only if $r < n$.

The vector $\vec{x} = \vec{0}$ is a solution to $A\vec{x} = \vec{0}$. The important case occurs when there are non-zero solutions. From the discussion in Definition(2.12), this occurs when there are free variables. In general there are $n - r$ free variables so the homogeneous problem has non-zero solutions when the number of pivots r is less than the number of unknowns n.

All of the previous has been illustrated in the examples discussed before Definition(2.3). In Example(2.2) (where $n = r = 2$ and $a_{22} \neq -1$) equation (2.9) illustrates a unique solution. In this case the homogeneous problem $A\vec{x} = \vec{0}$ has only the zero solution. Also, in Example(2.2) (where $a_{22} = -1$ and $b_2 = 3/2$) the nontrivial homogeneous solution $\vec{x}_h$ has one free variable and illustrates Theorem(2.13) with $n = 2 > r = 1$. In Example(2.3) the system is always consistent. In this example, $n = 3 > r = 2$ and the solution in (2.15) has $n - r = 1$ free variable. In contrast, the systems in Example(2.4) may or may not be consistent. The two consistent cases are (i) the case of a unique solution $n = 3 = r$ was illustrated in (2.21) and (ii) the case of infinitely many solutions $n = 3 > r = 2$ which is illustrated in (2.23). In Example(2.5) it is the case that $(n = r = 2)$. In the augmented matrix for equation (2.26) there are always two pivots no matter what the values of a_{32} and b_3. Hence, $\vec{0}$ is the only (unique) solution to $A\vec{x} = \vec{0}$. Example (2.4) will be used to illustrate a reduced row echelon form of a matrix.

Example 2.14 Beginning with (2.36) with $a_{33} = 2$ and $b_3 = 1$ proceed with the calculation

$$\left[A \mid \vec{b}\right] = \begin{bmatrix} 1 & 2 & 3 & 6 \\ 2 & 5 & 4 & 4 \\ 1 & 3 & 2 & 1 \end{bmatrix} \qquad \sim \qquad [\,U \mid \vec{b}\,]$$

$$\equiv \qquad \begin{bmatrix} 1 & 2 & 3 & 6 \\ 0 & 1 & -2 & -8 \\ 0 & 0 & 1 & 3 \end{bmatrix}$$

$$(2)\text{Eq3} + \text{Eq2} \qquad \begin{bmatrix} 1 & 2 & 3 & 6 \\ 0 & 1 & 0 & -2 \\ 0 & 0 & 1 & 3 \end{bmatrix}$$
$$\sim$$

$$(-3)\text{Eq3} + \text{Eq1} \qquad \begin{bmatrix} 1 & 2 & 0 & -3 \\ 0 & 1 & 0 & -2 \\ 0 & 0 & 1 & 3 \end{bmatrix}$$
$$\sim$$

$$(-2)\text{Eq2} + \text{Eq1} \qquad \begin{bmatrix} 1 & 0 & 0 & 1 \\ 0 & 1 & 0 & -2 \\ 0 & 0 & 1 & 3 \end{bmatrix}$$
$$\sim$$

$$\equiv \qquad [\, \mathcal{E} \mid \vec{b} \,]. \tag{2.36}$$

The augmented matrix after the first equivalent sign ($[\, U \mid \vec{b} \,]$) in the above calculation is the echelon form of $\left[A \mid \vec{b} \right]$ (see the last entry in (2.19)). The pivots are the numbers 1, 1 and 1. The four steps above to get to the reduced row echelon form are to convert all of the pivots to the number 1 and to introduce the zeros above these 1's. The last matrix is in reduced row echelon form ($[\, \mathcal{E} \mid \vec{b} \,]$). There are $n = 3$ unknowns and there are $r = 3$ pivots. From this reduced form it follows that

$$\vec{x} = \begin{bmatrix} x_1 \\ x_2 \\ x_3 \end{bmatrix} = \begin{bmatrix} 1 \\ -2 \\ 3 \end{bmatrix}$$

is the unique solution. This is the result found from (2.21) with $a_{33} = 2$ and $b_3 = 1$.

Whether one solves the original system using row echelon form $[\, U \mid \vec{b} \,]$ in (2.19) or using the reduced row echelon form $[\, \mathcal{E} \mid \vec{b} \,]$ in (2.36) really does not matter. Equivalent systems have the same solution. The system $[\, \mathcal{E} \mid \vec{b} \,]$ is simpler than the system $[\, U \mid \vec{b} \,]$, in the sense that the former has more zero entries. Whether the extra work (row operations) to go from $[\, U \mid \vec{b} \,]$ to $[\, \mathcal{E} \mid \vec{b} \,]$ in (2.36) makes it easier (compared to the back substitution) to solve the system in (2.19) is in the eyes of the beholder. Using the back substitution from the system $[\, U \mid \vec{b} \,]$ seems as simple as the extra steps to obtain $[\, \mathcal{E} \mid \vec{b} \,]$ from $[\, U \mid \vec{b} \,]$. There are, however, other uses for the reduced row echelon form occurring in the next chapter that are quite important.

Example 2.15 If $a_{33} = 1$ and $b_3 + 2 = 0$ then beginning with (2.36), continue the calculation to find

$$\left[A \mid \vec{b} \right] = \begin{bmatrix} 1 & 2 & 3 & 6 \\ 2 & 5 & 4 & 4 \\ 1 & 3 & 1 & b_3 \end{bmatrix} \qquad \sim \qquad \begin{bmatrix} 1 & 2 & 3 & 6 \\ 0 & 1 & -2 & -8 \\ 0 & 0 & 0 & 0 \end{bmatrix}$$

$$(-2)\text{Eq2} + \text{Eq1} \qquad \begin{bmatrix} 1 & 0 & 7 & 22 \\ 0 & 1 & -2 & -8 \\ 0 & 0 & 0 & 0 \end{bmatrix}. \tag{2.37}$$
$$\sim$$

The reduced row echelon form in (2.37) gives

$$x_2 = 2x_3 - 8$$
$$x_1 = -7x_3 + 22$$

or in vector form

$$\begin{bmatrix} x_1 \\ x_2 \\ x_3 \end{bmatrix} = \begin{bmatrix} -7x_3 + 22 \\ 2x_3 - 8 \\ x_3 \end{bmatrix} + x_3 \begin{bmatrix} -7 \\ 2 \\ 1 \end{bmatrix} = \begin{bmatrix} 22 \\ -8 \\ 0 \end{bmatrix}$$

which reproduces (2.23). There are $r = 2$ pivots and there is $n - r = 3 - 2 = 1$ free variable. This is why in Example(2.4) the variable x_3 was declared the free variable. When a matrix is transformed to reduced row echelon form, the free variables will be the variables that are not in the pivot positions.

The closing example illustrates row and reduced row reductions to obtain the general solution for a "semi-large problem" (see also Exercise(2.8)).

Example 2.16 Solve the linear system

$$A\vec{x} = \begin{bmatrix} 1 & 2 & 3 & 4 \\ 2 & 4 & 4 & 4 \\ 3 & 6 & 9 & a_{34} \end{bmatrix} \begin{bmatrix} x_1 \\ x_2 \\ x_3 \\ x_4 \end{bmatrix} = \begin{bmatrix} 6 \\ 4 \\ b_3 \end{bmatrix}$$

by first finding the row echelon form of the augmented matrix for the system. In the following calculations the steps on the right hand side of the augmented matrix are the row operations used to get to the equivalent augmented matrix which follows:

$$\begin{bmatrix} A \mid \vec{b} \end{bmatrix} = \begin{bmatrix} 1 & 2 & 3 & 4 & \Big| & 6 \\ 2 & 4 & 4 & 4 & \Big| & 4 \\ 3 & 6 & 9 & a_{34} & \Big| & b_3 \end{bmatrix} \quad \begin{cases} (-2)\text{Eq1} + \text{Eq2} \\ (-3)\text{Eq1} + \text{Eq3} \end{cases}$$

$$\sim \begin{bmatrix} 1 & 2 & 3 & 4 & \Big| & 6 \\ 0 & 0 & -2 & -4 & \Big| & -8 \\ 0 & 0 & 0 & a_{34} - 12 & \Big| & b_3 - 18 \end{bmatrix}. \qquad (2.38)$$

The number of pivots in the row echelon form is three if $a_{34} \neq 12$ and it is two if $a_{34} = 12$. Each of these cases will be considered.

1. Take $a_{34} \neq 12$, say $a_{34} = 13$ to be specific, and continue the calculation in (2.38)

$$\begin{bmatrix} A \mid \vec{b} \end{bmatrix} \sim \begin{bmatrix} 1 & 2 & 3 & 4 & \Big| & 6 \\ 0 & 0 & -2 & -4 & \Big| & -8 \\ 0 & 0 & 0 & 1 & \Big| & b_3 - 18 \end{bmatrix} \quad \begin{cases} 4\text{Eq3} + \text{Eq2} \\ (-4)\text{Eq3} + \text{Eq1} \end{cases}$$

$$\sim \begin{bmatrix} 1 & 2 & 3 & 0 & | & -4b_3 + 78 \\ 0 & 0 & -2 & 0 & | & 4b_3 - 80 \\ 0 & 0 & 0 & 1 & | & b_3 - 18 \end{bmatrix} \quad \{ -(3/2)\text{Eq2} + \text{Eq1}$$

$$\sim \begin{bmatrix} 1 & 2 & 0 & 0 & | & 2b_3 - 42 \\ 0 & 0 & -2 & 0 & | & 4b_3 - 80 \\ 0 & 0 & 0 & 1 & | & b_3 - 18 \end{bmatrix} \quad \{ -(1/2)\text{Eq2}$$

$$\sim \begin{bmatrix} 1 & 2 & 0 & 0 & | & 2b_3 - 42 \\ 0 & 0 & 1 & 0 & | & -2b_3 + 40 \\ 0 & 0 & 0 & 1 & | & b_3 - 18 \end{bmatrix} \equiv [\, \mathcal{E} \mid \vec{\tilde{b}} \,] \qquad (2.39)$$

where the latter is the notation for the reduced echelon matrix in Definition(2.12). Since there is no restriction on b_3, this system is always consistent. Using Definition(2.12), there are $r = 3$ pivots and there is $n - r = 4 - 3 = 1$ free variable which is x_2 since this is column number of the non-pivot position. Finally, this system is always consistent and the general solution is

$$\vec{x} = \begin{bmatrix} x_1 \\ x_2 \\ x_3 \\ x_4 \end{bmatrix} = \begin{bmatrix} -2x_2 + 2b_3 - 42 \\ x_2 \\ -2b_3 + 40 \\ b_3 - 18 \end{bmatrix}$$

$$= x_2 \begin{bmatrix} -2 \\ 1 \\ 0 \\ 0 \end{bmatrix} + \begin{bmatrix} 2b_3 - 42 \\ 0 \\ -2b_3 + 40 \\ b_3 - 18 \end{bmatrix} = \vec{x}_h + \vec{x}_p. \qquad (2.40)$$

As a specific case, take $b_3 = 1$ so that a particular solution is $\vec{x}_p = \begin{bmatrix} -40 \\ 0 \\ 38 \\ -17 \end{bmatrix}$ and the

homogeneous solution $\vec{x}_h = x_2 \begin{bmatrix} -2 \\ 1 \\ 0 \\ 0 \end{bmatrix}$. To check this particular solution calculate

the matrix product

$$A\vec{x}_p = \begin{bmatrix} 1 & 2 & 3 & 4 \\ 2 & 4 & 4 & 4 \\ 3 & 6 & 9 & 13 \end{bmatrix} \begin{bmatrix} -40 \\ 0 \\ 38 \\ -17 \end{bmatrix} = \begin{bmatrix} -40 + 0 + 3(38) + 4(-17) \\ 2(-40) + 0 + 4(38) + 4(-17) \\ 3(-40) + 0 + 9(38) + 13(-17) \end{bmatrix} = \begin{bmatrix} 6 \\ 4 \\ 1 \end{bmatrix}$$

and the homogeneous solution satisfies

$$A\vec{x}_h = \begin{bmatrix} 1 & 2 & 3 & 4 \\ 2 & 4 & 4 & 4 \\ 3 & 6 & 9 & 13 \end{bmatrix} \left(x_2 \begin{bmatrix} -2 \\ 1 \\ 0 \\ 0 \end{bmatrix} \right) = x_2 \begin{bmatrix} 1 & 2 & 3 & 4 \\ 2 & 4 & 4 & 4 \\ 3 & 6 & 9 & 13 \end{bmatrix} \begin{bmatrix} -2 \\ 1 \\ 0 \\ 0 \end{bmatrix} = \begin{bmatrix} 0 \\ 0 \\ 0 \end{bmatrix}.$$

2. Take $a_{34} = 12$ in (2.39) so that

$$\left[\, A \mid \vec{b} \,\right] \sim \begin{bmatrix} 1 & 2 & 3 & 4 & 6 \\ 0 & 0 & -2 & -4 & -8 \\ 0 & 0 & 0 & 0 & b_3 - 18 \end{bmatrix}. \tag{2.41}$$

In contrast to part 1 where the system is always consistent, in this system if $b_3 - 18 \neq 0$ the system is inconsistent. Hence, in order for (2.41) to have solutions one must require $b_3 = 18$. The reduced echelon form beginning with (2.41) proceeds as

$$\left[\, A \mid \vec{b} \,\right] \sim \begin{bmatrix} 1 & 2 & 3 & 4 & 6 \\ 0 & 0 & -2 & -4 & -8 \\ 0 & 0 & 0 & 0 & 0 \end{bmatrix} \qquad \left\{ \begin{array}{c} b_3 = 18 \\ (3/2)\text{Eq2} + \text{Eq1} \end{array} \right.$$

$$\sim \begin{bmatrix} 1 & 2 & 0 & -2 & -6 \\ 0 & 0 & -2 & -4 & -8 \\ 0 & 0 & 0 & 0 & 0 \end{bmatrix} \qquad \left\{ \; (-1/2)\text{Eq2} \right.$$

$$\sim \begin{bmatrix} 1 & 2 & 0 & -2 & -6 \\ 0 & 0 & 1 & 2 & 4 \\ 0 & 0 & 0 & 0 & 0 \end{bmatrix}. \tag{2.42}$$

There are $r = 2$ pivots and $n - r = 4 - 2 = 2$ free variables which are x_2 and x_4 since these are the column numbers of the non-pivot positions. The general solution is

$$\vec{x} = \begin{bmatrix} x_1 \\ x_2 \\ x_3 \\ x_4 \end{bmatrix} = \begin{bmatrix} -2x_2 + 2x_4 - 6 \\ x_2 \\ -2x_4 + 4 \\ x_4 \end{bmatrix}$$

$$= \left\{ x_2 \begin{bmatrix} -2 \\ 1 \\ 0 \\ 0 \end{bmatrix} + x_4 \begin{bmatrix} 2 \\ 0 \\ -2 \\ 1 \end{bmatrix} \right\} + \begin{bmatrix} -6 \\ 0 \\ 4 \\ 0 \end{bmatrix} = \{\vec{x}_h\} + \vec{x}_p. \tag{2.43}$$

Using the matrix product in (2.32) (twice) to see that

$$A\vec{x}_h = \begin{bmatrix} 1 & 2 & 3 & 4 \\ 2 & 4 & 4 & 4 \\ 3 & 6 & 9 & 12 \end{bmatrix} \left\{ x_2 \begin{bmatrix} -2 \\ 1 \\ 0 \\ 0 \end{bmatrix} + x_4 \begin{bmatrix} 2 \\ 0 \\ -2 \\ 1 \end{bmatrix} \right\}$$

$$= \begin{bmatrix} 1 & 2 & 3 & 4 \\ 2 & 4 & 4 & 4 \\ 3 & 6 & 9 & 12 \end{bmatrix} \left(x_2 \begin{bmatrix} -2 \\ 1 \\ 0 \\ 0 \end{bmatrix} \right) + \begin{bmatrix} 1 & 2 & 3 & 4 \\ 2 & 4 & 4 & 4 \\ 3 & 6 & 9 & 12 \end{bmatrix} \left(x_4 \begin{bmatrix} 2 \\ 0 \\ -2 \\ 1 \end{bmatrix} \right)$$

$$= x_2 \left(\begin{bmatrix} 1 & 2 & 3 & 4 \\ 2 & 4 & 4 & 4 \\ 3 & 6 & 9 & 12 \end{bmatrix} \begin{bmatrix} -2 \\ 1 \\ 0 \\ 0 \end{bmatrix} \right) + x_4 \left(\begin{bmatrix} 1 & 2 & 3 & 4 \\ 2 & 4 & 4 & 4 \\ 3 & 6 & 9 & 12 \end{bmatrix} \begin{bmatrix} 2 \\ 0 \\ -2 \\ 1 \end{bmatrix} \right)$$

$$= x_2 \begin{bmatrix} -2+2 \\ -4+4 \\ -6+6 \end{bmatrix} + x_4 \begin{bmatrix} 2-6+4 \\ 4-8+4 \\ 6-18+12 \end{bmatrix} = \begin{bmatrix} 0 \\ 0 \\ 0 \end{bmatrix}.$$

The second equality follows from the fact that the dot product distributes over the sum of two vectors (from Definition(1.8)) and apply this with each row of A. There will be a lot more of this in the next chapter. The calculation

$$A\vec{x}_p = \begin{bmatrix} 1 & 2 & 3 & 4 \\ 2 & 4 & 4 & 4 \\ 3 & 6 & 9 & 12 \end{bmatrix} \begin{bmatrix} -6 \\ 0 \\ 4 \\ 0 \end{bmatrix} = \begin{bmatrix} -6+3(4) \\ 2(-6)+4(4) \\ 3(-6)+4(9) \end{bmatrix} = \begin{bmatrix} 6 \\ 4 \\ 18 \end{bmatrix}$$

provides a check on the the validity of the particular solution.

2.8 Exercise Set

Exercise 2.1 For each of the following linear systems, write down the system as a matrix equation, write down the augmented matrix for the system and then find the unique solution to the linear systems using Gauss Elimination.

1. $\begin{cases} 2x_1 - 2x_2 = 1 \\ x_1 + x_2 = 3 \ . \end{cases}$ See Example(2.2) where $a_{22} = 1$ and $b_2 = 3$ in (2.19).

2. $\begin{cases} x_1 + 2x_2 + 3x_3 = 6 \\ 2x_1 + 5x_2 + 4x_3 = 4 \\ x_1 + 3x_2 + 3x_3 = 2 \end{cases}$ See Example(2.4) with $a_{33} = 3$ and $b_3 = 2$ and (2.19).

3. $\begin{cases} x_1 + 2x_2 + 3x_3 = 6 \\ 2x_1 + 5x_2 + 4x_3 = 4 \\ x_1 + 3x_2 - 2x_3 = 2 \end{cases}$ See Example(2.4) with $a_{33} = -2$ and $b_3 = 2$ and (2.19).

4. $\begin{cases} x_1 + x_2 = 2 \\ x_1 + 2x_2 = 1 \\ 2x_1 + 5x_2 = 1 \end{cases}$ See Example(2.5) with $a_{32} = 5$ and $b_3 = 1$.

5. $\begin{cases} x_1 + x_2 = 2 \\ x_1 + 2x_2 = 1 \\ 2x_1 - 2x_2 = 8 \end{cases}$ See Example(2.5) with $a_{32} = -2$ and $b_3 = 8$.

Exercise 2.2 For each of the following linear systems, write down the system as a matrix equation, write down the augmented matrix for the system and then show that the system is inconsistent via Gauss elimination. See the discussion in Definition(2.10).

1. $\begin{cases} 2x_1 - 2x_2 = 3 \\ x_1 - x_2 = 2 \ . \end{cases}$ See Example(2.2) with $a_{22} = -1$ and $b_2 = 2$.

2. $\begin{cases} x_1 + 2x_2 + 3x_3 = 6 \\ 2x_1 + 5x_2 + 4x_3 = 4 \\ x_1 + 3x_2 + x_3 = 3 \ . \end{cases}$ See Example(2.4) with $a_{33} = 1$ and $b_3 = 3$.

3. $\begin{cases} x_1 + x_2 = 2 \\ x_1 + 2x_2 = 1 \\ 2x_1 + 4x_2 = 3 \ . \end{cases}$ See Example(2.5) with $a_{32} = 4$, $b_3 = 2$.

Exercise 2.3 Find a value for b_2 so that the system $\begin{cases} x_1 + 2x_2 + 3x_3 = 6 \\ 2x_1 + 4x_2 + 6x_3 = b_2 \end{cases}$ has infinitely many solutions. Find these solutions. Compare to (2.16).

Exercise 2.4 The general solution to the problem $\begin{cases} 2x_1 - 2x_2 = 3 \\ x_1 - x_2 = \dfrac{3}{2} \end{cases}$ is given by $\vec{x} \equiv$

$x_2 \begin{bmatrix} 1 \\ 1 \end{bmatrix} + \begin{bmatrix} 3/2 \\ 0 \end{bmatrix}$ where x_2 is a free variable. This was found in Example(2.2). Define

$\vec{x}_h \equiv x_2 \begin{bmatrix} 1 \\ 1 \end{bmatrix}$ and $\vec{x}_p \equiv \begin{bmatrix} 3/2 \\ 0 \end{bmatrix}$ and $A = \begin{bmatrix} 2 & -2 \\ 1 & -1 \end{bmatrix}$. Verify that $A\vec{x}_h = \begin{bmatrix} 0 \\ 0 \end{bmatrix}$ and $A\vec{x}_p =$

$\begin{bmatrix} 3 \\ 3/2 \end{bmatrix}$. Show that $\vec{\tilde{x}}_p = \begin{bmatrix} 1/2 \\ -1 \end{bmatrix}$ is also a particular solution to the problem. Recall that the free variable x_2 can be assigned any value.

Exercise 2.5 The row echelon form for $A\vec{x} = \begin{bmatrix} 1 & 2 & 3 \\ 2 & 5 & 4 \end{bmatrix} \begin{bmatrix} x_1 \\ x_2 \\ x_3 \end{bmatrix} = \begin{bmatrix} 6 \\ 4 \end{bmatrix}$ is

$$\left[\begin{array}{ccc|c} 1 & 2 & 3 & 6 \\ 2 & 5 & 4 & 4 \end{array}\right] \sim \left[\begin{array}{ccc|c} 1 & 2 & 3 & 6 \\ 0 & 1 & -2 & -8 \end{array}\right] \sim \left[\begin{array}{ccc|c} 1 & 0 & 7 & 22 \\ 0 & 1 & -2 & -8 \end{array}\right]$$

where the first equivalence is from (2.14) and the second gives the reduced echelon form for the system (Definition(2.12)) . Find x_1 and x_2 from the reduced echelon form. Compare this to the lines preceding the solution in (2.15).

Exercise 2.6 The matrix of Example(2.4) with $a_{33} = 1$ is $A = \begin{bmatrix} 1 & 2 & 3 \\ 2 & 5 & 4 \\ 1 & 3 & 1 \end{bmatrix}$ and the

general solution to $A\vec{x} = \vec{b} = \begin{bmatrix} 6 \\ 4 \\ -2 \end{bmatrix}$, from (2.23), is given by

$$\vec{x} = \begin{bmatrix} x_1 \\ x_2 \\ x_3 \end{bmatrix} = x_3 \begin{bmatrix} -7 \\ 2 \\ 1 \end{bmatrix} + \begin{bmatrix} 22 \\ -8 \\ 0 \end{bmatrix} = \vec{x}_h + \vec{x}_p.$$

1. Verify that

$$A\vec{x}_h \equiv \begin{bmatrix} 1 & 2 & 3 \\ 2 & 5 & 4 \\ 1 & 3 & 1 \end{bmatrix} \left(x_3 \begin{bmatrix} -7 \\ 2 \\ 1 \end{bmatrix} \right) = \vec{0} = \begin{bmatrix} 0 \\ 0 \\ 0 \end{bmatrix}$$

and

$$A\vec{x}_p = \begin{bmatrix} 1 & 2 & 3 \\ 2 & 5 & 4 \\ 1 & 3 & 1 \end{bmatrix} \begin{bmatrix} 22 \\ -8 \\ 0 \end{bmatrix} = \begin{bmatrix} 6 \\ 4 \\ -2 \end{bmatrix}.$$

2. Another form for the general solution to this problem is obtained as follows. From the second row in augmented system in (2.22), instead of solving for x_2 as was done

following (2.22), solve for x_3 to find $x_3 = \dfrac{x_2 + 8}{2}$. Here x_2 is the free variable. Use $x_1 + 2x_2 + 3x_3 = 6$ to find x_1 in terms of x_2 and x_3. Show that the solution of the system takes the form

$$\vec{x} = \begin{bmatrix} x_1 \\ x_2 \\ x_3 \end{bmatrix} = x_2 \begin{bmatrix} -7/2 \\ 1 \\ 1/2 \end{bmatrix} + \begin{bmatrix} -6 \\ 0 \\ 4 \end{bmatrix} \equiv \vec{x}_h + \vec{x}_p.$$

As in part 1, $A\vec{x}_h = \vec{0}$ and $A\vec{x}_p = \vec{b}$. A connection between this new and the old solution is given by

$$\hat{\vec{x}}_h = \frac{1}{2}\vec{x}_h \quad \text{and} \quad \hat{\vec{x}}_p = 4\vec{x}_h + \vec{x}_p.$$

Indeed, if x_2 is replaced by $2x_3 - 8$ in the solution $\hat{\vec{x}}$ then this solution becomes the solution $\vec{x}$. That is, either x_2 or x_3 can be the free variable.

Exercise 2.7 Change the system in (2.25) to

$$A\vec{x} \equiv \begin{bmatrix} 1 & 1 \\ 1 & 2 \\ 2 & a_{32} \end{bmatrix} \begin{bmatrix} x_1 \\ x_2 \end{bmatrix} = \begin{bmatrix} 2 \\ b_2 \\ b_3 \end{bmatrix}.$$

The second equation in (2.25), $x_1 + 2x_2 = 1$, is replaced by the equation $x_1 + 2x_2 = b_2$.

1. Assume that $b_2 = 3$. Find a condition on a_{33} and b_3 (analogous to (2.29)) so that the system is consistent. Identify the case of three distinct lines as in Part 3 of Example(2.5).

2. Assume that $b_2 = 2$. Argue that, in the case of consistency, b_3 is uniquely determined independent of the value for a_{32}.

Exercise 2.8 The reduction of the augmented matrix for the system

$$A\vec{x} = \begin{bmatrix} 1 & 2 & 3 & 4 \\ 2 & 4 & 4 & 5 \\ 3 & a_{32} & 5 & 6 \end{bmatrix} \begin{bmatrix} x_1 \\ x_2 \\ x_3 \\ x_4 \end{bmatrix} = \begin{bmatrix} 1 \\ 0 \\ b_3 \end{bmatrix}$$

reads

$$\left[A \mid \vec{b} \right] = \left[\begin{array}{cccc|c} 1 & 2 & 3 & 4 & 1 \\ 0 & 0 & -2 & -3 & -2 \\ 0 & a_{32} - 6 & -4 & -6 & b_3 - 3 \end{array} \right].$$

1. Let $a_{32} = 6$ so that the augmented system reads $\left[\begin{array}{cccc|c} 1 & 2 & 3 & 4 & 1 \\ 0 & 0 & -2 & -3 & -2 \\ 0 & 0 & -4 & -6 & b_3 - 3 \end{array} \right]$. Find a condition on b_3 so that the system is consistent. Further, show that the general

solution is given by

$$
\vec{x} =
\begin{bmatrix}
-2x_2 + (1/2)x_4 - 2 \\
x_2 \\
(-3/2)x_4 + 1 \\
x_4
\end{bmatrix}
=
\begin{bmatrix}
-2x_2 + (1/2)x_4 \\
x_2 \\
-(3/2)x_4 \\
x_4
\end{bmatrix}
+
\begin{bmatrix}
-2 \\
0 \\
1 \\
0
\end{bmatrix}
$$

$$
=
\left\{
x_2
\begin{bmatrix}
-2 \\
1 \\
0 \\
0
\end{bmatrix}
+ x_4
\begin{bmatrix}
1/2 \\
0 \\
-3/2 \\
1
\end{bmatrix}
\right\}
+
\begin{bmatrix}
2 \\
0 \\
1 \\
0
\end{bmatrix}
= \{\vec{x}_h\} + \vec{x}_p .
$$

There are $n = 4$ unknowns and $r = 2$ pivots and there are $n - r = 4 - 2 = 2$ free variables.

2. Show that if $a_{32} = 7$ then the system is solvable for any value of b_3. Let $b_3 = -1$, show that the general solution is

$$
\vec{x} =
\begin{bmatrix}
x_1 \\
x_2 \\
x_3 \\
x_4
\end{bmatrix}
=
\begin{bmatrix}
(1/2)x_4 - 2 \\
0 \\
-(3/2)x_4 + 1 \\
x_4
\end{bmatrix}
= x_4
\begin{bmatrix}
1/2 \\
0 \\
-3/2 \\
1
\end{bmatrix}
+
\begin{bmatrix}
-2 \\
0 \\
1 \\
0
\end{bmatrix}
$$

In contrast to part 1 there are $r = 3$ pivots and there is $n - r = 4 - 3 = 1$ free variable.

Exercise 2.9 The system $\begin{cases} 2x_1 - 2x_2 = 1 \\ x_1 + (1/2)x_2 = 0 \end{cases}$ has the augmented matrix $\begin{bmatrix} 2 & -2 & | & 1 \\ 1 & 1/2 & | & 0 \end{bmatrix}$

1. Transform the augmented system to reduced row echelon form and show that the solution to this reduced system is $\vec{x} \equiv \vec{\hat{a}}_1 = \begin{bmatrix} 1/6 \\ -1/3 \end{bmatrix}$. This means the matrix product

$$
A\vec{\hat{a}}_1 =
\begin{bmatrix}
2 & -2 \\
1 & -1/2
\end{bmatrix}
\begin{bmatrix}
1/6 \\
-1/3
\end{bmatrix}
=
\begin{bmatrix}
1 \\
0
\end{bmatrix}
$$

is satisfied.

2. Repeat part 1 for the system $\begin{cases} 2x_1 - 2x_2 = 0 \\ x_1 + x_2 = 1 \end{cases}$. Show that the solution to this reduced system is $\vec{x} \equiv \vec{\hat{a}}_2 = \begin{bmatrix} 2/3 \\ 2/3 \end{bmatrix}$ which means

$$
A\vec{\hat{a}}_2 =
\begin{bmatrix}
2 & -2 \\
1 & 1
\end{bmatrix}
\begin{bmatrix}
2/3 \\
2/3
\end{bmatrix}
=
\begin{bmatrix}
0 \\
1
\end{bmatrix}.
$$

3. Define the matrix $\hat{A} = [\vec{a}_1 \ \vec{a}_2] = \begin{bmatrix} 1/6 & 2/3 \\ -1/3 & 2/3 \end{bmatrix}$ whose columns are the solution vectors from parts 1 and 2. Further, define the matrix product $A[\vec{a}_1 \ \vec{a}_2] \equiv [A\vec{a}_1 \ A\vec{a}_2]$ which is the definition in equation (2.6) applied to each column of the matrix $\hat{A}$. Show that

$$A\hat{A} = \begin{bmatrix} 1 & 0 \\ 0 & 1 \end{bmatrix} \equiv I = \hat{A}A.$$

4. Let $B = \begin{bmatrix} b_{11} & b_{12} \\ b_{21} & b_{22} \end{bmatrix}$. Use the definition of the matrix product in part 3 to show that

$$\begin{bmatrix} b_{11} & b_{12} \\ b_{21} & b_{22} \end{bmatrix} \begin{bmatrix} 1 & 0 \\ 0 & 1 \end{bmatrix} = \begin{bmatrix} 1 & 0 \\ 0 & 1 \end{bmatrix} \begin{bmatrix} b_{11} & b_{12} \\ b_{21} & b_{22} \end{bmatrix}$$

and conclude that $BI = IB = B$. It's for this reason the matrix $I = \begin{bmatrix} 1 & 0 \\ 0 & 1 \end{bmatrix}$ is called the multiplicative identity. Its action in multiplication of 2×2 matrices is the same as the action of the number 1 for real number multiplication, that is $1a = a1 = a$, where a is a real number. From part 3, and borrowing the notion of exponents it is tempting to write $\hat{A} = A^{-1}$.

2.9 Sample Quizzes

Name_____   Date_____

2.9.1 Sample Quiz 1

1. Answer each of the following for the system $\begin{cases} 2x_1 - 2x_2 = b_1 \\ x_1 + a_{22}x_2 = b_2 \end{cases}$.

   (a) Assume that $a_{22} = 1$. Find b_1 and b_2 so that $\vec{x} = \begin{bmatrix} x_1 \\ x_2 \end{bmatrix} = \begin{bmatrix} 7/4 \\ 5/4 \end{bmatrix}$ is the unique solution to the linear system.

   (b) Assume that $a_{22} = -1$ and $b_1 = 3$. Find b_2 so that the system has infinitely many solutions. Write down this solution set.

   (c) Assume that $a_{22} = -1$ and $b_1 = 3$. Find a value of b_2 so that the system is inconsistent.

2. Assume that A is 3×4 and the system $A\vec{x} = \vec{b} = \begin{bmatrix} b_1 \\ b_2 \\ b_3 \end{bmatrix}$ is row reduced as follows

$$[\, A \mid \vec{b} \,] \sim [\, U \mid \vec{b} \,] = \begin{bmatrix} 2 & 4 & 0 & -2 & \vline & b_1 \\ 0 & 0 & 1 & 2 & \vline & b_2 - 2b_1 \\ 0 & 0 & 0 & 0 & \vline & b_3 - b_2 - b_1 \end{bmatrix}. \qquad (*)$$

(a) (6 points) The matrix A has ____ pivots. If $\vec{b} = \begin{bmatrix} 2 \\ 2 \\ 3 \end{bmatrix}$ then augmented matrix

$[\, A \mid \vec{b} \,]$ has ____ pivots. If $\vec{b} = \begin{bmatrix} 1 \\ 2 \\ 3 \end{bmatrix}$ then $[\, A \mid \vec{b} \,]$ has ____ pivots.

(b) Find the general solution to the problem $A\vec{x} = \vec{b} = \begin{bmatrix} b_1 \\ b_2 \\ b_3 \end{bmatrix} = \begin{bmatrix} 1 \\ 2 \\ 3 \end{bmatrix}$. It is okay

to start with $(*)$. Identify the homogeneous solution and a particular solution to the problem.

2.9.2 Sample Quiz 2

Name_____   Date_____

1. Consider the linear system $\begin{cases} 2x_1 - 2x_2 = 3 \\ -x_1 + x_2 = b_2 \end{cases}$ (*)

   (a) Write down the augmented matrix for (*) and row reduce this matrix to row echelon form.

   (b) Find a value for b_2 so that the linear system is inconsistent.

   (c) Find a value for b_2 so that the linear system is consistent.

   (d) Assume b_2 has the value in part (c). Find the solution of (*).

   (e) If $x_2 = -1$ in part (d) what is the value of x_1?

   (f) Verify that the ordered pair found in part (e) satisfies the second equation in (*). Don't forget part (c).

2. Let $A = \begin{bmatrix} 1 & 2 & 3 & 4 \\ 2 & 4 & 4 & 5 \\ 3 & 6 & 5 & 6 \end{bmatrix}$. Assume that the linear system $A\vec{x} = \vec{b} = \begin{bmatrix} b_1 \\ b_2 \\ b_3 \end{bmatrix}$ has been **correctly** row reduced as follows

$$[\,A \mid \vec{b}\,] \sim [\,U \mid \tilde{b}\,] = \begin{bmatrix} 1 & 2 & 3 & 4 & \bigm| & b_1 \\ 0 & 0 & -2 & -3 & \bigm| & b_2 - 2b_1 \\ 0 & 0 & 0 & 0 & \bigm| & b_3 - 2b_2 + b_1 \end{bmatrix}. \qquad (*)$$

(a) The matrix A has ____ pivots. If $\vec{b} = \begin{bmatrix} 2 \\ 2 \\ 3 \end{bmatrix}$ then augmented matrix $[\,A \mid \vec{b}\,]$ has

____ pivots. If $\vec{b} = \begin{bmatrix} 2 \\ 2 \\ 2 \end{bmatrix}$ then $[\,A \mid \vec{b}\,]$ has ____ pivots.

(b) Find the general solution to the problem $A\vec{x} = \vec{b} = \begin{bmatrix} b_1 \\ b_2 \\ b_3 \end{bmatrix} = \begin{bmatrix} 2 \\ 2 \\ 2 \end{bmatrix}$. It is

perfectly alright to begin with $(*)$. Write the general solution $\vec{x} = \vec{x}_h + \vec{x}_p$ where $\vec{x}_h$ is the homogeneous solution and $\vec{x}_p$ is a particular solution to the problem.

Chapter 3

Matrices

The last chapter introduced a matrix as an object used to simplify writing down a linear system. Matrices are objects in their own right and there is an arithmetic which is almost completely analogous to the arithmetic of the real number system. The arithmetic of the addition of matrices is simply a restatement of vector addition in Definition(1.1). Here the analogy with real number addition is in complete agreement. The multiplication of matrices presents some challenges. As opposed to an obstacle these challenges impart interest to the topic. As a bit of publicity here, recall that if a and b are real numbers then the commutative law of multiplication $ab = ba$ holds. For matrices, this is not true in general. Indeed, even if ab (as a matrix) is defined then the matrix ba may not equal ab. Actually the matrix product ba may not be defined. As a consequence, the case when $ab = ba$ is quite interesting. In addition $ab = 0$ need not imply that one of a or b is zero. This curiosity is exemplified in Exercise(3.4). In contrast, the equality $ab = 1$ gives rise to the most interesting matrix analogue with the real number multiplication. All eighteen exercises are illustrative and/or computational. Some of the exercises introduce certain named matrices: Exercise(3.4) (Nilpotent and zero divisor), Exercise(3.12) (triangular), Exercise(3.16) (skew-symmetric) and the very important Exercise(3.18) (orthogonal). One of the main goals of this chapter is its final Theorem(3.28). This theorem forecasts the definition of null spaces in Chapter Four and also plays a prominent role in the eigenvalue problem in Chapter Five.

3.1 Arithmetic of Matrices

In Examples(2.2), (2.3), and (2.4) the coefficient matrices of the linear systems were given by the following 2×2, 2×3 and 3×3 ordered arrays

$$A_1 = \begin{bmatrix} 2 & -2 \\ 1 & 0 \end{bmatrix}, \ A_2 = \begin{bmatrix} 1 & 2 & 3 \\ 2 & 5 & 4 \end{bmatrix} \ . \ \text{and} \ A_3 = \begin{bmatrix} 1 & 2 & 3 \\ 2 & 5 & 4 \\ 1 & 3 & 0 \end{bmatrix}$$

where $a_{22} = a_{33} = 0$. The word order refers to the fact it matters what order the rows (columns) are listed. For example, the matrices

$$\hat{A}_1 = \begin{bmatrix} 1 & 0 \\ 2 & -2 \end{bmatrix} \ \text{or} \ \tilde{A}_1 = \begin{bmatrix} -2 & 2 \\ 0 & 1 \end{bmatrix}$$

are obtained from the matrix A_1 by interchanging the rows ($\hat{A}_1$) or columns ($\tilde{A}_1$) of A_1, respectively. In Example(2.5) the 3×2 coefficient matrix was given by the matrix

$$A_4 = \begin{bmatrix} 1 & 1 \\ 1 & 2 \\ 2 & 0 \end{bmatrix}$$

if $a_{32} = 0$. The focus in those examples was finding the solution (or showing such a solution does not exist) in the linear system whose coefficient matrix is A_k, $k = 1, 2, 3, 4$. That is, find (if possible) a vector $\vec{x}_k$ so that $A_k \vec{x}_k = \vec{b}_k$, $k = 1, 2, 3$, or 4. In Definition(2.8) the notion of coefficient and augmented matrices were introduced in conjunction with linear systems. In this chapter, the arithmetic and the properties of the matrices themselves will be studied. Where appropriate, the interplay of a matrix property and a corresponding property of a linear system will be given.

Definition 3.1 Matrix Sums, Equality, Scalar Multiple, the Zero Matrix, and the Matrix Transpose: An ordered $m \times n$ array A is called an $m \times n$ matrix. If a_{ij} is an element of the array, then the index i refers to the row in which a_{ij} appears and the index j refers to the column in which a_{ij} appears. Hence, the first index $1 \le i \le m$ is a count on the number of rows in A and the second index $1 \le j \le n$ is a count on the number of columns in A. In displayed form the matrix A is

$$A \equiv [a_{ij}]_{mn} = \begin{bmatrix} a_{11} & a_{12} & \cdots & \cdots & a_{1j} & \cdots & a_{1n} \\ a_{21} & a_{22} & \cdots & \cdots & a_{2j} & \cdots & a_{2n} \\ \vdots & \vdots & \ddots & \cdots & \vdots & \vdots & \vdots \\ a_{i1} & a_{i2} & \cdots & \cdots & a_{ij} & \cdots & a_{in} \\ \vdots & \vdots & \cdots & \cdots & \vdots & \vdots & \vdots \\ a_{m1} & a_{m2} & \cdots & \cdots & a_{mj} & \cdots & a_{mn} \end{bmatrix} .$$

If $n = 1$ the matrix A is a $m \times 1$ matrix or, referring to Chapter One, an $m-$vector. If $m = 1$ the matrix A is an $1 \times n$ matrix or, again referring to Chapter One, is the transpose of an $n-$vector. More generally, the jth column of A is an $m \times 1$ vector for any fixed column number j and for any fixed row number i the ith row of A is the transpose of a $n \times 1$ vector. Let B be another $m \times n$ matrix

$$B = [b_{ij}]_{mn} = \begin{bmatrix} b_{11} & b_{12} & \cdots & \cdots & b_{1j} & \cdots & b_{1n} \\ b_{21} & b_{22} & \cdots & \cdots & b_{2j} & \cdots & b_{2n} \\ \vdots & \vdots & \ddots & \cdots & \vdots & \vdots & \vdots \\ b_{i1} & b_{i2} & \cdots & \cdots & b_{ij} & \cdots & b_{in} \\ \vdots & \vdots & \cdots & \cdots & \vdots & \vdots & \vdots \\ b_{m1} & b_{m2} & \cdots & \cdots & b_{mj} & \cdots & b_{mn} \end{bmatrix}.$$

The **sum** of A and B is the $m \times n$ matrix defined by

$$A + B = [a_{ij} + b_{ij}]_{mn} = [b_{ij} + a_{ij}]_{mn} = B + A$$

so that addition is commutative. If $n = 1$ then each of A and B are $n-$vectors and this definition is the matrix version of Definition(1.3). The discussion in Example(1.17) highlighted the futility in trying to define the sum of two vectors of different sizes. The same sort of futility is met in trying to define the sum of two matrices of different sizes. Hence, if A and B are not the same size then the **sum is undefined**. There are similar difficulties in trying to define the equality of two matrices of different sizes. Hence, if A and B are both $m \times n$ matrices then $A = B$ if and only if $a_{ij} = b_{ij}$ for all $1 \le i \le m$ and $1 \le j \le n$. If A and B are **different sizes, then they are not equal**. If α is a scalar then the **scalar multiple** of A is the $m \times n$ matrix defined by

$$\alpha A = [\alpha a_{ij}]_{mn}.$$

If $\alpha = -1$ then the matrix $(-1)A = [-a_{ij}]_{mn}$ is called the negative of A and has the property

$$A + (-A) = [a_{ij} - a_{ij}]_{mn} = [0]_{mn} \equiv \mathcal{O}_{mn} \equiv \mathcal{O}$$

where $\mathcal{O}$ is the $m \times n$ **zero matrix**. The subscripts on the zero matrix $\mathcal{O}$ will be deleted if the context makes the size of the matrix clear. Finally, the **transpose** of the $m \times n$ matrix A is defined by

$$A^T \equiv [a_{ji}]_{nm} = \begin{bmatrix} a_{11} & a_{21} & \cdots & a_{i1} & \cdots & a_{m1} \\ a_{12} & a_{22} & \cdots & a_{i2} & \cdots & a_{m2} \\ \vdots & \vdots & \ddots & \vdots & \vdots & \vdots \\ \vdots & \vdots & \cdots & \vdots & \vdots & \vdots \\ a_{1j} & a_{2j} & \cdots & a_{ij} & \cdots & a_{mj} \\ \vdots & \vdots & \cdots & \vdots & \vdots & \vdots \\ a_{1n} & a_{2n} & \cdots & a_{in} & \cdots & a_{mn} \end{bmatrix},$$

which is the $n \times m$ matrix obtained from A by interchanging the rows and columns of A. Row one of A becomes column one of A^T, row two of A becomes column two of A^T and continue until the mth row of A becomes the mth column of A^T.

Example 3.2 All of the ideas in the previous definition can be illustrated using the matrices $A_k, k = 1, 2, 3, 4$ and $\hat{A}_1$, which occurred in the opening of this chapter. The sum of the matrices A_1 and $\hat{A}_1$ is given by

$$A_1 + \hat{A}_1 = \begin{bmatrix} 2 & -2 \\ 1 & 0 \end{bmatrix} + \begin{bmatrix} 1 & 0 \\ 2 & -2 \end{bmatrix} = \begin{bmatrix} 3 & -2 \\ 3 & -2 \end{bmatrix} = \hat{A}_1 + A_1$$

so that the matrices commute. If $k \neq p$ the matrix sums $A_k + A_p$ are undefined since the summands A_k and A_p are different sizes. The negative of the matrix A_3 is

$$(-1)A_2 = (-1) \begin{bmatrix} 1 & 2 & 3 \\ 2 & 5 & 4 \end{bmatrix} = \begin{bmatrix} -1 & -2 & -3 \\ -2 & -5 & -4 \end{bmatrix}$$

and the sum (difference)

$$A_2 + (-1)A_2 = A_2 - A_2 = \begin{bmatrix} 0 & 0 & 0 \\ 0 & 0 & 0 \end{bmatrix} = \mathcal{O}$$

is the 2×3 zero matrix. The scalar multiple

$$0A_2 = \begin{bmatrix} 0 & 0 & 0 \\ 0 & 0 & 0 \end{bmatrix} = \mathcal{O}$$

also gives the 2×3 zero matrix. If $\mathcal{O}$ is the 2×3 zero matrix then the sums $A_1 + \mathcal{O}$, $A_3 + \mathcal{O}$ and $A_4 + \mathcal{O}$ are all undefined because the summands are different sizes. However, the sum $A_2 + \mathcal{O} = A_2$ is defined. The transpose of A_2 can be added to A_4

$$(A_2)^T + A_4 = \begin{bmatrix} 1 & 2 \\ 2 & 5 \\ 3 & 4 \end{bmatrix} + \begin{bmatrix} 1 & 1 \\ 1 & 2 \\ 2 & 0 \end{bmatrix} = \begin{bmatrix} 2 & 3 \\ 3 & 7 \\ 5 & 4 \end{bmatrix}$$

and $(A_4)^T$ can be subtracted from A_2

$$A_2 - (A_4)^T = \begin{bmatrix} 1 & 2 & 3 \\ 2 & 5 & 4 \end{bmatrix} - \begin{bmatrix} 1 & 1 & 2 \\ 1 & 2 & 0 \end{bmatrix} = \begin{bmatrix} 0 & 1 & 1 \\ 1 & 3 & 4 \end{bmatrix}.$$

The transpose of the transpose of A_1 reads

$$\left(A_1^T\right)^T = \left(\begin{bmatrix} 2 & -2 \\ 1 & 0 \end{bmatrix}^T\right)^T = \left(\begin{bmatrix} 2 & 1 \\ -2 & 0 \end{bmatrix}\right)^T = \begin{bmatrix} 2 & -2 \\ 1 & 0 \end{bmatrix} = A_1$$

and for A_3

$$\left(A_3^T\right)^T = \left(\begin{bmatrix} 1 & 2 & 3 \\ 2 & 5 & 4 \\ 1 & 3 & 0 \end{bmatrix}^T\right)^T = \left(\begin{bmatrix} 1 & 2 & 1 \\ 2 & 5 & 3 \\ 3 & 4 & 0 \end{bmatrix}\right)^T = \begin{bmatrix} 1 & 2 & 3 \\ 2 & 5 & 4 \\ 1 & 3 & 0 \end{bmatrix} = A_3.$$

which exemplifies the general rule $\left(A^T\right)^T = A$ which is true for any $m \times n$ matrix A.

Theorem 3.3 Laws of Matrix Addition and Scalar Multiplication: Let A, B, and C be $m \times n$ matrices. Further, let $\mathcal{O}$ be the $m \times n$ zero matrix and α and β be scalars; then

1. $A + B = B + A$ 5. $\alpha(A + B) = \alpha A + \alpha B$

2. $(A + B) + C = A + (B + C)$ 6. $\alpha(\beta(A)) = (\alpha\beta)A$

3. $A + \mathcal{O} = A$ 7. $(\alpha + \beta)A = \alpha A + \beta A$

4. $A + (-A) = \mathcal{O}$ 8. $1A = A$.

The addition and the scalar multiplication laws in the above theorem are the same as are the vector rules in Theorem(1.5). This is to be expected since if in Theorem(3.3) each of A, B and C are $m \times 1$ matrices then they are vectors and the above rules reduce to the corresponding rules for vectors.

From (2.27) the product of an $m \times p$ matrix A and a $p \times 1$ vector is given by the m vector of dot products

$$
A\vec{x} =
\begin{bmatrix}
a_{11} & a_{12} & \cdots & \cdots & a_{1j} & \cdots & a_{1p} \\
a_{21} & a_{22} & \cdots & \cdots & a_{2j} & \cdots & a_{2p} \\
\vdots & \vdots & \ddots & \cdots & \vdots & \vdots & \vdots \\
a_{i1} & a_{i2} & \cdots & \cdots & a_{ij} & \cdots & a_{ip} \\
\vdots & \vdots & \ddots & \cdots & \cdots & \ddots & \vdots \\
\vdots & \vdots & \cdots & \cdots & \vdots & \vdots & \vdots \\
a_{m1} & a_{m2} & \cdots & \cdots & a_{mj} & \cdots & a_{mp}
\end{bmatrix}
\begin{bmatrix}
x_1 \\ x_2 \\ \vdots \\ x_i \\ \vdots \\ x_j \\ \vdots \\ x_p
\end{bmatrix}
=
\begin{bmatrix}
\vec{a_{1*}}^T \vec{x} \\
\vec{a_{2*}}^T \vec{x} \\
\vdots \\
\vec{a_{i*}}^T \vec{x} \\
\vdots \\
\vec{a_{m*}}^T \vec{x}
\end{bmatrix}. \tag{3.1}
$$

These products are defined, since each p-vector $\vec{a_{i*}}^T = [a_{i1}\ a_{i2} \cdots a_{ij} \cdots a_{ip}]$, $1 \le i \le m$ is the same length as the vector $\vec{x} = [x_1\ x_2\ \cdots\ x_i\ \cdots\ x_j \cdots x_p]^T$. Another way to write the product in (3.1) is to switch emphasis from the rows of A to the columns of A. To see this write the m vector $\vec{a_{*j}}$, $1 \le j \le p$ for the jth column of A, that is,

$$
\vec{a_{*j}} = [\ a_{1j}\ a_{2j}\ \cdots\ a_{ij}\ \cdots\ a_{mj}\ ]^T
$$

and the product reads

$$
A\vec{x} = [\vec{a_{*1}}\ \vec{a_{*2}}\ \cdots\ \cdots \vec{a_{*p}}]
\begin{bmatrix}
x_1 \\ x_2 \\ \vdots \\ x_p
\end{bmatrix}
$$

$$
= x_1\vec{a_{*1}} + x_2\vec{a_{*2}} + \cdots + x_p\vec{a_{*p}} = \sum_{k=1}^{p} x_k\vec{a_{*k}} \tag{3.2}
$$

which is a linear combination of the p columns of A.

Definition 3.4 Matrix Product: Let B be the $p \times n$ matrix

$$B = [b_{ij}]_{pn} = \begin{bmatrix} b_{11} & b_{12} & \cdots & \cdots & b_{1j} & \cdots & b_{1n} \\ b_{21} & b_{22} & \cdots & \cdots & b_{2j} & \cdots & b_{2n} \\ \vdots & \vdots & \ddots & \cdots & \vdots & \vdots & \vdots \\ b_{i1} & b_{i2} & \cdots & \cdots & b_{ij} & \cdots & b_{in} \\ \vdots & \vdots & \cdots & \cdots & \vdots & \vdots & \vdots \\ b_{p1} & b_{p2} & \cdots & \cdots & b_{pj} & \cdots & b_{pn} \end{bmatrix} = [\vec{b}_{*1}\ \vec{b}_{*2} \cdots \vec{b}_{*j} \cdots \vec{b}_{*n}] \qquad (3.3)$$

where each p-vector $\vec{b}_{*j}$ is the $j^{th}, 1 \leq j \leq n$ column of B. Let A be the $m \times p$ matrix (3.1). The product AB is the $m \times n$ matrix defined by

$$AB = \begin{bmatrix} \vec{a}_{1*}^{\,T} \\ \vec{a}_{2*}^{\,T} \\ \vdots \\ \vec{a}_{i*}^{\,T} \\ \vdots \\ \vec{a}_{m*}^{\,T} \end{bmatrix} [\vec{b}_{*1}\ \vec{b}_{*2} \cdots \vec{b}_{*j} \cdots \vec{b}_{*n}] \equiv \left[\vec{a}_{i*}^{\,T}\vec{b}_{*j}\right]_{i,j}^{m,n} = \left[\sum_{k=1}^{p} a_{ik}b_{kj}\right]_{i,j=1}^{m,n}$$

$$= \begin{bmatrix} \vec{a}_{1*}^{\,T}\vec{b}_{*1} & \vec{a}_{1*}^{\,T}\vec{b}_{*2} & \cdots & \cdots & \vec{a}_{1*}^{\,T}\vec{b}_{*j} & \cdots & \vec{a}_{1*}^{\,T}\vec{b}_{*n} \\ \vec{a}_{2*}^{\,T}\vec{b}_{*1} & \vec{a}_{2*}^{\,T}\vec{b}_{2} & \cdots & \cdots & \vec{a}_{2*}^{\,T}\vec{b}_{*j} & \cdots & \vec{a}_{2*}^{\,T}\vec{b}_{*n} \\ \vdots & \vdots & \ddots & \cdots & \vdots & \vdots & \vdots \\ \vec{a}_{i*}^{\,T}\vec{b}_{*1} & \vec{a}_{i*}^{\,T}\vec{b}_{*2} & \cdots & \cdots & \vec{a}_{i*}^{\,T}\vec{b}_{*j} & \cdots & \vec{a}_{i*}^{\,T}\vec{b}_{*n} \\ \vdots & \vdots & \cdots & \cdots & \vdots & \vdots & \vdots \\ \vec{a}_{m*}^{\,T}\vec{b}_{*1} & \vec{a}_{m*}^{\,T}\vec{b}_{*2} & \cdots & \cdots & \vec{a}_{m*}^{\,T}\vec{b}_{*j} & \cdots & \vec{a}_{m*}^{\,T}\vec{b}_{*n} \end{bmatrix}. \qquad (3.4)$$

In words, the product matrix AB is the $m \times n$ matrix whose ij^{th} entry is the dot product of the ith row of A with the jth column of B. This is why the number of columns p in the left multiplier A has to be the same as the number of rows p in the right multiplier B. This guarantees that the mn dot products in (3.4) are defined. For the matrices A and B the product $B_{pn}A_{mp}$ may or may not be defined. **If $n = m$ the product is defined but if $n \neq m$ the product $B_{pn}A_{mp}$ is undefined.** Even in the cases when BA is defined it may or may not be equal to AB. In general **matrix multiplication is not commutative.** Another form of the matrix product which is frequently useful reads

$$AB = A\left[\vec{b}_{*1}\ \vec{b}_{*2} \cdots \vec{b}_{*j} \cdots \vec{b}_{*n}\right] = \left[A\vec{b}_{*1}\ A\vec{b}_{*2} \cdots A\vec{b}_{*j} \cdots A\vec{b}_{*n}\right] \qquad (3.5)$$

so that the matrix product consists of $n-$vectors each of which is obtained by multiplying each column of B by A.

Theorem 3.5 If A, B and C have the appropriate sizes then

    1. $A(B + C) = AB + AC$,   2. $(A + B)C = AC + BC$ and   3. $A(BC) = (AB)C$.

In part 1 B and C must be the same size (so that the sum $B+C$ is defined), say $p \times n$. This implies that A is $m \times p$ where m is arbitrary. The resulting matrix is $m \times p$. In subscripted symbols this is

$$A_{mp}\left(B_{pn} + C_{pn}\right) = A_{mp}\left(B + C\right)_{pn} = [A(B+C)]_{mn}\,.$$

On the right hand side of part 1 each of AB and AC are $m \times n$ so that this sum is defined. In part 2 A and B must be the same size (so that the sum $A + B$ is defined), say $m \times p$. This implies that C is $p \times n$ where n is arbitrary. The resulting matrix is $m \times p$. In part 3, assume that B is $p \times q$ and that C is $q \times n$ so that the product BC is defined and has size $p \times n$. Now the matrix A must be $m \times p$ so that the product

$$A_{mp}\left(B_{pq}C_{qn}\right) = A_{mp}\left(BC\right)_{pn} = [A(BC)]_{mn}$$

is $m \times n$. Also the product AB is $m \times q$ which when multiplied by the $q \times n$ matrix C on the right gives the same $m \times n$ matrix.

Example 3.6 Recall the matrices from Example(3.2):

$$A_1 = \begin{bmatrix} 2 & -2 \\ 1 & 0 \end{bmatrix},\; \hat{A}_1 = \begin{bmatrix} 1 & 0 \\ 2 & -2 \end{bmatrix},\; A_2 = \begin{bmatrix} 1 & 2 & 3 \\ 2 & 5 & 4 \end{bmatrix}\; A_3 = \begin{bmatrix} 1 & 2 & 3 \\ 2 & 5 & 4 \\ 1 & 3 & 0 \end{bmatrix},\; A_4 = \begin{bmatrix} 1 & 1 \\ 1 & 2 \\ 2 & 0 \end{bmatrix}.$$

The two products in the calculation

$$\begin{aligned}
A_1\hat{A}_1 &= \begin{bmatrix} 2 & -2 \\ 1 & 0 \end{bmatrix}\begin{bmatrix} 1 & 0 \\ 2 & -2 \end{bmatrix} \\
&= \begin{bmatrix} 2(1) - 2(2) & 2(0) - 2(-2) \\ 1(1) + 0(2) & 1(0) + 0(-2) \end{bmatrix} = \begin{bmatrix} -2 & 4 \\ 1 & 0 \end{bmatrix} \\
&\neq \begin{bmatrix} 2 & -2 \\ 2 & -4 \end{bmatrix} = \begin{bmatrix} 1 & 0 \\ 2 & -2 \end{bmatrix}\begin{bmatrix} 2 & -2 \\ 1 & 0 \end{bmatrix} = \hat{A}_1 A_1
\end{aligned}$$

illustrates the matrix multiplication is not commutative. The first product consists of the four dot products, the first two of which are obtained from the dot product of row one of A_1 with the two columns of $\hat{A}_1$. This is row one of the product matrix. The next two are obtained from the dot product of row two of A_1 with the two columns of $\hat{A}_1$. This is row two of the product matrix. The product

$$\begin{aligned}
A_1 A_2 &= \begin{bmatrix} 2 & -2 \\ 1 & 0 \end{bmatrix}\begin{bmatrix} 1 & 2 & 3 \\ 2 & 5 & 4 \end{bmatrix} \\
&= \begin{bmatrix} 2(1) - 2(2) & 2(2) - 2(5) & 2(3) - 2(4) \\ 1(1) + 0(2) & 1(2) + 0(5) & 1(3) + 0(4) \end{bmatrix} = \begin{bmatrix} -2 & -6 & -2 \\ 1 & 2 & 3 \end{bmatrix}
\end{aligned}$$

consists of the six dot products, three of which are obtained from the dot product of row one of A_1 with the three columns of A_2. This is row one of the product matrix. The next three are obtained from the dot product of row two of A_1 with the three columns of A_2. This is row two of the product matrix. The product $A_2 A_1$ is undefined since A_2 has three columns and A_1 has two rows. In the discussion following (3.4) $n = 3 \neq 2 = m$. This product provides a dramatic case of the failure of the commutativity of products since $A_2 A_1$ is not defined. Similarly, the product

$$
A_3 A_4 = \begin{bmatrix} 1 & 2 & 3 \\ 2 & 5 & 4 \\ 1 & 3 & 0 \end{bmatrix} \begin{bmatrix} 1 & 1 \\ 1 & 2 \\ 2 & 0 \end{bmatrix}
$$

$$
= \begin{bmatrix} 1(1) + 2(1) + 3(2) & 1(1) + 2(2) + 3(0) \\ 2(1) + 5(1) + 4(2) & 2(1) + 5(2) + 4(0) \\ 1(1) + 3(1) + 0(2) & 1(1) + 3(1) + 0(0) \end{bmatrix} = \begin{bmatrix} 9 & 5 \\ 15 & 12 \\ 4 & 4 \end{bmatrix}
$$

consist of the six displayed dot products but $A_4 A_3$ is undefined. Both products $A_2 A_4$ and $A_4 A_2$ are defined but

$$
A_2 A_4 = \begin{bmatrix} 1 & 2 & 3 \\ 2 & 5 & 4 \end{bmatrix} \begin{bmatrix} 1 & 1 \\ 1 & 2 \\ 2 & 0 \end{bmatrix}
$$

$$
= \begin{bmatrix} 1(1) + 2(1) + 3(2) & 1(1) + 2(2) + 3(0) \\ 2(1) + 5(1) + 4(2) & 2(1) + 5(2) + 4(0) \end{bmatrix} = \begin{bmatrix} 9 & 5 \\ 15 & 12 \end{bmatrix}
$$

while

$$
A_4 A_2 = \begin{bmatrix} 1 & 1 \\ 1 & 2 \\ 2 & 0 \end{bmatrix} \begin{bmatrix} 1 & 2 & 3 \\ 2 & 5 & 4 \end{bmatrix}
$$

$$
= \begin{bmatrix} 1(1) + 1(2) & 1(2) + 1(5) & 1(3) + 1(4) \\ 1(1) + 2(2) & 1(2) + 2(5) & 1(3) + 2(4) \\ 2(1) + 0(2) & 2(2) + 0(5) & 2(3) + 0(4) \end{bmatrix} = \begin{bmatrix} 3 & 7 & 7 \\ 5 & 12 & 11 \\ 2 & 4 & 6 \end{bmatrix} .
$$

The two resulting product matrices are different sizes and therefore not equal. The product

$$
A_2^T A_4^T = \begin{bmatrix} 1 & 2 \\ 2 & 5 \\ 3 & 4 \end{bmatrix} \begin{bmatrix} 1 & 1 & 2 \\ 1 & 2 & 0 \end{bmatrix}
$$

$$
= \begin{bmatrix} 1(1) + 2(1) & 1(1) + 2(2) & 1(2) + 2(0) \\ 2(1) + 5(1) & 2(1) + 5(2) & 2(2) + 5(0) \\ 3(1) + 4(1) & 3(1) + 4(2) & 3(2) + 4(0) \end{bmatrix}
$$

$$
= \begin{bmatrix} 3 & 5 & 2 \\ 7 & 12 & 4 \\ 7 & 11 & 6 \end{bmatrix} = \begin{bmatrix} 3 & 7 & 7 \\ 5 & 12 & 11 \\ 2 & 4 & 6 \end{bmatrix}^T = (A_4 A_2)^T
$$

where the last two equalities follows from the previous display. This equality is true in general. That is, for any two matrices A and B for which AB is defined it is the case that

$(AB)^T = B^T A^T$. It will be helpful to see one more example of this transposition rule. Let $\vec{b} = \begin{bmatrix} -1 \\ 2 \\ 1 \end{bmatrix}$ and calculate

$$
\begin{aligned}
(A_2 \vec{b})^T &= \left(\begin{bmatrix} 1 & 2 & 3 \\ 2 & 5 & 4 \end{bmatrix} \begin{bmatrix} -1 \\ 2 \\ 1 \end{bmatrix} \right)^T = \left(\begin{bmatrix} 1(-1) + 2(2) + 3(1) \\ 2(-1) + 5(2) + 4(1) \end{bmatrix} \right)^T = \left(\begin{bmatrix} 6 \\ 12 \end{bmatrix} \right)^T \\
&= \begin{bmatrix} 6 & 12 \end{bmatrix} = \begin{bmatrix} -1 & 2 & 1 \end{bmatrix} \begin{bmatrix} 1 & 2 \\ 2 & 5 \\ 3 & 4 \end{bmatrix} = \vec{b}^T A_2^T .
\end{aligned}
$$

3.2 Matrix Transpose

A number of properties of the transpose of a matrix have appeared in the last two examples. The last portion of the previous example is more subtle than the other properties of the transpose that appeared in those examples.

Theorem 3.7 The matrix transpose satisfies each of the properties:

1. $(A^T)^T = A$,

2. $(A + B)^T = A^T + B^T$, A and B are the same size and

3. $[(AB)_{mn}]^T = [B^T A^T]_{nm}$, the product AB is defined.

If A is an $m \times p$ matrix then

$$
(A^T)^T = \left([a_{ij}]^T \right)^T = ([a_{ji}])^T = [a_{ij}] = A
$$

since the first transpose interchanges the rows of A with its columns and then the second transpose puts them back. Now suppose that B is also an $m \times p$ so that $A + B$ is an $m \times p$ matrix and the transpose $(A + B)^T$ is the $p \times m$ matrix given by

$$
\begin{aligned}
(A + B)^T &= ([a_{ij}] + [b_{ij}])^T \\
&\equiv [c_{ij}]^T , \quad c_{ij} = a_{ij} + b_{ij} \\
&= [c_{ji}] \qquad \text{definition of transpose} \\
&= [a_{ji}] + [b_{ji}] \\
&= A^T + B^T .
\end{aligned}
$$

A little deeper property of transposition of matrices is in part 3. Assume A is $m \times p$ and write $A = [\vec{a}_{*1} \ \vec{a}_{*2} \ \cdots \vec{a}_{*j} \cdots \vec{a}_{*p}]$ where the m vector $\vec{a}_{*j}$ is a column of A. Assume that B

is $p \times n$ and that the first column of B is $\vec{b}_{*1} = [b_{11} \ b_{21} \ \cdots \ b_{p1}]^T$. To establish part 3 for the product $A\vec{b}_{*1}$ begin by writing the product out as in (3.2) combined with part 2 to find

$$
\begin{aligned}
(A\vec{b}_{*1})^T &= \left([\vec{a}_{*1} \ \vec{a}_{*2} \ \cdots \vec{a}_{*j} \cdots \vec{a}_{*p}] \begin{bmatrix} b_{11} \\ b_{21} \\ \vdots \\ b_{p1} \end{bmatrix} \right)^T = \left(\sum_{j=1}^{p} b_{j1}\vec{a}_{*j} \right)^T \\
&= \sum_{j=1}^{p} b_{j1}\vec{a}_{*j}^{\ T} \qquad \vec{a}_{*j}^{\ T} = [a_{1j} \ a_{2j} \cdots a_{mj}] \\
&= b_{11}[a_{11} \ a_{21} \ \cdots \ a_{m1}] + b_{21}[a_{12} \ a_{22} \ \cdots \ a_{m2}] + \cdots + b_{p1}[a_{1p} \ a_{2p} \ \cdots \ a_{mp}] \\
&= [b_{11} \ b_{21} \ \cdots \ b_{p1}] \begin{bmatrix} a_{11} & a_{21} & \cdots & a_{m1} \\ a_{12} & a_{22} & \cdots & a_{m2} \\ \vdots & \cdots & \cdots & \vdots \\ a_{1p} & a_{2p} & \cdots & a_{mp} \end{bmatrix} = \vec{b}_{*1}^{\ T} A^T ,
\end{aligned}
$$

which establishes part 3 if B is a column vector. Combine this last identity with the matrix product from (3.5) in the calculation

$$
\begin{aligned}
(AB)^T &= \left(A[\vec{b}_{*1} \ \vec{b}_{*2} \ \cdots \vec{b}_{*j} \cdots \vec{b}_{*n}] \right)^T = \left([A\vec{b}_{*1} \ A\vec{b}_{*2} \ \cdots A\vec{b}_{*j} \ \cdots A\vec{b}_{*n}] \right)^T \\
&= \begin{bmatrix} (A\vec{b}_{*1})^T \\ (A\vec{b}_{*2})^T \\ \vdots \\ (A\vec{b}_{*j})^T \\ \vdots \\ (A\vec{b}_{*n})^T \end{bmatrix} = \begin{bmatrix} \vec{b}_{*1}^{\ T} A^T \\ \vec{b}_{*2}^{\ T} A^T \\ \vdots \\ \vec{b}_{*j}^{\ T} A^T \\ \vdots \\ \vec{b}_{*n}^{\ T} A^T \end{bmatrix} = \begin{bmatrix} \vec{b}_{*1}^{\ T} \\ \vec{b}_{*2}^{\ T} \\ \vdots \\ \vec{b}_{*j}^{\ T} \\ \vdots \\ \vec{b}_{*n}^{\ T} \end{bmatrix} A^T = B^T A^T
\end{aligned}
$$

which verifies part 3.

3.3 Square and Symmetric Matrices

Definition 3.8 Square Matrix and Symmetric Matrices: If the matrix A has the same number of rows as columns then the matrix A is called a **square** matrix. To form the matrix product AA of the $m \times n$ matrix A with itself the definition of multiplication requires the number of columns of the left multiplier n to be the same as the number of rows of the right multiplier m. That is $AA \equiv A^2$ is defined if and only if A is square. A **symmetric matrix** is an $n \times n$ matrix A which is equal to its transpose. In symbols the equality reads

$$
A = \begin{bmatrix} a_{11} & a_{12} & \cdots & a_{1n} \\ a_{21} & a_{22} & \cdots & a_{2n} \\ \vdots & \ddots & \cdots & \vdots \\ a_{n1} & a_{n2} & \cdots & a_{nn} \end{bmatrix} = \begin{bmatrix} a_{11} & a_{21} & \cdots & a_{n1} \\ a_{12} & a_{22} & \cdots & a_{n2} \\ \vdots & \ddots & \cdots & \vdots \\ a_{1n} & a_{2n} & \cdots & a_{nn} \end{bmatrix} = A^T,
$$

so that symmetry requires $a_{ij} = a_{ji}$ for all i, j. In words, the matrix A is symmetric if the matrix A is unchanged when its rows and columns are interchanged.

Example 3.9 Change the $a_{21} = 1$ in $A_1 = \begin{bmatrix} 2 & -2 \\ 1 & 0 \end{bmatrix}$ to a -2 so that $\begin{bmatrix} 2 & -2 \\ -2 & 0 \end{bmatrix}$ is symmetric. Similarly, change the a_{31} to 3 and the a_{32} to 4 in $A_3 = \begin{bmatrix} 1 & 2 & 3 \\ 2 & 5 & 4 \\ 1 & 3 & 0 \end{bmatrix}$ to obtain the

symmetric matrix $\begin{bmatrix} 1 & 2 & 3 \\ 2 & 5 & 4 \\ 3 & 4 & 0 \end{bmatrix}$. The two matrices $A_2 = \begin{bmatrix} 1 & 2 & 3 \\ 2 & 5 & 4 \end{bmatrix}$ and $A_4 = \begin{bmatrix} 1 & 1 \\ 1 & 2 \\ 2 & 0 \end{bmatrix}$

are not symmetric since neither are square. However, the product matrix

$$
A_2 A_2^T = \begin{bmatrix} 1 & 2 & 3 \\ 2 & 5 & 4 \end{bmatrix} \begin{bmatrix} 1 & 2 \\ 2 & 5 \\ 3 & 4 \end{bmatrix} = \begin{bmatrix} 14 & 24 \\ 24 & 45 \end{bmatrix}
$$

is symmetric as is the matrix

$$
A_2^T A_2 = \begin{bmatrix} 1 & 2 \\ 2 & 5 \\ 3 & 4 \end{bmatrix} \begin{bmatrix} 1 & 2 & 3 \\ 2 & 5 & 4 \end{bmatrix} = \begin{bmatrix} 5 & 12 & 11 \\ 12 & 29 & 26 \\ 11 & 26 & 25 \end{bmatrix}.
$$

In general, for an arbitrary $m \times p$ matrix B the $m \times m$ matrix $V = BB^T$ satisfies

$$
V^T = \left(BB^T\right)^T = \left(B^T\right)^T B^T = BB^T = V \tag{3.6}
$$

so that V is symmetric. The second equality uses part 3 of Theorem(3.7). Similarly, the $p \times p$ matrix $W = B^T B$ is also symmetric.

From Exercise(2.9), the two matrices $A = \begin{bmatrix} 2 & -2 \\ 1 & 1/2 \end{bmatrix}$ and $\hat{A} = \begin{bmatrix} 1/6 & 2/3 \\ -1/3 & 2/3 \end{bmatrix}$ have the property

$$
\begin{aligned}
A\hat{A} = \begin{bmatrix} 2 & -2 \\ 1 & 1/2 \end{bmatrix} \begin{bmatrix} 1/6 & 2/3 \\ -1/3 & 2/3 \end{bmatrix} &= \begin{bmatrix} 1 & 0 \\ 0 & 1 \end{bmatrix} \equiv I \\
&= \begin{bmatrix} 1/6 & 2/3 \\ -1/3 & 2/3 \end{bmatrix} \begin{bmatrix} 2 & -2 \\ 1 & 1/2 \end{bmatrix} = \hat{A}A. \tag{3.7}
\end{aligned}
$$

where $I \equiv \begin{bmatrix} 1 & 0 \\ 0 & 1 \end{bmatrix}$ is called the (2×2) identity matrix. The matrices A and $\hat{A}$ are representative examples of a special class of matrices called invertible matrices. One motivation for considering invertible matrices is provided by studying the coefficient matrix of a linear system in conjunction with the solution process for the linear system. All of this is included in the following review of Example(2.2).

Example 3.10 The matrix formulation for the problem

$$
\begin{aligned}
2x_1 - 2x_2 &= 3 \\
x_1 + (1/2)x_2 &= b_2
\end{aligned}
$$

is given by

$$
A\vec{x} = \begin{bmatrix} 2 & -2 \\ 1 & 1/2 \end{bmatrix} \begin{bmatrix} x_1 \\ x_2 \end{bmatrix} = \begin{bmatrix} 3 \\ b_2 \end{bmatrix}.
$$

The augmented system and its row reduction

$$
\begin{bmatrix} 2 & -2 & | & 3 \\ 1 & -1/2 & | & b_2 \end{bmatrix} \sim \begin{bmatrix} 2 & -2 & | & 3 \\ 0 & 3/2 & | & b_2 - (3/2) \end{bmatrix}
$$

lead, by way of back substitution, to the unique solution of the linear system

$$
\vec{x} = \begin{bmatrix} x_1 \\ x_2 \end{bmatrix} = \begin{bmatrix} 1/2 + (2/3)b_2 \\ -1 + (2/3)b_2 \end{bmatrix}.
$$

Multiply both sides of $A\vec{x} = \begin{bmatrix} 3 \\ b_2 \end{bmatrix}$ by $\hat{A} = \begin{bmatrix} 1/6 & 2/3 \\ -1/3 & 2/3 \end{bmatrix}$ and using the product $\hat{A}A = I$ from (3.7) gives

$$
\left(\hat{A}A \right) \vec{x} = \begin{bmatrix} 1 & 0 \\ 0 & 1 \end{bmatrix} \begin{bmatrix} x_1 \\ x_2 \end{bmatrix} = \begin{bmatrix} x_1 \\ x_2 \end{bmatrix} = \vec{x} = \hat{A} \begin{bmatrix} 3 \\ b_2 \end{bmatrix}
$$

$$
= \begin{bmatrix} 1/6 & 2/3 \\ -1/3 & 2/3 \end{bmatrix} \begin{bmatrix} 3 \\ b_2 \end{bmatrix}
$$

$$
= \begin{bmatrix} 1/2 + (2/3)b_2 \\ -1 + (2/3)b_2 \end{bmatrix}
$$

which is the same solution as that found by the row reduction method. Indeed, if $b_2 = 3/4$ then the previous display is

$$
\vec{x} = \begin{bmatrix} 1/2 + (2/3)b_2 \\ -1 + (2/3)b_2 \end{bmatrix} \Bigg|_{b_2 = 3/4} = \begin{bmatrix} 1/2 + (2/3)(3/4) \\ -1 + (2/3)(3/4) \end{bmatrix} = \begin{bmatrix} 1/2 + 1/2 \\ -1 + 1/2 \end{bmatrix} = \begin{bmatrix} 1 \\ -1/2 \end{bmatrix}
$$

which agrees with the result from Example(2.2). The matrix $\hat{A}$ is called the inverse of A and is denoted by $\hat{A} = A^{-1}$. Hence, the unique solution from the row reduction is associated with the coefficient matrix A having an inverse. It gives rise to the speculation that if the system has no solution or has infinitely many solutions then there may not be a matrix inverse for the corresponding coefficient matrix. To pursue the latter point consider the linear system with $a_{22} = -1$ so the augmented system with the row reduction reads

$$
\left[\begin{array}{c|c} A & \begin{array}{c} b_1 \\ b_2 \end{array} \end{array}\right] = \left[\begin{array}{cc|c} 2 & -2 & b_1 \\ 1 & -1 & b_2 \end{array}\right] \sim \left[\begin{array}{cc|c} 2 & -2 & 3 \\ 0 & 0 & b_2 - 3/2 \end{array}\right]. \tag{3.8}
$$

If $b_2 - 3/2 \neq 0$ the system is inconsistent and if $b_2 - 3/2 = 0$ there are infinitely many solutions. In either case, suppose there is a matrix $B = \left[\begin{array}{cc} b_{11} & b_{12} \\ b_{21} & b_{22} \end{array}\right]$ satisfying $AB = I$ where $A = \left[\begin{array}{cc} 2 & -2 \\ 1 & -1 \end{array}\right]$ is the coefficient matrix. If this is to occur, then

$$
AB = \left[\begin{array}{cc} 2 & -2 \\ 1 & -1 \end{array}\right] \left[\begin{array}{cc} b_{11} & b_{12} \\ b_{21} & b_{22} \end{array}\right] = \left[\begin{array}{cc} 2b_{11} - 2b_{21} & 2b_{12} - 2b_{22} \\ b_{11} - b_{21} & b_{12} - b_{22} \end{array}\right] = \left[\begin{array}{cc} 1 & 0 \\ 0 & 1 \end{array}\right]
$$

where, upon equating the components from the first column, gives $b_{11} - b_{21} = 1/2$ and $b_{11} - b_{21} = 0$. The second of these give $b_{11} = b_{21}$ which when substituted into the first leads to the contradiction $0 = 1/2$. Hence there is no B such that $AB = I$. This form of argument is called *proof by contradiction*. Generally this means to assume the negative of what is to be proved (there is a matrix B such that $AB = I$ following (3.8)) and then in the course of the argument arrive at an absurdity (the statement that $0 = 1/2$). The lack of an inverse for the coefficient matrix A is advertised in the row reduction by the two zeros in the first two columns in (3.8). To pursue this more generally, assume that if

$$
B = \left[\begin{array}{cc} b_{11} & b_{12} \\ b_{21} & b_{22} \end{array}\right] \quad \text{is to be an inverse for } A = \left[\begin{array}{cc} 2 & -2 \\ 1 & a_{22} \end{array}\right]
$$

then the product

$$
AB = \left[\begin{array}{cc} 2 & -2 \\ 1 & a_{22} \end{array}\right] \left[\begin{array}{cc} b_{11} & b_{12} \\ b_{21} & b_{22} \end{array}\right] = \left[\begin{array}{cc} 2b_{11} - 2b_{21} & 2b_{12} - 2b_{22} \\ b_{11} + a_{22}b_{21} & b_{12} + a_{22}b_{22} \end{array}\right] = \left[\begin{array}{cc} 1 & 0 \\ 0 & 1 \end{array}\right]
$$

must be satisfied. Equating the entries in the first column yields the two equations

$$
b_{11} - b_{21} = 1/2 \quad \text{and} \quad b_{11} + a_{22}b_{21} = 0 \quad \text{or} \quad b_{11} = -a_{22}b_{21}.
$$

Substituting $b_{11} = -a_{22}b_{21}$ into $b_{11} - b_{21} = 1/2$ gives

$$
(a_{22} + 1)b_{21} = -1/2 \quad \text{or} \quad b_{21} = \frac{-1}{2(a_{22} + 1)} \quad \text{assuming } a_{22} \neq -1.
$$

Substitute this result in

$$
b_{11} - b_{21} = 1/2 \quad \text{to find } b_{11} = \frac{a_{22}}{2(a_{22} + 1)}.
$$

Similarly, the quantities b_{12} and b_{22} are found by equating the entries in the second column which leads to $b_{12} = b_{22}$ and $b_{12} = \dfrac{1}{a_{22} + 1}$. Collecting all of these quantities gives

$$B = \begin{bmatrix} b_{11} & b_{12} \\ b_{21} & b_{22} \end{bmatrix} = \frac{1}{2(a_{22} + 1)} \begin{bmatrix} a_{22} & 2 \\ -1 & 2 \end{bmatrix} = A^{-1} \quad \text{if } a_{22} \neq -1$$

for the inverse of the matrix A. Notice that the eliminated case $a_{22} \neq -1$ led to the row reduction in (3.8). If $a_{22} = 1/2$ then

$$B = \frac{1}{2(a_{22} + 1)} \begin{bmatrix} a_{22} & 2 \\ -1 & 2 \end{bmatrix}\Bigg|_{a_{22}=1/2} = \frac{1}{3}\begin{bmatrix} 1/2 & 2 \\ -1 & 2 \end{bmatrix} = \begin{bmatrix} 1/6 & 2/3 \\ -1/3 & 2/3 \end{bmatrix}$$

is the matrix $\hat{A}$ from (3.7) used in the opening of this example.

The last two examples included a number of important properties of some 2×2 matrices that are illustrative of the same property for more general $n \times n$ matrices. Many of these properties are housed in the following definition.

3.4   Invertible Matrices

Definition 3.11 Diagonal, Scalar, and the Identity Matrix. Matrix Inverse and Invertible Matrices: Assume A is $n \times n$. The **main diagonal** of A consists of the n elements $a_{ii}, i = 1, 2, \ldots, n$. The $n \times n$ matrix

$$D \equiv \begin{bmatrix} a_{11} & 0 & 0 & \cdots & 0 \\ 0 & a_{22} & 0 & \cdots & 0 \\ 0 & 0 & a_{33} & \cdots & 0 \\ \vdots & \vdots & \vdots & \ddots & 0 \\ 0 & 0 & 0 & \cdots & a_{nn} \end{bmatrix}$$

is called a **diagonal** matrix. If all $a_{ii} = s$, $i = 1, 2, \ldots, n$, a common value, the resulting diagonal matrix

$$S \equiv \begin{bmatrix} s & 0 & 0 & \cdots & 0 \\ 0 & s & 0 & \cdots & 0 \\ 0 & 0 & s & \cdots & 0 \\ \vdots & \vdots & \vdots & \ddots & 0 \\ 0 & 0 & 0 & \cdots & s \end{bmatrix} = s \begin{bmatrix} 1 & 0 & 0 & \cdots & 0 \\ 0 & 1 & 0 & \cdots & 0 \\ 0 & 0 & 1 & \cdots & 0 \\ \vdots & \vdots & \vdots & \ddots & 0 \\ 0 & 0 & 0 & \cdots & 1 \end{bmatrix} = sI$$

is called a **scalar** matrix where, if $s = 1$, the $n \times n$ matrix I is called the **identity matrix**. The identity matrix gets its name from the property $AI = IA = A$. If there is an $n \times n$ matrix B so that

$$AB = I \quad \text{and} \quad BA = I$$

then the matrix A is called **invertible** and the matrix B is called the **inverse** of A. The matrix inverse B of A is designated $B = A^{-1}$. If no such matrix B exists A has **no inverse** and is **not invertible**. Interchanging the roles of A and B shifts the emphasis to the invertibility of the matrix B, that is, B is called **invertible** and the matrix A is called the **inverse** of B and is designated $A = B^{-1}$. If A is invertible then A is also called **nonsingular** and if A has no inverse it is called **singular**.

As indicated in Example(3.10) some square matrices have no inverse. However, when a matrix has an inverse, the inverse has a number of properties.

Theorem 3.12 Assume that the $n \times n$ matrix A is invertible, then

1. A^{-1} is unique.

   Let B denote another inverse for A. This means that $AA^{-1} = AB = I$. Subtraction gives $A(A^{-1} - B) = \mathcal{O}$. Multiply both sides of this equation by A^{-1} to find $A^{-1} - B = \mathcal{O}$ or $A^{-1} = B$.

2. $(A^{-1})^{-1} = A$.

   If $AB = I$ then $B = A^{-1}$. Now by definition B has an inverse so that

   $$B^{-1} = (I)(B)^{-1} = (AB)(B)^{-1} = A(BB^{-1}) = A.$$

   Hence $B^{-1} = (A^{-1})^{-1} = A$.

3. $(A^T)^{-1} = (A^{-1})^T$.

   Transpose both sides of the equality $I = AA^{-1}$ to find $I = I^T = (AA^{-1})^T = (A^{-1})^T A^T$. Multiply both sides of this equality by $(A^T)^{-1}$ on the right to get $(A^T)^{-1} = (A^{-1})^T$.

4. If, in addition, the $n \times n$ matrix B is invertible then the product AB is invertible and satisfies $(AB)^{-1} = B^{-1}A^{-1}$.

   To see that the product AB is invertible use the fact that each of A and B are invertible and write

   $$B^{-1}A^{-1}(AB) = B^{-1}(A^{-1}A)B = B^{-1}(I)B = B^{-1}B = I.$$

   This shows that AB is invertible. To see the given formula for the inverse write $(AB)(AB)^{-1} = I$. Multiply on the left of this identity by A^{-1} followed by B^{-1} to find that $(AB)^{-1} = B^{-1}A^{-1}$.

5. If A symmetric then A^{-1} is symmetric.

   This follows from part 3 above since $(A^{-1})^T = (A^T)^{-1} = A^{-1}$ by the symmetry of the matrix A..

Example 3.13 Using the two matrices from Example(3.10),

$$A = \begin{bmatrix} 2 & -2 \\ 1 & -1/2 \end{bmatrix} \text{ and } A^{-1} = \begin{bmatrix} -1/2 & 2 \\ -1 & 2 \end{bmatrix}$$

a matrix multiplication shows that

$$A^{-1}\left(A^{-1}\right)^{-1} = \begin{bmatrix} -1/2 & 2 \\ -1 & 2 \end{bmatrix}\begin{bmatrix} 2 & -2 \\ 1 & -1/2 \end{bmatrix} = \begin{bmatrix} 1 & 0 \\ 0 & 1 \end{bmatrix},$$

which illustrates the equality $\left(A^{-1}\right)^{-1} = A$. This is part 2 of Theorem(3.12). Another matrix multiplication

$$A^T\left(A^T\right)^{-1} = A^T\begin{bmatrix} -1/2 & -1 \\ 2 & 2 \end{bmatrix} = \begin{bmatrix} 2 & 1 \\ -2 & -1/2 \end{bmatrix}\begin{bmatrix} -1/2 & -1 \\ 2 & 2 \end{bmatrix} = \begin{bmatrix} 1 & 0 \\ 0 & 1 \end{bmatrix}$$

shows that

$$\left(A^T\right)^{-1} = \begin{bmatrix} -1/2 & -1 \\ 2 & 2 \end{bmatrix} = \left(A^{-1}\right)^T,$$

which is part 3 of Theorem(3.12). If $B = \begin{bmatrix} 3 & 1 \\ 2 & 1 \end{bmatrix}$ then a matrix multiplication $(BB^{-1} = I)$ shows $B^{-1} = \begin{bmatrix} 1 & -1 \\ -2 & 3 \end{bmatrix}$. The calculation

$$\begin{aligned} (AB)^{-1} &= \left(\begin{bmatrix} 2 & -2 \\ 1 & -1/2 \end{bmatrix}\begin{bmatrix} 3 & 1 \\ 2 & 1 \end{bmatrix}\right)^{-1} = \left(\begin{bmatrix} 2 & 0 \\ 2 & 1/2 \end{bmatrix}\right)^{-1} \\ &= \begin{bmatrix} 1/2 & 0 \\ -2 & 2 \end{bmatrix} = \begin{bmatrix} 1 & -1 \\ -2 & 3 \end{bmatrix}\begin{bmatrix} -1/2 & 2 \\ -1 & 2 \end{bmatrix} = B^{-1}A^{-1} \end{aligned}$$

illustrates part 4 of Theorem(3.12). Lastly, since

$$AA^{-1} = \begin{bmatrix} 1 & 2 \\ 2 & 3 \end{bmatrix}\begin{bmatrix} -3 & 2 \\ 2 & -1 \end{bmatrix} = I = \begin{bmatrix} 1 & 0 \\ 0 & 1 \end{bmatrix} = \begin{bmatrix} -3 & 2 \\ 2 & -1 \end{bmatrix}\begin{bmatrix} 1 & 2 \\ 2 & 3 \end{bmatrix} = A^{-1}A,$$

the inverse of the symmetric matrix A is the symmetric matrix A^{-1}.

Example(3.13) illustrates a number of 2×2 matrices that are invertible while Example(3.10) illustrated a matrix that is not invertible. To study which square matrices are invertible, a lot can be learned from the 2×2 case. Use Gauss elimination to solve the linear system

$$A\vec{x}^{\,1} = \begin{bmatrix} a_{11} & a_{12} \\ a_{21} & a_{22} \end{bmatrix}\begin{bmatrix} x_{11} \\ x_{21} \end{bmatrix} = \begin{bmatrix} 1 \\ 0 \end{bmatrix}. \tag{3.9}$$

Row operations applied to the augmented system lead to

$$\left[\, A \,\middle|\, \begin{bmatrix} 1 \\ 0 \end{bmatrix} \,\right] = \left[\begin{array}{cc|c} a_{11} & a_{12} & 1 \\ a_{21} & a_{22} & 0 \end{array}\right] \sim \left[\begin{array}{cc|c} 1 & 0 & x_{11} \\ 0 & 1 & x_{21} \end{array}\right].$$

where, if the quantity $a_{11}a_{22} - a_{12}a_{21} \neq 0$

$$x_{21} = \frac{-a_{21}}{a_{11}a_{22} - a_{12}a_{21}} \quad \text{and} \quad x_{11} = \frac{a_{22}}{a_{11}a_{22} - a_{12}a_{21}}. \tag{3.10}$$

Similarly, the solution to the linear system

$$A\vec{x}^{\,2} = \begin{bmatrix} a_{11} & a_{12} \\ a_{21} & a_{22} \end{bmatrix} \begin{bmatrix} x_{12} \\ x_{22} \end{bmatrix} = \begin{bmatrix} 0 \\ 1 \end{bmatrix}$$

is

$$x_{22} = \frac{a_{11}}{a_{11}a_{22} - a_{12}a_{21}} \quad \text{and} \quad x_{12} = \frac{-a_{12}}{a_{11}a_{22} - a_{12}a_{21}}. \tag{3.11}$$

Define the matrix of solutions $X = [\vec{x}^{\,1} \ \vec{x}^{\,2}]$ and using (3.5) for matrix products

$$AX = A[\vec{x}^{\,1} \ \vec{x}^{\,2}] = [A\vec{x}^{\,1} \ A\vec{x}^{\,2}] = \begin{bmatrix} 1 & 0 \\ 0 & 1 \end{bmatrix},$$

which shows that $X = A^{-1}$. The steps in the Gauss elimination to obtain (3.10) and (3.11) are the same. That is the problems could have been done simultaneously as follows

$$[\, A \mid I \,] = \left[\begin{array}{cc|cc} a_{11} & a_{12} & 1 & 0 \\ a_{21} & a_{22} & 0 & 1 \end{array}\right] \sim \left[\begin{array}{cc|cc} 1 & 0 & x_{11} & x_{12} \\ 0 & 1 & x_{21} & x_{22} \end{array}\right] = [\, I \mid X \,]. \tag{3.12}$$

The components for the formula for $X = A^{-1}$ are housed in (3.10) and (3.11) and these formulas focus attention on the quantity $a_{11}a_{22} - a_{12}a_{21}$ in their denominators.

Theorem 3.14 The **determinant** of $A = \begin{bmatrix} a_{11} & a_{12} \\ a_{21} & a_{22} \end{bmatrix}$ is defined by the scalar

$$\det(A) \equiv |A| \equiv a_{11}a_{22} - a_{12}a_{21}. \tag{3.13}$$

If $\det(A) = |A| \neq 0$ it follows from (3.10) and (3.11) that

$$A^{-1} = X = \begin{bmatrix} x_{11} & x_{12} \\ x_{21} & x_{22} \end{bmatrix} = \frac{1}{|A|} \begin{bmatrix} a_{22} & -a_{12} \\ -a_{21} & a_{11} \end{bmatrix}. \tag{3.14}$$

The 2×2 matrix A is invertible if and only if $\det(A) = |A| \neq 0$.

Example 3.15 In Example(3.10) the matrix $A = \begin{bmatrix} 2 & -2 \\ 1 & a_{22} \end{bmatrix}$ did or did not have an inverse depending on the value of a_{22}. At the end of that example it was shown that

$$A^{-1} = \frac{1}{2(a_{22}+1)} \begin{bmatrix} a_{22} & 2 \\ -1 & 2 \end{bmatrix} \quad \text{if} \quad a_{22} \neq -1.$$

Using (3.13), $\det(A) = 2a_{22} + 2$ so that the assumption $a_{22} \neq -1$ is the statement that the determinant of A must be different from zero for A to have an inverse. Alternatively, if $a_{22} = -1$ then $\det(A) = 2a_{22} + 2 = 0$ and the row reductions take the form

$$[A \mid I] = \begin{bmatrix} 2 & -2 & | & 1 & 0 \\ 1 & a_{22} & | & 0 & 1 \end{bmatrix} \sim \begin{bmatrix} 2 & -2 & | & 1 & 0 \\ 1 & -1 & | & 0 & 1 \end{bmatrix} \sim \begin{bmatrix} 2 & -2 & | & 1 & 0 \\ 0 & 0 & | & -1/2 & 1 \end{bmatrix}.$$

It is impossible to use row reductions to transform the matrix A to the identity by row operations. As pointed out in Example(3.10), this zero row in the first two columns in the row reduction of $[A \mid I]$ means that A is not invertible. It is instructive to mimic the row reduction procedure in (3.12) for a 3×3 matrix. This is illustrated for the 3×3 matrix $A = \begin{bmatrix} 1 & 2 & 3 \\ 2 & 5 & 4 \\ 1 & 3 & a_{33} \end{bmatrix}$. Apply row reductions to the augmented system $[A \mid I]$ to find

$$[A \mid I] = \begin{bmatrix} 1 & 2 & 3 & | & 1 & 0 & 0 \\ 2 & 5 & 4 & | & 0 & 1 & 0 \\ 1 & 3 & a_{33} & | & 0 & 0 & 1 \end{bmatrix}$$

$$\sim \begin{bmatrix} 1 & 2 & 3 & | & 1 & 0 & 0 \\ 0 & 1 & -2 & | & -2 & 1 & 0 \\ 0 & 1 & a_{33}-3 & | & -1 & 0 & 1 \end{bmatrix} \quad \begin{cases} (-2)\text{Eq1} + \text{Eq2} \\ (-1)\text{Eq1} + \text{Eq3} \end{cases}$$

$$\sim \begin{bmatrix} 1 & 2 & 3 & | & 1 & 0 & 0 \\ 0 & 1 & -2 & | & -2 & 1 & 0 \\ 0 & 0 & a_{33}-1 & | & 1 & -1 & 1 \end{bmatrix} \quad (-2)\text{Eq2} + \text{Eq3}. \tag{3.15}$$

Further assumptions on the value of the quantity a_{33} need to be introduced in order to proceed. If $a_{33} = 1$

$$[A \mid I] = \begin{bmatrix} 1 & 2 & 3 & | & 1 & 0 & 0 \\ 2 & 5 & 4 & | & 0 & 1 & 0 \\ 1 & 3 & 1 & | & 0 & 0 & 1 \end{bmatrix}$$

$$\sim \begin{bmatrix} 1 & 2 & 3 & | & 1 & 0 & 0 \\ 0 & 1 & -2 & | & -2 & 1 & 0 \\ 0 & 0 & 0 & | & 1 & -1 & 1 \end{bmatrix}$$

and the procedure stops due to the zero row in the first three columns of the row reduction of $[A \mid I]$. This means that the matrix A is not invertible. If $a_{33} = 2$ in (3.15) the calculation can continue:

$$[A \mid I] \sim \left[\begin{array}{ccc|ccc} 1 & 2 & 3 & 1 & 0 & 0 \\ 0 & 1 & -2 & -2 & 1 & 0 \\ 0 & 0 & 1 & 1 & -1 & 1 \end{array}\right] \quad \text{put } a_{33} = 2 \text{ in (3.15)}$$

$$\sim \left[\begin{array}{ccc|ccc} 1 & 2 & 0 & -2 & 3 & -3 \\ 0 & 1 & 0 & 0 & -1 & 2 \\ 0 & 0 & 1 & 1 & -1 & 1 \end{array}\right] \quad \left\{\begin{array}{l} (2)\text{Eq3} + \text{Eq2} \\ (-3)\text{Eq3} + \text{Eq1} \end{array}\right.$$

$$\sim \left[\begin{array}{ccc|ccc} 1 & 0 & 0 & -2 & 5 & -7 \\ 0 & 1 & 0 & 0 & -1 & 2 \\ 0 & 0 & 1 & 1 & -1 & 1 \end{array}\right] \quad (-2)\text{Eq2} + \text{Eq1} \tag{3.16}$$

$$= [\, I \mid A^{-1} \,]$$

so that $A^{-1} = \left[\begin{array}{ccc} -2 & 5 & -7 \\ 0 & -1 & 2 \\ 1 & -1 & 1 \end{array}\right]$. This can be checked by computing the product

$$AA^{-1} = \left[\begin{array}{ccc} 1 & 2 & 3 \\ 2 & 5 & 4 \\ 1 & 3 & 2 \end{array}\right]\left[\begin{array}{ccc} -2 & 5 & -7 \\ 0 & -1 & 2 \\ 1 & -1 & 1 \end{array}\right] = \left[\begin{array}{ccc} 1 & 0 & 0 \\ 0 & 1 & 0 \\ 0 & 0 & 1 \end{array}\right]$$

$$= \left[\begin{array}{ccc} -2 & 5 & -7 \\ 0 & -1 & 2 \\ 1 & -1 & 1 \end{array}\right]\left[\begin{array}{ccc} 1 & 2 & 3 \\ 2 & 5 & 4 \\ 1 & 3 & 2 \end{array}\right] = A^{-1}A.$$

The solution to the problem $A\vec{x} = \vec{b} = \left[\begin{array}{c} 6 \\ 4 \\ 1 \end{array}\right]$ can be found using the matrix multiplication:

$$\vec{x} = A^{-1}\vec{b} = \left[\begin{array}{ccc} -2 & 5 & -7 \\ 0 & -1 & 2 \\ 1 & -1 & 1 \end{array}\right]\left[\begin{array}{c} 6 \\ 4 \\ 1 \end{array}\right] = \left[\begin{array}{c} -12 + 20 - 7 \\ -4 + 2 \\ 6 - 4 + 1 \end{array}\right] = \left[\begin{array}{c} 1 \\ -2 \\ 3 \end{array}\right].$$

which is the solution found in Example(2.14) following (2.18). If A^{-1} is known then multiplying each side of the equation $A\vec{x} = \vec{b}$ by A^{-1} gives the (unique) solution $\vec{x} = A^{-1}\vec{b}$. The procedure outlined in the row reductions in (3.15) and (3.16) can be performed for any $n \times n$ matrix A. This is recorded in the next definition.

3.5 Inverses and the Gauss-Jordan Reduction

Definition 3.16 Gauss-Jordan reduction: Let A be an $n \times n$ matrix. The process of transforming the $n \times 2n$ augmented system $[A \mid I]$ to $[I \mid B]$ using elementary row operations (if possible) is called the **Gauss-Jordan reduction** of A. If the process can be completed then $B = A^{-1}$. If the reduction breaks down (a zero row in the first n columns of the reduction) then A has no inverse. Specifically, if at some point in the row reduction process the augmented system reaches the form

$$
\left[\begin{array}{cccc|cccc}
a_{11} & a_{12} & \cdots & a_{1n} & 1 & 0 & \cdots & 0 \\
a_{21} & a_{22} & \cdots & a_{2n} & 0 & 1 & \cdots & 0 \\
\vdots & \vdots & \ddots & \vdots & \vdots & \vdots & \ddots & \vdots \\
a_{n1} & a_{n2} & \cdots & a_{nn} & 0 & 0 & \cdots & 1
\end{array}\right]
\sim
\left[\begin{array}{cccc|cccc}
a_{11} & a_{12} & \cdots & a_{1n} & b_{11} & b_{12} & \cdots & b_{1n} \\
0 & \hat{a}_{22} & \cdots & \hat{a}_{2n} & b_{21} & b_{22} & \cdots & b_{2n} \\
\vdots & \vdots & \ddots & \vdots & \vdots & \vdots & \ddots & \vdots \\
0 & 0 & \cdots & 0 & b_{n1} & b_{n2} & \cdots & b_{nn}
\end{array}\right],
$$

then the matrix A has no inverse. If A is 3×3 this has the form

$$
\left[\begin{array}{ccc|ccc}
a_{11} & a_{12} & a_{13} & 1 & 0 & 0 \\
a_{21} & a_{22} & a_{23} & 0 & 1 & 0 \\
a_{31} & a_{32} & a_{33} & 0 & 0 & 1
\end{array}\right]
\sim
\left[\begin{array}{ccc|ccc}
a_{11} & a_{12} & a_{1n} & b_{11} & b_{12} & b_{13} \\
0 & \hat{a}_{22} & \hat{a}_{2n} & b_{21} & b_{22} & b_{23} \\
0 & 0 & 0 & b_{31} & b_{32} & b_{33}
\end{array}\right],
$$

which was illustrated in Example(3.15).

Theorem(3.14) gives a formula for the inverse of a 2×2 matrix A which includes the non-vanishing determinant condition for invertibility. There is also such a condition for an $n \times n$ matrix A. To build this formula the following notation is needed.

Definition 3.17 Cofactor: Given the $n \times n$ matrix

$$
A \equiv [a_{ij}]_{nn} =
\left[\begin{array}{cccccc}
a_{11} & a_{12} & \cdots & \cdots & a_{1j} & \cdots & a_{1n} \\
a_{21} & a_{22} & \cdots & \cdots & a_{2j} & \cdots & a_{2n} \\
\vdots & \vdots & \ddots & \cdots & \vdots & \vdots & \vdots \\
a_{i1} & a_{i2} & \cdots & \cdots & a_{ij} & \cdots & a_{in} \\
\vdots & \vdots & \cdots & \cdots & \vdots & \vdots & \vdots \\
a_{n1} & a_{n2} & \cdots & \cdots & a_{nj} & \cdots & a_{nn}
\end{array}\right],
\tag{3.17}
$$

define the $(n-1) \times (n-1)$ matrix A_{ij} to be the matrix obtained from A by removing the ith row and j^{th} column of A

$$
A_{ij} \equiv
\left[\begin{array}{cccccc}
a_{11} & a_{12} & \cdots & a_{1,j-1} & a_{1,j+1} & \cdots & a_{1n} \\
a_{21} & a_{22} & \cdots & a_{2,j-1} & a_{2,j+1} & \cdots & a_{2n} \\
\vdots & \vdots & \ddots & \cdots & \vdots & \vdots & \vdots \\
a_{i-1,1} & a_{i-1,2} & \cdots & a_{i-1,j-1} & a_{i-1,j+1} & \cdots & a_{i-1,n} \\
a_{i+1,1} & a_{i+1,2} & \cdots & a_{i+1,j-1} & a_{i+1,j+1} & \cdots & a_{i+1,n} \\
\vdots & \vdots & \cdots & \cdots & \vdots & \vdots & \vdots \\
a_{n1} & a_{n2} & \cdots & a_{n,j-1} & a_{n,j+1} & \cdots & a_{nn}
\end{array}\right]
\tag{3.18}
$$

where the notation

$$
a_{i\pm1,q} \text{ for } q = 1, 2, \cdots, j-1, j+1, \cdots, n
$$

and

$$
a_{p,j\pm1} \text{ for } p = 1, 2, \cdots, i-1, i+1, \cdots, n
$$

has been temporarily introduced for clarity. For example $a_{i-1,2}$ is clearer than is a_{i-12}. The numbers $(-1)^{i+j}\det(A_{ij}) = (-1)^{i+j}|A_{ij}|$ are called the **cofactors** of a_{ij}. If $n = 2$ then the four cofactors $A_{11} = [a_{22}], A_{12} = [a_{21}], A_{21} = [a_{12}]$ and $A_{22} = [a_{11}]$ are 1×1 matrices whose determinant is just the element in the matrix, that is, $|A_{11}| = \det([a_{22}]) = a_{22}$.

3.6 Determinants by the Laplace Cofactor Expansion

Theorem 3.18 Laplace's Cofactor Expansions: The determinant of the $n \times n$ matrix A is given by any one of the n row expansions

$$\det(A) = |A| = \sum_{j=1}^{n}(-1)^{i+j}a_{ij}|A_{ij}|, \quad i = 1, 2, \ldots, n \tag{3.19}$$

or any one of the n column expansions

$$\det(A) = |A| = \sum_{i=1}^{n}(-1)^{i+j}a_{ij}|A_{ij}|, \quad j = 1, 2, \ldots, n. \tag{3.20}$$

It is implied and is true that the number obtained from any of the $2n$ expansions in (3.19) and (3.20) are the same.

Example 3.19 This example illustrates the consistency of the different expressions for the determinant of A in (3.19) and (3.20). Assume $n = 2$ so that $A = \begin{bmatrix} a_{11} & a_{12} \\ a_{21} & a_{22} \end{bmatrix}$ and if $i = 1$ in (3.19) the Laplace expansion around the first row reads

$$\det(A) = |A| = \sum_{j=1}^{2}(-1)^{1+j}a_{1j}|A_{1j}| = a_{11}|A_{11}| - a_{12}|A_{12}| = a_{11}a_{22} - a_{12}a_{21}.$$

since from Definition(3.17) $|A_{11}| = a_{22}$ and $|A_{12}| = a_{21}$. This is the determinant formula in equation (3.13). See Exercise(3.8) to check that the other row expansion for the determinant of A from Theorem(3.18) agrees with the last display. Now let $n = 3$ and $i = 1$ in (3.19) so the Laplace expansion of a 3×3 matrix A around the first row reads

$$\det(A) = \begin{vmatrix} a_{11} & a_{12} & a_{13} \\ a_{21} & a_{22} & a_{23} \\ a_{31} & a_{32} & a_{33} \end{vmatrix} = \sum_{j=1}^{3}(-1)^{1+j}a_{1j}|A_{1j}|$$

$$= (-1)^{1+1}a_{11}|A_{11}| + (-1)^{1+2}a_{12}|A_{12}| + (-1)^{1+3}a_{13}|A_{13}|$$

$$= a_{11}\begin{vmatrix} a_{22} & a_{23} \\ a_{32} & a_{33} \end{vmatrix} - a_{12}\begin{vmatrix} a_{21} & a_{23} \\ a_{31} & a_{33} \end{vmatrix} + a_{13}\begin{vmatrix} a_{21} & a_{22} \\ a_{31} & a_{32} \end{vmatrix}.$$

$$= a_{11}[a_{22}a_{33} - a_{23}a_{32}] - a_{12}[a_{21}a_{33} - a_{23}a_{31}] + a_{13}[a_{21}a_{32} - a_{22}a_{31}].$$

The last equality uses the 2×2 determinant formula in equation (3.13). See Exercise(3.9) to check that the row expansion using $i = 2$ in Theorem(3.18) leads to same formula for the determinant of A. Applying the formula to the matrix $A = \begin{bmatrix} 1 & 2 & 3 \\ 2 & 5 & 4 \\ 1 & 3 & a_{33} \end{bmatrix}$ gives

$$
\begin{aligned}
\det(A) &= (-1)^{1+1}(1) \begin{vmatrix} 5 & 4 \\ 3 & a_{33} \end{vmatrix} + (-1)^{1+2}(2) \begin{vmatrix} 2 & 4 \\ 1 & a_{33} \end{vmatrix} + (-1)^{1+3}(3) \begin{vmatrix} 2 & 5 \\ 1 & 3 \end{vmatrix} \\
&= (1)\left[5a_{33} - 4(3)\right] - (2)\left[2a_{33} - 4(1)\right] + (3)\left[2(3) - 5(1)\right] \\
&= 5a_{33} - 12 - 4a_{33} + 8 + 3 = a_{33} - 1.
\end{aligned}
$$

Using any of the expansions in Theorem(3.18) will also give $\det(A) = a_{33} - 1$. However, a more efficient procedure for computing a determinant uses row reductions. It was shown in (3.15) that the following matrix equivalences occur

$$
A \sim \tilde{A}_1 \equiv \begin{bmatrix} 1 & 2 & 3 \\ 0 & 1 & -2 \\ 0 & 1 & a_{33} - 3 \end{bmatrix} \sim \tilde{A}_2 \equiv \begin{bmatrix} 1 & 2 & 3 \\ 0 & 1 & -2 \\ 0 & 0 & a_{33} - 1 \end{bmatrix}.
$$

The determinant of $\tilde{A}_1$ using the expansion around column one gives

$$
\det(\tilde{A}_1) = (1) \begin{bmatrix} 1 & -2 \\ 1 & a_{33} - 3 \end{bmatrix} = (a_{33} - 3) - (-2)(1) = a_{33} - 1.
$$

Similarly, expanding around column one of $\tilde{A}_2$ shows

$$
\det(\tilde{A}_2) = (1) \begin{bmatrix} 1 & -2 \\ 0 & a_{33} - 1 \end{bmatrix} = a_{33} - 1.
$$

The determinant of a matrix A is unchanged if an elementary row operation of type 1 in Definition(2.9) is applied to A, that is, a row of the matrix A is multiplied by a scalar and added to another row of A. A number of properties of the determinant and row operations impact on the determinant are contained in the following theorem.

Theorem 3.20 Properties of Determinants: Let A and B be $n \times n$ matrices.

1. If B is obtained from A by multiplying a row of A by a scalar and added to another row of A then $\det(A) = \det(B)$.

2. If B is obtained from A by multiplying a row (or a column) of A by a scalar α then $\det(B) = \alpha(\det(A))$. If instead, the determinant of a scalar multiple of the entire matrix A is given by $\det(\alpha A) = \alpha^n \det(A)$. Hence, $\det(-A) = (-1)^n \det(A)$.

3. If B is obtained from A by interchanging two rows of A then $\det(A) = -\det(B)$.

4. $\det(A) = \det(A^T)$.

5. $\det(AB) = \det(A)\det(B)$.

6. If A is invertible, then $\det(A^{-1}) = \dfrac{1}{\det(A)}$.

Example 3.21 Part 1 is illustrated preceding Theorem(3.20) and is actually one of the more useful tools used in finding the $\det(A)$. Let

$$A = \begin{bmatrix} a_{11} & a_{12} \\ a_{21} & a_{22} \end{bmatrix} \text{ and } B = \alpha A = \begin{bmatrix} \alpha a_{11} & \alpha a_{12} \\ a_{21} & a_{22} \end{bmatrix}.$$

Use the definition of the determinant in (3.13) to see

$$\det(B) = \begin{vmatrix} \alpha a_{11} & \alpha a_{12} \\ a_{21} & a_{22} \end{vmatrix} = \alpha a_{11} a_{22} - \alpha a_{12} a_{21} = \alpha\left(a_{11}a_{22} - \alpha a_{12}a_{21}\right) = \alpha\left(\det(A)\right).$$

This is an example of the first portion of part 2. Now set $B = \alpha A$ and calculate

$$\det(B) = \det(\alpha A) = \begin{vmatrix} \alpha a_{11} & \alpha a_{12} \\ \alpha a_{21} & \alpha a_{22} \end{vmatrix} = \alpha^2\left(a_{11}a_{22} - a_{12}a_{21}\right) = \alpha^2\left(\det(A)\right).$$

This illustrates the second portion of part 2. Interchange the two rows of A and define the resulting matrix to be $B = \begin{bmatrix} a_{21} & a_{22} \\ a_{11} & a_{12} \end{bmatrix}$. The calculation

$$\det(A) = a_{11}a_{22} - a_{21}a_{12} = -\left(a_{21}a_{12} - a_{11}a_{22}\right) = -\det(B)$$

illustrates part 3 of Theorem(3.20). Part 4 is a straight forward application of (3.19) and (3.20). If the $\det(A)$ is found, for example, by applying (3.19) with $i = 1$ and $\det(A^T)$ is found by applying (3.20) with $j = 1$ then the two expansions are exactly the same (the first row of A (expansion from (3.19)) with $i = 1$) is the first column of A^T (expansion from (3.20) with $j = 1$). Part 5 requires more tools than have been developed but consider the two matrices

$$A = \begin{bmatrix} 2 & -2 \\ 1 & a_{22} \end{bmatrix} \text{ and } B = \begin{bmatrix} 4 & 1 \\ 1 & 2 \end{bmatrix} \text{ and their product } AB = \begin{bmatrix} 6 & -2 \\ 4 + a_{22} & 1 + 2a_{22} \end{bmatrix}.$$

Using the determinant formula in (3.13) yields

$$\begin{aligned} (\det(A))\,(\det(B)) &= (2a_{22} + 2)(8 - 1) = 14(a_{22} + 1) \\ (\det(AB)) &= 6(1 + 2a_{22}) + 2(4 + a_{22}) = 14(a_{22} + 1) \end{aligned}$$

so that $\det(A)\det(B) = \det(AB)$. If $a_{22} = -1$ then $\det(A) = \det(AB) = 0$ so neither of the matrices A or the product AB are invertible. See Exercise(3.13). Finally, if A is invertible then $AA^{-1} = I$ so that $\det(AA^{-1}) = \det(I) = 1$. See Exercise(3.12) for the determinant of a diagonal matrix. Using part 5 on the left hand side of $\det(AA^{-1}) = 1$ gives $\det(A)\det(A^{-1}) = 1$ which is part 6.

An important application of Theorem(3.20) for the calculation of the determinant of a matrix emerges as a consequence of adroit combinations of parts 1 and 3 of that theorem. Here is an illustration of this application in the case of a 4×4 matrix. Using elementary row operations one finds

$$
|A| = \begin{vmatrix} 0 & 3 & 2 & 3 \\ 1 & 2 & 0 & 4 \\ 3 & 8 & 2 & 1 \\ 1 & 3 & 1 & 1 \end{vmatrix} = (-1)\begin{vmatrix} 1 & 2 & 0 & 4 \\ 0 & 3 & 2 & 3 \\ 3 & 8 & 2 & 1 \\ 1 & 3 & 1 & 1 \end{vmatrix} \quad \left\{ \begin{array}{l} (-3)\text{Eq1} + \text{Eq3} \\ (-1)\text{Eq1} + \text{Eq4} \end{array} \right.
$$

$$
= (-1)\begin{vmatrix} 1 & 2 & 0 & 4 \\ 0 & 3 & 2 & 3 \\ 0 & 2 & 2 & -11 \\ 0 & 1 & 1 & -3 \end{vmatrix} \quad \left\{ \begin{array}{l} (-2/3)\text{Eq2} + \text{Eq3} \\ (-1/3)\text{Eq2} + \text{Eq4} \end{array} \right.
$$

$$
= (-1)\begin{vmatrix} 1 & 2 & 0 & 4 \\ 0 & 3 & 2 & 3 \\ 0 & 0 & \frac{2}{3} & -13 \\ 0 & 0 & \frac{1}{3} & -4 \end{vmatrix} \quad (-1/2)\text{Eq3} + \text{Eq4}
$$

$$
= (-1)\begin{vmatrix} 1 & 2 & 0 & 4 \\ 0 & 3 & 2 & 3 \\ 0 & 0 & \frac{2}{3} & -13 \\ 0 & 0 & 0 & \frac{5}{2} \end{vmatrix} = (-1)(1)(3)\left(\frac{2}{3}\right)\left(\frac{5}{2}\right) = -5.
$$

The (-1) which appears after the second equality arises due to the interchange of row one and row two in the first step which is part 3 of Theorem(3.20). The two zeros which appear in the a_{31} and a_{41} positions after the third equality arise by using part 1 of Theorem(3.20) twice. The other zeros arise from similar applications of Theorem(3.20). The last matrix determinant is in row echelon form with pivots $1, 3, \frac{2}{3}$ and $\frac{5}{2}$. The last equality follows from the fact that the determinant of an upper triangular matrix is the product of its diagonal elements. See Exercise(3.12). This calculation provides one of the most economical means to evaluate a determinant. See Exercise(3.14).

3.7 Inverse of an $n \times n$ Matrix by the Adjoint Formula

The Gauss-Jordan row reduction gives an algorithm in Definition(3.16) for computing the inverse of a matrix or showing that the matrix has no inverse. Alternatively, if A is 2×2 the formula in (3.14) gives the inverse of A when it has one. There is an $n \times n$ analogue of (3.14) contained in the following formula.

Theorem 3.22 Inverse and Adjoint Formula: Let A be the $n \times n$ matrix in (3.17) and assume that $\det(A) = |A| \neq 0$ then

$$
A^{-1} \equiv \frac{1}{|A|}\mathrm{adj}(A) = \frac{1}{|A|}
\begin{bmatrix}
|A_{11}| & -|A_{12}| & \cdots & (-1)^{n+1}|A_{1n}| \\
-|A_{21}| & |A_{22}| & \cdots & (-1)^{n+2}|A_{2n}| \\
\vdots & \vdots & \ddots & \vdots \\
\vdots & \vdots & \cdots & \vdots \\
(-1)^{n+1}|A_{n1}| & (-1)^{n+2}|A_{n2}| & \cdots & |A_{nn}|
\end{bmatrix}^T
$$

$$
= \frac{1}{|A|}
\begin{bmatrix}
|A_{11}| & -|A_{21}| & \cdots & (-1)^{n+1}|A_{n1}| \\
-|A_{12}| & |A_{22}| & \cdots & (-1)^{n+2}|A_{n2}| \\
\vdots & \vdots & \ddots & \vdots \\
\vdots & \vdots & \cdots & \vdots \\
(-1)^{n+1}|A_{1n}| & (-1)^{n+2}|A_{2n}| & \cdots & |A_{nn}|
\end{bmatrix}
\tag{3.21}
$$

where the $n \times n$ matrix $\mathrm{adj}(A) = \left[(-1)^{i+j}|A_{ij}|\right]^T$ is called the **adjoint of A** and A_{ij} is the $(n-1) \times (n-1)$ matrix in (3.18).

Example 3.23 For the 2×2 matrix $A = \begin{bmatrix} a_{11} & a_{12} \\ a_{21} & a_{22} \end{bmatrix}$ it has already been mentioned that the four matrices A_{ij} are the 1×1 matrices $A_{11} = [a_{22}]$ $A_{12} = [a_{21}]$, $A_{21} = [a_{12}]$ and $A_{22} = [a_{11}]$ so that the adjoint formula in (3.21) reads

$$
A^{-1} = \frac{1}{|A|}
\begin{bmatrix}
(-1)^{1+1}|A_{11}| & (-1)^{1+2}|A_{12}| \\
(-1)^{2+1}|A_{21}| & (-1)^{2+2}|A_{22}|
\end{bmatrix}^T
= \frac{1}{|A|}
\begin{bmatrix}
|A_{11}| & -|A_{12}| \\
-|A_{21}| & |A_{22}|
\end{bmatrix}^T
$$

$$
= \frac{1}{|A|}
\begin{bmatrix}
a_{22} & -a_{21} \\
-a_{12} & a_{11}
\end{bmatrix}^T
= \frac{1}{|A|}
\begin{bmatrix}
a_{22} & -a_{12} \\
-a_{21} & a_{11}
\end{bmatrix}
$$

which is the formula in (3.14).

Theorem 3.24 Cramer's Rule Here is a use for the inverse formula in the last example. Assume that the coefficient matrix A in the system

$$
A\vec{x} = \begin{bmatrix} a_{11} & a_{12} \\ a_{21} & a_{22} \end{bmatrix} \begin{bmatrix} x_1 \\ x_2 \end{bmatrix} = \begin{bmatrix} b_1 \\ b_2 \end{bmatrix}.
\tag{3.22}
$$

is invertible. The system in (3.22) has a unique solution given by $\vec{x} = A^{-1}\vec{b}$ which when written out reads

$$
\vec{x} = \begin{bmatrix} x_1 \\ x_2 \end{bmatrix} = \frac{1}{|A|}
\begin{bmatrix}
|A_{11}| & -|A_{21}| \\
-|A_{12}| & |A_{22}|
\end{bmatrix} \vec{b}
= \frac{1}{|A|}
\begin{bmatrix}
b_1|A_{11}| - b_2|A_{21}| \\
-b_1|A_{12}| + b_2|A_{22}|
\end{bmatrix}
$$

$$= \frac{1}{|A|} \begin{bmatrix} b_1 a_{22} - b_2 a_{12} \\ -b_1 a_{21} + b_2 a_{11} \end{bmatrix} = \frac{1}{|A|} \begin{bmatrix} \begin{vmatrix} b_1 & a_{12} \\ b_2 & a_{22} \end{vmatrix} \\ \\ \begin{vmatrix} a_{11} & b_1 \\ a_{21} & b_2 \end{vmatrix} \end{bmatrix}. \tag{3.23}$$

Equating components gives the two scalar identities

$$x_1 = \frac{1}{|A|} \begin{vmatrix} b_1 & a_{12} \\ b_2 & a_{22} \end{vmatrix} \quad \text{and} \quad x_2 = \frac{1}{|A|} \begin{vmatrix} a_{11} & b_1 \\ a_{21} & b_2 \end{vmatrix}.$$

Define A^j to be the matrix obtained from the matrix A by replacing the jth column of A with the vector $\vec{b}$, $j = 1, 2$. The previous display shows that the solution of (3.22) is given by the formula

$$x_1 = \frac{|A^1|}{|A|} = \frac{1}{|A|} \begin{vmatrix} b_1 & a_{12} \\ b_2 & a_{22} \end{vmatrix} \quad \text{and} \quad x_2 = \frac{|A^2|}{|A|} = \frac{1}{|A|} \begin{vmatrix} a_{11} & b_1 \\ a_{21} & b_2 \end{vmatrix} \tag{3.24}$$

which is known as **Cramer's Rule** for the 2×2 linear system in (3.22). Assume that the $\det(A) = |A| \neq 0$ for the matrix in the system

$$A\vec{x} = \begin{bmatrix} a_{11} & a_{12} & \cdots & \cdots & a_{1j} & \cdots & a_{1n} \\ a_{21} & a_{22} & \cdots & \cdots & a_{2j} & \cdots & a_{2n} \\ \vdots & \vdots & \ddots & \cdots & \vdots & \vdots & \vdots \\ a_{i1} & a_{i2} & \cdots & \cdots & a_{ij} & \cdots & a_{in} \\ \vdots & \vdots & \ddots & \cdots & \cdots & \ddots & \vdots \\ \vdots & \vdots & \cdots & \cdots & \vdots & \vdots & \vdots \\ a_{n1} & a_{n2} & \cdots & \cdots & a_{nj} & \cdots & a_{nn} \end{bmatrix} \begin{bmatrix} x_1 \\ x_2 \\ \vdots \\ x_i \\ \vdots \\ x_j \\ \vdots \\ x_n \end{bmatrix} = \vec{b} = \begin{bmatrix} b_1 \\ b_2 \\ \vdots \\ b_i \\ \vdots \\ b_j \\ \vdots \\ b_n \end{bmatrix}$$

and define A^j, $j = 1, 2, \ldots, n$ to be the matrix obtained from A by replacing the jth column of A with the vector $\vec{b}$. The components of the solution vector $\vec{x}$ are given by

$$x_j = \frac{|A^j|}{|A|} = \frac{1}{|A|} \begin{vmatrix} a_{11} & a_{12} & \cdots & \cdots & b_1 & \cdots & a_{1n} \\ a_{21} & a_{22} & \cdots & \cdots & b_2 & \cdots & a_{2n} \\ \vdots & \vdots & \ddots & \cdots & \vdots & \vdots & \vdots \\ a_{i1} & a_{i2} & \cdots & \cdots & b_i & \cdots & a_{in} \\ \vdots & \vdots & \ddots & \cdots & \cdots & \ddots & \vdots \\ \vdots & \vdots & \cdots & \cdots & \vdots & \vdots & \vdots \\ a_{n1} & a_{n2} & \cdots & \cdots & b_n & \cdots & a_{nn} \end{vmatrix}, \ j = 1.2.\ldots, n. \tag{3.25}$$

This is obtained in exactly the same fashion as in the 2×2 case. The first step is to multiply both sides of the system $A\vec{x} = \vec{b}$ by A^{-1} and use the inverse formula (3.21) in

$\vec{x} = A^{-1}\vec{b}$. Observe that the jth component of this product is the cofactor expansion (3.20) with the coefficients a_{ij} replaced by b_i. This is the determinant expansion of A^j around its jth column. The formula in (3.25) is **Cramer's Rule** for an $n \times n$ linear system.

Example 3.25 Here are a few applications of Cramer's rule. For the linear system

$$A\vec{x} = \begin{bmatrix} 2 & -2 \\ 1 & 1/2 \end{bmatrix} \begin{bmatrix} x_1 \\ x_2 \end{bmatrix} = \begin{bmatrix} 3 \\ 3/4 \end{bmatrix}$$

the coefficient matrix A has the determinant

$$|A| = \begin{vmatrix} 2 & -2 \\ 1 & 1/2 \end{vmatrix} = 2(1/2) + 2(1) = 3.$$

The determinants of the matrices $A^j, j = 1, 2$ are given by

$$|A^1| = \begin{vmatrix} 3 & -2 \\ 3/4 & 1/2 \end{vmatrix} = 3(1/2) + (2)(3/4) = 3 \quad \text{and} \quad |A^2| = \begin{vmatrix} 2 & 3 \\ 1 & 3/4 \end{vmatrix} = 3/2 - 3 = -3/2.$$

Hence, the solution to the system is

$$x_1 = \frac{|A^1|}{|A|} = \frac{3}{3} = 1 \quad \text{and} \quad x_2 = \frac{|A^2|}{|A|} = \frac{-3/2}{3} = \frac{-1}{2}$$

which agrees with the solution found in Example(3.10). In Example(3.15) the matrix system

$$A\vec{x} = \begin{bmatrix} 1 & 2 & 3 \\ 2 & 5 & 4 \\ 1 & 3 & 2 \end{bmatrix} \begin{bmatrix} x_1 \\ x_2 \\ x_3 \end{bmatrix} = \begin{bmatrix} 6 \\ 4 \\ 1 \end{bmatrix} = \vec{b}$$

was solved by finding the inverse A^{-1} and performing the matrix multiplication

$$\vec{x} = \begin{bmatrix} x_1 \\ x_2 \\ x_3 \end{bmatrix} = A^{-1}\vec{b} = \begin{bmatrix} -2 & 5 & -7 \\ 0 & -1 & 2 \\ 1 & -1 & 1 \end{bmatrix} \begin{bmatrix} 6 \\ 4 \\ 1 \end{bmatrix} = \begin{bmatrix} 1 \\ -2 \\ 3 \end{bmatrix}. \tag{3.26}$$

In order to verify this solution using Cramer's rule, the four determinants $|A|, |A^1|, |A^2|$ and $|A^3|$ need to be calculated. It was found in Example(3.15) that $\det(A) = |A| = 1$. Use part 1 of Theorem(3.20) twice to find

$$|A^1| = \begin{vmatrix} 6 & 2 & 3 \\ 4 & 5 & 4 \\ 1 & 3 & 2 \end{vmatrix} \quad \begin{cases} (-2/3)\text{Eq1} + \text{Eq2} \\ (-1/6)\text{Eq1} + \text{Eq3} \end{cases}$$

$$\sim \begin{vmatrix} 6 & 2 & 3 \\ 0 & 11/3 & 2 \\ 0 & 8/3 & 3/2 \end{vmatrix} = 6\left(\frac{11}{3}\left(\frac{3}{2}\right) - 2\left(\frac{8}{3}\right)\right) = 6\left(\frac{33-32}{6}\right) = 1.$$

Combining this result with $|A| = 1$ and (3.25) gives the first component of the solution

$$x_1 = \frac{|A^1|}{|A|} = \frac{1}{1} = 1$$

which agrees with the result in (3.26). Continuing with the calculation of the determinant of the matrix A^2 and again using part 1 of determinants in Theorem(3.20) yields

$$|A^2| = \begin{vmatrix} 1 & 6 & 3 \\ 2 & 4 & 4 \\ 1 & 1 & 2 \end{vmatrix} \quad \left\{ \begin{array}{l} (-2)\text{Eq1} + \text{Eq2} \\ (-1)\text{Eq1} + \text{Eq3} \end{array} \right.$$

$$\sim \begin{vmatrix} 1 & 6 & 3 \\ 0 & -8 & -2 \\ 0 & -5 & -1 \end{vmatrix} = (-8)(-1) - (-2)(-5) = 8 - 10 = -2.$$

The second component of the solution is, by (3.25),

$$x_2 = \frac{|A^2|}{|A|} = \frac{-2}{1} = -2.$$

The last determinant needed in Cramer's rule is

$$|A^3| = \begin{vmatrix} 1 & 2 & 6 \\ 2 & 5 & 4 \\ 1 & 3 & 1 \end{vmatrix} \sim \begin{vmatrix} 1 & 2 & 1 \\ 0 & 1 & -8 \\ 0 & 1 & -5 \end{vmatrix} = (1)(-5) - (1)(-8) = -5 + 8 = 3$$

so that (3.25) gives the last component of the solution

$$x_3 = \frac{|A^3|}{|A|} = \frac{3}{1} = 3.$$

Cramer's rule is not as efficient for solving the system $A\vec{x} = \vec{b}$ as is the method of Gauss elimination. However, the formula in (3.21) which gives rise to Cramer's rule and the unique solution to $A\vec{x} = \vec{b}$ in (3.25) is an important part of the following theorem.

Theorem 3.26 Matrix Invertibility: The $n \times n$ matrix A is invertible if and only if $\det(A) \neq 0$. Equivalently, the $n \times n$ matrix A is not invertible if and only if $\det(A) = 0$.

By Definition(3.11) the matrix A is invertible if A has an inverse. This is a matrix A^{-1} so that $AA^{-1} = I$. By part 5 of Theorem(3.20) $\det(AA^{-1}) = \det(A)\det(A^{-1}) = 1$ so that neither $\det(A)$ nor $\det(A^{-1})$ can be zero, that is, $\det(A) \neq 0$. If $\det(A) \neq 0$ then formula (3.21) defines the inverse of A.

Example 3.27 Using the row reduction

$$A = \begin{bmatrix} 2 & -2 \\ 1 & -1 \end{bmatrix} \sim \begin{bmatrix} 2 & -2 \\ 0 & 0 \end{bmatrix},$$

it was shown in Example(3.10) that the matrix A is not invertible. As is guaranteed from Theorem(3.26), $\det(A) = 2(-1) - (-2)(1) = 0$. Here is another (equivalent) method to illustrate that the matrix A is not invertible. Calculate the product

$$A \begin{bmatrix} 1 \\ 1 \end{bmatrix} = \begin{bmatrix} 2 & -2 \\ 1 & -1 \end{bmatrix} \begin{bmatrix} 1 \\ 1 \end{bmatrix} = \begin{bmatrix} 0 \\ 0 \end{bmatrix}. \tag{3.27}$$

If A were invertible then, upon multiplying both sides of (3.27) by A^{-1}, it follows that

$$A^{-1} \left(A \begin{bmatrix} 1 \\ 1 \end{bmatrix} \right) = A^{-1} \begin{bmatrix} 0 \\ 0 \end{bmatrix}. \tag{3.28}$$

The left hand side of (3.28) reads

$$\left(A^{-1}A \right) \begin{bmatrix} 1 \\ 1 \end{bmatrix} = \begin{bmatrix} 1 & 0 \\ 0 & 1 \end{bmatrix} \begin{bmatrix} 1 \\ 1 \end{bmatrix} = \begin{bmatrix} 1 \\ 1 \end{bmatrix} \tag{3.29}$$

while the right hand side reads

$$A^{-1} \begin{bmatrix} 0 \\ 0 \end{bmatrix} = \begin{bmatrix} 0 \\ 0 \end{bmatrix}. \tag{3.30}$$

Putting (3.29) and (3.30) into (3.28) leads to the impossible equality $\begin{bmatrix} 1 \\ 1 \end{bmatrix} = \begin{bmatrix} 0 \\ 0 \end{bmatrix}$. The assumption that led to this contradictory situation is that A has an inverse. Hence A has no inverse. This is another example of *proof by contradiction*. In this case the assumption that A is invertible following (3.27) led to the contradictory statement that the vectors $\begin{bmatrix} 1 \\ 1 \end{bmatrix}$ and $\begin{bmatrix} 0 \\ 0 \end{bmatrix}$ are equal. From Example(3.15) the matrix $A = \begin{bmatrix} 1 & 2 & 3 \\ 2 & 5 & 4 \\ 1 & 3 & 1 \end{bmatrix}$ is not invertible. A short calculation shows that

$$A\vec{x} = \begin{bmatrix} 1 & 2 & 3 \\ 2 & 3 & 4 \\ 3 & 4 & 5 \end{bmatrix} \begin{bmatrix} -7 \\ 2 \\ 1 \end{bmatrix} = \begin{bmatrix} 0 \\ 0 \\ 0 \end{bmatrix}$$

and the previous argument shows that A is not invertible.

In both of these cases the augmented system $[\, A \mid \vec{0} \,]$ has a zero row in the row reduction which means there is a free variable in the solution. If this variable is assigned a non-zero value then the homogeneous system has a non-zero solution. In addition, since A is row equivalent to a matrix with a zero row it follows that $\det(A) = |A| = 0$ See Exercise(3.13). This provides another condition for a matrix not to be invertible. It plays an important role in Chapter Five.

Theorem 3.28 Assume that A is $n \times n$ and that $\vec{0}$ is the $n \times 1$ zero vector. There is a non-zero vector $\vec{x}$ satisfying $A\vec{x} = \vec{0}$ if and only if the matrix A is not invertible. Equivalently, $\vec{x} = \vec{0}$ is the unique solution of the system $A\vec{x} = \vec{0}$ if and only if A is invertible.

Compare this result with Theorem(2.13). If in Theorem(3.28) the vector $\vec{0}$ is replaced with an arbitrary vector $\vec{b}$ then the last line is also equivalent to the statement that the $n \times n$ system $A\vec{x} = \vec{b}$ has a unique solution if and only if $\det(A) \neq 0$. Here is a use for Theorem(3.28) that advertises parts of both Chapter Four and Chapter Five.

Example 3.29 Suppose $A = \begin{bmatrix} 2 & 4 \\ 4 & 2 \end{bmatrix}$ and it is required to find, if possible, a non-zero vector $\vec{p}$ and a scalar λ satisfying $A\vec{p} = \lambda\vec{p}$. Why one would want to find such vectors and scalars is the subject of Chapter Five. In terms of matrix multiplication this is a search for vectors $\vec{p}$ where the resulting product is about as simple as can be expected. If $A\vec{p} = \lambda\vec{p}$ then $A\vec{p} - \lambda\vec{p} = \vec{0}$ so if I is introduced into the last equality the equation takes the form $A\vec{p} - \lambda I\vec{p} = (A - \lambda I)\vec{p} = \vec{0}$. So the opening sentence can be formulated as follows: find non-zero vectors $\vec{p}$ so that $(A - \lambda I)\vec{p} = \vec{0}$. Theorem(3.28) implies that the search should begin for numbers λ so that the matrix

$$B = A - \lambda I = \begin{bmatrix} 2 & 4 \\ 4 & 2 \end{bmatrix} - \lambda \begin{bmatrix} 1 & 0 \\ 0 & 1 \end{bmatrix} = \begin{bmatrix} 2-\lambda & 4 \\ 4 & 2-\lambda \end{bmatrix}$$

is not invertible. Again by Theorem(3.28), the matrix B is not invertible if its determinant is zero. This leads to

$$0 = \det(B) = \begin{vmatrix} 2-\lambda & 4 \\ 4 & 2-\lambda \end{vmatrix} = (2-\lambda)(2-\lambda) - 16$$

$$= \lambda^2 - 4\lambda - 12 = (\lambda + 2)(\lambda - 6)$$

and the matrix B is not invertible if $\lambda_1 = -2$ or $\lambda_2 = 6$. Define the two matrices $B_1 = A - \lambda_1 I$ and $B_2 = A - \lambda_2 I$. According to Theorem(3.28) there is a non-zero vector $\vec{p}_1$ so that $B_1\vec{p}_1 = \vec{0}$. To find $\vec{p}_1$ a simple row reduction gives

$$\begin{bmatrix} A - \lambda_1 I \mid \vec{0} \end{bmatrix} = \begin{bmatrix} A + 2I \mid \vec{0} \end{bmatrix} = \begin{bmatrix} 4 & 4 & | & 0 \\ 4 & 4 & | & 0 \end{bmatrix} \sim \begin{bmatrix} 4 & 4 & | & 0 \\ 0 & 0 & | & 0 \end{bmatrix}$$

and a non-zero solution is $\vec{p}_1 = \begin{bmatrix} 1 \\ -1 \end{bmatrix}$. So it has been shown that

$$B_1\vec{p}_1 = (A - \lambda_1 I)\vec{p}_1 = \begin{bmatrix} 4 & 4 \\ 4 & 4 \end{bmatrix} \begin{bmatrix} 1 \\ -1 \end{bmatrix} = \begin{bmatrix} 0 \\ 0 \end{bmatrix}$$

which can also be written

$$A\vec{p}_1 = \begin{bmatrix} 2 & 4 \\ 4 & 2 \end{bmatrix} \begin{bmatrix} 1 \\ -1 \end{bmatrix} = \lambda_1\vec{p}_1 = (-2)\begin{bmatrix} 1 \\ -1 \end{bmatrix}. \tag{3.31}$$

Notice that any multiple $\vec{q} \equiv \alpha \vec{p}_1$ will also either of the previous displays. This is an example of one of four important subspaces (the set of all scalar multiples of $\vec{p}_1$ is a subspace of $\mathcal{R}^2$) studied in Chapter Four. To see that any multiple $\vec{q} \equiv \alpha \vec{p}_1$ satisfies (3.31) calculate

$$
\begin{aligned}
A\vec{q} = A(\alpha \vec{p}_1) &= \begin{bmatrix} 2 & 4 \\ 4 & 2 \end{bmatrix} \left(\alpha \begin{bmatrix} 1 \\ -1 \end{bmatrix} \right) \\
&= \alpha \left(\begin{bmatrix} 2 & 4 \\ 4 & 2 \end{bmatrix} \begin{bmatrix} 1 \\ -1 \end{bmatrix} \right) \\
&= \alpha(\lambda_1 \vec{p}_1) = \lambda_1(\alpha \vec{p}_1) = \lambda_1 \vec{q}.
\end{aligned}
$$

Similarly, if $\lambda_2 = 6$ the homogeneous system

$$
B_2 \vec{p}_2 = (A - 6I)\vec{p}_2 = \begin{bmatrix} -4 & 4 \\ 4 & -4 \end{bmatrix} \vec{p}_2 = \begin{bmatrix} 0 \\ 0 \end{bmatrix}
$$

has the solution $\vec{p}_2 = \begin{bmatrix} 1 \\ 1 \end{bmatrix}$. Form the matrix $P = [\vec{p}_1 \ \vec{p}_2] = \begin{bmatrix} 1 & 1 \\ -1 & 1 \end{bmatrix}$ and since $\det(P) = |P| = 2 \neq 0$ Theorem(3.14) guarantees that P is invertible and formula (3.14) yields

$$
P^{-1} = \frac{1}{|P|} \begin{bmatrix} 1 & -1 \\ 1 & 1 \end{bmatrix} = \frac{1}{2} \begin{bmatrix} 1 & -1 \\ 1 & 1 \end{bmatrix}.
$$

Finally, the matrix multiplication

$$
\begin{aligned}
P^{-1}AP &= \frac{1}{2} \begin{bmatrix} 1 & -1 \\ 1 & 1 \end{bmatrix} \begin{bmatrix} 2 & 4 \\ 4 & 2 \end{bmatrix} \begin{bmatrix} 1 & 1 \\ -1 & 1 \end{bmatrix} \\
&= \begin{bmatrix} -2 & 0 \\ 0 & 6 \end{bmatrix} = \begin{bmatrix} \lambda_1 & 0 \\ 0 & \lambda_2 \end{bmatrix} = \Lambda
\end{aligned}
\tag{3.32}
$$

transforms, via the indicated multiplication, the matrix A to a diagonal matrix. As it turns out the two vectors $\vec{p}_1$ and $\vec{p}_2$ are orthogonal. From Theorem(1.10), part 6 this means that the dot product $\vec{p}_1 \cdot \vec{p}_2 = 0$. Define the two unit vectors (see Definition(1.6))

$$
\vec{q}_1 = \frac{1}{\|\vec{p}_1\|} \vec{p}_1 = \frac{1}{\sqrt{2}} \begin{bmatrix} 1 \\ 1 \end{bmatrix} \quad \text{and} \quad \vec{q}_1 = \frac{1}{\|\vec{p}_1\|} \vec{p}_1 = \frac{1}{\sqrt{2}} \begin{bmatrix} 1 \\ -1 \end{bmatrix}
$$

and the matrix $Q = [\vec{q}_1 \ \vec{q}_2]$. If P in (3.32) is replaced by Q that equation remains true and, further, the matrix Q satisfies $Q^{-1} = Q^T$. See Exercise(3.18). Matrices Q which satisfy $Q^{-1} = Q^T$ are called orthogonal matrices and play a fundamental role in Chapter Five. The notion of orthogonal vectors play a very important role in the manner in which the various subspaces of the matrix A fit together. This is the subject of Chapter Four.

3.8   Exercise Set

Exercise 3.1 Let $A = \begin{bmatrix} 2 & 0 & -1 \\ 1 & 2 & 2 \end{bmatrix}$, $B = \begin{bmatrix} 1 & -1 \\ 0 & 0 \\ 2 & 2 \end{bmatrix}$ and $C = \begin{bmatrix} 0 & -2 & 0 \\ -2 & 4 & 0 \\ 0 & 0 & 0 \end{bmatrix}$ and

$\mathcal{O} = \begin{bmatrix} 0 & 0 & 0 \\ 0 & 0 & 0 \end{bmatrix}$. Find the following matrices or state that the quantity is undefined.

	Additions		Multiplications
(i)	$A + B$	(i)	AB
(ii)	$A + B^T$	(ii)	BA
(iii)	$A + C$	(iii)	CB
(iv)	$A + \mathcal{O}$	(iv)	$A\mathcal{O}$
(v)	$B + \mathcal{O}$	(v)	$\mathcal{O}A$
(vi)	$A^T + B$	(vi)	BC
(vii)	$\mathcal{O} + B^T$	(vii)	$C^T B^T$
(viii)	$B + C$	(viii)	$B^T C^T$
(ix)	$A^T + B^T$	(ix)	$(CB)^T$

Exercise 3.2 Let $A = \begin{bmatrix} a_{11} & a_{12} \\ a_{21} & a_{22} \end{bmatrix}$ and set $A_c = [\,\vec{a}_{*1}\ \vec{a}_{*2}]$ so that $\vec{a}_{*j} = \begin{bmatrix} a_{1j} \\ a_{2j} \end{bmatrix}, j = 1, 2$
are the two columns of A. Call this the column form of the representation of A. In a similar
fashion, $A_r = \begin{bmatrix} \vec{a}_{1*}^{\,T} \\ \vec{a}_{2*}^{\,T} \end{bmatrix}$ where $\vec{a}_{i*}^{\,T} = [a_{i1}\ a_{i1}], i = 1, 2$ are the two rows of A. Call this the
row form of the representation of A. Finally, let $\Lambda = \begin{bmatrix} \lambda_1 & 0 \\ 0 & \lambda_2 \end{bmatrix}$.

1. Show, by direct calculation or using (3.4), that $\Lambda A = \Lambda A_r = \begin{bmatrix} \lambda_1 \vec{a}_{1*}^{\,T} \\ \lambda_2 \vec{a}_{2*}^{\,T} \end{bmatrix}$. Left
   multiplication by a diagonal matrix is row multiplication of row i by the diagonal
   entry $\lambda_i, i = 1, 2$.

2. Similarly, show by direct calculation or using (3.4), $A\Lambda = A_c\Lambda = [\lambda_1\vec{a}_{*1}\ \lambda_2\vec{a}_{*2}]$. Right
   multiplication by a diagonal matrix is column multiplication of column j by the di-
   agonal entry $\lambda_j, j = 1, 2$.

3. Show that part 2 follows by taking the transpose of part 1 and using Theorem(3.7).

4. Just a note that parts 1 and 2 of this problem are true for $n \times n$ matrices A and
   diagonal matrices Λ. The column and row representations for A is in equation(3.2)
   and equation(3.4), respectively

Exercise 3.3 Let $A_4 = \begin{bmatrix} 1 & 1 \\ 1 & 2 \\ 2 & 0 \end{bmatrix}$.

1. Show that $A_4 A_4^T$ is a 3×3 symmetric matrix.

2. Show that $A_4^T A_4$ is a 2×2 symmetric matrix.

3. If B is an $m \times p$ matrix the calculation in (3.8) shows that $V = BB^T$ is an $m \times m$ symmetric matrix. Show that $W = B^T B$ is a $p \times p$ symmetric matrix.

Exercise 3.4 Let $A = \begin{bmatrix} 1 & 0 \\ 0 & 0 \end{bmatrix}$, $B = \begin{bmatrix} 0 & 0 \\ 1 & 2 \end{bmatrix}$ and $C = \begin{bmatrix} 0 & 1 \\ 0 & 0 \end{bmatrix}$.

1. Show that

$$AB = \begin{bmatrix} 0 & 0 \\ 0 & 0 \end{bmatrix} \neq \begin{bmatrix} 0 & 0 \\ 1 & 0 \end{bmatrix} = BA.$$

This shows that if $AB = \mathcal{O}$ one can not necessarily conclude that one of A or B is the zero matrix. The real number analogue of the above equation reads: if α and β are real numbers then the equation $\alpha\beta = 0$ implies that $\alpha = 0$ or $\beta = 0$ or both are zero. It is also the case that

$$AC = \begin{bmatrix} 0 & 1 \\ 0 & 0 \end{bmatrix} \neq \begin{bmatrix} 0 & 0 \\ 0 & 0 \end{bmatrix} = CA.$$

Any of the matrices A, B or C is called a **zero divisor**.

2. Use the above identity to show that neither A nor B is invertible. (Argue indirectly, if A is invertible then multiply both sides of $AB = \mathcal{O}$ by A^{-1}. Conclude that this implies that $B = \mathcal{O}$. Since B is not the zero matrix this is a contradiction so A is not invertible).

3. Show also that

$$CC = C^2 = \begin{bmatrix} 0 & 1 \\ 0 & 0 \end{bmatrix} \begin{bmatrix} 0 & 1 \\ 0 & 0 \end{bmatrix} = \begin{bmatrix} 0 & 0 \\ 0 & 0 \end{bmatrix}.$$

That is, even if $CC = C^2 = \mathcal{O}$ one can not necessarily conclude that C is the zero matrix. The matrix C is an example of a **Nilpotent** matrix.

Exercise 3.5 It was mentioned in Definition(3.1) that matrix multiplication is not, in general, commutative. It should not be concluded that matrices **never** commute. Let

$$A = \begin{bmatrix} 3 & 2 \\ 0 & 1 \end{bmatrix}, B = \begin{bmatrix} 1 & 5 \\ 5 & 1 \end{bmatrix} \text{ and } C = \begin{bmatrix} 2 & -1 \\ -1 & 2 \end{bmatrix},$$

1. Find each of AB and BA. Conclude that the expansion $(A \pm B)^2 = A^2 \pm AB \pm BA + B^2$ for this A and B cannot be simplified to $(A \pm B)^2 = A^2 \pm 2AB + B^2$.

2. Find each of BC and CB. Conclude that the expansion $(B \pm C)^2 = B^2 \pm 2BC + C^2$, in this case is valid. Exercise(5.6) gives some insight as to how such commuting matrices arise.

Exercise 3.6 Find, if possible, A^{-1} for the matrices. It is wise to check to see if $\det(A) = 0$ since in this case you are done.

1. $A = \begin{bmatrix} 1 & 2 \\ 2 & 1 \end{bmatrix}$

5. $A = \begin{bmatrix} 2 & 0 \\ 2 & 0 \end{bmatrix}$

2. $A = \begin{bmatrix} 1 & 1 \\ 1 & 2 \end{bmatrix}$

6. $A = \begin{bmatrix} 1 & 1 \\ 2 & 2 \end{bmatrix}$

3. $A = \begin{bmatrix} 2 & -1 & 3 \\ 4 & 0 & 2 \\ 0 & -1 & 3 \end{bmatrix}$

7. $A = \begin{bmatrix} 2 & -1 & 3 \\ 4 & 0 & 2 \\ 0 & -1 & 2 \end{bmatrix}$

4. $A = \begin{bmatrix} 0 & -1 & 3 & 1 \\ 4 & 0 & 2 & 2 \\ 0 & -1 & 2 & 0 \\ 1 & 0 & 1 & 0 \end{bmatrix}$

8. $A = \begin{bmatrix} 2 & -1 & 3 & 1 \\ 4 & 0 & 2 & 2 \\ 0 & -1 & 2 & 0 \\ 1 & 0 & 1 & 0 \end{bmatrix}$

Exercise 3.7 For $n \geq 2$ define the $n \times n$ matrix $T_n = \begin{bmatrix} 2 & -1 & 0 & \cdots & 0 \\ -1 & 2 & -1 & \vdots & 0 \\ \vdots & \ddots & \ddots & \ddots & \vdots \\ 0 & 0 & \ddots & 2 & -1 \\ 0 & 0 & \cdots & -1 & 2 \end{bmatrix}$. This matrix is an example of what is called a **Tridiagonal matrix**. Nonzero elements are on the main diagonal or just above (or below) the main diagonal.

1. Find the inverse of T_n for $n = 2, 3$ and 4.

2. Define $|T_0| = 1$ and $|T_1| = 2$ and find each of the following.

(a) $|T_2| = \begin{vmatrix} 2 & -1 \\ -1 & 2 \end{vmatrix} = 2|T_1| - 1 = 2|T_1| - |T_0| = 3.$

(b) $|T_3| = \begin{vmatrix} 2 & -1 & 0 \\ -1 & 2 & -1 \\ 0 & -1 & 2 \end{vmatrix} = 2|T_2| + \begin{vmatrix} -1 & 0 \\ -1 & 2 \end{vmatrix} = 2|T_2| - 2 = 2|T_2| - |T_1| = 4.$

(c) $|T_4| = \begin{vmatrix} 2 & -1 & 0 & 0 \\ -1 & 2 & -1 & 0 \\ 0 & -1 & 2 & -1 \\ 0 & 0 & -1 & 2 \end{vmatrix} = 2|T_3| + \begin{vmatrix} -1 & 0 & 0 \\ -1 & 2 & -1 \\ 0 & -1 & 2 \end{vmatrix} = 2|T_3| - |T_2| = 5.$

(d) The previous determinants give a reason to believe the formula

$$|T_{n+1}| = 2|T_n| - |T_{n-1}| = n + 2, \ n \geq 1 \text{ where } |T_1| \equiv 2 \text{ and } |T_0| \equiv 1.$$

Expand the determinant $|T_{n+1}|$ around row one to verify the recursion formula. The identity $|T_{n+1}| = n + 2$ proceeds by induction.

3. **Principle of Mathematical Induction** - Let $S(n)$ be a statement about the positive integers. If $S(1)$ is true and the truth of $S(k)$ implies the truth of $S(k + 1)$ then the statement $S(n)$ is true for all positive integers. Alternatively;

Little stick people induction.

Hypothesis:

(1) Knock down   (2) Each person is taller (t) than the
the first person.   distance (d) to the person behind them.

$\downarrow$ "$S(1)$ is true."   "$S(k)$ implies $S(k + 1)$"

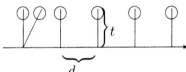

$t > d$

Conclusion: Everybody falls down.
"$S(n)$ is always true".

To see how this applies to part 2 (d) above let $S(n)$ be the statement that $|T_{n+1}| = n+2$ for all $n \geq 1$. $S(1)$ is the statement $|T_2| = 3$ which follows from $|T_2| = \begin{vmatrix} 2 & -1 \\ -1 & 2 \end{vmatrix} = 4 - 1 = 3$. Assume that $S(k)$ is true. This means that $|T_{k+1}| = k + 2$ which also implies $|T_k| = k + 1$ (all of the stick people up to the $(k + 1)^{st}$ is knocked down). Use this to show that $|T_{k+2}| = k + 3$. Begin with the recursion formula to write

$$
\begin{aligned}
|T_{k+2}| &= 2|T_{k+1}| - |T_k| &&\text{inductive hypothesis applied to} \\
&= 2(k + 2) - (k + 1) &&|T_{k+1}| = k + 2 \text{ and } |T_k| = k + 1 \\
&= 2k + 4 - (k + 1) = k + 3.
\end{aligned}
$$

See part 3 of Exercise(5.4) for a different procedure to find this determinant formula.

Exercise 3.8 If $A = \begin{bmatrix} a_{11} & a_{12} \\ a_{21} & a_{22} \end{bmatrix}$ and $i = 1$ in (3.19) the determinant of A is given by

$$\det(A) = |A| = \begin{vmatrix} a_{11} & a_{12} \\ a_{21} & a_{22} \end{vmatrix} = a_{11}a_{22} - a_{12}a_{21}.$$

which agrees with equation (3.13). If $i = 2$ in (3.19) then

$$\det(A) = |A| = (-1)^3 a_{21}|A_{21}| + (-1)^{2+2}a_{22}|A_{22}|.$$

Use Definition(3.17) to show the last display agrees with (3.13).

Exercise 3.9 Let $A = \begin{bmatrix} a_{11} & a_{12} & a_{13} \\ a_{21} & a_{22} & a_{23} \\ a_{31} & a_{32} & a_{33} \end{bmatrix}$ be an arbitrary 3×3 matrix. Use $i = 2$ in the expansion in (3.19) to write

$$\det(A) = |A| = -a_{21}\begin{vmatrix} a_{12} & a_{13} \\ a_{32} & a_{33} \end{vmatrix} + a_{22}\begin{vmatrix} a_{11} & a_{13} \\ a_{31} & a_{33} \end{vmatrix} - a_{23}\begin{vmatrix} a_{11} & a_{12} \\ a_{31} & a_{32} \end{vmatrix}.$$

Expand these determinants and show that this result is the same as the expansion found in Example(3.19).

Exercise 3.10 Assume that the determinant of the matrix $A = \begin{bmatrix} a_{11} & a_{12} & a_{13} \\ a_{21} & a_{22} & a_{23} \\ a_{31} & a_{32} & a_{33} \end{bmatrix}$ is non-zero. Use (3.21) to show that the inverse matrix is given by

$$A^{-1} = \frac{1}{|A|} \begin{bmatrix} \begin{vmatrix} a_{22} & a_{23} \\ a_{32} & a_{33} \end{vmatrix} & -\begin{vmatrix} a_{12} & a_{13} \\ a_{32} & a_{33} \end{vmatrix} & \begin{vmatrix} a_{12} & a_{13} \\ a_{22} & a_{23} \end{vmatrix} \\ -\begin{vmatrix} a_{21} & a_{23} \\ a_{31} & a_{33} \end{vmatrix} & \begin{vmatrix} a_{11} & a_{13} \\ a_{31} & a_{33} \end{vmatrix} & -\begin{vmatrix} a_{11} & a_{13} \\ a_{21} & a_{23} \end{vmatrix} \\ \begin{vmatrix} a_{21} & a_{22} \\ a_{31} & a_{32} \end{vmatrix} & -\begin{vmatrix} a_{11} & a_{12} \\ a_{31} & a_{32} \end{vmatrix} & \begin{vmatrix} a_{11} & a_{12} \\ a_{21} & a_{22} \end{vmatrix} \end{bmatrix}.$$

Apply the result just obtained to find A^{-1} for $A = \begin{bmatrix} 1 & 2 & 3 \\ 2 & 5 & 4 \\ 1 & 3 & 2 \end{bmatrix}$. This is the result found in equation (3.16) from Example(3.15).

Exercise 3.11 Let $A = \begin{bmatrix} 1 & -2 & 2 \\ -2 & 1 & 2 \\ 2 & 2 & 1 \end{bmatrix}$ in the linear system $A\begin{bmatrix} x_1 \\ x_2 \\ x_3 \end{bmatrix} = \vec{b} = \begin{bmatrix} 3 \\ 0 \\ -3 \end{bmatrix}$.

1. Find $x_1, x_2,$ and x_3 by row reducing $[\,A \mid \vec{b}\,]$ and using back substitution.

2. Find A^{-1} by row reducing $[\,A \mid I\,] \sim [\,I \mid A^{-1}\,]$ as in the Gauss-Jordan reduction in Definition(3.16).

3. Check your answer by constructing A^{-1} using formula in Exercise(3.10).

4. Check your answer to part 1 by calculating $A^{-1}\vec{b}$.

Exercise 3.12 Upper and Lower Triangular Matrices: The $n \times n$ matrices

$$U = \begin{bmatrix} u_{11} & u_{12} & u_{13} & \cdots & u_{1n} \\ 0 & u_{22} & u_{23} & \cdots & u_{2n} \\ 0 & 0 & u_{33} & \cdots & u_{3n} \\ \vdots & \vdots & \vdots & \ddots & \vdots \\ 0 & 0 & 0 & \cdots & u_{nn} \end{bmatrix} \text{ and } L = \begin{bmatrix} l_{11} & 0 & 0 & \cdots & 0 \\ l_{21} & l_{22} & 0 & \cdots & 0 \\ l_{31} & l_{32} & l_{33} & \cdots & 0 \\ \vdots & \vdots & \vdots & \ddots & 0 \\ l_{n1} & l_{n2} & l_{n3} & \cdots & l_{nn} \end{bmatrix}$$

are called **upper and lower triangular** matrices, respectively. In an **upper triangular** matrix the non-zero elements occur on or above the main diagonal. In a **lower triangular** matrix the non-zero elements occur on or below the main diagonal. The diagonal matrix $D = [d_{ii}]_{nn}$ and $d_{ij} = 0$ for $i \neq j$ from Definition(3.11) is both upper and lower triangular.

1. Show that $\det(U) = u_{11}u_{22}\cdots u_{nn}$, $\det(L) = l_{11}l_{22}\cdots l_{nn}$ and $\det(D) = d_{11}d_{22}\cdots d_{nn}$. When is U (L or D) invertible?

2. Use formula (3.21) in the display from Exercise(3.10) to show that $U^{-1} = \begin{bmatrix} 1 & -1 & 2 \\ 0 & 1 & -1 \\ 0 & 0 & 1 \end{bmatrix}$

   is the inverse $U = \begin{bmatrix} 1 & 1 & -1 \\ 0 & 1 & 1 \\ 0 & 0 & 1 \end{bmatrix}$.

3. Show that the inverse of any 3×3 upper triangular U is upper triangular.

4. Find L^{-1} for $L = \begin{bmatrix} 1 & 0 & 0 \\ 1 & 1 & 0 \\ -1 & 1 & 1 \end{bmatrix}$. Note that $L = U^T$ and then use part 3 of Theorem(3.12).

Exercise 3.13 One conclusion of Theorem(3.28) is that the matrix A is not invertible if and only if $\det(A) = |A| = 0$. Here are some more instances when the determinant of the matrix A is zero. The first was mentioned in the lines preceding Theorem(3.28). Show that

1. if A has a zero row or column then $\det(A) = 0$.

2. if A has two equal rows (or columns) then $\det(A) = 0$.

3. if A has two rows (or columns) that are proportional then $\det(A) = 0$.

4. if A and B are $n \times n$ and either A or B is not invertible then the product AB is not invertible (see Example(3.21)).

Exercise 3.14 This exercise provides some practice computing determinants as discussed at the close of Example(3.21).

1. Verify that $\det(A) = \begin{vmatrix} 1 & 2 & 0 & 2 \\ -1 & 1 & 0 & 2 \\ 0 & 1 & 2 & 1 \\ 1 & -1 & 0 & -2 \end{vmatrix} = 0$ by using $i = 1$ in (3.19) and using $j = 3$

   in (3.20). The method described at the close of Example(3.21) proceeds as follows: use two row operations to show that $A \sim B$, followed by two more row operations on $B \sim U$, that is,

$$[\,A\,] \sim \begin{bmatrix} 1 & 2 & 0 & 2 \\ 0 & 3 & 0 & 4 \\ 0 & 1 & 2 & 1 \\ 0 & -3 & 0 & -4 \end{bmatrix} \equiv B \sim \begin{bmatrix} 1 & 2 & 0 & 2 \\ 0 & 3 & 0 & 4 \\ 0 & 0 & 2 & -1/3 \\ 0 & 0 & 0 & 0 \end{bmatrix} \equiv U.$$

   Verify $\det(A) = \det(B) = \det(U) = (1)(3)(2)(0) = 0$ which is the first part 1 of Theorem(3.20). The matrix U is the row echelon form of the matrix A. For matrices larger than 2×2 it usually simplifies a determinant calculation by introducing zeros, for example in column 1 by part 1 of Theorem(3.20), and computing the determinant of the similar matrix.

2. Find the determinant of $A = \begin{bmatrix} 1 & 2 & 0 & 4 \\ 0 & 3 & 2 & 3 \\ 3 & 8 & 2 & 1 \\ 1 & 3 & 1 & 1 \end{bmatrix}$ by comparing this matrix to the example

   worked out at the close of Example(3.21).

3. Find $|A|$ for $A = \begin{bmatrix} 1 & 2 & 0 & 4 \\ 0 & 1 & 2 & 3 \\ 3 & 2 & 0 & 1 \\ 1 & 1 & 2 & 1 \end{bmatrix}$ and $\hat{A} = \begin{bmatrix} 1 & 2 & 0 & 4 \\ 3 & 2 & 0 & 1 \\ 0 & 2 & 4 & 6 \\ 1 & 1 & 2 & 1 \end{bmatrix}.$

4. Let $A = \begin{bmatrix} 1 & 2 & 3 & 4 \\ 2 & 3 & 4 & 5 \\ 3 & 4 & a_{33} & 6 \\ 4 & 5 & 6 & a_{44} \end{bmatrix}$. If $a_{33} = 5$ is there any value for a_{44} so that the matrix

   is invertible? Now let $a_{33} = 6$. Find the unique value for a_{44} so that the matrix is not invertible.

5. For the $n \times n$ matrix A let U be the row echelon form [see Definition(2.10ed)] obtained using only row operations of types one and three (parts 1 and 3 of Theorem(3.20)). Label the pivots $p_j, j = 1, 2, 3, \cdots, k$ where $k \leq n$. The determinant of A is given by the formula

$$\det(A) = \begin{cases} (-1)^s p_1 p_2 \cdots p_n, & k = n \\ 0, & k < n \end{cases}.$$

where s is the number of row switches made in the row reduction of A to U. Notice that if $k < n$ then $\det(A) = 0$ since U has at least one zero row. See part 1 of this problem. Finally, if no row switches are made and $k = n$ then the result states that the determinant of A is the product of its pivots.

Exercise 3.15 Let $A = \begin{bmatrix} 1 & 2 & 0 & 2 \\ -1 & 1 & 0 & 2 \\ 0 & 1 & 2 & 1 \\ 1 & -1 & 0 & -3 \end{bmatrix}$.

1. Show that $\det(A) = 2 \begin{bmatrix} 1 & 2 & 2 \\ -1 & 1 & 2 \\ 1 & -1 & -3 \end{bmatrix} = -6$.

2. Show that $A^{-1} = \dfrac{1}{6} \begin{bmatrix} 2 & -8 & 0 & -4 \\ 2 & 10 & 0 & 8 \\ -1 & -2 & 3 & -1 \\ 0 & -6 & 0 & -6 \end{bmatrix}$ by row reducing $[\,A \mid I\,] \sim [\,I \mid A^{-1}\,]$.

3. Start constructing A^{-1} using formula (3.21) and continue until you've had enough.

Exercise 3.16 Let $A_1 = \begin{bmatrix} 0 & 1 \\ -1 & 0 \end{bmatrix}$ and $A_2 = \begin{bmatrix} 0 & 1 & -2 \\ -1 & 0 & 3 \\ 2 & -3 & 0 \end{bmatrix}$.

1. Show that $A_1^T = -A_1$ and $\det(A_1) = 1$

2. Show that $A_2^T = -A_2$ and $\det(A_2) = 0$

3. Use part 2 to show that $\det(A_2) = 0$. It is helpful to use part 4 in Theorem(3.20) and the identity $\det(-A_2) = (-1)^3 \det(A_2) = -\det(A_2)$.

   For any $n \times n$ matrix A, if $A^T = -A$ the matrix is called **skew-symmetric**.

4. If A is skew-symmetric, show that the diagonal entries of A are all zero, that is, $a_{ii} = 0$ for $i = 1, 2, \ldots, n$.

5. If n is odd and A is skew-symmetric show that $\det(A) = 0$. Your work in part 3 should work fine here. By part 4 of Theorem(3.20) $\det(-A) = (-1)^n \det(A)$.

Exercise 3.17 Let $A = \begin{bmatrix} 8 & -5 \\ 10 & -7 \end{bmatrix}$.

1. Find numbers λ so that $A - \lambda I$ is not invertible. See Example(3.29).

2. Define $\lambda_1 = -2$ and $\lambda_2 = 3$ and let $\vec{p}_1 = \begin{bmatrix} 1 \\ 2 \end{bmatrix}$ and $\vec{p}_2 = \begin{bmatrix} 1 \\ 1 \end{bmatrix}$. Show that

$$A\vec{p}_1 = \begin{bmatrix} 8 & -5 \\ 10 & -7 \end{bmatrix} \vec{p}_1 = -2 \begin{bmatrix} 1 \\ 2 \end{bmatrix} = \lambda_1 \vec{p}_1$$

and

$$A\vec{p}_2 = \begin{bmatrix} 8 & -5 \\ 10 & -7 \end{bmatrix} \vec{p}_2 = 3 \begin{bmatrix} 1 \\ 1 \end{bmatrix} = \lambda_2 \vec{p}_2 \ .$$

3. Define the matrix $P = [\vec{p}_1 \ \vec{p}_2] = \begin{bmatrix} 1 & 1 \\ 2 & 1 \end{bmatrix}$ and show

$$P^{-1}AP = \Lambda \equiv \begin{bmatrix} \lambda_1 & 0 \\ 0 & \lambda_2 \end{bmatrix} = \begin{bmatrix} -2 & 0 \\ 0 & 3 \end{bmatrix} \ .$$

4. Repeat parts 1, 2 and 3 for $A = \begin{bmatrix} 1 & 2 \\ 2 & 1 \end{bmatrix}$. In this case show that the dot product $\vec{p}_1 \cdot \vec{p}_2 = 0$.

5. What happens in part 1 if $A = \begin{bmatrix} 2 & -1 \\ 4 & 6 \end{bmatrix}$?

Exercise 3.18 An $n \times n$ matrix Q satisfying $Q^T Q = I$ is called an **orthogonal matrix**. The columns (or the rows) of Q are orthogonal vectors. The definition implies that $Q^T = Q^{-1}$. Here are a few examples.

1. Multiply the matrix $P = \begin{bmatrix} 1 & -1 \\ 1 & 1 \end{bmatrix}$ by $1/\sqrt{2}$ and define $Q = \dfrac{1}{\sqrt{2}} \begin{bmatrix} 1 & -1 \\ 1 & 1 \end{bmatrix}$. Show that Q is orthogonal.

2. Let $Q = \begin{bmatrix} \cos(\theta) & -\sin(\theta) \\ \sin(\theta) & \cos(\theta) \end{bmatrix}$. Show Q is orthogonal for all angles θ. What matrix do you obtain if $\theta = \dfrac{\pi}{4}$?

3. An $n \times n$ invertible symmetric matrix having a number of interesting properties is the **backwards identity** $J_n = [j_{ik}]$, which is defined by

$$j_{ik} = \begin{cases} 1 & \text{if } k = n - i + 1 \\ \\ 0 & \text{if } k \neq n - i + 1 \end{cases} \qquad i = 1, 2, \ldots, n \quad .$$

Take $n = 2$ and $n = 3$ to see that

$$J_2 = \begin{bmatrix} 0 & 1 \\ 1 & 0 \end{bmatrix} \quad \text{and} \quad J_3 = \begin{bmatrix} 0 & 0 & 1 \\ 0 & 1 & 0 \\ 1 & 0 & 0 \end{bmatrix}.$$

If $\vec{x} = \begin{bmatrix} x_1 \\ x_2 \end{bmatrix}$ show that $J_2 \vec{x} = \begin{bmatrix} x_2 \\ x_1 \end{bmatrix}$. It follows that

$$(J_2)^2 \, \vec{x} = J_2 \, (J_2 \vec{x}) = J_2 \left(\begin{bmatrix} x_2 \\ x_1 \end{bmatrix} \right) = \begin{bmatrix} x_1 \\ x_2 \end{bmatrix}.$$

It follows that $(J_2)^2 = I$ and therefore $J_2 = J_2^T = J_2^{-1}$. The matrix J_2 is an symmetric orthogonal matrix. Analogously, if $\vec{x} = \begin{bmatrix} x_1 \\ x_2 \\ x_3 \end{bmatrix}$ show that $J_3 \vec{x} = \begin{bmatrix} x_3 \\ x_2 \\ x_1 \end{bmatrix}$. It is also the case that $(J_3)^2 = I$ and $J_3^T = J_3$ so that J_3 is orthogonal. The matrix J_n gets its name since, after multiplication, it lists the vector $\vec{x}$ backwards.

3.9 Sample Tests

3.9.1 Sample Test 1

Name_____   Date_____

1. Find the matrix or write that it is undefined (UND) in the $\begin{bmatrix} & \\ & \end{bmatrix}$.

(a) $\begin{bmatrix} 1 & 2 \\ 2 & 3 \end{bmatrix} + \begin{bmatrix} 0 & 0 & 0 \\ 0 & 0 & 0 \end{bmatrix} = \begin{bmatrix} & \\ & \end{bmatrix}$

(b) $\begin{bmatrix} 1 & 2 & 0 \\ 2 & 3 & 0 \end{bmatrix} + \begin{bmatrix} 2 & 0 & 0 \\ 0 & 3 & 0 \end{bmatrix} = \begin{bmatrix} & \\ & \end{bmatrix}$

(c) $\begin{bmatrix} 2 & 0 & 0 \\ 0 & 3 & 0 \end{bmatrix} \begin{bmatrix} 1 & 2 & 0 \\ 2 & 3 & 0 \\ 0 & 0 & 0 \end{bmatrix} = \begin{bmatrix} & \\ & \end{bmatrix}$

(d) $\begin{bmatrix} 1 & 2 & 0 \\ 2 & 3 & 0 \\ 0 & 0 & 0 \end{bmatrix} \begin{bmatrix} 2 & 0 & 0 \\ 0 & 3 & 0 \end{bmatrix} = \begin{bmatrix} & \\ & \end{bmatrix}$

(e) the inverse of $\begin{bmatrix} 2 & 2 \\ 1 & 3 \end{bmatrix} = \begin{bmatrix} & \\ & \end{bmatrix}$

(f) the inverse of $\begin{bmatrix} 2 & 2 & 0 \\ 1 & 3 & 0 \end{bmatrix} = \begin{bmatrix} & \\ & \end{bmatrix}$

(g) Find $\begin{bmatrix} 1 & 0 \\ 1 & 0 \end{bmatrix} \begin{bmatrix} 0 & 0 \\ 1 & 1 \end{bmatrix} = \begin{bmatrix} & \\ & \end{bmatrix}$

(h) $J^2 = \begin{bmatrix} 0 & 1 \\ 1 & 0 \end{bmatrix}^2 = \begin{bmatrix} 0 & 1 \\ 1 & 0 \end{bmatrix} \begin{bmatrix} 0 & 1 \\ 1 & 0 \end{bmatrix} = \begin{bmatrix} & \\ & \end{bmatrix}$ so that $J^{-1} = \begin{bmatrix} & \\ & \end{bmatrix}$

(i) $N^2 = \begin{bmatrix} 0 & 1 & 0 \\ 0 & 0 & 1 \\ 0 & 0 & 0 \end{bmatrix}^2 = \begin{bmatrix} 0 & 1 & 0 \\ 0 & 0 & 1 \\ 0 & 0 & 0 \end{bmatrix} \begin{bmatrix} 0 & 1 & 0 \\ 0 & 0 & 1 \\ 0 & 0 & 0 \end{bmatrix} =$

(j) $N^3 = NN^2 = \begin{bmatrix} 0 & 1 & 0 \\ 0 & 0 & 1 \\ 0 & 0 & 0 \end{bmatrix} N^2 =$

2. Suppose the matrix B is $p \times q$. Assume that the product ABC is defined and it's size is $m \times n$. Answer each of the following

   (a) The size of A is _____.

   (b) The size of C is _____.

   (c) The size of AB is _____.

   (d) The size of BC is _____.

   (e) The size of $(ABC)^T$ is _____.

3. Find the determinant $\begin{vmatrix} 1 & 2 & 0 & 4 \\ 0 & 1 & 2 & 0 \\ 1 & 1 & 3 & 0 \\ 1 & 0 & 2 & 2 \end{vmatrix} =$

4. Let $A = \begin{bmatrix} 1 & 1 & 2 & 1 \\ 2 & 0 & 2 & -4 \\ 0 & 1 & -1 & -1 \\ 0 & 1 & 0 & 1 \end{bmatrix}$.

   (a) Calculate the product

   $$\begin{bmatrix} 1 & 1 & 2 & 1 \\ 2 & 0 & 2 & -4 \\ 0 & 1 & -1 & -1 \\ 0 & 1 & 0 & 1 \end{bmatrix} \begin{bmatrix} 4 \\ -1 \\ -2 \\ 1 \end{bmatrix} = \begin{bmatrix} \\ \\ \\ \end{bmatrix}.$$

   (b) The matrix A has an inverse__True__ False____ (Circle One).

   (c) The determinant of A _____

5. Let $A = \begin{bmatrix} 1 & 0 & 1 \\ 1 & 1 & \alpha \\ 0 & 1 & 1 \end{bmatrix}$.

(a) Find α so that $|A| = \det(A) = 0$.

(b) Find α so that $|A| = \det(A) = 1$.

(c) Using the value of α from part (b), find A^{-1}.

(d) Let A be the matrix from part (c). Find the solution to the linear system
$$A\vec{x} = \begin{bmatrix} 1 & 0 & 1 \\ 1 & 1 & \alpha \\ 0 & 1 & 1 \end{bmatrix} \begin{bmatrix} x_1 \\ x_2 \\ x_3 \end{bmatrix} = \begin{bmatrix} 1 \\ 2 \\ 3 \end{bmatrix}$$
using the result found in part (c),

3.9.2 Sample Test 2

Name_____   Date_____

1. Find the quantity or state that it is undefined (UND) for the matrices

$$A = \begin{bmatrix} 3 & 0 \\ 1 & 2 \end{bmatrix} \quad B = \begin{bmatrix} -3 & 0 \\ 2 & 3 \end{bmatrix}, \quad \mathcal{O} = \begin{bmatrix} 0 & 0 & 0 \\ 0 & 0 & 0 \end{bmatrix} \quad C = \begin{bmatrix} 3 & 0 \\ 1 & 2 \\ 0 & 0 \end{bmatrix}, \quad D = \begin{bmatrix} 1 & 2 & 0 \\ 2 & 3 & 0 \\ 0 & 0 & 0 \end{bmatrix}.$$

(a) $A + B =$

(f) $AB =$

(b) $B^T + C =$

(g) $\mathcal{O} + C =$

(c) $DC =$

(h) $C^T D^T =$

(d) $\mathcal{O} C =$

(i) $D \mathcal{O} =$

(e) $A^{-1} = \dfrac{1}{6} \begin{bmatrix} & \\ & \end{bmatrix}$

(j) $C^{-1} = \dfrac{1}{6} \begin{bmatrix} & \\ & \end{bmatrix}$

2. Let A and B be the same as in #1. Find each of the determinants.

(a) $\det(A)$_____

(b) $\det(B)$_____

(c) $\det(AB)$_____

(d) $\det(BA)$_____

(e) $\det(A + B)$_____

3. Find a_{44} so that the matrix $A = \begin{bmatrix} 1 & 2 & 3 & 4 \\ 2 & 3 & 4 & 5 \\ 3 & 4 & 6 & 6 \\ 4 & 5 & 6 & a_{44} \end{bmatrix}$ is not invertible.

4. Consider the system $A \begin{bmatrix} x_1 \\ x_2 \\ x_3 \end{bmatrix} = \vec{b} = \begin{bmatrix} 1 \\ 0 \\ 1 \end{bmatrix}$ where $A = \begin{bmatrix} 1 & 1 & 0 \\ 0 & 1 & 3 \\ 2 & 3 & 4 \end{bmatrix}$.

(a) Perform the row reduction $[\, A \mid I \,] \sim [\, I \mid A^{-1} \,]$ to find A^{-1}.

(b) Calculate $A^{-1}\vec{b}$.

5. Assume that A, B are invertible $n \times n$ matrices and set $C = A + B$. Answer each of the following T (true) or F (false).

   (a) __T   F__ $\det(C) = \det(A) + \det(B)$.

   (b) __T   F__   The matrix C is invertible.

   (c) __T   F__ $\det(AB) = \det(A)\det(B)$.

   (d) __T   F__ $(AB)^{-1} = A^{-1}B^{-1}$

   (e) __T   F__   The problem $A\vec{x} = \vec{b}$ has a unique solution for all $\vec{b} \in \mathcal{R}^3$.

6. Let $A = \begin{bmatrix} 1 & 2 \\ 2 & 1 \end{bmatrix}$.

   (a) Find numbers λ so that the matrix

   $$B = A - \lambda I = \begin{bmatrix} 1 & 2 \\ 2 & 1 \end{bmatrix} - \lambda \begin{bmatrix} 1 & 0 \\ 0 & 1 \end{bmatrix} = \begin{bmatrix} 1 - \lambda & 2 \\ 2 & 1 - \lambda \end{bmatrix}$$

   is not invertible. Label the results $\lambda_1 < \lambda_2$.

   (b) Find nonzero vectors $\vec{p}_j, j = 1, 2$ which satisfy $(A - \lambda_j I)\vec{p}_j = \begin{bmatrix} 0 \\ 0 \end{bmatrix}$.

Chapter 4

Matrix Subspaces

For any $m \times n$ matrix A the subspaces mentioned in the chapter title are related to the row and column structure of A. These subspaces, two in $\mathcal{R}^n$ and two in $\mathcal{R}^m$, fit together in a very pretty manner which culminates in the elegant **Orthogonal Decomposition Theorem** in Theorem(4.28). This theorem requires the introduction to the idea of a vector space. Example(4.5) discusses and illustrates the vector space of all 2×2 matrices as well as the subspace of symmetric matrices and the subspace of skew-symmetric matrices. Following this example, the chapter concentrates on the vector space $\mathcal{R}^n$ and its subspaces. A number of definitions and theorems are developed using the column space and null space of A for examples. The ten Exercises(4.1) through (4.10) are fairly routine. These exercises explore the manner in which the subspaces are related to the solution or lack of a solution to the system given by $A\vec{x} = \vec{b}$. Exercise(4.11) and Exercise(4.12) illustrates and fills in a few details on the orthogonal decomposition theorem. The three problems on the rank of a matrix in Exercises(4.13) through (4.15) have important consequences. Exercise(4.16) is a discussion of the development of the Gram-Schmidt process. This development reveals the important formula for the projection of a vector onto a subspace. This is the generalization of the projection of a vector onto a vector from Definition(1.10). The latter part of Exercise(4.16) begs a mention of least squares which is the closing Exercise(4.17). Indeed, the rank theorem in Exercise(4.15) is fundamental to the least squares procedure. To sort of complete the circle, the least squares discussion provides an adroit application of the **Orthogonal Decomposition Theorem**. This is the first of the Big Two mentioned in the preface.

4.1   The $m \times n$ matrix A as a function

If A is an $m \times n$ matrix and $\vec{b}$ is a given $m \times 1$ vector then the problem

$$A\vec{x} = \vec{b} , \qquad (4.1)$$

is to find, if possible, an $n-$vector $\vec{x}$ so that (4.1) is a true statement. Another point of view is to regard the matrix A as a function whose action is left multiplication

$$A\vec{x} = \begin{bmatrix} a_{11} & a_{12} & \cdots & \cdots & a_{1j} & \cdots & a_{1n} \\ a_{21} & a_{22} & \cdots & \cdots & a_{2j} & \cdots & a_{2n} \\ \vdots & \vdots & \ddots & \cdots & \vdots & \vdots & \vdots \\ a_{i1} & a_{i2} & \cdots & \cdots & a_{ij} & \cdots & a_{in} \\ \vdots & \vdots & \ddots & \cdots & \cdots & \ddots & \vdots \\ \vdots & \vdots & \cdots & \cdots & \vdots & \vdots & \vdots \\ a_{m1} & a_{m2} & \cdots & \cdots & a_{mj} & \cdots & a_{mn} \end{bmatrix} \begin{bmatrix} x_1 \\ x_2 \\ \vdots \\ x_i \\ \vdots \\ x_j \\ \vdots \\ x_n \end{bmatrix} = \begin{bmatrix} \vec{a_{1*}}^T \vec{x} \\ \vec{a_{2*}}^T \vec{x} \\ \vdots \\ \vec{a_{i*}}^T \vec{x} \\ \vdots \\ \vec{a_{m*}}^T \vec{x} \end{bmatrix} \qquad (4.2)$$

where $\vec{a_{i*}}^T$ is the ith row of A. For each n-vector $\vec{x}$ in $\mathcal{R}^n$ this multiplication associates with $\vec{x}$ exactly one m-vector $A\vec{x}$ called the image of $\vec{x}$. The set $\mathcal{R}^n$ is called the domain of the function A and the set of all the images $\{A\vec{x}\}$ is called the range of A. The question implied by the equation in (4.1) is the following: as the n-vectors vary over $\mathcal{R}^n$ are any of these images equal to the given $m-$vector $\vec{b}$ in $\mathcal{R}^m$? The domain $\mathcal{R}^n$ as well as the set of all images $\{A\vec{x}\} \subseteq \mathcal{R}^m$ (the symbol $\subseteq$ is read "is a subset of") are examples of vector spaces. The general definition of a vector space is as follows:

4.2   Vector Spaces

Definition 4.1 Vector Space: A vector space $\mathcal{V}$ is a set of objects equipped with two operations called addition and scalar multiplication. Let $\vec{v}, \vec{w}$ and $\vec{u}$ be elements of $\mathcal{V}$ and α and β be real scalars, elements of $\mathcal{R}$. These elements satisfy following properties:

A1	$\vec{v} + \vec{w} \in \mathcal{V}$	M1	$\alpha\vec{v} \in \mathcal{V}$
A2	$\vec{v} + \vec{w} = \vec{w} + \vec{v}$	M2	$\alpha(\beta(\vec{v})) = (\alpha\beta)\vec{v}$
A3	$(\vec{v} + \vec{w}) + \vec{u} = \vec{v} + (\vec{w} + \vec{u})$	M3	$\alpha(\vec{v} + \vec{w}) = \alpha\vec{v} + \alpha\vec{w}$
A4	There exist $\vec{0} \in \mathcal{V}$ so that $\vec{v} + \vec{0} = \vec{v}$	M4	$(\alpha + \beta)\vec{v} = \alpha\vec{v} + \beta\vec{v}$
A5	For every $\vec{v}$ there is $-\vec{v}$ so that $\vec{v} + (-\vec{v}) = \vec{0}$	M5	$1\vec{v} = \vec{v}$.

The symbol $\in$ reads "is an element of". The notation $\vec{v} + \vec{w} \in \mathcal{V}$ is read: the sum of the vectors $\vec{v}$ and $\vec{w}$ is an element of $\mathcal{V}$. It is equivalent to say that $\mathcal{V}$ is **closed** with respect to addition. Similarly, $\alpha\vec{v} \in V$ is read: the scalar multiple $\alpha\vec{v}$ is an element of V or V is **closed** with respect scalar multiplication. Recall from Definition(1.6) if $\vec{v}$ and $\vec{w}$ are $n-$vectors then the sum $\alpha\vec{v} + \beta\vec{w}$ is called a linear combination of $\vec{v}$ and $\vec{w}$. This language is retained for general vectors. In this language the properties A1 and M1 say that the space V is closed with respect to linear combinations. The properties A2 through A5 and M2 through M5 are the addition and scalar multiplication laws listed in Theorem(1.5) and Theorem(3.3). This is because the set of all $n-$vectors (Theorem(1.5)) as well as the set of all $m \times n$ (Theorem(3.3)) matrices are examples of vector spaces. The element $\vec{0}$ is called the **zero** vector and $-\vec{v}$ is called the **negative** of $\vec{v}$.

Example 4.2 Suppose $\vec{0}$ and $\widehat{\vec{0}}$ are zero vectors in V. For any $\vec{v} \in V$ it follows from A4

$$\vec{v} + \vec{0} = \vec{v} \quad \text{and} \quad \vec{v} + \widehat{\vec{0}} = \vec{v}.$$

Use $\vec{v} = \widehat{\vec{0}}$ in the first and $\vec{v} = \vec{0}$ in the second to see that

$$\widehat{\vec{0}} + \vec{0} = \widehat{\vec{0}} \quad \text{and} \quad \vec{0} + \widehat{\vec{0}} = \vec{0}.$$

By the commutativity axiom A2 the left hand sides are equal: $\widehat{\vec{0}} + \vec{0} = \vec{0} + \widehat{\vec{0}}$. Hence the right hand-sides are equal $\vec{0} = \widehat{\vec{0}}$. This means that the zero vector in V is unique. A similar line of thinking shows that the negative of $\vec{v}$, $-\vec{v}$ is unique.

Example 4.3 Let a be arbitrary and define the sets

$$V_a = \left\{ \begin{bmatrix} x_1 \\ x_2 \end{bmatrix} : x_1 + x_2 = a \right\} .$$

In words V_a is the set of $2-$vectors whose components sum to the fixed number a. Suppose $a = 1$ so that $V_1 = \left\{ \begin{bmatrix} x_1 \\ x_2 \end{bmatrix} : x_1 + x_2 = 1 \right\}$. The two vectors $\vec{v} = \begin{bmatrix} 1 \\ 0 \end{bmatrix}$ and $\vec{w} = \begin{bmatrix} 0 \\ 1 \end{bmatrix}$ belong to V_1 since $1 + 0 = 0 + 1 = 1$. Now $\vec{v} + \vec{w} = \begin{bmatrix} 1 \\ 1 \end{bmatrix}$ but since $1 + 1 = 2 \neq 1$ the set is not closed under addition. Hence V_1 is not a vector space. Notice also that there is no vector $\vec{0} \in V_1$ so that A4 in Definition(4.1) fails. In addition, there is no vector $-\vec{v} \in V_1$ for $\vec{v} \in V_1$. This is just an indication of the number of items in Definition(4.1) which fail. However, to show that a set is not a vector space one just has to demonstrate one case of failure.

Now set $a = 0$ so that $V_0 = \left\{ \begin{bmatrix} x_1 \\ x_2 \end{bmatrix} : x_1 + x_2 = 0 \right\}$. This set can also be written as

$$V_0 = \left\{ \begin{bmatrix} x_1 \\ -x_1 \end{bmatrix} : x_1 \text{ is arbitrary} \right\} = \left\{ x_1 \begin{bmatrix} 1 \\ -1 \end{bmatrix} : x_1 \text{ is arbitrary} \right\}$$

since $x_2 = -x_1$ for all elements in $\mathcal{V}_0$. Let α and β be arbitrary so that the two elements
$\alpha \begin{bmatrix} 1 \\ -1 \end{bmatrix} \in \mathcal{V}_0$ and $\beta \begin{bmatrix} 1 \\ -1 \end{bmatrix} \in \mathcal{V}_0$ and the linear combination

$$\alpha \begin{bmatrix} 1 \\ -1 \end{bmatrix} + \beta \begin{bmatrix} 1 \\ -1 \end{bmatrix} = (\alpha + \beta) \begin{bmatrix} 1 \\ -1 \end{bmatrix} \in \mathcal{V}_0 \, .$$

That is $\mathcal{V}_0$ is closed under linear combinations. Each of A1 and M1 of Definition(4.1) are satisfied. The remaining eight properties in the definition of a vector space are automatically satisfied since the set of all 2−vectors satisfy these properties. This shows $\mathcal{V}_0$ is a vector space that is a subset of $\mathcal{R}^2$. For this reason, $\mathcal{V}_0$ is called a vector subspace of $\mathcal{R}^2$.

4.3   Linear Combinations, Spans and Vector Subspaces

Definition 4.4 Linear Combinations, Spans, Vector Subspaces, and the Trivial Subspace: Let the vectors $\vec{v}_i$, $i = 1, 2, \ldots, m$ be elements of the vector space $\mathcal{V}$. The vector

$$\vec{u} = \alpha_1 \vec{v}_1 + \alpha_2 \vec{v}_2 + \cdots + \alpha_m \vec{v}_m \in \mathcal{V} \text{ for arbitrary } \alpha_1, \alpha_2, \ldots, \alpha_m \in \mathcal{R}$$

is called a **linear combination** of the vectors $\{\vec{v}_i\}_{i=1}^m$. Let $S = \{\vec{v}_1, \vec{v}_2, \ldots, \vec{v}_m\}$ denote the set of m elements in the vector space $\mathcal{V}$. The set of all linear combinations defined by

$$\mathcal{W} = \{\vec{u} : \vec{u} = \alpha_1 \vec{v}_1 + \alpha_2 \vec{v}_2 + \cdots + \alpha_m \vec{v}_m, \ \alpha_1, \alpha_2, \ldots \alpha_m \in \mathcal{R}\} \, ,$$

is called the **span** of the set $\{\vec{v}_i\}_{i=1}^m$ and is denoted by

$$\mathcal{W} = \text{span} \{\vec{v}_i\}_{i=1}^m = \text{span}\{S\}.$$

Built into the definition of the **span** is the closure of $\mathcal{W}$ with respect to addition and scalar multiplication. All the other vector space properties for the elements of $\mathcal{W}$ are inherited from the "big" space $\mathcal{V}$. This means that $\mathcal{W}$ is a vector space in its own right and is a **vector subspace** of $\mathcal{V}$. If S is the subset of $\mathcal{V}$ with the single element $\vec{0}$ then span$\{S\} = \mathcal{W} = \{\vec{0}\}$ is the vector subspace of $\mathcal{V}$ consisting only of the zero vector. This is called the **trivial subspace** of $\mathcal{V}$.

Given a vector space $\mathcal{V}$ and some subset $\mathcal{V}_0$ of $\mathcal{V}$ one way to show that $\mathcal{V}_0$ is a subspace of $\mathcal{V}$ is to exhibit a spanning set for $\mathcal{V}_0$. This is actually what was done for $\mathcal{V}_0$ in Example (4.3). Although the focus of this chapter will be the vector space $\mathcal{R}^n$ and various of its subspaces there are vector spaces whose elements are not $n-$vectors.

Example 4.5 The set of 2×2 matrices is defined by

$$\mathcal{V} = \left\{ \begin{bmatrix} a_{11} & a_{12} \\ a_{21} & a_{22} \end{bmatrix} : \ a_{11}, a_{12}, a_{21}, \text{ and } a_{22} \in \mathcal{R} \right\}.$$

For $A \in \mathcal{V}$ and $\hat{A} \in \mathcal{V}$ the component-wise definition of addition

$$A + \hat{A} = \begin{bmatrix} a_{11} & a_{12} \\ a_{21} & a_{22} \end{bmatrix} + \begin{bmatrix} \hat{a}_{11} & \hat{a}_{12} \\ \hat{a}_{21} & \hat{a}_{22} \end{bmatrix}$$

$$\equiv \begin{bmatrix} a_{11} + \hat{a}_{11} & a_{12} + \hat{a}_{12} \\ a_{21} + \hat{a}_{21} & a_{22} + \hat{a}_{22} \end{bmatrix} \in \mathcal{V}$$

implies closure with respect to addition. The component-wise definition of scalar multiplication

$$\alpha A = \alpha \begin{bmatrix} a_{11} & a_{12} \\ a_{21} & a_{22} \end{bmatrix} \equiv \begin{bmatrix} \alpha a_{11} & \alpha a_{12} \\ \alpha a_{21} & \alpha a_{22} \end{bmatrix}$$

implies closure with respect to multiplication. Define the set

$$S = \{e_1, e_2, e_3, e_4\} \equiv \left\{ \begin{bmatrix} 1 & 0 \\ 0 & 0 \end{bmatrix}, \begin{bmatrix} 0 & 1 \\ 0 & 0 \end{bmatrix}, \begin{bmatrix} 0 & 0 \\ 1 & 0 \end{bmatrix}, \begin{bmatrix} 0 & 0 \\ 0 & 1 \end{bmatrix} \right\},$$

and for $A \in \mathcal{V}$ write

$$\begin{bmatrix} a_{11} & a_{12} \\ a_{21} & a_{22} \end{bmatrix} = a_{11} \begin{bmatrix} 1 & 0 \\ 0 & 0 \end{bmatrix} + a_{12} \begin{bmatrix} 0 & 1 \\ 0 & 0 \end{bmatrix} + a_{21} \begin{bmatrix} 0 & 0 \\ 1 & 0 \end{bmatrix} + a_{22} \begin{bmatrix} 0 & 0 \\ 0 & 1 \end{bmatrix}$$

$$= a_{11} e_1 + a_{12} e_2 + a_{21} e_3 + a_{22} e_4.$$

This shows that any element of $\mathcal{V}$ is a linear combination of the elements of S so by Definition(4.4) the vector space $\mathcal{V} = \text{span}\,\{S\}$. Now define the subset $\mathcal{V}_S$ of $\mathcal{V}$ consisting of 2×2 symmetric matrices

$$\mathcal{V}_S = \left\{ \begin{bmatrix} a_{11} & a_{12} \\ a_{12} & a_{22} \end{bmatrix} : a_{11}, a_{12}, a_{22} \in \mathcal{R} \right\}.$$

Any vector in $\mathcal{V}_S$ can be written

$$\begin{bmatrix} a_{11} & a_{12} \\ a_{12} & a_{22} \end{bmatrix} = a_{11} \begin{bmatrix} 1 & 0 \\ 0 & 0 \end{bmatrix} + a_{12} \begin{bmatrix} 0 & 1 \\ 1 & 0 \end{bmatrix} + a_{22} \begin{bmatrix} 0 & 0 \\ 0 & 1 \end{bmatrix} = a_{11} e_1 + a_{12}(e_2 + e_3) + a_{22} e_4$$

so that $\mathcal{V}_S$ is a linear combination of the three matrices $\{e_1, (e_2 + e_3), e_4\}$. Hence,

$$\mathcal{V}_S = \text{span}\{e_1, (e_2 + e_3), e_4\} = \text{span} \left\{ \begin{bmatrix} 1 & 0 \\ 0 & 0 \end{bmatrix}, \begin{bmatrix} 0 & 1 \\ 1 & 0 \end{bmatrix}, \begin{bmatrix} 0 & 0 \\ 0 & 1 \end{bmatrix} \right\}.$$

and $\mathcal{V}_S$ is a subspace of the vector space $\mathcal{V}$. A 2×2 matrix is skew-symmetric if

$$A = \begin{bmatrix} a_{11} & a_{12} \\ a_{21} & a_{22} \end{bmatrix} = -A^T = \begin{bmatrix} -a_{11} & -a_{21} \\ -a_{12} & -a_{22} \end{bmatrix}.$$

This implies that $a_{11} = a_{22} = 0$ and $a_{12} = -a_{21}$. See Exercise(3.14). The set of all 2×2 skew-symmetric matrices

$$\mathcal{V}_{\hat{S}} = \left\{ \begin{bmatrix} 0 & a_{12} \\ -a_{12} & 0 \end{bmatrix} : a_{12} \in \mathcal{R} \right\}$$

$$= \text{span}\left\{(e_2 - e_3)\right\} \equiv \text{span}\left\{ \begin{bmatrix} 0 & 1 \\ -1 & 0 \end{bmatrix} \right\}.$$

is another subspace of $\mathcal{V}$ whose span is the single element $(e_2 - e_3)$.

4.4   The Column Space of A

Recall from equation (3.2) that the matrix product $A\vec{x}$ in (4.2) can also be written

$$A\vec{x} = [\vec{a_{*1}}\ \vec{a_{*2}}\ \cdots \vec{a_{*n}}] \begin{bmatrix} x_1 \\ x_2 \\ \vdots \\ x_n \end{bmatrix} = x_1\vec{a}_{*1} + x_2\vec{a}_{*2} + \cdots + x_n\vec{a}_{*n}$$

$$= x_1 \begin{bmatrix} a_{11} \\ a_{21} \\ \vdots \\ a_{m1} \end{bmatrix} + x_2 \begin{bmatrix} a_{12} \\ a_{22} \\ \vdots \\ a_{m2} \end{bmatrix} \cdots + x_n \begin{bmatrix} a_{1n} \\ a_{2n} \\ \vdots \\ a_{mn} \end{bmatrix} = \begin{bmatrix} b_1 \\ b_2 \\ \vdots \\ b_m \end{bmatrix}. \qquad (4.3)$$

which displays the product $A\vec{x}$ as a linear combination of the columns of the matrix A. From this point of view the problem $A\vec{x} = \vec{b}$ is consistent if the vector $\vec{b}$ is a linear combination of the columns of A.

Definition 4.6 Column Space: The product on   the left hand side of (4.3) is a linear combination of the n columns of A. Define the set of vectors

$$S = \left\{ \vec{a}_{*j} = \begin{bmatrix} a_{1j} \\ a_{2j} \\ \vdots \\ a_{mj} \end{bmatrix} \quad j = 1, 2, \ldots, n \right\}. \qquad (4.4)$$

The set of all linear combinations of the n columns of A is by Definition(4.4) a vector space and is called the **column space** of A. This is written

$$\mathcal{C}_A \equiv \text{span}\{S\} = \text{span}\left\{ \begin{bmatrix} a_{11} \\ a_{21} \\ \vdots \\ a_{m1} \end{bmatrix}, \ldots, \begin{bmatrix} a_{1j} \\ a_{2j} \\ \vdots \\ a_{mj} \end{bmatrix}, \ldots, \begin{bmatrix} a_{1n} \\ a_{2n} \\ \vdots \\ a_{mn} \end{bmatrix} \right\} \subseteq \mathcal{R}^m. \qquad (4.5)$$

In light of the lines following (4.2) the subspace $\mathcal{C}_A$ is also referred to as the **range** of A. Throughout this and the next chapter, the space $\mathcal{C}_A$ will be called the column space of A.

Example 4.7 The column space, $\mathcal{C}_A$, for the matrix $A = [\vec{a}_{*1} \; \vec{a}_{*2} \; \vec{a}_{*2}] = \begin{bmatrix} 1 & 2 & 3 \\ 2 & 5 & 4 \\ 1 & 3 & 1 \end{bmatrix}$ is,

from (4.5),

$$\mathcal{C}_A = \text{span}\{\vec{a}_{*1}, \vec{a}_{*2}, \vec{a}_{*3}\} = \text{span}\left\{ \begin{bmatrix} 1 \\ 2 \\ 1 \end{bmatrix}, \begin{bmatrix} 2 \\ 5 \\ 3 \end{bmatrix}, \begin{bmatrix} 3 \\ 4 \\ 1 \end{bmatrix} \right\}. \tag{4.6}$$

The equation

$$\vec{a}_{*3} = \begin{bmatrix} 3 \\ 4 \\ 1 \end{bmatrix} = (7) \begin{bmatrix} 1 \\ 2 \\ 1 \end{bmatrix} - (2) \begin{bmatrix} 2 \\ 5 \\ 3 \end{bmatrix} = (7)\vec{a}_{*1} - (2)\vec{a}_{*2} \tag{4.7}$$

shows that the third column of A is a linear combination of the first two columns of A so the column space is also spanned by just $\vec{a}_{*2}$ and $\vec{a}_{*2}$. For example, the vector

$$\vec{v} = \alpha_1 \vec{a}_{*1} + \alpha_2 \vec{a}_{*2} + \alpha_3 \vec{a}_{*3}$$

is an element of $\mathcal{C}_A$ since it is a linear combination of the columns of A. Using the identity in (4.7), the vector $\vec{v}$ can also be written as

$$\begin{aligned} \vec{v} &= \alpha_1 \vec{a}_{*1} + \alpha_2 \vec{a}_{*2} + \alpha_3 \vec{a}_{*3} \\ &= \alpha_1 \vec{a}_{*1} + \alpha_2 \vec{a}_{*2} + \alpha_3 \left(7\vec{a}_{*1} - (2)\vec{a}_{*2}\right) \\ &= \left(\alpha_1 + 7\right) \vec{a}_{*1} + \left(\alpha_2 - 2\right) \vec{a}_{*2} \end{aligned}$$

so that $\vec{v}$ is a linear combination of $\vec{a}_{*1}$ and $\vec{a}_{*2}$. In symbols

$$\begin{aligned} \mathcal{C}_A = \text{span}\{\vec{a}_{*1}, \vec{a}_{*2}, \vec{a}_{*3}\} &= \text{span}\left\{ \begin{bmatrix} 1 \\ 2 \\ 1 \end{bmatrix}, \begin{bmatrix} 2 \\ 5 \\ 3 \end{bmatrix} \right\} \\ &= \text{span}\{\vec{a}_{*1}, \vec{a}_{*2}\} \\ &= \text{span}\{\vec{a}_{*1}, \vec{a}_{*3}\} \\ &= \text{span}\{\vec{a}_{*2}, \vec{a}_{*2}\} \end{aligned} \tag{4.8}$$

where the last two equalities are obtained by solving for $\vec{a}_{*2}$ and then solving for $\vec{a}_{*1}$ in equation (4.7). Geometrically, the two vectors $\vec{a}_{*1}$ and $\vec{a}_{*2}$ span a plane in $\mathcal{R}^3$. The last two equalities are just different spanning sets for this plane. Lastly, the second equality (passing from three vectors to two vectors) illustrates that using three vectors is an over prescription of the space describing $\mathcal{C}_A$. For the remainder of this example, $\mathcal{C}_A = \text{span}\{\vec{a}_{*1}, \vec{a}_{*1}\}$.

There is an interesting connection between the column space of A and the consistency of the problem $A\vec{x} = \vec{b}$. To illustrate this connection consider the problem

$$A\vec{x} \equiv [\vec{a}_{*1} \; \vec{a}_{*2} \; \vec{a}_{*2}] \, \vec{x} = \begin{bmatrix} 1 & 2 & 3 \\ 2 & 5 & 4 \\ 1 & 3 & 1 \end{bmatrix} \begin{bmatrix} x_1 \\ x_2 \\ x_3 \end{bmatrix} = \begin{bmatrix} b_1 \\ b_2 \\ b_3 \end{bmatrix}$$

which was discussed in Example(2.4) if $b_1 = 6$ and $b_2 = 4$. From Definition(2.10) the consistency of $A\vec{x} = \vec{b}$ was stated in terms of the row reduction

$$\begin{bmatrix} 1 & 2 & 3 & b_1 \\ 2 & 5 & 4 & b_2 \\ 1 & 3 & 1 & b_3 \end{bmatrix} \sim \begin{bmatrix} 1 & 2 & 3 & b_1 \\ 0 & 1 & -2 & b_2 - 2b_1 \\ 0 & 0 & 0 & b_3 - b_2 + b_1 \end{bmatrix} \tag{4.9}$$

which shows that the system is consistent if $b_3 - b_2 + b_1 = 0$. The algebraic relation connecting the components of $\vec{b}$ can be written in the vector form

$$\begin{bmatrix} b_1 \\ b_2 \\ b_3 \end{bmatrix} = \begin{bmatrix} b_1 \\ b_2 \\ -b_1 + b_2 \end{bmatrix} = b_1 \begin{bmatrix} 1 \\ 0 \\ -1 \end{bmatrix} + b_2 \begin{bmatrix} 0 \\ 1 \\ 1 \end{bmatrix}$$

$$\equiv b_1 \vec{c}_1 + b_2 \vec{c}_2$$

$$= \operatorname{span} \{\vec{c}_1, \vec{c}_2\} \tag{4.10}$$

$$= \operatorname{span} \left\{ \begin{bmatrix} 1 \\ 0 \\ -1 \end{bmatrix}, \begin{bmatrix} 0 \\ 1 \\ 1 \end{bmatrix} \right\} \equiv \mathcal{C}$$

where the use of the word span is justified since b_1 and b_2 are arbitrary. The connection between $\mathcal{C}$ and $\mathcal{C}_A$ is $\mathcal{C} = \mathcal{C}_A$. Here is one way to see this. The three equalities

$$\vec{a}_{*1} = \begin{bmatrix} 1 \\ 2 \\ 1 \end{bmatrix} = \begin{bmatrix} 1 \\ 0 \\ -1 \end{bmatrix} + 2 \begin{bmatrix} 0 \\ 1 \\ 1 \end{bmatrix} = \vec{c}_1 + 2\vec{c}_2,$$

$$\vec{a}_{*2} = \begin{bmatrix} 2 \\ 5 \\ 3 \end{bmatrix} = 2 \begin{bmatrix} 1 \\ 0 \\ -1 \end{bmatrix} + 5 \begin{bmatrix} 0 \\ 1 \\ 1 \end{bmatrix} = 2\vec{c}_1 + 5\vec{c}_2$$

and

$$\vec{a}_{*3} = \begin{bmatrix} 3 \\ 4 \\ 1 \end{bmatrix} = 3 \begin{bmatrix} 1 \\ 0 \\ -1 \end{bmatrix} + 4 \begin{bmatrix} 0 \\ 1 \\ 1 \end{bmatrix} = 3\vec{c}_1 + 4\vec{c}_2$$

show that each column of A is a linear combination of the two vectors $\vec{c}_1$ and $\vec{c}_2$ so that any linear combination of the columns of A can be written as a linear combination of the two vectors $\vec{c}_1$ and $\vec{c}_2$. For example if $\vec{v} \in \mathcal{C}_A$ then using the previous identities

$$\begin{aligned} \vec{v} &= \alpha_1 \vec{a}_{*1} + \alpha_2 \vec{a}_{*2} + \alpha_3 \vec{a}_{*3} \\ &= \alpha_1 \left(\vec{c}_1 + 2\vec{c}_2 \right) + \alpha_2 \left(2\vec{c}_1 + 5\vec{c}_2 \right) + \alpha_3 \left(3\vec{c}_1 + 4\vec{c}_2 \right) \\ &= \left(\alpha_1 + 2\alpha_2 + 3\alpha_3 \right) \vec{c}_1 + \left(2\alpha_1 + 5\alpha_2 + 4\alpha_3 \right) \vec{c}_2 \end{aligned}$$

which shows that $\vec{v} \in \mathcal{C}$. Hence, any vector $\vec{v}$ in $\mathcal{C}_A$ is also an element of $\mathcal{C}$, or $\mathcal{C}_A \subseteq \mathcal{C}$. Reciprocally, the two identities

$$\vec{c}_1 = \begin{bmatrix} 1 \\ 0 \\ -1 \end{bmatrix} = 5 \begin{bmatrix} 1 \\ 2 \\ 1 \end{bmatrix} + (-2) \begin{bmatrix} 2 \\ 5 \\ 3 \end{bmatrix} = 5\vec{a}_{*1} + (-2)\vec{a}_{*2}$$

$$(4.11)$$

and

$$\vec{c}_2 = \begin{bmatrix} 0 \\ 1 \\ 1 \end{bmatrix} = (-2) \begin{bmatrix} 1 \\ 2 \\ 1 \end{bmatrix} + (1) \begin{bmatrix} 2 \\ 5 \\ 3 \end{bmatrix} = (-2)\vec{a}_{*1} + (1)\vec{a}_{*2}$$

show that each element of $\mathcal{C}$ is a linear combination of the first two columns of A. Now assume that $\vec{w} = \gamma_1 \vec{c}_1 + \gamma_2 \vec{c}_2 \in \mathcal{C}$ and write

$$\begin{aligned} \vec{w} &= \gamma_1 \vec{c}_1 + \gamma_2 \vec{c}_2 \\ &= \gamma_1 \left(5\vec{a}_{*1} + (-2)\vec{a}_{*2} \right) + \gamma_2 \left((-2)\vec{a}_{*1} + (1)\vec{a}_{*2} \right) \\ &= \left(5\gamma_1 - 2\gamma_2 \right) \vec{a}_{*1} + \left(-2\gamma_1 + \gamma_2 \right) \vec{a}_{*2} \end{aligned}$$

where the second equality uses (4.11). The original assumption was $\vec{w} \in \mathcal{C}$ and the previous display shows that $\vec{w} \in \mathcal{C}_A$. With the previous inclusion it follows that

$$\mathcal{C}_A = \text{span} \left\{ \begin{bmatrix} 1 \\ 2 \\ 3 \end{bmatrix}, \begin{bmatrix} 2 \\ 3 \\ 4 \end{bmatrix} \right\} = \mathcal{C} = \text{span} \left\{ \begin{bmatrix} 1 \\ 0 \\ -1 \end{bmatrix}, \begin{bmatrix} 0 \\ 1 \\ 2 \end{bmatrix} \right\}. \qquad (4.12)$$

The last display highlights the fact that spanning sets are not unique. Indeed, although A has three columns, it's column space is described by the span of only two vectors. The following definition helps get a handle on this count.

4.5   Independent Sets, Dimension and Basis

Definition 4.8 Linearly Dependent and Independent Sets: Let $\vec{v}_j, j = 1, 2, \ldots, n$ be elements of a vector space $\mathcal{V}$. The set $S = \{\vec{v}_1 \ \vec{v}_2 \ \cdots \vec{v}_n\}$ is called a **linearly dependent** set of elements if there are scalars $\{\alpha_j\}_{j=1}^n$, at least one of which is non-zero, so that the equation

$$\alpha_1 \vec{v}_1 + \alpha_2 \vec{v}_2 + \cdots + \alpha_k \vec{v}_k + \cdots + \alpha_n \vec{v}_n = \vec{0} \qquad (4.13)$$

is satisfied. For brevity, the set $S = \{\vec{v}_1 \ \vec{v}_2 \ \cdots \vec{v}_n\}$ is called a **dependent** set. The set $S = \{\vec{v}_1 \ \vec{v}_2 \ \cdots \vec{v}_n\}$ is called a **linearly independent** set if it is not linearly dependent. In a positive formulation the set S is linearly independent if the equation (4.13) is satisfied only for $\alpha_1 = \alpha_2 = \cdots = \alpha_n = 0$. Again, for brevity, the set $S = \{\vec{v}_1 \ \vec{v}_2 \ \cdots \vec{v}_n\}$ is called an **independent** set. If any one of the elements, say $\vec{v}_k$, is the **zero element** then the set $S = \{\vec{v}_1 \ \vec{v}_2 \ \cdots \ \vec{0} \cdots \vec{v}_n\}$ is **dependent**. Just take $\alpha_k \neq 0$ in (4.13). This means that the set consisting only of the zero element, that is, $S = \{\vec{0}\}$ is a **dependent** set. Any set with a single non-zero element is an independent set. To see this set $n = 1$ in equation (4.13) so that $\alpha_1 \vec{v}_1 = \vec{0}$ implies $\alpha_1 = 0$ since $\vec{v}_1$ is assumed non-zero. In the specific case that each $\vec{v}_j \in \mathcal{R}^m$ then, upon setting

$$\vec{v}_j = \begin{bmatrix} a_{1j} \\ a_{2j} \\ \vdots \\ a_{mj} \end{bmatrix}, \quad j = 1, 2, \ldots, n,$$

equation (4.13) takes the matrix form

$$A\vec{\alpha} \equiv \begin{bmatrix} a_{11} & a_{12} & \cdots & a_{1n} \\ a_{21} & a_{21} & \cdots & a_{2n} \\ \vdots & \vdots & \ddots & \vdots \\ a_{m1} & a_{m2} & \cdots & a_{mn} \end{bmatrix} \begin{bmatrix} \alpha_1 \\ \alpha_2 \\ \vdots \\ \vdots \\ \alpha_n \end{bmatrix} = \begin{bmatrix} 0 \\ 0 \\ \vdots \\ 0 \end{bmatrix}. \tag{4.14}$$

The vector of coefficients $\vec{\alpha} = \begin{bmatrix} \alpha_1 \\ \alpha_2 \\ \vdots \\ \alpha_n \end{bmatrix} = \vec{0} = \begin{bmatrix} 0 \\ 0 \\ \vdots \\ 0 \end{bmatrix}$ render both equations (4.13) or (4.14)

true statements. What is important in differentiating between dependent or independent sets is whether the zero vector is the only solution of equations (4.13) or (4.14). That is, to decide whether the set S is a **dependent** or an **independent** set of vectors is equivalent to determining whether (4.14) has a **non-zero** or **only the zero** solution, respectively.

In Example (4.7) the span of the three vectors consisting of the columns of the matrix A defines the column space $\mathcal{C}_A$. This set is a dependent set of vectors which is illustrated in (4.7) which can be connected to (4.13) and (4.14) (take $n = 3$ and $\alpha_1 = -7$, $\alpha_2 = 2$ and $\alpha_3 = 1$) by writing

$$(-7)\vec{a}_{*1} + (2)\vec{a}_{*2} + (1)\vec{a}_{*3} = \begin{bmatrix} 1 & 2 & 3 \\ 2 & 5 & 4 \\ 1 & 3 & 1 \end{bmatrix} \begin{bmatrix} -7 \\ 2 \\ 1 \end{bmatrix} = \vec{0}.$$

Equation (4.12) gives a second description for $\mathcal{C}_A = \text{span}\{\vec{a}_{*1}, \vec{a}_{*2}\}$. To check whether the this set is an independent or dependent set using Definition(4.8) requires the calculation

$$\alpha_1 \vec{a}_{*1} + \alpha_2 \vec{a}_{*2} = \alpha_1 \begin{bmatrix} 1 \\ 2 \\ 3 \end{bmatrix} + \alpha_2 \begin{bmatrix} 2 \\ 3 \\ 4 \end{bmatrix} = \begin{bmatrix} \alpha_1 + 2\alpha_2 \\ 2\alpha_1 + 3\alpha_2 \\ 3\alpha_1 + 4\alpha_2 \end{bmatrix} = \begin{bmatrix} 0 \\ 0 \\ 0 \end{bmatrix} = \vec{0}.$$

Equate the first two components and solve for α_1 and α_2 in the two equations

$$\begin{cases} \alpha_1 + 2\alpha_2 = 0 \\ 2\alpha_1 + 3\alpha_2 = 0 \end{cases},$$

to see that the unique solution to this pair of equations is $\alpha_1 = \alpha_2 = 0$. By Definition(4.8) the set $\{\vec{a}_{*1}, \vec{a}_{*2}\}$ is an independent set. Here is another way to check whether the set of two vectors $\{\vec{a}_{*1}\ \vec{a}_{*2}\}$ or any set of two vectors $\{\vec{v}_1, \vec{v}_2\}$ is a dependent or independent set. Assume that

$$\alpha_1 \vec{v}_1 + \alpha_2 \vec{v}_2 = \vec{0}$$

is valid with at least one of α_1 or α_2 not zero. Assume $\alpha_1 \neq 0$ and write the last display as

$$\vec{v}_1 = -\frac{\alpha_2}{\alpha_1} \vec{v}_2.$$

The vectors are multiples if and only if they form a dependent set of vectors. In terms of independence this statement reads: two non-zero vectors are independent if and only if one vector is not a multiple of the other. This can be used to see that the set consisting of the two vectors whose span is $\mathcal{C}$ in (4.12) form an independent set of vectors. The identities in (4.8) and (4.12) give three different descriptions of the space $\mathcal{C}_A$. There are infinitely many descriptions of this space and one thing in common to all of the descriptions is that it will take at least two vectors to describe $\mathcal{C}_A$.

Definition 4.9 Dimension and Basis: Let $\mathcal{V}$ be a vector space. If $\{\vec{v}_1\ \vec{v}_2\ \cdots \vec{v}_n\}$ is an independent set of vectors spanning $\mathcal{V}$ then the number n is called the **dimension** of $\mathcal{V}$. The notation for this is $\dim \mathcal{V} = n$. The independent set of vectors which span $\mathcal{V}$ is called a **basis** for $\mathcal{V}$. In the case that $\mathcal{V} = \{\vec{0}\}$ (the trivial space consisting only of the zero vector) set $\dim \mathcal{V} = 0$. The trivial space has no basis since (see Definition(4.8)) the set consisting only of the zero vector has been declared to be a dependent set. All that is needed is the dimension statement $\dim \{\vec{0}\} = 0$.

Example 4.10 The vector space $\mathcal{C}_A$ in Example(4.7) is a two dimensional vector subspace of $\mathcal{R}^3$. Either of the sets in (4.12) is a basis for $\mathcal{C}_A$. The set consisting of all of the columns of A in (4.6) is a spanning set for $\mathcal{C}_A$ but it is not a basis. This is because the set is a dependent set of vectors. **A basis for a vector space $\mathcal{V}$ is always a spanning set for $\mathcal{V}$, but a spanning set for $\mathcal{V}$ is not necessarily a basis.**

The vector space $\mathcal{R}^n$ is an n dimensional vector space. A simple set of independent vectors which span the space is the **canonical** or **standard** basis defined by the $n-$vectors $\vec{e}_j$ which are the vectors defined by inserting a 1 in the jth position of the $n \times 1$ zero vector. See the display preceding Example(1.16). In the case of $n = 3$ these three vectors are

$$\vec{e}_1 = \begin{bmatrix} 1 \\ 0 \\ 0 \end{bmatrix} \quad \vec{e}_2 = \begin{bmatrix} 0 \\ 1 \\ 0 \end{bmatrix} \quad \vec{e}_3 = \begin{bmatrix} 0 \\ 0 \\ 1 \end{bmatrix}$$

so that the vector space $\mathcal{R}^3$ is three dimensional. This means that the three vectors $\{\vec{e}_1, \vec{e}_2, \vec{e}_3\}$ are linearly independent and any vector in $\mathcal{R}^3$ can be written as a linear combination of the $\{\vec{e}_j\}_{j=1}^3$. This was illustrated in Example(1.16).

The space $\mathcal{V}$ in Example(4.5) of 2×2 matrices is four dimensional since the set of matrices

$$S = \{e_1, e_2, e_3, e_4\} \equiv \left\{ \begin{bmatrix} 1 & 0 \\ 0 & 0 \end{bmatrix}, \begin{bmatrix} 0 & 1 \\ 0 & 0 \end{bmatrix}, \begin{bmatrix} 0 & 0 \\ 1 & 0 \end{bmatrix}, \begin{bmatrix} 1 & 0 \\ 0 & 1 \end{bmatrix} \right\}$$

is an independent set of vectors (use (4.13) with $\vec{v}_j$ replaced by e_j). The subspace of 2×2 symmetric matrices $\mathcal{V}_S$ is three dimensional since the set $S_S = \{e_1, e_2 + e_3, e_4\}$ span $\mathcal{V}$ and S_S is an independent set of three vectors. The subspace of 2×2 skew-symmetric matrices $\mathcal{V}_{\hat{S}}$ is a one dimensional subspace since the set consisting of the single element $S_{\hat{S}} = \{e_2 - e_3\}$ spans $\mathcal{V}_{\hat{S}}$. Recall that a set with a single non-zero element is an independent set.

4.6   Null Space of A

If the columns of the $m \times n$ matrix A in (4.14) form a dependent set of vectors then there is a non-zero vector $\vec{\alpha}$ so that (4.14) is satisfied. Such non-zero vectors are very important and receive there own special designation.

Definition 4.11 Null Space of A: Let A be an $m \times n$ matrix. The set of vectors

$$\mathcal{N}(A) = \text{span}\{\vec{x} \in \mathcal{R}^n : A\vec{x} = \vec{0}\} \subseteq \mathcal{R}^n$$

is a subspace of the vector space $\mathcal{R}^n$ and is called the **null space** of the matrix A.

The language in the definition of the null space implies that the set $\mathcal{N}(A)$ is a vector space. To see that $\mathcal{N}(A)$ is a vector space, let $\vec{x}_1$ and $\vec{x}_2$ belong to $\mathcal{N}(A)$. This means that $A\vec{x}_1 = \vec{0}$ and $A\vec{x}_2 = \vec{0}$. Let α and β be scalars. The calculation

$$\begin{aligned} A(\alpha\vec{x}_1 + \beta\vec{x}_2) &= A(\alpha\vec{x}_1) + A(\beta\vec{x}_2) \\ &= \alpha(A\vec{x}_1) + \beta(A\vec{x}_2) = \vec{0} \end{aligned}$$

shows that $\alpha\vec{x}_1 + \beta\vec{x}_2 \in \mathcal{N}(A)$. This shows that $\mathcal{N}(A)$ is closed with respect to addition and scalar multiplication so that $\mathcal{N}(A)$ is a subspace of $\mathcal{R}^n$. The dimension of $\mathcal{N}(A)$ is less than or equal to n since $\mathcal{N}(A)$ is a subspace of the $n-$dimensional space $\mathcal{R}^n$.

Two subspaces have been associated with the $m \times n$ matrix A: the column space $\mathcal{C}_A \subseteq \mathcal{R}^m$ and the null space $\mathcal{N}(A) \subseteq \mathcal{R}^n$. Each of these subspaces play a role in the general solution of the problem $A\vec{x} = \vec{b}$. The following definition is a review of Definition(2.12) using the subspaces $\mathcal{C}_A$ and $\mathcal{N}(A)$.

Definition 4.12 General, Homogeneous, and Particular Solutions: Assume that the problem $A\vec{x} = \vec{b}$ is consistent and write its **general solution** as $\vec{x} = \vec{x}_h + \vec{x}_p$ where the **homogeneous solution** $\vec{x}_h$ satisfies $A\vec{x}_h = \vec{0}$ and a **particular solution** $\vec{x}_p$ satisfies $A\vec{x}_p = \vec{b}$ so that the general solution satisfies

$$A\vec{x} = A\vec{x}_h + A\vec{x}_p = \vec{0} + \vec{b} = \vec{b}.$$

To say that the problem $A\vec{x} = \vec{b}$ is consistent is the same as saying that $\vec{b} \in \mathcal{C}_A$. By definition $\vec{x}_h \in \mathcal{N}(A)$. All that can be said about the particular solution $\vec{x}_p \in \mathcal{R}^n$ at this point is that $\vec{x}_p$ is not in $\mathcal{N}(A)$ (assuming that $\vec{b} \neq \vec{0}$). There is some other portion of $\mathcal{R}^n$ where $\vec{x}_p$ resides. This portion will be identified before the end of this chapter.

Example 4.13 The row reduction in (4.9) reads

$$\left[\, A \mid \vec{b} \,\right] = \begin{bmatrix} 1 & 2 & 3 & b_1 \\ 2 & 5 & 4 & b_2 \\ 1 & 3 & 1 & b_3 \end{bmatrix} \sim \begin{bmatrix} 1 & 2 & 3 & b_1 \\ 0 & 1 & -2 & b_2 - 2b_1 \\ 0 & 0 & 0 & b_3 - b_2 + b_1 \end{bmatrix}.$$

The problem is consistent if $b_3 - b_2 + b_1 = 0$ and the general solution of $A\vec{x} = \vec{b}$ is given by

$$\vec{x} = \begin{bmatrix} x_1 \\ x_2 \\ x_3 \end{bmatrix} = x_3 \begin{bmatrix} -7 \\ 2 \\ 1 \end{bmatrix} + \begin{bmatrix} 5b_1 - 2b_2 \\ -2b_1 + b_2 \\ 0 \end{bmatrix} \equiv \vec{x}_h + \vec{x}_p. \tag{4.15}$$

The homogeneous solution $\vec{x}_h$ has the property $A\vec{x}_h = \vec{0}$ so the vector $\vec{x}_h$ is in the null space of the matrix A, $\vec{x}_h \in \mathcal{N}(A)$. Since x_3 is a free variable the null space of A is the one dimensional subspace of $\mathcal{R}^3$ given by

$$\vec{x}_h = \begin{bmatrix} x_1 \\ x_2 \\ x_3 \end{bmatrix} = \begin{bmatrix} -7x_3 \\ 2x_3 \\ x_3 \end{bmatrix} = x_3 \begin{bmatrix} -7 \\ 2 \\ 1 \end{bmatrix} = \mathcal{N}(A) = \mathrm{span}\left\{ \begin{bmatrix} -7 \\ 2 \\ 1 \end{bmatrix} \right\}.$$

In general the number of free variables and the dimension of the null space of A are always the same. Further, if $b_1 = 6$ and $b_2 = 4$ ($b_3 = 4 - 6 = -2$ for consistency) then

$$\vec{x}_p = \begin{bmatrix} 5b_1 - 2b_2 \\ -2b_1 + b_2 \\ 0 \end{bmatrix} = \begin{bmatrix} 22 \\ -8 \\ 0 \end{bmatrix}$$ is a particular solution which was found in Example(2.15).

In the language of Example(4.7) the vector $\vec{b} = \begin{bmatrix} 6 \\ 4 \\ -2 \end{bmatrix} = 6 \begin{bmatrix} 1 \\ 0 \\ -1 \end{bmatrix} + 4 \begin{bmatrix} 0 \\ 1 \\ 1 \end{bmatrix} \in \mathcal{C}_A.$

Definition(4.12) refers to "a" particular solution in contrast to "the" particular solution. Besides $\vec{x}_p$ it is straightforward to check that $\vec{x}_r = \dfrac{1}{27}\begin{bmatrix} -1 \\ -46 \\ 85 \end{bmatrix}$ is another particular solution.

See Exercise(4.4). Neither of these particular solutions are in $\mathcal{N}(A)$ since $A\vec{x}_p = A\vec{x}_r \neq \vec{0}$. However the dot product

$$\vec{x}_r \cdot \vec{x}_h = (\vec{x}_r)^T \vec{x}_h = \frac{1}{27}[-1 \ -46 \ 85]\left(x_3 \begin{bmatrix} -7 \\ 2 \\ 1 \end{bmatrix} \right)$$

$$= \frac{x_3}{27}\left(-1(-7) - 46(2) + 85(1) \right)$$

$$= \frac{x_3}{27}\left(7 - 92 + 85 \right) = 0$$

shows that the particular solution $\vec{x}_r$ is orthogonal to any vector in $\mathcal{N}(A)$. In contrast $\vec{x}_p \cdot \vec{x}_h = (\vec{x}_p)^T \vec{x}_h = -7(22) + 4(2) + 1(0) = -146$ so that one distinction between these particular solutions is that one is orthogonal to $\mathcal{N}(A)$ and the other is not. This distinction between particular solutions will emerge as this chapter develops. For this example the two dimensional column space of A is a subspace of the three dimensional subspace $\mathcal{R}^3$. The dimension of the null space of A is one and these are related by the equality

$$3 = \dim \mathcal{R}^3 = 2 + 1 = \dim \mathcal{C}_A + \dim \mathcal{N}(A) \ .$$

This is a special case of a very general equality. For this example the row reduced form $[\, A \mid \vec{b}\,] \sim [\, U \mid \vec{\tilde{b}}\,]$ has two pivots, namely, the numbers 1 and -1. This is the same as the dimension of the column space $\mathcal{C}_A$. This advertises another general equality.

4.7   The Rank of a Matrix

Definition 4.14 The Rank of the $m \times n$ matrix A and the rank of $[\, A \mid \vec{b}\,]$:   Assume that Gauss elimination gives the the row echelon form $[\, A \mid \vec{b}\,] \sim [\, U \mid \vec{\tilde{b}}\,]$. If the number of pivots in U is r then the non-negative integer r is called the **rank** of A. The **rank** of $[\, A \mid \vec{b}\,]$ is the number of pivots in $[\, U \mid \vec{\tilde{b}}\,]$.

Theorem 4.15 Rank, Consistency, and Free variables: Suppose that the matrix A in the problem $A\vec{x} = \vec{b}$ has rank r. The problem $A\vec{x} = \vec{b}$ is consistent if and only if the rank of A is the same as the rank of $[A \mid \vec{b}\,]$. In this case the general solution has $n - r$ free variables.

Recall from Definition(2.10) that the the number of pivots in $[\, U \mid \vec{\tilde{b}}\,]$ is either r or $r + 1$. Since rank is defined in terms of pivots the following discussion is a review of the discussion following Definition(2.10) with the word "pivot" replaced by the word "rank." Gauss elimination gives the row echelon form $[\, A \mid \vec{b}\,] \sim [\, U \mid \vec{\tilde{b}}\,]$. The assumption that the rank of A is r means, from Definition(4.14), that the row echelon form U of A has r pivots. If the vector $\vec{\tilde{b}}$ has $r + 1$ or more non-zero components then the rank of $[A \mid \vec{b}\,]$ is $r + 1$. In this case the problem $A\vec{x} = \vec{b}$ is inconsistent. The reason for this is that the $(r + 1)^{st}$ row in $[U \mid \vec{\tilde{b}}\,]$ written in terms of the variables of the system reads

$$0x_1 + 0x_2 + \cdots + 0x_n = \tilde{b}_{r+1} \neq 0$$

where $\tilde{b}_{r+1}$ is the non-zero $(r + 1)^{st}$ component of $\vec{\tilde{b}}$. For the system to be consistent, the number $\tilde{b}_{r+1} = 0$. In this case the rank of $[\, U \mid \vec{\tilde{b}}\,]$ is r which is the statement of the theorem. Finally, since a free variable corresponds to a non-pivot position in $A \sim U$ and A has n columns, it follows that there are $n - r$ free variables. As an illustration, from equation (4.15) the 3×3 matrix A has rank $r = 2$. If the problem $A\vec{x} = \vec{b}$ is consistent, then the components of $\vec{b}$ satisfy $b_3 + b_1 - 2b_2 = 0$. In this case the rank of $[\, U \mid \vec{\tilde{b}}\,]$ in (4.15) is two and, from Example(4.13), there is $n - r = 3 - 2 = 1$ free variable. If $b_3 - b_2 + b_1 \neq 0$ the rank of $[\, U \mid \vec{\tilde{b}}\,]$ in (4.15) is three and the problem $A\vec{x} = \vec{b}$ is inconsistent.

Example 4.16 Since the matrix A in the system

$$A\vec{x} = \begin{bmatrix} 1 & 2 & 3 \\ 2 & 4 & 4 \end{bmatrix} \begin{bmatrix} x_1 \\ x_2 \\ x_3 \end{bmatrix} = \begin{bmatrix} b_1 \\ b_2 \end{bmatrix}$$

is 2×3 the domain of A is $\mathcal{R}^3$ and $\mathcal{C}_A \subseteq \mathcal{R}^2$. The augmented system and row reduction takes the form

$$[\, A \mid \vec{b}\,] = \begin{bmatrix} 1 & 2 & 3 & b_1 \\ 2 & 4 & 4 & b_2 \end{bmatrix} \sim \begin{bmatrix} 1 & 2 & 3 & b_1 \\ 0 & 0 & -2 & b_2 - 2b_1 \end{bmatrix} = [\, U \mid \vec{b}\,]. \qquad (4.16)$$

From Theorem(4.15), the problem $A\vec{x} = \vec{b}$ is consistent since the rank of A and the rank of $[\, A \mid \vec{b}\,]$ is two for every vector $\vec{b}$. Since there is no restriction on the components of $\vec{b}$ it follows that $\mathcal{C}_A = \mathcal{R}^2$. This means that any two independent vectors in $\mathcal{R}^2$ is a basis for $\mathcal{C}_A$. For reasons that will emerge in Example(4.18) select the columns of A which correspond to the pivot columns of U. Not the pivot columns in U but the columns of A corresponding to the columns in U where the pivots occur. In (4.16) this selection is given by columns one and three

$$\mathcal{C}_A = \operatorname{span}\left\{ \begin{bmatrix} 1 \\ 2 \end{bmatrix}, \begin{bmatrix} 3 \\ 4 \end{bmatrix} \right\}.$$

From the row reduction in (4.16) the general solution is

$$\begin{bmatrix} x_1 \\ x_2 \\ x_3 \end{bmatrix} = x_2 \begin{bmatrix} -2 \\ 1 \\ 0 \end{bmatrix} + \begin{bmatrix} -2b_1 + (3/2)b_2 \\ 0 \\ \dfrac{2b_1 - b_2}{2} \end{bmatrix} = \vec{x}_h + \vec{x}_p, \qquad (4.17)$$

so that $\mathcal{N}(A) = \operatorname{span}\left\{ \begin{bmatrix} -2 \\ 1 \\ 0 \end{bmatrix} \right\}$. In the specific case that $b_1 = 6$ and $b_2 = 4$ the particular solution is given by

$$\vec{x}_p = \begin{bmatrix} -2b_1 + (3/2)b_2 \\ 0 \\ \dfrac{2b_1 - b_2}{2} \end{bmatrix}\Bigg|_{b_1=6, b_2=4} = \begin{bmatrix} -12 + (3/2)4 \\ 0 \\ \dfrac{12 - 4}{2} \end{bmatrix} = \begin{bmatrix} -6 \\ 0 \\ 4 \end{bmatrix}.$$

This is the solution found in Example(2.3). As in the last example, the rank of A is the same as the dimension of $\mathcal{C}_A$. There is one free variable in the general solution so that the null space of A is the one dimensional subspace defined by the homogeneous solution in (4.17). The equality

$$3 = \dim \mathcal{R}^3 = 2 + 1 = r + \dim \mathcal{N}(A) = \dim \mathcal{C}_A + \dim \mathcal{N}(A) \,.$$

replicates the equality at the end of Example(4.13). Now apply the above discussion to the linear system

$$B\vec{x} \equiv A^T\vec{x} = \begin{bmatrix} 1 & 2 \\ 2 & 4 \\ 3 & 4 \end{bmatrix} \begin{bmatrix} x_1 \\ x_2 \end{bmatrix} = \begin{bmatrix} b_1 \\ b_2 \\ b_3 \end{bmatrix} \tag{4.18}$$

where the coefficient matrix B is the transpose of the matrix A in (4.16). The domain of B is $\mathcal{R}^2$ and its range is in $\mathcal{R}^3$. Row reduction gives the equivalent system

$$[B \mid \vec{b}\,] = \begin{bmatrix} 1 & 2 & b_1 \\ 2 & 4 & b_2 \\ 3 & 4 & b_3 \end{bmatrix} \sim \begin{bmatrix} 1 & 2 & b_1 \\ 0 & 0 & b_2 - 2b_1 \\ 0 & -2 & b_3 - 3b_1 \end{bmatrix}$$

$$\tag{4.19}$$

$$\sim \begin{bmatrix} 1 & 2 & b_1 \\ 0 & -2 & b_3 - 3b_1 \\ 0 & 0 & b_2 - 2b_1 \end{bmatrix}.$$

This reduction illustrates both situations described in Theorem(4.15). The system is inconsistent if $b_2 - 2b_1 \neq 0$, since

$$2 = \text{rank}\left(\begin{bmatrix} 1 & 2 \\ 2 & 4 \\ 3 & 4 \end{bmatrix}\right) \neq \text{rank}\left(\begin{bmatrix} 1 & 2 & b_1 \\ 0 & -2 & b_3 - 3b_1 \\ 0 & 0 & b_2 - 2b_1 \end{bmatrix}\right) = 3.$$

If $b_2 - 2b_1 = 0$ then the rank of the echelon form on the right-hand side is two and the system is consistent. The equation $b_2 - 2b_1 = 0$ also defines the column space of B as follows

$$\mathcal{C}_B = \begin{bmatrix} b_1 \\ b_2 \\ b_3 \end{bmatrix} = \begin{bmatrix} b_1 \\ 2b_1 \\ b_3 \end{bmatrix} = b_1 \begin{bmatrix} 1 \\ 2 \\ 0 \end{bmatrix} + b_3 \begin{bmatrix} 0 \\ 0 \\ 1 \end{bmatrix}$$

$$\tag{4.20}$$

$$= \text{span}\left\{\begin{bmatrix} 1 \\ 2 \\ 0 \end{bmatrix}, \begin{bmatrix} 0 \\ 0 \\ 1 \end{bmatrix}\right\}.$$

so the dim $\mathcal{C}_B = 2$. It is equivalent to say that the two columns defining the matrix B are linearly independent since column one is not a multiple of column two. By setting $b_1 = b_2 = 0$ in (4.19) it follows that

$$\mathcal{N}(B) = \{\vec{0}\} = \left\{\begin{bmatrix} 0 \\ 0 \end{bmatrix}\right\} \tag{4.21}$$

and therefore, using the last part of Definition (4.9), the dimension of $\mathcal{N}(B)$ is zero. The equality for the dimension of the subspaces associated with the matrix B reads

$$2 = \dim \mathcal{R}^2 = 2 + 0 = r + \dim \mathcal{N}(B) = \dim \mathcal{C}_B + \dim \mathcal{N}(B) .$$

4.8 The Row Space of A

Let $\vec{a}_{1*}^{T} = [\,1\ 2\ 3\,]$ and $\vec{a}_{2*}^{T} = [\,2\ 4\ 4\,]$ be the two rows of the matrix A in (4.16). Define the subspace R_A of $\mathcal{R}^3$ by

$$R_A = \text{span}\left\{\vec{a}_{1*}^{T}, \vec{a}_{2*}^{T}\right\} = \text{span}\left\{\vec{a}_{1*}^{T}, [\,0\ 0\ -2\,]\right\}$$

where the second equality follows from the row reduction in (4.16). Using the two independent vectors defining the column space $\mathcal{C}_B$ in (4.20) the rows of A can be written as the linear combinations

$$\vec{a}_{1*}^{T} = \begin{bmatrix} 1 \\ 2 \\ 3 \end{bmatrix} = 1\begin{bmatrix} 1 \\ 2 \\ 0 \end{bmatrix} + 3\begin{bmatrix} 0 \\ 0 \\ 1 \end{bmatrix} \quad \text{and} \quad \vec{a}_{2*}^{T} = \begin{bmatrix} 2 \\ 4 \\ 4 \end{bmatrix} = 2\begin{bmatrix} 1 \\ 2 \\ 0 \end{bmatrix} + 4\begin{bmatrix} 0 \\ 0 \\ 1 \end{bmatrix}.$$

This shows that $\mathcal{C}_B = R_A$ is the column space of the matrix $B = A^T$ in (4.18), that is, the two dimensional subspace spanned by the rows of A. Mimicking the language used in defining the column space of a matrix A it seems natural to call the space R_A the row space of A.

Definition 4.17 Row Space of A: Let A be an $m \times n$ matrix. Define the m vectors

$$\vec{a}_{i*}^{T} = [a_{i1}\ a_{i2}\ \cdots\ a_{in}] \equiv \vec{r}_i \quad i = 1, 2, \ldots, m$$

so that $\vec{r}_i$ is the ith row of A and therefore has n components. The vector subspace

$$R_A = \text{span}\,\{\vec{r}_1, \vec{r}_2,\ \cdots\ ,\vec{r}_m\} = \mathcal{C}_{A^T} \subseteq \mathcal{R}^n$$

is called the **row space** of A. The second equality in the last display emphasizes that the row space is really not a new space, it is the **column space of the matrix** A^T. The latter notation $\mathcal{C}_{A^T}$ will be used only sparingly as the notation R_A is simpler.

In Example(4.16), the rank of A and the rank of $B = A^T$ are the same. As a consequence, the dimension of $\mathcal{C}_A$ and the dimension of $\mathcal{C}_B = \mathcal{C}_{A^T} = R_A$ are equal. This is true even though these two subspace are subsets of different vector spaces; $\mathcal{C}_A \subseteq R^2$ and $R_A \subseteq R^3$. As it turns out, this is not just a coincidence. Before turning to this equality of the ranks of A and A^T, which is equivalent to the statement that the dimension of $\mathcal{C}_A$ is the same as the dimension of R_A, it is helpful to work through a more encompassing (read "bigger") example.

Example 4.18 The row reduction of the linear system

$$A\vec{x} = \begin{bmatrix} 1 & 2 & 3 & 4 \\ 2 & 4 & 4 & 5 \\ 3 & 6 & 5 & 6 \end{bmatrix}\begin{bmatrix} x_1 \\ x_2 \\ x_3 \\ x_4 \end{bmatrix} = \begin{bmatrix} b_1 \\ b_2 \\ b_3 \end{bmatrix} \tag{4.22}$$

is given by

$$
\left[\, A \mid \vec{b}\, \right] \;=\; \begin{bmatrix} 1 & 2 & 3 & 4 & b_1 \\ 0 & 0 & -2 & -3 & b_2 - 2b_1 \\ 0 & 0 & -4 & -6 & b_3 - 3b_1 \end{bmatrix}
$$

$$
\sim\; \begin{bmatrix} 1 & 2 & 3 & 4 & b_1 \\ 0 & 0 & -2 & -3 & b_2 - 2b_1 \\ 0 & 0 & 0 & 0 & b_3 - 2b_2 + b_1 \end{bmatrix} = [\, U \mid \vec{b}\,]. \tag{4.23}
$$

The rank of A is two so by Theorem(4.15) the components of $\vec{b}$ determine whether the problem is consistent. If $b_3 - 2b_2 + b_1 \neq 0$ then the rank of $[\, A \mid \vec{b}\,]$ is three and the problem is inconsistent. If $b_3 - 2b_2 + b_1 = 0$ the rank of $[\, A \mid \vec{b}\,]$ is two and the general solution to (4.22) reads

$$
\vec{x} \;=\; \begin{bmatrix} x_1 \\ x_2 \\ x_3 \\ x_4 \end{bmatrix} = \begin{bmatrix} -2x_2 + (1/2)x_4 - 2b_1 + (3/2)b_2 \\ x_2 \\ -(3/2)x_4 + b_1 - (1/2)b_2 \\ x_4 \end{bmatrix}
$$

$$
\;=\; \begin{bmatrix} -2x_2 + (1/2)x_4 \\ x_2 \\ -(3/2)x_4 \\ x_4 \end{bmatrix} + \begin{bmatrix} -2b_1 + (3/2)b_2 \\ 0 \\ b_1 - (1/2)b_2 \\ 0 \end{bmatrix}
$$

$$
\;=\; \left\{ x_2 \begin{bmatrix} -2 \\ 1 \\ 0 \\ 0 \end{bmatrix} + x_4 \begin{bmatrix} 1/2 \\ 0 \\ -3/2 \\ 1 \end{bmatrix} \right\} + \begin{bmatrix} -2b_1 + (3/2)b_2 \\ 0 \\ b_1 - (1/2)b_2 \\ 0 \end{bmatrix}
$$

$$
\tag{4.24}
$$

$$
\equiv\; \{x_2 \vec{n}_1 + x_4 \vec{n}_2\} + \vec{x}_p = \{\vec{x}_h\} + \vec{x}_p.
$$

Set $\vec{b} = \vec{0}$ in (4.24) to find $\vec{x}_h = x_2 \vec{n}_1 + x_4 \vec{n}_2$ so the null space of A is

$$
\mathcal{N}(A) = \mathrm{span}\,\{\vec{n}_1, \vec{n}_2\} = \mathrm{span} \left\{ \begin{bmatrix} -2 \\ 1 \\ 0 \\ 0 \end{bmatrix}, \begin{bmatrix} 1/2 \\ 0 \\ -3/2 \\ 1 \end{bmatrix} \right\}. \tag{4.25}
$$

Again the number of free variables in the homogeneous solution and the dimension of $\mathcal{N}(A)$ are the same. There are a number of ways to find $\mathcal{C}_A$. By Definition(4.6) the column space of A is the span of all the columns of A. This does not necessarily give a basis for $\mathcal{C}_A$. It is a spanning set but it may not be an independent set. As in Example(4.7), the vector $\vec{b} \in \mathcal{C}_A$ if the consistency condition $b_3 - 2b_2 + b_1 = 0$ is satisfied. Writing this condition in vector form gives

$$\begin{bmatrix} b_1 \\ b_2 \\ b_3 \end{bmatrix} = \begin{bmatrix} b_1 \\ b_2 \\ -b_1 + 2b_2 \end{bmatrix} = b_1 \begin{bmatrix} 1 \\ 0 \\ -1 \end{bmatrix} + b_2 \begin{bmatrix} 0 \\ 1 \\ 2 \end{bmatrix} = \text{span} \left\{ \begin{bmatrix} 1 \\ 0 \\ -1 \end{bmatrix}, \begin{bmatrix} 0 \\ 1 \\ 2 \end{bmatrix} \right\} = \mathcal{C}_A. \quad (4.26)$$

Here is yet another way to find $\mathcal{C}_A$ (recall the discussion following equation (4.16)). An inspection of $[\, U \mid \vec{b}\,]$ in (4.23) shows that the columns of U corresponding to the two pivot columns (one and three) are independent. These columns in A are also independent and form a basis for

$$\mathcal{C}_A = \text{span} \left\{ \begin{bmatrix} 1 \\ 2 \\ 3 \end{bmatrix}, \begin{bmatrix} 3 \\ 4 \\ 5 \end{bmatrix} \right\}.$$

Here is a way to see why this works. Write out the two products $A\vec{n}_1 = \vec{0}$ and $A\vec{n}_2 = \vec{0}$ to see that column two of A is a multiple of column one and column four of A is a linear combination of columns one and three of A, respectively. In equation form

$$\vec{a}_{*2} = 2\vec{a}_{*1} \quad \text{and} \quad \vec{a}_{*4} = \frac{3}{2}\vec{a}_{*3} - \frac{1}{2}\vec{a}_{*1}.$$

where $\vec{a}_{*j}, j = 1, 2, 3$ and 4 are the four columns of A. These two equations show that $\vec{a}_{*2}$ and $\vec{a}_{*4}$ can be written in terms of $\vec{a}_{*1}$ and $\vec{a}_{*3}$. This means that if $\vec{y} = \alpha_1 \vec{a}_{*1} + \alpha_2 \vec{a}_{*2} + \alpha_3 \vec{a}_{*3} + \alpha_4 \vec{a}_{*4}$ is an arbitrary element of $\mathcal{C}_A$, then

$$\begin{aligned} \vec{y} &= \alpha_1 \vec{a}_{*1} + \alpha_2 (2\vec{a}_{*1}) + \alpha_3 \vec{a}_{*3} + \alpha_4 (\frac{3}{2}\vec{a}_{*3} - \frac{1}{2}\vec{a}_{*1}) \\ &= (\alpha_1 + 2\alpha_2 - \frac{1}{2}\alpha_4)\vec{a}_{*1} + (\alpha_3 + \frac{3}{2}\alpha_4)\vec{a}_{*3}, \end{aligned} \quad (4.27)$$

which shows that any $\vec{y} \in \mathcal{C}_A$ can be expressed as a linear combination of columns $\vec{a}_{*1}$ and $\vec{a}_{*3}$ of A. These are the columns of A corresponding to the pivot columns in U. Specifically, if U is the echelon form of A then $U\vec{n}_1 = \vec{0}$ and $U\vec{n}_2 = \vec{0}$ yields

$$\vec{u}_{*2} = 2\vec{u}_{*1} \quad \text{and} \quad \vec{u}_{*4} = \frac{3}{2}\vec{u}_{*3} - \frac{1}{2}\vec{u}_{*1}.$$

which shows the linear dependence among the columns of A and its echelon form U are identical. As it turns out this is always the case. If $A \sim U$ then **the columns of A corresponding to the pivot columns in U form a basis for $\mathcal{C}_A$.** This description of $\mathcal{C}_A$ (columns one and three of A) and the description in (4.26) display two different basis for $\mathcal{C}_A$. It can be shown (see Exercise(4.2)) that

$$\mathcal{C}_A = \text{span} \left\{ \begin{bmatrix} 1 \\ 2 \\ 3 \end{bmatrix}, \begin{bmatrix} 3 \\ 4 \\ 5 \end{bmatrix} \right\} = \text{span} \left\{ \begin{bmatrix} 1 \\ 0 \\ -1 \end{bmatrix}, \begin{bmatrix} 0 \\ 1 \\ 2 \end{bmatrix} \right\}.$$

Finally, the dimension of the domain of A is four and

$$4 = \dim \mathcal{R}^4 = 2 + 2 = r + \dim \mathcal{N}(A) = \dim \mathcal{C}_A + \dim \mathcal{N}(A).$$

Let B be the transpose of the matrix A in (4.22) and consider

$$B\vec{x} \equiv A^T \vec{x} = \begin{bmatrix} 1 & 2 & 3 \\ 2 & 4 & 6 \\ 3 & 4 & 5 \\ 4 & 5 & 6 \end{bmatrix} \begin{bmatrix} x_1 \\ x_2 \\ x_3 \end{bmatrix} = \begin{bmatrix} b_1 \\ b_2 \\ b_3 \\ b_4 \end{bmatrix}. \qquad (4.28)$$

Row reduction gives the equivalent system

$$[B \mid \vec{b}] = \begin{bmatrix} 1 & 2 & 3 & b_1 \\ 2 & 4 & 6 & b_2 \\ 3 & 4 & 5 & b_3 \\ 4 & 5 & 6 & b_4 \end{bmatrix}$$

$$\sim \begin{bmatrix} 1 & 2 & 3 & b_1 \\ 0 & 0 & 0 & b_2 - 2b_1 \\ 0 & -2 & -4 & b_3 - 3b_1 \\ 0 & -3 & -6 & b_4 - 4b_1 \end{bmatrix}$$

$$\sim \begin{bmatrix} 1 & 2 & 3 & b_1 \\ 0 & 0 & 0 & b_2 - 2b_1 \\ 0 & -2 & -4 & b_3 - 3b_1 \\ 0 & 0 & 0 & b_4 - (3/2)b_3 + (1/2)b_1 \end{bmatrix}$$

$$\sim \begin{bmatrix} 1 & 2 & 3 & b_1 \\ 0 & -2 & -4 & b_3 - 3b_1 \\ 0 & 0 & 0 & b_2 - 2b_1 \\ 0 & 0 & 0 & b_4 - (3/2)b_3 + (1/2)b_1 \end{bmatrix}.$$

The problem (4.28) is consistent if the last two entries in the fourth column of the reduced form are zero. This means that the column space can be found by enforcing the consistency conditions: $b_2 - 2b_1 = 0$ and $b_4 - (3/2)b_3 + (1/2)b_1 = 0$. Solve for b_2 and b_4 and write $\vec{b} \in \mathcal{C}_B$ in the vector form

$$\vec{b} = \begin{bmatrix} b_1 \\ b_2 \\ b_3 \\ b_4 \end{bmatrix} = \begin{bmatrix} b_1 \\ 2b_1 \\ b_3 \\ (3/2)b_3 - (1/2)b_1 \end{bmatrix} = b_1 \begin{bmatrix} 1 \\ 2 \\ 0 \\ -1/2 \end{bmatrix} + b_3 \begin{bmatrix} 0 \\ 0 \\ 1 \\ 3/2 \end{bmatrix}.$$

Alternatively, the column space of B can be found using the lines following (4.27) which dictate selecting the first two columns of B as a basis for $\mathcal{C}_B$. This is because the two pivots in the row reduced form of B are in columns one and two. Hence the column space of B admits the two descriptions

$$\mathcal{C}_B = \text{span} \left\{ \begin{bmatrix} 1 \\ 2 \\ 3 \\ 4 \end{bmatrix}, \begin{bmatrix} 2 \\ 4 \\ 4 \\ 5 \end{bmatrix} \right\} = \text{span} \left\{ \begin{bmatrix} 1 \\ 2 \\ 0 \\ -1/2 \end{bmatrix}, \begin{bmatrix} 0 \\ 0 \\ 1 \\ 3/2 \end{bmatrix} \right\} \qquad (4.29)$$

where the first span is defined by the first two columns of B. From the discussion preceding Definition(4.17), the subspace $\mathcal{C}_B$ is also given by the span of the rows of $A = B^T$, the row space R_A. Using the row reduction in (4.23) gives the further (equivalent by Exercise(4.7)) representation for

$$\mathcal{C}_B = R_A = \text{span}\left\{ \begin{bmatrix} 1 \\ 2 \\ 3 \\ 4 \end{bmatrix}, \begin{bmatrix} 0 \\ 0 \\ -2 \\ -3 \end{bmatrix} \right\}.$$

Assume that $\vec{b} \in \mathcal{C}_B$ so that the general solution of (4.28) is given by

$$
\begin{aligned}
\vec{x} = \begin{bmatrix} x_1 \\ x_2 \\ x_3 \end{bmatrix} &= \begin{bmatrix} x_3 - 2b_1 + b_3 \\ -2x_3 + (3/2)b_1 - (1/2)b_3 \\ x_3 \end{bmatrix} \\
&= \begin{bmatrix} x_3 \\ -2x_3 \\ x_3 \end{bmatrix} + \begin{bmatrix} -2b_1 + b_3 \\ (3/2)b_1 - (1/2)b_3 \\ 0 \end{bmatrix} \\
&= x_3 \begin{bmatrix} 1 \\ -2 \\ 1 \end{bmatrix} + \begin{bmatrix} -2b_1 + b_3 \\ (3/2)b_1 - (1/2)b_3 \\ 0 \end{bmatrix} = \vec{x}_h + \vec{x}_p
\end{aligned}
\tag{4.30}
$$

where x_3 is a free variable. Setting $\vec{b} = \vec{0}$ shows that

$$\mathcal{N}(B) = \text{span}\left\{ \begin{bmatrix} 1 \\ -2 \\ 1 \end{bmatrix} \right\}$$

so the $\dim \mathcal{N}(B) = 1$. The dimension of the domain of B is three and the equality of the dimensions of the various subspaces associated with the matrix B satisfy

$$3 = \dim \mathcal{R}^3 = 2 + 1 = r + \dim \mathcal{N}(B) = \dim \mathcal{C}_B + \dim \mathcal{N}(B).$$

As in the previous example, the rank of A and the rank of $B = A^T$ are the same. This means that $\dim \mathcal{C}_A = \dim R_A = 2$ and, as mentioned earlier, these two spaces are very different spaces. Specifically, the subspace $\mathcal{C}_A$ in (4.26) is contained in $\mathcal{R}^3$ and the subspace R_A in (4.29) is contained in $\mathcal{R}^4$.

4.9 Column Space = Row Space Dimension

In general if the matrix A is $m \times n$ then $\mathcal{C}_A \subset R^m$ and $R_A \subset R^n$. It is somewhat surprising that the dimension of these two subspaces are related but the actual equality $\dim \mathcal{C}_A = \dim R_A$ is amazing. From Definition(4.14) the rank of a matrix A is the number of pivots in the row echelon form of A. From Definition(4.6) the number given by $\dim \mathcal{C}_A$ is the number of independent columns of the matrix A. By definition the dimension of the row space of A

is the number of independent rows of A. In all the previous examples these three numbers, the rank of A, dim $\mathcal{C}_A$ and dim R_A, are the same. This section provides an outline of why this is true. First, a result on how to obtain a basis for R_A

Theorem 4.19 The Rank r of the matrix A is equal to the dimension of the row space of A = dim R_A. A basis for R_A: Let A be an $m \times n$, rank r matrix with the row echelon form U. The number r is the dimension of the **row space** of A and the r non-zero rows of U are a **basis** for the row space R_A.

The following discussion gives a reason to believe the theorem. The row reduction in (4.23) of the 3×4 matrix A in Example(4.18) can be broken down into the following steps

$$
A = \begin{bmatrix} \vec{r}_1 \\ \vec{r}_2 \\ \vec{r}_3 \end{bmatrix} \equiv \begin{bmatrix} a_{11} & a_{12} & a_{13} & a_{14} \\ a_{21} & a_{22} & a_{23} & a_{24} \\ a_{31} & a_{32} & a_{33} & a_{34} \end{bmatrix}
$$

$$
= \begin{bmatrix} 1 & 2 & 3 & 4 \\ 2 & 4 & 4 & 5 \\ 3 & 6 & 5 & 6 \end{bmatrix} \sim \begin{bmatrix} 1 & 2 & 3 & 4 \\ 0 & 0 & -2 & -3 \\ 3 & 6 & 5 & 6 \end{bmatrix} \equiv \hat{U} \qquad -2\text{Eq}1 + \text{Eq}2
$$

$$
\sim \begin{bmatrix} 1 & 2 & 3 & 4 \\ 0 & 0 & -2 & -3 \\ 0 & 0 & -4 & -6 \end{bmatrix} \qquad -3\text{Eq}1 + \text{Eq}3 \qquad\qquad (4.31)
$$

$$
\sim \begin{bmatrix} 1 & 2 & 3 & 4 \\ 0 & 0 & -2 & -3 \\ 0 & 0 & 0 & 0 \end{bmatrix} \qquad -2\text{Eq}2 + \text{Eq}3
$$

$$
= \begin{bmatrix} u_{11} & u_{12} & u_{13} & u_{14} \\ u_{21} & u_{22} & u_{23} & u_{24} \\ 0 & 0 & 0 & 0 \end{bmatrix} = \begin{bmatrix} \vec{u}_1 \\ \vec{u}_2 \\ \vec{0} \end{bmatrix} \equiv U.
$$

The notation $\vec{r}_i, i = 1, 2, 3$ denotes the three rows of the matrix A and $\vec{u}_i, i = 1, 2$ the two (independent) rows of U corresponding to the two pivots in U. Since U has two pivots the rank of A is two. A careful inspection of the steps in reducing A to the row echelon form U shows that each row of U is a linear combination of the rows of A. Specifically, the two equations

$$
\begin{aligned}
\vec{u}_1 &= \vec{r}_1 \\
\vec{u}_2 &= -2\vec{r}_1 + \vec{r}_2
\end{aligned} \qquad\qquad (4.32)
$$

show that each non-zero row of U is a linear combination of the rows of A. The first equation in (4.32) reflects the fact that the first row of A is never altered. The second equation in (4.32) represents the row operation $-2\text{Eq}1 + \text{Eq}2$. The two equations taken together shows that each row of U is a linear combination of the rows of A. This means the two dimensional row space of U is contained in the row space of A, $R_U \subseteq R_A$. All of the above steps are reversible. For example, the operation $2\text{Eq}1 + \text{Eq}2$ applied to $\hat{U}$ in (4.31) returns $\hat{U}$ to the matrix A. Indeed, reversing all of the steps gives

$$\begin{array}{ll}
\vec{r_1} &= \vec{u_1} + 0\vec{u_2} \\
\vec{r_2} &= 2\vec{u_1} + \vec{u_2} \\
\vec{r_3} &= 3\vec{u_1} + \vec{u_2}
\end{array} = \begin{bmatrix} 1 & 0 \\ 2 & 1 \\ 3 & 1 \end{bmatrix} \begin{bmatrix} \vec{u_1} \\ \vec{u_2} \end{bmatrix}. \tag{4.33}$$

These equations show that each row of A is a linear combination of the rows of U so that the row space of A is contained in the row space of U, $R_A \subseteq R_U$. Combining these two inclusions gives $R_A = R_U$. This implies that the non-zero rows of U are a basis for the row space of A. Since the matrix U has two independent rows corresponding to the $r = 2$ pivots this implies that the row space of A has dimension $r = 2$.

Example(4.18) can be taken further. Rewrite (4.33) with the matrix A written out

$$\begin{aligned}
A &= \begin{bmatrix} a_{11} & a_{12} & a_{13} & a_{14} \\ a_{21} & a_{22} & a_{23} & a_{24} \\ a_{31} & a_{32} & a_{33} & a_{34} \end{bmatrix} = \begin{bmatrix} \vec{a}_{*1} & \vec{a}_{*2} & \vec{a}_{*3} & \vec{a}_{*4} \end{bmatrix} \\
&= \begin{bmatrix} 1 & 0 \\ 2 & 1 \\ 3 & 1 \end{bmatrix} \begin{bmatrix} u_{11} & u_{12} & u_{13} & u_{14} \\ u_{21} & u_{22} & u_{23} & u_{24} \end{bmatrix} \\
&= \begin{bmatrix} u_{1j} \begin{bmatrix} 1 \\ 2 \\ 3 \end{bmatrix} + u_{2j} \begin{bmatrix} 0 \\ 1 \\ 1 \end{bmatrix} \end{bmatrix}_{3 \times 4} \quad j = 1,2,3,4
\end{aligned} \tag{4.34}$$

where $\vec{a}_{*j}, j = 1,2,3,4$ is the jth column of A and the three by four matrix on the right hand side has the vector $u_{1j} \begin{bmatrix} 1 \\ 2 \\ 3 \end{bmatrix} + u_{2j} \begin{bmatrix} 0 \\ 1 \\ 1 \end{bmatrix}$ in the jth column. Equating the columns of A on the left with the columns of the matrix on the right hand of side of (4.34) gives the four equalities

$$\vec{a}_{*j} = \begin{bmatrix} a_{1j} \\ a_{2j} \\ a_{3j} \end{bmatrix} = u_{1j} \begin{bmatrix} 1 \\ 2 \\ 3 \end{bmatrix} + u_{2j} \begin{bmatrix} 0 \\ 1 \\ 1 \end{bmatrix} \ , \ j = 1,2,3,4. \tag{4.35}$$

This shows that each column of A is a linear combination of the single set of $r = 2$ elements $\left\{ \begin{bmatrix} 1 \\ 2 \\ 3 \end{bmatrix}, \begin{bmatrix} 0 \\ 1 \\ 1 \end{bmatrix} \right\}$. Hence, the dimension of the column space of A is less than or equal to the $r = 2$ dimensional row space of A:

$$\dim(\text{column space of } A) \leq \dim(\text{row space of } A).$$

Replace the matrix A in (4.31) by $B = A^T$ to find (see the calculation following (4.28))

$$B = A^T = \begin{bmatrix} a_{11} & a_{21} & a_{31} \\ a_{12} & a_{22} & a_{32} \\ a_{13} & a_{23} & a_{33} \\ a_{14} & a_{24} & a_{34} \end{bmatrix} \sim \begin{bmatrix} 1 & 2 & 3 \\ 0 & -1 & -4 \\ 0 & 0 & 0 \\ 0 & 0 & 0 \end{bmatrix}.$$

Use the reasoning following (4.35) to conclude that dimension of the column space of B (which is is row space of A) is less than or equal to the dimension of the row space of B (which is the column space of A):

$$\dim(\text{row space of } A) \leq \dim(\text{column space of } A).$$

Except for "more" notation in the case of an $m \times n$ matrix A with rank r the methodology outlined above implies the following important theorem.

Theorem 4.20 The dimension of $\mathcal{C}_A$, R_A and the Ranks of A and A^T: If the rank of A is r then the rank of A^T is also r. Equivalently, $\dim \mathcal{C}_A = \dim R_A = r$.

Assume the matrix A is $m \times n$ and that the rank of A is r so that there are r independent columns among the n columns of A. The r independent columns are a basis for the $r-$dimensional subspace $\mathcal{C}_A$. As pointed out in Theorem(4.15) there are $n - r$ free variables. These free variables provide a count on the number of independent vectors in the homogeneous solution. This count is the dimension of the null space of A. Calculating this homogeneous solution provides a basis for the null space of the matrix A.

Theorem 4.21 A Basis for $\mathcal{N}(A)$ or $\mathcal{N}(A^T)$: Let A be an $m \times n$ matrix with rank r. If $r = n$ then $\vec{0}$ is the unique solution to $A\vec{x} = \vec{0}$ by Theorem(2.13). In the case that the rank $r < n$ there are $n - r$ free variables (review the discussion in Definition(2.12)). Label the $n - r$ free variables by $x_{r+1}, x_{r+2}, \ldots, x_n$. This may require some relabeling of variables which is simply a rearrangement of the columns of A. See the illustration below. With this convention, write the homogeneous solution to $A\vec{x} = \vec{0}$ in the form

$$\vec{x}_h = x_{r+1}\vec{n}_{r+1} + x_{r+2}\vec{n}_{r+2} + \cdots + x_n\vec{n}_n \text{ where } A\vec{n}_j = \vec{0}, \; j = r + 1, r + 2, \ldots, n \quad (4.36)$$

are the vectors found by solving, using row reductions, $A\vec{x} = \vec{0}$. The structure of the row echelon form of A implies that the set of vectors $\{\vec{n}_{r+1}, \vec{n}_{r+2}, \ldots, \vec{n}_n\}$ is linearly independent. Since the dimension of $\mathcal{N}(A)$ is $n - r$ the $n - r$ vectors in the set are a basis for the null space of A. Hence a basis for $\mathcal{N}(A)$ is defined implicitly by solving the homogeneous problem $A\vec{x} = \vec{0}$.

Here is an illustration of the above discussion. It is straightforward to show, using the row reduction, that

$$\widehat{A} = \begin{bmatrix} 1 & 3 & 2 & 4 \\ 2 & 4 & 4 & 5 \\ 3 & 5 & 6 & 6 \end{bmatrix} \sim \begin{bmatrix} 1 & 3 & 2 & 4 \\ 0 & -2 & 0 & -3 \\ 0 & 0 & 0 & 0 \end{bmatrix}.$$

The homogeneous solution to $\widehat{A}\vec{x} = \vec{0}$ is

$$\vec{x}_h = \begin{bmatrix} x_1 \\ x_2 \\ x_3 \\ x_4 \end{bmatrix} = \begin{bmatrix} -2x_3 + (1/2)x_4 \\ -(3/2)x_4 \\ x_3 \\ x_4 \end{bmatrix}$$

$$= x_3 \begin{bmatrix} -2 \\ 0 \\ 1 \\ 0 \end{bmatrix} + x_4 \begin{bmatrix} 1/2 \\ -3/2 \\ 0 \\ 1 \end{bmatrix} \equiv x_3 \vec{n}_3 + x_4 \vec{n}_4$$

and $\mathcal{N}(A) = \text{span}\{\vec{n}_3, \vec{n}_4\}$. This is (4.36) for $r = 2$ and $n = 3$. A review of the solution in (4.24) for the problem (4.22) with the coefficient matrix

$$A = \begin{bmatrix} 1 & 2 & 3 & 4 \\ 2 & 4 & 4 & 5 \\ 3 & 6 & 5 & 6 \end{bmatrix} \sim \begin{bmatrix} 1 & 2 & 3 & 4 \\ 0 & 0 & -2 & -3 \\ 0 & 0 & 0 & 0 \end{bmatrix}$$

has x_2 and x_4 as free variables. The relabeling would require x_2 to be relabeled x_3. This amounts to interchanging columns 2 and 3 of the matrix A. This is the matrix $\widehat{A}$ above. In other words, the relabeling is simply a convenience aimed toward a general argument. In either case, the two independent vectors in the homogeneous solution of the problem are a basis for the null space of A. This is the procedure used in computing $\mathcal{N}(A)$ in equations (4.17) and (4.24). Similarly, a basis for $\mathcal{N}(A^T)$ is defined implicitly by finding the $m - r$ components of the homogeneous problem $A^T \vec{x} = \vec{0}$. This was illustrated in computing $\mathcal{N}(A^T)$ in equations (4.19) and (4.30).

4.10   Dimension Theorem

Since the dim $\mathcal{N}(A) = n - r$ for the $m \times n$ rank r matrix A one has the equality

$$n = \text{the number of columns of } A = r + (n - r) = \text{rank of } A + \dim \mathcal{N}(A).$$

A similar statement holds for the transpose of A. This is housed in the following theorem.

Theorem 4.22 Dimension Theorem for A and for A^T: Assume that A is an $m \times n$ matrix with $r = \text{rank of } A = \dim R_A$. The null space $\mathcal{N}(A) \subset \mathcal{R}^n$ and the row space $R_A \subset \mathcal{R}^n$ and their dimensions satisfy

$$n = \dim \mathcal{R}^n = r + \dim \mathcal{N}(A) = \dim R_A + \dim \mathcal{N}(A).$$

The matrix A^T is an $n \times m$ matrix. The null space $\mathcal{N}(A^T) \subset \mathcal{R}^m$ and the column space $\mathcal{C}_A \subset \mathcal{R}^m$. The rank of A^T is $r = \dim \mathcal{C}_A$ and their dimensions satisfy

$$m = \dim \mathcal{R}^m = r + \dim \mathcal{N}(A^T) = \dim \mathcal{C}_A + \dim \mathcal{N}(A^T).$$

The statement dim $\mathcal{C}_A = 0$ (or dim $R_A = 0$) is possible and can occur only if the matrix A (or A^T) is the $m \times n$ (or $n \times m$) zero matrix. This doesn't require much study. The statement dim $\mathcal{N}(A) = 0$ (dim $\mathcal{N}(A^T) = 0$) implies that the null space of A (or A^T) consists only of the $n \times 1$ (or $m \times 1$) zero vector. See the last sentence in Definition(4.9). This will be isolated as a special case of the dimension theorem.

Special Case: The $n \times n$ matrix A is invertible if and only if the columns of A are independent.

If $m = n$ the theorem gives

$$n = \dim R_A + \dim \mathcal{N}(A) = \dim \mathcal{C}_A + \dim \mathcal{N}(A)$$

where the second equality uses $\dim R_A = \dim \mathcal{C}_A$ from Theorem(4.20). By Theorem(3.28) the matrix A is invertible if and only if $\vec{x} = \vec{0}$ is the unique solution of $A\vec{x} = \vec{0}$. In the language of this chapter the last sentence reads: the matrix A is invertible if and only if $\mathcal{N}(A) = \{\vec{0}\}$. This gives $\dim \mathcal{N}(A) = 0$ and the last display reads $\dim \mathcal{C}_A = n$. This equality is equivalent to the statement that the columns of A form an independent set of vectors. This gives another equivalence, which can be added to Theorem(3.28).

Many specific cases of this theorem have occurred in the examples of this chapter. In Example(4.16) for the 3×2 matrix B, which has rank two, it was found in (4.21) that $\mathcal{N}(B) = \{\vec{0}\}$. This illustrates the first part of the theorem since $r = n = 2$. The general solutions listed in the equations (4.15), (4.17), and (4.30) all have $r = 2$ and $n = 3$. Each of these have an $n - r = 1$ dimensional null space, and a basis for these null spaces is derived from the homogeneous part of the general solution as described in Theorem(4.21). For the general solution in (4.24) $r = 2, n = 4$ and the $n - r = 2$ dimensional null space is listed in (4.25). The dimension theorem was illustrated for the 3×3, the 2×3, and 3×4 matrices defining the systems in Example(4.13), Example(4.16), and Example (4.18), respectively. In Examples (4.16) and (4.18) the dimension theorem was also illustrated for 3×2 and 4×3 matrices derived from the systems using the transpose matrices $B = A^T$. Calculating the homogeneous solution for these two examples provides an illustration of finding a basis for $\mathcal{N}(A^T)$. For Example(4.13), the dimension theorem for the 3×3 rank $r = 2$ matrix A read $n = 3 = r + \dim \mathcal{N}(A) = 2 + 1$. There is more to the dimension theorem than just the numerical count of the dimensions. There are four subspaces referenced, namely $\mathcal{C}_A$ and $\mathcal{N}(A^T)$, which are both subspaces of $\mathcal{R}^m$ as well as R_A and $\mathcal{N}(A)$, which are both subspaces of $\mathcal{R}^n$. The following continuation of Example(4.16) and (4.18) show how these subspaces are connected.

Example 4.23 In Example (4.16) the null space

$$\mathcal{N}(A) = \mathcal{N}\left(\begin{bmatrix} 1 & 2 & 3 \\ 2 & 4 & 4 \end{bmatrix}\right) = \text{span}\left\{\begin{bmatrix} -2 \\ 1 \\ 0 \end{bmatrix}\right\} \equiv \text{span}\{\vec{n}\} \subset \mathcal{R}^3$$

and the row space (see (4.20))

$$R_A = \text{span}\left\{\begin{bmatrix} 1 \\ 2 \\ 0 \end{bmatrix}, \begin{bmatrix} 0 \\ 0 \\ 1 \end{bmatrix}\right\} = \text{span}\left\{\vec{r}_1^T, \vec{r}_2^T\right\} \subset \mathcal{R}^3$$

were found. The row vectors $\vec{r}_1 = [\,1\ 2\ 0\,]$ and $\vec{r}_2 = [\,0\ 0\ 1\,]$ span the row space of A. If α and β are arbitrary scalars then $\alpha\vec{r}_1 + \beta\vec{r}_2$ is an arbitrary vector in R_A. Take the dot product of $\alpha\vec{r}_1 + \beta\vec{r}_2$ with $\vec{n} \in \mathcal{N}(A)$

$$\vec{n} \cdot (\alpha\vec{r}_1 + \beta\vec{r}_2) = \alpha\vec{n} \cdot \vec{r}_1 + \beta\vec{n} \cdot \vec{r}_2 = 0$$

since both $\vec{n}\cdot\vec{r}_1 = \vec{n}\cdot\vec{r}_2 = 0$. It follows from Theorem(1.10) that $\vec{n}$ is orthogonal to the vector $\alpha\vec{r}_1 + \beta\vec{r}_2$. In words, every vector in R_A is orthogonal to every vector (any scalar multiple of $\vec{n}$) in $\mathcal{N}(A)$. The notation for these orthogonal subspaces is taken from the notation for orthogonal vectors, $\mathcal{N}(A) \perp R_A$. This will be formalized in Definition(4.24). The other two subspaces associated with the matrix A are $\mathcal{C}_A = \mathcal{R}^2$, and $\mathcal{N}(A^T) = \text{span}\left\{\begin{bmatrix} 0 \\ 0 \end{bmatrix}\right\}$. These subspaces are orthogonal, $\mathcal{N}(A^T) \perp \mathcal{C}_A$, since the zero vector is orthogonal to every vector (Definition(1.9)). From Example (4.18), a basis for the null space of A was found in (4.25)

$$\mathcal{N}(A) = \mathcal{N}\left(\begin{bmatrix} 1 & 2 & 3 & 4 \\ 2 & 4 & 4 & 5 \\ 3 & 6 & 5 & 6 \end{bmatrix}\right) = \text{span}\left\{\begin{bmatrix} -2 \\ 1 \\ 0 \\ 0 \end{bmatrix}, \begin{bmatrix} 1/2 \\ 0 \\ -3/2 \\ 1 \end{bmatrix}\right\} \equiv \text{span}\{\vec{n}_1, \vec{n}_2\}.$$

A basis for the column space $B = A^T$ was found in (4.29)

$$\mathcal{C}_B = R_A = \text{span}\left\{\begin{bmatrix} 1 \\ 2 \\ 0 \\ -1/2 \end{bmatrix}, \begin{bmatrix} 0 \\ 0 \\ 1 \\ 3/2 \end{bmatrix}\right\} \equiv \text{span}\left\{\vec{r}_1^{\,T}, \vec{r}_2^{\,T}\right\}$$

so the two vectors $\vec{r}_1 = \begin{bmatrix} 1 \\ 2 \\ 0 \\ -1/2 \end{bmatrix}$ and $\vec{r}_2 = \begin{bmatrix} 0 \\ 0 \\ 1 \\ 3/2 \end{bmatrix}$ span the row space of A. The calculation of the two dot products

$$\vec{r}_1 \cdot \vec{n}_1 = [\,1\ 2\ 0\ -1/2\,]\begin{bmatrix} -2 \\ 1 \\ 0 \\ 0 \end{bmatrix} = 1(-2) + 2(1) + 0(0) - 1/2(0) = 0$$

$$(4.37)$$

$$\vec{r}_1 \cdot \vec{n}_2 = [\,1\ 2\ 0\ -1/2\,]\begin{bmatrix} 1/2 \\ 0 \\ -3/2 \\ 1 \end{bmatrix} = 1(1/2) + 2(0) + 0(-3/2) - 1/2(1) = 0$$

shows that every vector in $\mathcal{N}(A)$ is orthogonal to $\vec{r}_1$. For every $\vec{n} \in \mathcal{N}(A)$ there are scalars α and β so that $\vec{n} = \alpha\vec{n}_1 + \beta\vec{n}_2$ and therefore

$$\vec{r}_1 \cdot \vec{n} = \vec{r}_1 \cdot (\alpha\vec{n}_1 + \beta\vec{n}_2) = \alpha(\vec{r}_1 \cdot \vec{n}_1) + \beta(\vec{r}_1 \cdot \vec{n}_2) = \alpha 0 + \beta 0 = 0\ .$$

Replacing $\vec{r}_1$ by $\vec{r}_2$ in (4.37) shows that

$$\vec{r}_2 \cdot \vec{n}_1 = [\,0\ 0\ 1\ 3/2\,]^T \begin{bmatrix} -2 \\ 1 \\ 0 \\ 0 \end{bmatrix} = 0(-2) + 0(1) + 1(0) + 3/2(0) = 0$$

$$\vec{r}_2 \cdot \vec{n}_2 = [\,0\ 0\ 1\ 3/2\,]^T \begin{bmatrix} 1/2 \\ 0 \\ -3/2 \\ 1 \end{bmatrix} = 0(1/2) + 0(0) + 1(-3/2) + 3/2(1) = 0. \tag{4.38}$$

Since the vector $\vec{n} = \alpha\vec{n}_1 + \beta\vec{n}_2 \in \mathcal{N}(A)$ is an arbitrary element in the null space of A the result in (4.38) shows

$$\vec{r}_2 \cdot \vec{n} = \vec{r}_2 \cdot (\alpha\vec{n}_1 + \beta\vec{n}_2) = \alpha(\vec{r}_2 \cdot \vec{n}_1) + \beta(\vec{r}_2 \cdot \vec{n}_2) = \alpha 0 + \beta 0 = 0.$$

In words, every vector in $\mathcal{N}(A)$ is orthogonal to $\vec{r}_2$. Let $\vec{r} = \hat{\alpha}\vec{r}_1 + \hat{\beta}\vec{r}_2$ be an arbitrary element in R_A. Using the dot product results in (4.37) and (4.38) in the calculation

$$\begin{aligned} \vec{r} \cdot \vec{n} &= \left(\hat{\alpha}\vec{r}_1 + \hat{\beta}\vec{r}_2\right) \cdot (\alpha\vec{n}_1 + \beta\vec{n}_2) \\ &= (\hat{\alpha}\vec{r}_1 \cdot \alpha\vec{n}_1 + \hat{\alpha}\vec{r}_1 \cdot \beta\vec{n}_2) + \left(\hat{\beta}\vec{r}_2 \cdot \alpha\vec{n}_1 + \hat{\beta}\vec{r}_2 \cdot \beta\vec{n}_2\right) \\ &= \hat{\alpha}\alpha\,(\vec{r}_1 \cdot \vec{n}_1) + \hat{\alpha}\beta\,(\vec{r}_1 \cdot \vec{n}_2) + \hat{\beta}\alpha\,(\vec{r}_2 \cdot \vec{n}_1) + \hat{\beta}\beta\,(\vec{r}_2 \cdot \vec{n}_2) = 0 \end{aligned} \tag{4.39}$$

shows that every vector in $\mathcal{N}(A)$ is orthogonal to every vector in R_A that is, $\mathcal{N}(A) \perp R_A$. In a similar fashion $\mathcal{C}_A \perp \mathcal{N}(A^T)$ and these two subspaces are subspaces in $\mathcal{R}^3$.

The illustrations of orthogonality in the last two examples are not "cooked up." The fact that the vectors in the null space of a matrix A are orthogonal to the vectors in the row space of A, can be seen as follows. Assume that the vector $\vec{x}_h \in \mathcal{N}(A)$, which, by Definition(4.11), means the equality

$$\begin{bmatrix} 0 \\ 0 \\ \vdots \\ 0 \end{bmatrix} = A\vec{x}_h = \begin{bmatrix} a_{11} & a_{12} & a_{13} & \cdots & a_{1,n} \\ a_{21} & a_{22} & a_{23} & \cdots & a_{2,n} \\ \vdots & \vdots & \ddots & \ddots & \cdots \\ a_{m1} & a_{m2} & a_{m3} & \cdots & a_{mn} \end{bmatrix} \begin{bmatrix} x_1 \\ x_2 \\ x_3 \\ \vdots \\ x_n \end{bmatrix} = \begin{bmatrix} \vec{a}_{1*}^T \vec{x}_h \\ \vec{a}_{2*}^T \vec{x}_h \\ \vdots \\ \vec{a}_{m*}^T \vec{x}_h \end{bmatrix} \tag{4.40}$$

holds. This says that any vector $\vec{x}_h$ in the $\mathcal{N}(A)$ is orthogonal to every row of the matrix A. Since the rows of A span the space R_A, (4.40) means that the only intersection of the r dimensional subspace R_A with the $n - r$ dimensional subspace $\mathcal{N}(A)$ is the zero vector. Since $(n - r) + r = n$ the totality of the vectors in the two subspaces R_A and $\mathcal{N}(A)$ "fill out" the domain space $\mathcal{R}^n$. To see this statement for $B = A^T$ simply replace the matrix A in (4.40) by $B = A^T$ to see that the only intersection of the r dimensional subspace $\mathcal{C}_A$

with the $m - r$ dimensional subspace $\mathcal{N}(A^T)$ is the zero vector. Since $(m - r) + r = m$ the totality of the vectors in the two subspaces $\mathcal{C}_A$ and $\mathcal{N}(A^T)$ again "fill out" the domain space which is now $\mathcal{R}^m$. What is meant by fill out here is that the number of independent vectors in R_A (or $\mathcal{C}_A$) plus the number of independent vectors in $\mathcal{N}(A)$ (or $\mathcal{N}(A^T)$) totals $n = \dim \mathcal{R}^n$ (or $m = \dim \mathcal{R}^m$), the dimension of the domain of A (or A^T).

Definition 4.24 Orthogonal Subspaces, Complements and Perps: Two subspaces $\mathcal{V}$ and $\mathcal{W}$ of $\mathcal{R}^n$ are called orthogonal if every vector $\vec{v} \in \mathcal{V}$ is orthogonal to every vector $\vec{w} \in \mathcal{W}$. From Theorem(1.10) this happens if and only if the dot product $\vec{w} \cdot \vec{v} = \vec{w}^T \vec{v} = 0$. From Definition(1.9), the notation for orthogonality is $\vec{v} \perp \vec{w}$ (**read $\vec{v}$ perp $\vec{w}$**). The same notation will be used for the orthogonal subspaces $\mathcal{V}$ and $\mathcal{W}$, $\mathcal{V} \perp \mathcal{W}$. The **orthogonal complement** of the subspace $\mathcal{V}$ is the subspace of vectors in $\mathcal{R}^n$ defined by

$$\mathcal{V}^\perp = \{\vec{u} : \vec{u} \cdot \vec{v} = \vec{u}^T \vec{v} = 0 \text{ for every } \vec{v} \in \mathcal{V}\} \ .$$

The subspace $\mathcal{V}^\perp$ is read $\mathcal{V}$ **perp**. In words the space consists of the vectors $\vec{u}$ which are orthogonal to every vector in $\mathcal{V}$. As such $\mathcal{V} \perp \mathcal{V}^\perp$. To see that $\mathcal{V}^\perp$ is a subspace one only needs to show that $\mathcal{V}^\perp$ is closed with respect to scalar multiplication and addition. See Exercise(4.11). Suppose the dimension of $\mathcal{V} = r \leq n$. It follows from Theorem(4.26) that dimension of $\mathcal{V}^\perp = n - r$. This means that $\mathcal{V}^\perp \cap \mathcal{V} = \{\vec{0}\}$ and every vector $\vec{w} \in \mathcal{R}^n$ can be written in the form $\vec{w} = \vec{v} + \vec{v}^\perp$ where $\vec{v} \in \mathcal{V}$ and $\vec{v}^\perp \in \mathcal{V}^\perp$. **The notation for this orthogonal decomposition of $\mathcal{R}^n$ is $\mathcal{R}^n = \mathcal{V} \oplus \mathcal{V}^\perp$.**

Example 4.25 In Example(4.23) it was shown that the two subspaces

$$R_A = \text{span} \left\{ \begin{bmatrix} 1 \\ 2 \\ 0 \end{bmatrix}, \begin{bmatrix} 0 \\ 0 \\ 1 \end{bmatrix} \right\} \text{ and } \mathcal{N}(A) = \text{span} \left\{ \begin{bmatrix} -2 \\ 1 \\ 0 \end{bmatrix} \right\}$$

are orthogonal where $A = \begin{bmatrix} 1 & 2 & 3 \\ 2 & 4 & 4 \end{bmatrix}$. To see that $\mathcal{N}(A)^\perp = R_A$, let $\vec{u} = \begin{bmatrix} a \\ b \\ c \end{bmatrix}$ be an arbitrary element of R_A so that

$$\mathcal{N}(A)^\perp = \{\vec{u} : \vec{u}^T \vec{v} = 0 \text{ for every } \vec{v} \in \mathcal{N}(A)\} \ .$$

Since there is a single vector spanning $\mathcal{N}(A)$, the condition gives

$$\vec{u}^T \vec{v} = [\, a \ b \ c \,] \begin{bmatrix} -2 \\ 1 \\ 0 \end{bmatrix} = -2a + b = 0$$

so that $b = 2a$ and the parameter c is arbitrary. Hence, the vector

$$\vec{u} = \begin{bmatrix} a \\ b \\ c \end{bmatrix} = \begin{bmatrix} a \\ 2a \\ c \end{bmatrix} = a \begin{bmatrix} 1 \\ 2 \\ 0 \end{bmatrix} + c \begin{bmatrix} 0 \\ 0 \\ 1 \end{bmatrix}$$

is an arbitrary element of $\mathcal{N}(A)^\perp$. The right hand side of this display is a basis for R_A. This shows that $\mathcal{N}(A)^\perp = R_A$ so that these two subspaces are orthogonal complements. In the notation of Definition(4.24), $\mathcal{R}^3 = \mathcal{N}_A \oplus \mathcal{N}_A^\perp = \mathcal{N}_A \oplus R_A^\perp = R_A^\perp \oplus R_A$. The latter equality follows upon interchanging the roles of $\mathcal{N}(A)$ and R_A which shows that $\mathcal{N}(A) = R_A^\perp$.

Recall from (4.25) that

$$\mathcal{N}(A) = \text{span} \left\{ \begin{bmatrix} -2 \\ 1 \\ 0 \\ 0 \end{bmatrix}, \begin{bmatrix} 1/2 \\ 0 \\ -3/2 \\ 1 \end{bmatrix} \right\}$$

for the matrix $A = \begin{bmatrix} 1 & 2 & 3 & 4 \\ 2 & 4 & 4 & 5 \\ 3 & 6 & 5 & 6 \end{bmatrix}$ in Example(4.23). For the vector $\vec{u} = \begin{bmatrix} a \\ b \\ c \\ d \end{bmatrix}$ to belong

to the orthogonal complement of $\mathcal{N}(A)$ requires both

$$\vec{u}^T \begin{bmatrix} -2 \\ 1 \\ 0 \\ 0 \end{bmatrix} = -2a + b$$

and

$$\vec{u}^T \begin{bmatrix} 1/2 \\ 0 \\ -3/2 \\ 1 \end{bmatrix} = (1/2)a - (3/2)c + d = 0.$$

Solve the first for a and the second for d to find

$$\begin{bmatrix} a \\ 2a \\ c \\ -(1/2)a + (3/2)c \end{bmatrix} = a \begin{bmatrix} 1 \\ 2 \\ 0 \\ -1/2 \end{bmatrix} + c \begin{bmatrix} 0 \\ 0 \\ 1 \\ 3/2 \end{bmatrix} = \mathcal{N}(A)^\perp.$$

Compare this display with (4.29) to see that $\mathcal{N}(A)^\perp = R_A$. Hence, $\mathcal{R}^4 = \mathcal{N}_A \oplus \mathcal{N}_A^\perp = \mathcal{N}_A \oplus R_A^\perp = R_A^\perp \oplus R_A$.

4.11 Orthogonal Decomposition of $\mathcal{R}^n$

Theorem 4.26 Let $\mathcal{V}$ be a subspace of $\mathcal{R}^n$ and let $\mathcal{V}^\perp$ be the orthogonal complement of $\mathcal{V}$. Then

(a) $\mathcal{V}^\perp \cap \mathcal{V} = \{\vec{0}\}$.

(b) every vector $\vec{w} \in \mathcal{R}^n$ can be uniquely written as

$$\vec{w} = \vec{v} + \vec{v}^\perp \quad \text{where} \quad \vec{v} \in \mathcal{V} \quad \text{and} \quad \vec{v} \in \mathcal{V}^\perp.$$

Since a non-zero vector cannot be orthogonal to itself the intersection of the subspace $\mathcal{V}$ with the subspace $\mathcal{V}^\perp$ is the zero vector; $\mathcal{V}^\perp \cap \mathcal{V} = \{\vec{0}\}$. To see that any vector $\vec{w} \in \mathcal{R}^n$ can be written in the form $\vec{w} = \vec{v} + \vec{v}^\perp$ see part 4 of Exercise(4.16), which introduces the notion of a projection onto a subspace. This is a generalization of projecting one vector along another vector as in Definition(1.11). To see the uniqueness statement, assume that the vector $\vec{w}$ can also be written as $\vec{w} = \vec{u} + \vec{u}^\perp$ where $\vec{u} \in \mathcal{V}$ and $\vec{u}^\perp \in \mathcal{V}^\perp$. Take the dot product of $\vec{v}$ with each of $\vec{w} = \vec{v} + \vec{v}^\perp$ and $\vec{w} = \vec{u} + \vec{u}^\perp$ to find

$$\vec{v} \cdot \vec{w} = \vec{v} \cdot \left(\vec{v} + \vec{v}^\perp \right) = \vec{v} \cdot \vec{v} + \vec{v} \cdot \vec{v}^\perp = \vec{v} \cdot \vec{v} \quad \text{since } \vec{v} \cdot \vec{v}^\perp = 0$$

and

$$\vec{v} \cdot \vec{w} = \vec{v} \cdot \left(\vec{u} + \vec{u}^\perp \right) = \vec{v} \cdot \vec{u} + \vec{v} \cdot \vec{u}^\perp = \vec{v} \cdot \vec{u} \quad \text{since } \vec{v} \cdot \vec{u}^\perp = 0 .$$

Subtracting the last two displays gives

$$\begin{aligned} 0 = \vec{v} \cdot \vec{w} - \vec{v} \cdot \vec{w} &= \vec{v} \cdot \vec{v} - \vec{v} \cdot \vec{u} \\ &= \vec{v} \cdot (\vec{v} - \vec{u}) . \end{aligned}$$

Hence $\vec{v} \perp (\vec{v} - \vec{u})$. Since $\vec{v} \in \mathcal{V}$ it follows that $\vec{v} - \vec{u} \in \mathcal{V}^\perp$. By assumption each of the vectors $\vec{v}$ and $\vec{u}$ are in $\mathcal{V}$ so difference $\vec{v} - \vec{u} \in \mathcal{V}$ since $\mathcal{V}$ is a vector space. It follows that $\vec{v} - \vec{u}$ is in both $\mathcal{V}$ and $\mathcal{V}^\perp$. That is

$$(\vec{v} - \vec{u}) \in \mathcal{V} \cap \mathcal{V}^\perp = \left\{ \vec{0} \right\} .$$

Hence, $\vec{v} = \vec{u}$. Repeat the previous steps with $\vec{v}$ replaced by $\vec{v}^\perp$ and conclude that $\vec{v}^\perp = \vec{u}^\perp$. This shows that the decomposition is unique.

Example 4.27 Define two subspaces of $\mathcal{R}^3$ by

$$\mathcal{V} = \text{span} \left\{ \begin{bmatrix} 1 \\ 0 \\ 0 \end{bmatrix} \right\} \text{ and } \mathcal{W} = \text{span} \left\{ \begin{bmatrix} 0 \\ 1 \\ 0 \end{bmatrix} \right\} .$$

Geometrically $\mathcal{V}$ is the $x_1 = x$ axis and $\mathcal{W}$ is the $x_2 = y$ axis. These two subspaces are orthogonal, which is another way of saying that the two coordinate axis meet at right angles. Analytically, a vector $\begin{bmatrix} \alpha \\ 0 \\ 0 \end{bmatrix} \in \mathcal{V}$, $\alpha \in \mathcal{R}$ is orthogonal to $\begin{bmatrix} 0 \\ \beta \\ 0 \end{bmatrix} \in \mathcal{W}, \beta \in \mathcal{R}$ since the dot product of these two vectors is zero. The subspace $\mathcal{W}$ is not, however, the orthogonal complement of $\mathcal{V}$, since the vector $\begin{bmatrix} 0 \\ 0 \\ 1 \end{bmatrix}$ (geometrically the $x_3 = z$ axis) is orthogonal to every vector in $\mathcal{V}$ but this vector is not in $\mathcal{W}$. The orthogonal complement of $\mathcal{V}$ is the subspace defined by

$$\mathcal{V}^\perp = \text{span} \left\{ \begin{bmatrix} 0 \\ 1 \\ 0 \end{bmatrix} , \begin{bmatrix} 0 \\ 0 \\ 1 \end{bmatrix} \right\} \text{ and } \mathcal{R}^3 = \mathcal{V} \oplus \mathcal{V}^\perp .$$

The last statement says that every vector in $\mathcal{R}^3$ can be written as a sum of its component in the x-direction (the subspace $\mathcal{V}$) and its components in the $y - z$ plane (the subspace $\mathcal{V}^\perp$) and this decomposition is orthogonal. If $\vec{v} = \begin{bmatrix} 2 \\ 3 \\ 1 \end{bmatrix}$ then the decomposition is given by

$$\vec{v} = \begin{bmatrix} 2 \\ 3 \\ 1 \end{bmatrix} = \vec{v}_\mathcal{V} + \vec{v}_\mathcal{V}^\perp = \begin{bmatrix} 2 \\ 0 \\ 0 \end{bmatrix} + \begin{bmatrix} 0 \\ 3 \\ 1 \end{bmatrix}.$$

The orthogonal complement of $\mathcal{V}^\perp$ is found by finding all vectors $\vec{v} = \begin{bmatrix} v_1 \\ v_2 \\ v_3 \end{bmatrix}$ that are orthogonal to both of the vectors $\begin{bmatrix} 0 \\ 1 \\ 0 \end{bmatrix}$ and $\begin{bmatrix} 0 \\ 0 \\ 1 \end{bmatrix}$. That is each of the dot products

$$\begin{bmatrix} 0 \\ 1 \\ 0 \end{bmatrix} \cdot \vec{v} = v_2 = 0 \text{ and } \begin{bmatrix} 0 \\ 0 \\ 1 \end{bmatrix} \cdot \vec{v} = v_3 = 0$$

so that $\vec{v} = \begin{bmatrix} v_1 \\ v_2 \\ v_3 \end{bmatrix} = \begin{bmatrix} v_1 \\ 0 \\ 0 \end{bmatrix} = v_1 \begin{bmatrix} 1 \\ 0 \\ 0 \end{bmatrix}$. In words, the orthogonal complement of the orthogonal complement of $\mathcal{V}$ is $\mathcal{V}$. In symbols, $(\mathcal{V}^\perp)^\perp = \mathcal{V}$. There is nothing special in this example. It is always the case that the orthogonal complement of the orthogonal complement of a subspace is the subspace with which you began. Switching the emphasis from the subspace $\mathcal{V}$ to $\mathcal{W}$, one can write $\mathcal{R}^3 = \mathcal{W} \oplus \mathcal{W}^\perp$ where

$$\mathcal{W}^\perp = \text{span} \left\{ \begin{bmatrix} 1 \\ 0 \\ 0 \end{bmatrix}, \begin{bmatrix} 0 \\ 0 \\ 1 \end{bmatrix} \right\}$$

which is a different orthogonal decomposition of $\mathcal{R}^3$ than the one obtained from $\mathcal{V}$. For the vector $\vec{v}$ above

$$\vec{v} = \begin{bmatrix} 2 \\ 3 \\ 1 \end{bmatrix} = \vec{w}_\mathcal{W} + \vec{w}_\mathcal{W}^\perp = \begin{bmatrix} 0 \\ 3 \\ 0 \end{bmatrix} + \begin{bmatrix} 2 \\ 0 \\ 1 \end{bmatrix}.$$

The procedure is the same for finding $\mathcal{W}_2^\perp$ where $\mathcal{W}_2 = \text{span} \left\{ \begin{bmatrix} 0 \\ 1 \\ 1 \end{bmatrix}, \begin{bmatrix} 1 \\ -1/2 \\ 1/2 \end{bmatrix} \right\}$. For a vector $\begin{bmatrix} a \\ b \\ c \end{bmatrix} \in \mathcal{W}_2^\perp$ the vector must satisfy both of the equalities

$$\begin{bmatrix} 0 \\ 1 \\ 1 \end{bmatrix} \cdot \begin{bmatrix} a \\ b \\ c \end{bmatrix} = b + c = 0$$

and

$$\begin{bmatrix} 1 \\ -1/2 \\ 1/2 \end{bmatrix} \cdot \begin{bmatrix} a \\ b \\ c \end{bmatrix} = a - \frac{b}{2} + \frac{c}{2} = 0.$$

The first gives $b = -c$ and from the second $a = \frac{b}{2} - \frac{c}{2} = -c$. Using these results to write $b = -c = a$, where a is arbitrary gives

$$\begin{bmatrix} a \\ b \\ c \end{bmatrix} = \begin{bmatrix} a \\ a \\ -a \end{bmatrix} = a \begin{bmatrix} 1 \\ 1 \\ -1 \end{bmatrix} = \operatorname{span}\left(\begin{bmatrix} 1 \\ 1 \\ -1 \end{bmatrix} \right) = \mathcal{W}_2^\perp.$$

The orthogonal decomposition for $\vec{v}$ reads

$$\vec{v} = \begin{bmatrix} 2 \\ 3 \\ 1 \end{bmatrix} = \vec{w}_{\mathcal{W}_2} + \vec{w}_{\mathcal{W}_2}^\perp = \frac{1}{3} \begin{bmatrix} 2 \\ 5 \\ 7 \end{bmatrix} + \frac{4}{3} \begin{bmatrix} 1 \\ 1 \\ -1 \end{bmatrix}. \tag{4.41}$$

By construction the vector

$$\vec{w}_{\mathcal{W}_2}^\perp = \frac{4}{3} \begin{bmatrix} 1 \\ 1 \\ -1 \end{bmatrix} \in \mathcal{W}_2^\perp,$$

and writing $\vec{w}_{\mathcal{W}_2}$ as the linear combination

$$\vec{w}_{\mathcal{W}_2} = \frac{1}{3} \begin{bmatrix} 2 \\ 5 \\ 7 \end{bmatrix} = 2 \begin{bmatrix} 0 \\ 1 \\ 1 \end{bmatrix} + \frac{2}{3} \begin{bmatrix} 1 \\ -1/2 \\ 1/2 \end{bmatrix}$$

shows that $\vec{w}_{\mathcal{W}_2} \in \mathcal{W}_2$. The decomposition in (4.41) of the given vector $\vec{v}$ is the unique decomposition given in Theorem(4.26) with respect to the subspace $\mathcal{V} = \mathcal{W}_2$. It is, however, more subtle than the previous two decompositions. A formula to obtain the decomposition in (4.41), or the decomposition of an arbitrary $\vec{w} \in \mathcal{R}^3$ for $\mathcal{W}_2 \oplus \mathcal{W}_2^\perp$, is found in parts 3 and 4 of Exercise(4.16).

The equality $\mathcal{N}(A)^\perp = R_A$ was illustrated in Example(4.25) for two different matrices A. This equality is true in general. One way to see this equality is from an inspection of the equation $A\vec{x}_h = \vec{0}$. This is the statement that $x_h \in \mathcal{N}(A)$ and it shows that that any point in the null space of A is orthogonal to each row of the matrix A. Stated in terms of complementary subspaces, any point in the null space of A is in the orthogonal complement of the row space of A. Another way to see the equality $\mathcal{N}(A)^\perp = R_A$ is to take $\mathcal{V} = \mathcal{N}(A)$ (or $\mathcal{V} = R_A$) in Theorem(4.26). This leads to the decomposition theorem.

Theorem 4.28 Orthogonal Subspace Decomposition Theorem: If A is an $m \times n$ matrix then

$$\mathcal{R}^n = \mathcal{N}(A) \oplus R_A \quad \text{where} \quad R_A \cap \mathcal{N}(A) = \{\vec{0}\} \quad \text{and} \quad \begin{cases} \mathcal{N}(A)^\perp = R_A \\ \\ R_A^\perp = \mathcal{N}(A) \end{cases} .$$

Replacing A by A^T gives the alternative subspace decomposition

$$\mathcal{R}^m = \mathcal{N}(A^T) \oplus \mathcal{C}_A \quad \text{where} \quad \mathcal{C}_A \cap \mathcal{N}(A^T) = \{\vec{0}\} \quad \text{and} \quad \begin{cases} \mathcal{N}(A^T)^\perp = \mathcal{C}_A \\ \\ \mathcal{C}_A^\perp = \mathcal{N}(A^T) \end{cases} .$$

Suppose that A is an $m \times n$ matrix, $\vec{x}$ is an $n \times 1$ vector and $\vec{b} \in \mathcal{C}_A$ so that the system $A\vec{x} = \vec{b}$ is consistent. The solution of $A\vec{x} = \vec{b}$ is given by

$$\vec{x} = \vec{x}_h + \vec{x}_p \quad \text{where} \quad A\vec{x}_h = \vec{0} \quad \text{and} \quad A\vec{x}_p = \vec{b}$$

where $\vec{x}_p$ is **a particular** solution, not **the particular** solution of the problem. This is because there are many particular solutions. It follows from the orthogonal decomposition theorem that there is a **unique** row space solution $\vec{x}_r$ which satisfies $A\vec{x}_r = \vec{b}$. This is the particular solution $\vec{x}_r = \dfrac{1}{27} \begin{bmatrix} -1 \\ -46 \\ 85 \end{bmatrix}$ found in Example(4.16) which is orthogonal to the homogeneous solution $\vec{x}_h = x_3 \begin{bmatrix} -7 \\ 2 \\ 1 \end{bmatrix}$. This is to be expected from Theorem(4.28) since $\vec{x}_r \in R_A$, $\vec{x}_h \in \mathcal{N}_A$ and $R_A \perp \mathcal{N}_A$. Here is another example.

Example 4.29 From Example (4.23) the two subspaces of $\mathcal{R}^4$ given by

$$R_A = \text{span} \left\{ \begin{bmatrix} 1 \\ 2 \\ 0 \\ -1/2 \end{bmatrix} , \begin{bmatrix} 0 \\ 0 \\ 1 \\ 3/2 \end{bmatrix} \right\} \quad \text{and} \quad \mathcal{N}(A) = \left\{ \begin{bmatrix} -2 \\ 1 \\ 0 \\ 0 \end{bmatrix} , \begin{bmatrix} 1/2 \\ 0 \\ -3/2 \\ 1 \end{bmatrix} \right\}$$

are orthogonal complements so $R_A^\perp = \mathcal{N}(A)$ and $\mathcal{R}^4 = \mathcal{N}(A) \oplus R_A$. Using (4.26) and (4.30) from Example(4.18) gives

$$\mathcal{C}_A = \text{span} \left\{ \begin{bmatrix} 1 \\ 0 \\ -1 \end{bmatrix} , \begin{bmatrix} 0 \\ 1 \\ 2 \end{bmatrix} \right\} \quad \text{and} \quad \mathcal{N}(A^T) = \text{span} \left\{ \begin{bmatrix} 1 \\ -2 \\ 1 \end{bmatrix} \right\} .$$

Hence $\mathcal{R}^3 = \mathcal{N}(A^T) \oplus \mathcal{C}_A$. A geometrical realization of these four subspaces requires the use of your imagination. Here is what came out of mine.

$$\mathcal{N}(A) \oplus R_A = \text{span} \left\{ \begin{bmatrix} -2 \\ 1 \\ 0 \\ 0 \end{bmatrix}, \begin{bmatrix} 1/2 \\ 0 \\ -3/2 \\ 1 \end{bmatrix} \right\} \oplus \text{span} \left\{ \begin{bmatrix} 1 \\ 2 \\ 0 \\ -1/2 \end{bmatrix}, \begin{bmatrix} 0 \\ 0 \\ 1 \\ 3/2 \end{bmatrix} \right\} \quad \begin{matrix} A \\ \to \end{matrix} \quad \mathcal{R}^3$$

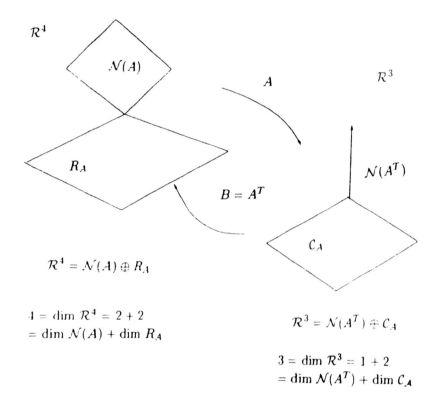

$$\mathcal{R}^4 = \mathcal{N}(A) \oplus R_A$$

$$4 = \dim \mathcal{R}^4 = 2 + 2$$
$$= \dim \mathcal{N}(A) + \dim R_A$$

$$\mathcal{R}^3 = \mathcal{N}(A^T) \oplus \mathcal{C}_A$$

$$3 = \dim \mathcal{R}^3 = 1 + 2$$
$$= \dim \mathcal{N}(A^T) + \dim \mathcal{C}_A$$

$$\mathcal{R}^4 \quad \begin{matrix} A^T \\ \leftarrow \end{matrix} \quad \text{span} \left\{ \begin{bmatrix} 1 \\ -2 \\ 1 \end{bmatrix} \right\} \oplus \text{span} \left\{ \begin{bmatrix} 1 \\ 0 \\ -1 \end{bmatrix}, \begin{bmatrix} 0 \\ 1 \\ 2 \end{bmatrix} \right\} = \mathcal{N}(A^T) \oplus \mathcal{C}_A$$

The solution to the linear system of equations

$$A\vec{x} = \begin{bmatrix} 1 & 2 & 3 & 4 \\ 2 & 4 & 4 & 5 \\ 3 & 6 & 5 & 6 \end{bmatrix} \begin{bmatrix} x_1 \\ x_2 \\ x_3 \\ x_4 \end{bmatrix} = \vec{b} = \begin{bmatrix} b_1 \\ b_2 \\ b_3 \end{bmatrix} \tag{4.42}$$

was discussed in Example (4.18). The solution in (4.24) and its connection to the various subspaces in the figure above will be reviewed. The components of $\vec{b}$ must satisfy

$$b_3 - 2b_2 + b_1 = 0 \quad \text{for} \quad \vec{b} \in \mathcal{C}_A.$$

To be specific let $\vec{b} = \begin{bmatrix} 1 \\ 1 \\ 1 \end{bmatrix} \in \mathcal{C}_A$ so from (4.24),

$$\vec{x} = \{\vec{x}_h\} + \vec{x}_p = \left\{ x_2 \begin{bmatrix} -2 \\ 1 \\ 0 \\ 0 \end{bmatrix} + x_4 \begin{bmatrix} 1/2 \\ 0 \\ -3/2 \\ 1 \end{bmatrix} \right\} + \begin{bmatrix} -1/2 \\ 0 \\ 1/2 \\ 0 \end{bmatrix} \qquad (4.43)$$

is the general solution to the linear system $A\vec{x} = \vec{b} = \begin{bmatrix} 1 \\ 1 \\ 1 \end{bmatrix}$ where $\vec{x}_p = [\ -\frac{1}{2}\ 0\ \frac{1}{2}\ 0\ ]^T$

is **a particular** solution. Check that $\tilde{\vec{x}}_p = [\ 0\ 0\ -1\ 1\ ]^T$ is another particular solution. Since $\mathcal{R}^4 = \mathcal{N}(A) \oplus R_A$ and $\vec{x}_h \in \mathcal{N}(A)$ some students want to conclude that the particular solution $\vec{x}_p$ must belong to the row space of A. By inspection neither $\vec{x}_p$ nor $\tilde{\vec{x}}_p$ is orthogonal to either of the vectors in $\mathcal{N}(A)$ which means that neither of these particular solutions belong to R_A. This scenario, a particular solution which does not lie in R_A, sometimes bothers students in light of the decomposition $\mathcal{R}^4 = \mathcal{N}(A) \oplus R_A$. Recall that this decomposition means that any $\vec{x} \in \mathcal{R}^4$ can be written as a sum, $\vec{x} = \vec{x}_r + \vec{x}_n$, where $\vec{x}_r \in R_A$ and $\vec{x}_n \in \mathcal{N}(A)$ where each of $\vec{x}_r$ and $\vec{x}_n$ are unique. It just happens to be the case that the particular solution written down in (4.43) does not belong to R_A. There is nothing wrong or bad about this. As pointed out following Theorem(4.26) there is a (unique) element $\vec{x}_r \in R_A$ which is a particular solution to (4.42). It is not hard (see Exercise(4.8)) to show that

$$\hat{\vec{x}} = \vec{x}_n + \vec{x}_r = \hat{x}_2 \begin{bmatrix} -2 \\ 1 \\ 0 \\ 0 \end{bmatrix} + \hat{x}_4 \begin{bmatrix} 1/2 \\ 0 \\ -3/2 \\ 1 \end{bmatrix} + \frac{1}{66} \begin{bmatrix} -5 \\ -10 \\ 9 \\ 16 \end{bmatrix} \qquad (4.44)$$

is another (form) of a general solution to (4.42). The x_2 and x_4 in (4.43) are different from the $\hat{x}_2$ and $\hat{x}_4$ in (4.44) but either set of coefficients are arbitrary. The identity $A\vec{x} = \vec{b} = A\hat{\vec{x}}$ does not in general imply that $\vec{x} = \hat{\vec{x}}$. All that can be concluded is that

$$A\vec{x} - A\hat{\vec{x}} = A\left(\vec{x} - \hat{\vec{x}}\right) = \vec{0} \text{ or } \vec{x} - \hat{\vec{x}} \in \mathcal{N}(A).$$

The figure in Exercise(4.8) is a geometrical illustration of each of the general solutions $\vec{x}$ from (4.43) and $\hat{\vec{x}}$ in (4.44). If there is a distinguished particular solution then the solution in (4.44) could play that role since it is the unique particular solution lying in the subspace R_A. As a consequence, $\vec{x}_r$ has a further distinguishing feature: of all particular solutions $\vec{x}_p$ satisfying $A\vec{x}_p = \vec{b}$ the row space solution satisfies $||\vec{x}_p||^2 \geq ||\vec{x}_r||^2$ with equality for $\vec{x}_p = \vec{x}_r$. To see this, first note that the vector $\vec{x}_p - \vec{x}_r \in \mathcal{N}(A)$ and $\vec{x}_r \in R_A$ so, by the orthogonal decomposition theorem(4.28), $\vec{x}_r \cdot (\vec{x}_p - \vec{x}_r) = 0$. Hence, $\vec{x}_r$ and $\vec{x}_p - \vec{x}_r$ are legs of a right triangle with hypotenuse $\vec{x}_p$ so

$$||\vec{x}_p||^2 = ||\vec{x}_r||^2 + ||\vec{x}_p - \vec{x}_r||^2 \geq ||\vec{x}_r||^2$$

since $||\vec{x}_p - \vec{x}_r||^2 \geq 0$. This is simply an interesting observation at this point. However, this minimum norm row space solution plays an important role in the least squares solution discussion in Exercise(4.17).

Finally, if the problem in $A\vec{x} = \vec{b}$ is solvable for any $\vec{b} \in \mathcal{R}^m$ then from the dimension theorem(4.22) the dimension of $\mathcal{C}_A = m$ so that dim $\mathcal{N}(A^T) = 0$, that is, the only solution to $A^T\vec{y} = \vec{0}$ is $\vec{0}$. Alternatively, if there is a $\vec{b} \in \mathcal{R}^m$ so that the problem in $A\vec{x} = \vec{b}$ is not solvable then, again from the dimension theorem, it follows that dim $\mathcal{C}_A < m$. This means there is a non-zero $\vec{y} \in \mathcal{R}^m$ satisfying $A^T\vec{y} = \vec{0}$. These observations are contained in the following theorem.

Theorem 4.30 Fredholm Alternative: Let A be an $m \times n$ matrix. Either $A\vec{x} = \vec{b}$ is solvable for any $\vec{b} \in \mathcal{R}^m$ **or** the problem $A^T\vec{y} = \vec{0}$ has a non-zero solution.

Example 4.31 In Example(4.16) for the 2×3 matrix $A = \begin{bmatrix} 1 & 2 & 3 \\ 2 & 4 & 4 \end{bmatrix}$ the column space $\mathcal{C}_A = \mathcal{R}^2$ so that the problem $A\vec{x} = \vec{b}$ is always solvable. The Fredholm Alternative tells you that the only solution to

$$A^T\vec{y} = \begin{bmatrix} 0 \\ 0 \\ 0 \end{bmatrix} \text{ is } \vec{0} = \begin{bmatrix} 0 \\ 0 \end{bmatrix}.$$

In Example(4.16) it was also shown that $\mathcal{N}(A^T) = \{\vec{0}\} = \left\{ \begin{bmatrix} 0 \\ 0 \end{bmatrix} \right\}$, which is precisely the identity in the last display. In Example(4.18) it was shown that the system

$$A\vec{x} = \begin{bmatrix} 1 & 2 & 3 & 4 \\ 2 & 4 & 4 & 5 \\ 3 & 6 & 5 & 6 \end{bmatrix} \begin{bmatrix} x_1 \\ x_2 \\ x_3 \\ x_4 \end{bmatrix} = \vec{b} = \begin{bmatrix} b_1 \\ b_2 \\ b_3 \end{bmatrix}$$

is solvable if the components of $\vec{b}$ satisfy $b_3 - 2b_2 + b_1 = 0$. Another way to say this is that there are vectors $\vec{b} \in \mathcal{R}^3$ for which the system is not solvable. From the dimension theorem, a positive equivalent statement is that there is a non-zero vector $\vec{y} \in \mathcal{R}^3$ such that

$$A^T\vec{y} = \begin{bmatrix} 1 & 2 & 3 \\ 2 & 4 & 6 \\ 3 & 4 & 5 \\ 4 & 5 & 6 \end{bmatrix} \begin{bmatrix} y_1 \\ y_2 \\ y_3 \end{bmatrix} = \vec{0} = \begin{bmatrix} 0 \\ 0 \\ 0 \\ 0 \end{bmatrix}.$$

The reason for this is that dim $\mathcal{N}(A^T) = m - $ dim $\mathcal{C}_A = 3 - 2 = 1$. The one-dimensional space $\mathcal{N}(A^T) = \text{span} \left\{ \begin{bmatrix} 1 \\ -2 \\ 1 \end{bmatrix} \right\}$ is listed in (4.30). In Exercise(4.6) you will show that for the matrix $A = \begin{bmatrix} 1 & 2 & 3 & 4 \\ 2 & 4 & 4 & 5 \\ 3 & 6 & 5 & 7 \end{bmatrix}$ there is no restriction on $\vec{b} \in R^3$ for the system $A\vec{x} = \vec{b}$ to be solvable. This means that $\mathcal{C}_A = \mathcal{R}^3$, so that, dim $\mathcal{C}_A = 3$. This is part 1 of Exercise(4.6). In this case the equation $A^T \vec{y} = \vec{0}$ has only $\vec{y} = \vec{0}$ as a solution. Reason: dim $\mathcal{N}(A^T) = m - $ dim $\mathcal{C}_A = 3 - 3 = 0$. This is part 3 of Exercise(4.6).

4.12 Exercises

Exercise 4.1 Decide whether the following are vector spaces. For those that are, find a basis.

1. $\mathcal{V} = \left\{ \begin{bmatrix} x_1 \\ x_2 \end{bmatrix} : x_2 = -x_1 \right\}$

2. $\mathcal{V} = \left\{ \begin{bmatrix} x_1 \\ x_2 \end{bmatrix} : x_2 = x_1 + 1 \right\}$

3. $\mathcal{V} = \left\{ \begin{bmatrix} x_1 \\ x_2 \\ x_3 \end{bmatrix} : x_1 + x_2 = 0, x_3 \in \mathcal{R} \right\}$

4. $\mathcal{V} = \left\{ \begin{bmatrix} x_1 \\ x_2 \\ 0 \end{bmatrix} : x_1 + x_2 = 1, \right\}$

5. $\mathcal{V} = \left\{ \begin{bmatrix} x_1 \\ x_1 + x_2 \\ x_2 \end{bmatrix} \quad x_1, x_2 \in \mathcal{R} \right\}$

6. $\mathcal{V} = \left\{ \begin{bmatrix} a_{11} & a_{12} \\ a_{21} & a_{22} \end{bmatrix} : \quad a_{11} + a_{22} = 0 \text{ and } a_{12}, a_{21} \in \mathcal{R} \right\}$

7. $\mathcal{V} = \left\{ \begin{bmatrix} a_{11} & a_{12} \\ a_{21} & a_{22} \end{bmatrix} : \quad a_{11} + a_{22} = 1 \text{ and } a_{12}, a_{21} \in \mathcal{R} \right\}$

Exercise 4.2 In Example(4.7) set containment (see (4.10) through (4.12)) was used to show

$$\mathcal{C}_A = \text{span} \left\{ \begin{bmatrix} 1 \\ 0 \\ -1 \end{bmatrix}, \begin{bmatrix} 0 \\ 1 \\ 2 \end{bmatrix} \right\} = \text{span} \left\{ \begin{bmatrix} 1 \\ 2 \\ 3 \end{bmatrix}, \begin{bmatrix} 2 \\ 3 \\ 4 \end{bmatrix} \right\}$$

Here is another approach. The equality means that a linear combination from the description of $\mathcal{C}_A$ on the left can be written in terms of a linear combination from the description of $\mathcal{C}_A$ on the right. In symbols, this means there are scalars $\alpha, \beta, \gamma,$ and δ so that

$$\alpha \begin{bmatrix} 1 \\ 0 \\ -1 \end{bmatrix} + \beta \begin{bmatrix} 0 \\ 1 \\ 2 \end{bmatrix} = \gamma \begin{bmatrix} 1 \\ 2 \\ 3 \end{bmatrix} + \delta \begin{bmatrix} 2 \\ 3 \\ 4 \end{bmatrix}.$$

1. Solve this for α and β in terms of γ and δ.

2. Why do you need to check that $-\alpha + 2\beta = 3\gamma + 4\delta$?

Exercise 4.3 Let a_{33} be a parameter $A = \begin{bmatrix} 1 & 2 & 3 \\ 2 & 5 & 4 \\ 1 & 3 & a_{33} \end{bmatrix}$.

1. Let $a_{33} = 2$. Show that the columns of A form an independent set of vectors.

2. What is a basis for the $\mathcal{C}_A$? What is the dimension of $\mathcal{C}_A$?

3. Why does this imply that the problem $A\vec{x} = \vec{b}$ is consistent for every $\vec{b} \in \mathcal{R}^3$?

4. If $a_{33} = 1$ it follows from the equation in (4.10) that dim $\mathcal{C}_A = 2$. Find a vector
$\vec{b} = \begin{bmatrix} b_1 \\ b_2 \\ b_3 \end{bmatrix}$ so that the problem $A\vec{x} = \vec{b}$ is not solvable. See the discussion following the display in (4.9).

Exercise 4.4 Let $A = \begin{bmatrix} 1 & 2 & 3 \\ 2 & 5 & 4 \\ 1 & 3 & 1 \end{bmatrix}$ and $\vec{x}_r = \dfrac{1}{27}\begin{bmatrix} -1 \\ -46 \\ 85 \end{bmatrix}$.

1. Verify that $A\vec{x}_r = \begin{bmatrix} 6 \\ 4 \\ -2 \end{bmatrix}$.

2. Here is a way to construct $\vec{x}_r$. Define $\vec{x}_r = \begin{bmatrix} \alpha \\ \beta \\ \gamma \end{bmatrix}$. It follows from Example(4.13) that
the $\mathcal{N}(A) = \text{span}\,\{\vec{n}\} = \text{span}\left\{\begin{bmatrix} -7 \\ 2 \\ 1 \end{bmatrix}\right\}$ and from Theorem(4.28) that $R_A = \mathcal{N}(A)^{\perp}$
so that the dot product $\vec{n} \cdot \vec{x}_r = 0$. Solve this for γ and put this result in $\vec{x}_r$.

3. Substitute the $\vec{x}_r$ from part 2 into $A\vec{x}_r = \begin{bmatrix} 6 \\ 4 \\ -2 \end{bmatrix}$ and solve this for α and β.

Exercise 4.5 In the Example(4.16) set $a_{22} = 5$ so the system reads

$$A\vec{x} = \begin{bmatrix} 1 & 2 & 3 \\ 2 & 5 & 4 \end{bmatrix}\begin{bmatrix} x_1 \\ x_2 \\ x_3 \end{bmatrix} = \begin{bmatrix} b_1 \\ b_2 \end{bmatrix}.$$

1. Show that the general solution of the system is

$$\begin{bmatrix} x_1 \\ x_2 \\ x_3 \end{bmatrix} = x_3\begin{bmatrix} -7 \\ 2 \\ 1 \end{bmatrix} + \begin{bmatrix} 5b_1 - 2b_2 \\ b_2 - 2b_1 \\ 0 \end{bmatrix} = \vec{x}_h + \vec{x}_p .$$

2. Show that $A\vec{x}_h = \vec{0}$ and $A\vec{x}_p = \vec{b}$. Conclude that the null space $\mathcal{N}(A) = \text{span}\left\{ \begin{bmatrix} -7 \\ 2 \\ 1 \end{bmatrix} \right\}$.

3. Is there any restriction on the components of $\vec{b}$ in the general solution? What is the column space $\mathcal{C}_A$?

4. Since, from part 4, $\dim \mathcal{C}_A = 2$ the columns of A are a dependent set. Find α_1, α_2 and α_3 so that

$$\alpha_1 \begin{bmatrix} 1 \\ 2 \end{bmatrix} + \alpha_2 \begin{bmatrix} 2 \\ 5 \end{bmatrix} + \alpha_3 \begin{bmatrix} 3 \\ 4 \end{bmatrix} = \begin{bmatrix} 0 \\ 0 \end{bmatrix}.$$

How are the scalars $\alpha_j, j = 1, 2, 3$ related to $\mathcal{N}(A)$?

Exercise 4.6 If the a_{34} entry for the matrix A of Example(4.18) is changed to $a_{34} = 7$ them the linear system reads

$$A\vec{x} = \begin{bmatrix} 1 & 2 & 3 & 4 \\ 2 & 4 & 4 & 5 \\ 3 & 6 & 5 & 7 \end{bmatrix} \begin{bmatrix} x_1 \\ x_2 \\ x_3 \\ x_4 \end{bmatrix} = \begin{bmatrix} b_1 \\ b_2 \\ b_3 \end{bmatrix}$$

1. Show that the row reduced form is

$$\begin{bmatrix} A \mid \vec{b} \end{bmatrix} \sim \begin{bmatrix} 1 & 2 & 3 & 4 & b_1 \\ 0 & 0 & -2 & -3 & b_2 - 2b_1 \\ 0 & 0 & 0 & 1 & b_3 - 2b_2 + b_1 \end{bmatrix}.$$

Compare this to (4.23). Here the value of $b_3 - 2b_2 + b_1$ is unrestricted. Why does this imply $\mathcal{C}_A = \mathcal{R}^3$?

2. Show that the general solution is

$$\vec{x} = \begin{bmatrix} x_1 \\ x_2 \\ x_3 \\ x_4 \end{bmatrix} = \left\{ x_2 \begin{bmatrix} -2 \\ 1 \\ 0 \\ 0 \end{bmatrix} \right\} + \begin{bmatrix} (b_3 + b_2 - 3b_1)/2 \\ 0 \\ (-3b_3 + 5b_2 - b_1)/2 \\ b_3 - 2b_2 + b_1 \end{bmatrix} = \{\vec{x}_h\} + \vec{x}_p.$$

It follows that $\mathcal{N}(A) = \text{span}\left\{ \begin{bmatrix} -2 \\ 1 \\ 0 \\ 0 \end{bmatrix} \right\}$. Compare this to the solution in (4.24).

3. Define $B = A^T = \begin{bmatrix} 1 & 2 & 3 \\ 2 & 4 & 6 \\ 3 & 4 & 5 \\ 4 & 5 & 7 \end{bmatrix}$ and show that

$$\mathcal{C}_B = \text{span}\left\{ \begin{bmatrix} 1 \\ 2 \\ 0 \\ 0 \end{bmatrix}, \begin{bmatrix} 0 \\ 0 \\ 1 \\ 0 \end{bmatrix}, \begin{bmatrix} 0 \\ 0 \\ 0 \\ 1 \end{bmatrix} \right\} \quad \text{and} \quad \mathcal{N}(B) = \text{span}\left\{ \begin{bmatrix} 0 \\ 0 \\ 0 \end{bmatrix} \right\}.$$

4. Verify that $\mathcal{C}_B^{\perp} = \mathcal{N}_A$.

Exercise 4.7 Let $A = \begin{bmatrix} 1 & 2 & 3 & 4 \\ 2 & 4 & 4 & 5 \\ 3 & 6 & 5 & 6 \end{bmatrix}$ be the matrix from (4.22) of Example(4.18).

1. Use the discussion following (4.27) to see the first equality

$$\mathcal{C}_A = \text{span}\left\{ \begin{bmatrix} 1 \\ 2 \\ 3 \end{bmatrix}, \begin{bmatrix} 3 \\ 4 \\ 5 \end{bmatrix} \right\} = \text{span}\left\{ \begin{bmatrix} 1 \\ 0 \\ -1 \end{bmatrix}, \begin{bmatrix} 0 \\ 1 \\ 2 \end{bmatrix} \right\}$$

and the method of Exercise(4.2) to see the second equality.

2. Similarly, use the method of Exercise(4.2) to see that

$$\text{span}\left\{ \begin{bmatrix} 1 \\ 2 \\ 0 \\ -1/2 \end{bmatrix}, \begin{bmatrix} 0 \\ 0 \\ 1 \\ 3/2 \end{bmatrix} \right\} = \text{span}\left\{ \begin{bmatrix} 1 \\ 2 \\ 3 \\ 4 \end{bmatrix}, \begin{bmatrix} 2 \\ 4 \\ 4 \\ 5 \end{bmatrix} \right\} = \text{span}\left\{ \begin{bmatrix} 1 \\ 2 \\ 3 \\ 4 \end{bmatrix}, \begin{bmatrix} 0 \\ 0 \\ -2 \\ -3 \end{bmatrix} \right\}.$$

Another way to see the set of equalities is as follows. The first equality is (4.29) and the second equality comes from the lines following (4.29). Hence any one of the sets define a basis for $R_A = \mathcal{C}_B$.

Exercise 4.8 Let A be the matrix in Exercise(4.7). By proceeding as in Exercise(4.4) here is an outline of the procedure to construct the vector $\vec{x}_r$ in

$$A\vec{x}_r \equiv \begin{bmatrix} 1 & 2 & 3 & 4 \\ 2 & 4 & 4 & 5 \\ 3 & 6 & 5 & 6 \end{bmatrix} \left(\frac{1}{66} \begin{bmatrix} -5 \\ -10 \\ 9 \\ 16 \end{bmatrix} \right) = \begin{bmatrix} 1 \\ 1 \\ 1 \end{bmatrix}.$$

1. Define $\vec{x}_r = \begin{bmatrix} \alpha \\ \beta \\ \gamma \\ \delta \end{bmatrix} \in R_A$. The decomposition $R_A^\perp = \mathcal{N}(A) = \text{span}\left\{ \begin{bmatrix} -2 \\ 1 \\ 0 \\ 0 \end{bmatrix}, \begin{bmatrix} 1/2 \\ 0 \\ -3/2 \\ 1 \end{bmatrix} \right\}$

gives the two equations

$$\vec{x}_r \cdot \begin{bmatrix} -2 \\ 1 \\ 0 \\ 0 \end{bmatrix} = -2\alpha + \beta = 0 \quad \text{and} \quad \vec{x}_r \cdot \begin{bmatrix} 1/2 \\ 0 \\ -3/2 \\ 1 \end{bmatrix} = \frac{1}{2}\alpha - \frac{3}{2}\gamma + \delta = 0.$$

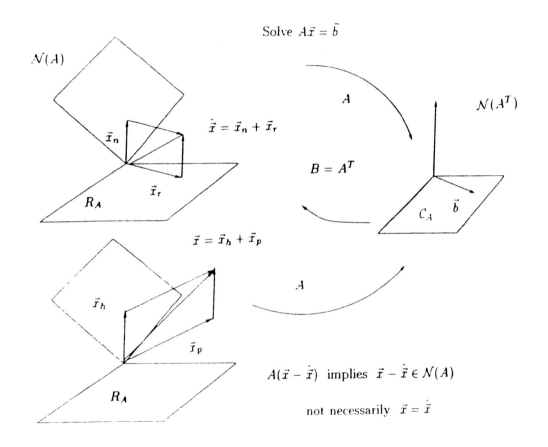

Solve $A\vec{x} = \vec{b}$

$\mathcal{N}(A)$

$\vec{x}_n$

$\vec{x} = \vec{x}_n + \vec{x}_r$

$\vec{x}_r$

R_A

A

$B = A^T$

$\mathcal{N}(A^T)$

C_A

$\vec{b}$

$\vec{x} = \vec{x}_h + \vec{x}_p$

$\vec{x}_h$

$\vec{x}_p$

A

R_A

$A(\vec{x} - \dot{\vec{x}})$ implies $\vec{x} - \dot{\vec{x}} \in \mathcal{N}(A)$

not necessarily $\vec{x} = \dot{\vec{x}}$

2. Substitute the result from part 1 into $\vec{x}_r$ to write $\vec{x}_r = \begin{bmatrix} \alpha \\ 2\alpha \\ \gamma \\ -(1/2)\alpha + (3/2)\gamma \end{bmatrix}$ and

evaluate $A\vec{x}_r = \vec{b}$ to find

$$A\vec{x}_r = \alpha \begin{bmatrix} 3 \\ 15/2 \\ 12 \end{bmatrix} + \gamma \begin{bmatrix} 9 \\ 23/2 \\ 14 \end{bmatrix} = \begin{bmatrix} 1 \\ 1 \\ 1 \end{bmatrix}.$$

3. Solve the first two equations in part 2 to find that $\alpha = -\dfrac{5}{66}$ and $\gamma = \dfrac{9}{66}$.

4. Check that $12\alpha + 14\gamma = 1$. This shows that $A\vec{x}_r = \begin{bmatrix} 1 \\ 1 \\ 1 \end{bmatrix}$. Substitute α and γ into the result of part 1 to find the desired row vector.

5. Show that

$$\vec{x} - \widehat{\vec{x}} = \begin{bmatrix} -1/2 \\ 0 \\ 1/2 \\ 0 \end{bmatrix} - (1/66) \begin{bmatrix} -5 \\ -10 \\ 9 \\ 16 \end{bmatrix} = (1/66) \begin{bmatrix} -28 \\ 10 \\ 24 \\ -16 \end{bmatrix} \in \mathcal{N}(A).$$

The above figure is an attempt to illustrate that $\vec{x} - \widehat{\vec{x}} \in \mathcal{N}(A)$.

Exercise 4.9 Assume A is a matrix with $\mathcal{C}_A = \operatorname{span}\{\vec{v}_1, \vec{v}_2, \vec{v}_3\}$ and $\mathcal{N}(A) = \operatorname{span}\{\vec{w}_1, \vec{w}_2\}$ where

$$\vec{v}_1 = \begin{bmatrix} 1 \\ 0 \\ 1 \\ 2 \end{bmatrix}, \vec{v}_2 = \begin{bmatrix} 1 \\ 1 \\ 1 \\ 2 \end{bmatrix}, \vec{v}_3 = \begin{bmatrix} 1 \\ 1 \\ 0 \\ 1 \end{bmatrix} \text{ and } \vec{w}_1 = \begin{bmatrix} 1 \\ -1 \\ 1 \\ -1 \\ 0 \end{bmatrix} \vec{w}_2 = \begin{bmatrix} 1 \\ -2 \\ 1 \\ 0 \\ 1 \end{bmatrix}.$$

1. The size of the matrix A is _____. Given that the $\vec{v}_j, j = 1, 2, 3$ are independent (you should check this) the dimension of $\mathcal{C}_A$ is _____. Theorem(4.20) then guarantees that the dimension of R_A is _____. Hence the dimension theorem implies that the dimension of $\mathcal{N}(A^T)$ is _____ and that the dimension of $\mathcal{N}(A)$ is _____.

2. Assume that $\vec{b} \in \mathcal{C}_A$ and $\vec{x}$ satisfies $A\vec{x} = \vec{b}$. How many free variables are in $\vec{x}_h$? Can you conclude that $\vec{x}_p \in R_A$?

3. Are there any **non-zero** solutions of $A^T \vec{w} = \vec{0}$?

Exercise 4.10 Add the two vectors $\vec{v}_4 = \begin{bmatrix} 1 \\ 0 \\ 0 \\ 1 \end{bmatrix}$ and $\vec{v}_5 = \begin{bmatrix} 0 \\ 1 \\ 1 \\ 1 \end{bmatrix}$ to the three vectors $\vec{v}_1, \vec{v}_2$ and $\vec{v}_3$ in Exercise(4.9) and form the matrix $A = [\vec{v}_1\ \vec{v}_2\ \vec{v}_3\ \vec{v}_4\ \vec{v}_5]$. Row reduction gives

$$[A \mid \vec{b}\,] = \begin{bmatrix} 1 & 1 & 1 & 1 & 0 & b_1 \\ 0 & 1 & 1 & 0 & 1 & b_2 \\ 1 & 1 & 0 & 0 & 1 & b_3 \\ 2 & 2 & 1 & 1 & 1 & b_4 \end{bmatrix}$$

$$\sim \begin{bmatrix} 1 & 1 & 1 & 1 & 0 & b_1 \\ 0 & 1 & 1 & 0 & 1 & b_2 \\ 0 & 0 & -1 & -1 & 1 & b_3 - b_1 \\ 0 & 0 & 0 & 0 & 0 & b_4 - b_1 - b_3 \end{bmatrix}.$$

1. Find a basis for span $\{\vec{v}_1\ \vec{v}_2\ \vec{v}_3\ \vec{v}_4\ \vec{v}_5\}$, that is, find a basis for $\mathcal{C}_A$. It is easiest to use the method outlined in the lines following (4.27). How is this connected to $b_4 - b_1 - b_3 = 0$? Use this result and the identity $\mathcal{N}(A^T) = \mathcal{C}_A^{\perp}$ to find $\mathcal{N}(A^T)$.

2. If $\vec{b} \in \mathcal{C}_A$, show that the solution of $A\vec{x} = \vec{b}$ is given by

$$\vec{x} = x_4 \begin{bmatrix} 1 \\ -1 \\ 1 \\ -1 \\ 0 \end{bmatrix} + x_5 \begin{bmatrix} 1 \\ -2 \\ 1 \\ 0 \\ 1 \end{bmatrix} + \begin{bmatrix} b_1 - b_2 \\ b_3 + b_2 - b_1 \\ b_1 - b_3 \\ 0 \\ 0 \end{bmatrix} = \vec{x}_h + \vec{x}_p.$$

3. How many free variables are in $\vec{x}_h$? Is the vector $\vec{x}_p \in R_A$?

Exercise 4.11 Let $\mathcal{V} = \mathrm{span}\left\{ \begin{bmatrix} 1 \\ 1 \end{bmatrix} \right\} = \mathrm{span}\{\vec{v}\}$ and $\mathcal{W} = \mathrm{span}\left\{ \begin{bmatrix} 1 \\ 1 \\ 1 \end{bmatrix}, \begin{bmatrix} 1 \\ 0 \\ -1 \end{bmatrix} \right\} = \mathrm{span}\{\vec{w}_1, \vec{w}_2\}$

1. Find $\mathcal{V}^{\perp}$. Write an arbitrary vector $\vec{x} = \begin{bmatrix} x_1 \\ x_2 \end{bmatrix} = \alpha\vec{v} + \beta\vec{v}^{\perp}$. That is find α and β in terms of x_1 and x_2.

2. Find $\mathcal{W}^{\perp}$. Write an arbitrary vector

$$\vec{x} = \begin{bmatrix} x_1 \\ x_2 \\ x_3 \end{bmatrix} = (\alpha\vec{w}_1 + \beta\vec{w}_2) + \gamma\vec{w}^{\perp}.$$

That is find α, β and γ in terms of x_1, x_2 and x_3. One method is to write out the matrix form of the displayed equation and invert the matrix to find α, β and γ. Alternatively, find α by taking the dot product of both sides of the displayed equation with $\vec{w}_1$. Proceed similarly for β and γ.

Exercise 4.12 Let $\mathcal{V} \subseteq \mathcal{R}^n$ be a vector subspace of $\mathcal{R}^n$. Show that the **orthogonal complement**

$$\mathcal{V}^{\perp} = \{\vec{u} : \vec{u} \cdot \vec{v} = \vec{u}^T\vec{v} = 0 \text{ for every } \vec{v} \in \mathcal{V}\}$$

is a subspace of $\mathcal{R}^n$.

1. Since $\mathcal{V}^{\perp} \subseteq \mathcal{R}^n$ it follows from Definition(4.4) that one only needs to show that $\mathcal{V}^{\perp}$ is closed with respect to addition and scalar multiplication. This means that if $\vec{u} \in \mathcal{V}^{\perp}$ and $\vec{\tilde{u}} \in \mathcal{V}^{\perp}$ then $\alpha\vec{u} + \beta\vec{\tilde{u}} \in \mathcal{V}^{\perp}$ where $\alpha \in \mathcal{R}$ and $\beta \in \mathcal{R}$ are arbitrary scalars.

2. Why is $\vec{0} \in \mathcal{V}^{\perp}$ (recall Definition(1.9))?

3. If $\mathcal{V} = \{\vec{0}\}$ (the trivial vector space), what is $\mathcal{V}^{\perp}$?

Exercise 4.13 Define $A = \begin{bmatrix} 1 & 1 & 0 \\ 0 & 1 & 1 \end{bmatrix}$ and $P = \begin{bmatrix} 1 & 2 & 3 \\ 1 & 1 & 1 \\ 1 & 2 & 3 \end{bmatrix}$ so that $AP = \begin{bmatrix} 2 & 3 & 4 \\ 2 & 3 & 4 \end{bmatrix}$.

1. Show that $\mathcal{C}_{AP} = \text{span}\left\{ \begin{bmatrix} 1 \\ 1 \end{bmatrix} \right\} \subset \mathcal{C}_A = \text{span}\left\{ \begin{bmatrix} 1 \\ 0 \end{bmatrix}, \begin{bmatrix} 0 \\ 1 \end{bmatrix} \right\} = R^2$ and conclude that $\text{rank}(AP) \leq \text{rank}(A)$.

2. Replace P by the invertible $\hat{P} = \begin{bmatrix} 1 & 2 & 3 \\ 1 & 1 & 1 \\ 1 & 2 & 4 \end{bmatrix}$ and find $\mathcal{C}_{A\hat{P}}$. Conclude that $\mathcal{C}_{A\hat{P}} = \mathcal{C}_A$.

and that $\text{rank}(A\hat{P}) = \text{rank}(A)$

Here is the general version of parts 1, 2 and 3. Let A be $m \times n$ and P be $n \times n$. If $\vec{b} \in \mathcal{C}_{AP}$ then there exists a $\vec{x} \in R^n$ so that $(AP)\vec{x} = A(P\vec{x}) \equiv A\vec{y} = \vec{b}$. The last equality implies that the problem $A\vec{y} = \vec{b}$ is solvable, namely by $\vec{y} = P\vec{x}$. This is the statement that $\vec{b} \in \mathcal{C}_A$. The discussion began with the assumption that $\vec{b} \in \mathcal{C}_{AP}$ and concluded with $\vec{b} \in \mathcal{C}_A$. This means that $\mathcal{C}_{AP} \subset \mathcal{C}_A$.

For the reverse inclusion for invertible P in part 3, assume $\vec{b} \in \mathcal{C}_A$ which means there is an $n-$vector $\vec{y}$ so that $A\vec{y} = \vec{b}$. Since P is invertible the identity $\vec{x} = P^{-1}\vec{y}$ is uniquely solvable, namely by $\vec{y} = P\vec{x}$ so that $A\vec{y} = AP\vec{x} = \vec{b}$ which shows that $\vec{b} \in \mathcal{C}_{AP}$ so that $\mathcal{C}_A \subset \mathcal{C}_{AP}$. Coupled with the reverse inclusion in the introduction to the problem one concludes that $\mathcal{C}_{AP} = \mathcal{C}_A$ so that $\text{rank}(PA) = \text{rank}(A)$ for invertible P.

Exercise 4.14 Let $B = A^T = \begin{bmatrix} 1 & 0 \\ 1 & 1 \\ 0 & 1 \end{bmatrix}$ and $Q = P^T = \begin{bmatrix} 1 & 1 & 1 \\ 2 & 1 & 2 \\ 3 & 1 & 3 \end{bmatrix}$

1. Show that $\mathcal{C}_{QB} = \text{span}\left\{ \begin{bmatrix} 2 \\ 3 \\ 4 \end{bmatrix} \right\}$ and $\mathcal{C}_B = \text{span}\left\{ \begin{bmatrix} 1 \\ 1 \\ 0 \end{bmatrix}, \begin{bmatrix} 0 \\ 1 \\ 1 \end{bmatrix} \right\}$. Conclude that

$\mathcal{C}_{QB}$ is not contained in $\mathcal{C}_B$. This requires showing that vector $[\, 2 \ 3 \ 4 \,]^T$ is not a linear combination of the two vectors $[\, 1 \ 1 \ 0 \,]^T$ and $[\, 0 \ 1 \ 1 \,]^T$. However, it is the case that the $\text{rank}(QB) = 1 \leq \text{rank}(B) = 2$. See Exercise(4.13).

2. Let $\hat{Q} = \hat{P}^T = \begin{bmatrix} 1 & 1 & 1 \\ 2 & 1 & 2 \\ 3 & 1 & 4 \end{bmatrix}$ and show that $\mathcal{C}_{\hat{Q}B} = \text{span}\left\{ \begin{bmatrix} 2 \\ 3 \\ 4 \end{bmatrix}, \begin{bmatrix} 2 \\ 3 \\ 5 \end{bmatrix} \right\}$. So in this

case, $\hat{Q}$ is invertible, $\text{rank}(QB) = \text{rank}(B)$.

Here is the general version of parts 1 and 2. If B be $m \times n$ and Q be $m \times m$ it is the case that $\text{rank}(QB) \leq \text{rank}(B)$. Consider the calculation

$$\begin{aligned} \text{rank}(QB) &= \text{rank}[(QB)^T] & \text{Theorem(4.20)} \\ &= \text{rank}(B^T Q^T) & \text{from part 3 of Theorem(3.7)} \end{aligned}$$

$$
\begin{aligned}
&= \operatorname{rank}(AP) \quad \text{identify } B^T = A \text{ and } Q^T = P \\
&\leq \operatorname{rank}(A) \quad \text{from part 1 of Exercise(4.13)} \\
&= \operatorname{rank}(B^T) \quad \text{identify } B^T = A \\
&= \operatorname{rank}(B) \quad \text{Theorem(4.20)}
\end{aligned}
$$

If Q is invertible, the inequality is an equality by part 2 of Exercise(4.13).

Exercise 4.15 Let $A = \begin{bmatrix} 1 & 1 & 0 \\ 0 & 1 & 1 \end{bmatrix}$ so that $A^T A = \begin{bmatrix} 1 & 1 & 0 \\ 1 & 2 & 1 \\ 0 & 1 & 1 \end{bmatrix}$.

1. Show that $\mathcal{N}(A) = \mathcal{N}(A^T A)$. Use part 1 and the Dimension Theorem(4.22) to show that $\operatorname{rank}(A^T A) = \operatorname{rank}(A) = 2$.

2. Now let $B = \begin{bmatrix} 1 & 0 \\ 1 & 1 \\ 0 & 1 \end{bmatrix}$ so that $B^T B = \begin{bmatrix} 2 & 1 \\ 1 & 2 \end{bmatrix}$ and show that $\mathcal{N}(B) = \mathcal{N}(B^T B)$.

This is part 1 for $B = A^T$.

Here is the general version of parts 1 and 2. If A be an $m \times n$ matrix then $\mathcal{N}(A) = \mathcal{N}(A^T A)$ and the matrix $A^T A$ is invertible if and only if the columns of A are linearly independent.

Assume $\vec{x} \in \mathcal{N}(A) \subset \mathcal{R}^n$ so that $A\vec{x} = \vec{0}_{m \times 1}$. The matrix A^T is an . Multiply both sides of this equality by the $n \times m$ matrix A^T to find $A^T(A\vec{x}) = (A^T A)\vec{x} = A^T\vec{0} = \vec{0}$. This is the statement that $\vec{x} \in \mathcal{N}(A^T A)$. The reverse inclusion proceeds as follows: assume $\vec{x} \in \mathcal{N}(A^T A)$ so that $(A^T A)\vec{x} = A^T(A\vec{x}) = \vec{0}$. This is the statement that $A\vec{x} \in \mathcal{N}(A^T)$. The vector $A\vec{x} \in \mathcal{C}_A$ since, by definition of matrix multiplication, the vector $A\vec{x}$ is a linear combination of the columns of A. Hence, $A\vec{x}$ is in both $\mathcal{N}(A^T)$ and $\mathcal{C}_A$ and the orthogonal decomposition Theorem(4.28) implies $A\vec{x} = \vec{0}$ or $\vec{x} \in \mathcal{N}(A)$. This completes the reverse inclusion $\mathcal{N}(A^T A) \subset \mathcal{N}(A)$ so that $\mathcal{N}(A) = \mathcal{N}(A^T A)$. Part 2 follows from part 1 with A replaced by A^T.

The invertibility statement follows from the special case of the Dimension Theorem(4.22) with the matrix A mentioned in the special case replaced by the $n \times n$ matrix $(A^T A)$.

Exercise 4.16 The Gram-Schmidt Process and Projection onto a subspace:

1. Let $\{\vec{w}_1, \vec{w}_2\}$ be given independent vectors and define

$$
\begin{aligned}
\vec{v}_1 &= \vec{w}_1 \\
\vec{v}_2 &= \vec{w}_2 - \left(\frac{\vec{w}_2 \cdot \vec{v}_1}{||\vec{v}_1||^2} \right) \vec{v}_1.
\end{aligned}
$$

Show that $\vec{v}_1 \cdot \vec{v}_2 = 0$. The vector $\dfrac{\vec{w}_2 \cdot \vec{v}_1}{||\vec{v}_1||^2} \vec{v}_1 = \operatorname{proj}_{\vec{v}_1}(\vec{w}_2)$ is the projection of $\vec{w}_2$ onto $\vec{v}_1$ (see Figure 1.5 and Definition(1.11)). The coefficient $\dfrac{\vec{w}_2 \cdot \vec{v}_1}{||\vec{v}_1||^2}$ is the multiple of $\vec{v}_1$, which forces the vector $\vec{w}_2 - \left(\dfrac{\vec{w}_2 \cdot \vec{v}_1}{||\vec{v}_1||^2}\right) \vec{v}_1$ to be orthogonal to $\vec{v}_1$. This is the calculation done in Definition(1.11).

2. Let $\mathcal{V}$ be an r–dimensional subspace of $\mathcal{R}^n$ and let $\{\vec{w}_1, \vec{w}_2, \ldots, \vec{w}_r\}$ where $\vec{w}_j \in \mathcal{R}^n, j = 1, 2, \ldots, r$ be a basis for $\mathcal{V}$. Define the sequence of vectors:

$$\left. \begin{aligned} \vec{v}_1 &= \vec{w}_1 \\[2ex] \vec{v}_2 &= \vec{w}_2 - \left(\frac{\vec{w}_2 \cdot \vec{v}_1}{||\vec{v}_1||^2}\right) \vec{v}_1 \\[2ex] \vec{v}_3 &= \vec{w}_3 - \left(\frac{\vec{w}_3 \cdot \vec{v}_1}{||\vec{v}_1||^2}\right) \vec{v}_1 - \left(\frac{\vec{w}_3 \cdot \vec{v}_2}{||\vec{v}_2||^2}\right) \vec{v}_2 \end{aligned} \right\} \tag{4.45}$$

It follows from the first two formulas that the span of $\{\vec{v}_1, \vec{v}_2\}$ is the same as the span of $\{\vec{w}_1, \vec{w}_2\}$ and part 1 shows that $\vec{v}_1 \cdot \vec{v}_2 = 0$, so the first two elements of the base for $\mathcal{V}$ have been replaced with an orthogonal pair of vectors. Show that $\vec{v}_1 \cdot \vec{v}_3 = 0$ and $\vec{v}_2 \cdot \vec{v}_3 = 0$. In general assume that $\vec{v}_{r-1}$ has been defined and set

$$\vec{v}_r = \vec{w}_r - \left(\frac{\vec{w}_r \cdot \vec{v}_1}{||\vec{v}_1||^2}\right) \vec{v}_1 - \left(\frac{\vec{w}_r \cdot \vec{v}_2}{||\vec{v}_2||^2}\right) \vec{v}_2 - \cdots - \left(\frac{\vec{w}_r \cdot \vec{v}_{r-1}}{||\vec{v}_{r-1}||^2}\right) \vec{v}_{r-1}. \tag{4.46}$$

The formula shows that

$$\mathcal{V} = \text{span}\{\vec{w}_1, \vec{w}_2, \cdots, \vec{w}_r\} = \text{span}\{\vec{v}_1, \vec{v}_2, \cdots, \vec{v}_r\}.$$

To see that $\vec{v}_i \cdot \vec{v}_j = 0$ if $i \neq j$ and $i, j \leq r$ proceeds by induction. The statement (from Exercise(3.7), part 3) for $S(r)$ is that

$$\text{span}\{\vec{w}_1, \vec{w}_2, \cdots, \vec{w}_{r+1}\} = \text{span}\{\vec{v}_1, \vec{v}_2, \cdots, \vec{v}_{r+1}\}$$

and $\vec{v}_j \cdot \vec{v}_i = 0$ for $i \neq j$ and $i, j \leq r + 1$. The statement $S(1)$ reads $\text{span}\{\vec{w}_1, \vec{w}_2,\} = \text{span}\{\vec{v}_1, \vec{v}_2\}$ and $\vec{v}_1 \cdot \vec{v}_2 = 0$ which is true from part 1 above. Now show that the validity of $S(r)$ implies the validity of $S(r + 1)$. Replacing r by $r + 2$ in equation (4.46) yields

$$\begin{aligned} \vec{v}_{r+2} &= \vec{w}_{r+2} - \left(\frac{\vec{w}_{r+2} \cdot \vec{v}_1}{||\vec{v}_1||^2}\right) \vec{v}_1 - \left(\frac{\vec{w}_{r+2} \cdot \vec{v}_2}{||\vec{v}_2||^2}\right) \vec{v}_2 - \cdots - \left(\frac{\vec{w}_{r+2} \cdot \vec{v}_{r+1}}{||\vec{v}_{r+1}||^2}\right) \vec{v}_{r+1} \\[1ex] &= \vec{w}_{r+2} - \sum_{i=1}^{r+1} \left(\frac{\vec{w}_{r+2} \cdot \vec{v}_i}{||\vec{v}_i||^2}\right) \vec{v}_i \\[1ex] &= \vec{w}_{r+2} - \left(\frac{\vec{w}_{r+2} \cdot \vec{v}_{r+1}}{||\vec{v}_{r+1}||^2}\right) \vec{v}_{r+1} - \sum_{i=1}^{k} \left(\frac{\vec{w}_{r+2} \cdot \vec{v}_i}{||\vec{v}_i||^2}\right) \vec{v}_i. \end{aligned}$$

This formula shows that $\vec{v}_{r+2} \in \text{span}\{\vec{w}_1, \vec{w}_2, \cdots, \vec{w}_{r+2}\}$. Now show that $\vec{v}_j \cdot \vec{v}_{r+2} = 0$ for every $j \leq r + 1$. The inductive hypothesis implies $\vec{v}_j \cdot \vec{v}_i = 0$ for $i \neq j$ and

$i, j \leq r + 1$. Now for all $j \leq r$

$$
\begin{aligned}
\vec{v}_j \cdot \vec{v}_{r+2} &= \vec{v}_j \cdot \vec{w}_{r+2} - \left(\frac{\vec{w}_{r+2} \cdot \vec{v}_{r+1}}{||\vec{v}_{r+1}||^2} \right) \vec{v}_j \cdot \vec{v}_{r+1} - \sum_{i=1}^{r} \left(\frac{\vec{w}_{r+2} \cdot \vec{v}_i}{||\vec{v}_i||^2} \right) \vec{v}_j \cdot \vec{v}_i \\
&= \vec{v}_j \cdot \vec{w}_{r+2} - 0 - \left(\frac{\vec{w}_{r+2} \cdot \vec{v}_j}{||\vec{v}_j||^2} \right) \vec{v}_j \cdot \vec{v}_j \\
&= \vec{v}_j \cdot \vec{w}_{r+2} - \vec{w}_{r+2} \cdot \vec{v}_j = 0
\end{aligned}
$$

since $\vec{v}_j \cdot \vec{v}_j = ||\vec{v}_j||^2$ and $\vec{v}_j \cdot \vec{w}_{r+2} = \vec{w}_{r+2} \cdot \vec{v}_j$. Lastly, since $\vec{v}_i \cdot \vec{v}_{r+1} = 0$ for all $i \leq r$

$$
\begin{aligned}
\vec{v}_{r+1} \cdot \vec{v}_{r+2} &= \vec{v}_{r+1} \cdot \vec{w}_{r+2} - \left(\frac{\vec{w}_{r+2} \cdot \vec{v}_{r+1}}{||\vec{v}_{r+1}||^2} \right) \vec{v}_{r+1} \cdot \vec{v}_{r+1} \\
&= \vec{v}_{r+1} \cdot \vec{w}_{r+2} - \vec{w}_{r+2} \cdot \vec{v}_{r+1} = 0
\end{aligned}
$$

again since $\vec{v}_{r+1} \cdot \vec{v}_{r+1} = ||\vec{v}_{r+1}||^2$ and $\vec{v}_{r+1} \cdot \vec{w}_{r+2} = \vec{w}_{r+2} \cdot \vec{v}_{r+1}$. This process of replacing the base $\{\vec{w}_1, \vec{w}_2, \ldots, \vec{w}_r\}$ for $\mathcal{V}$ by the orthogonal base $\{\vec{v}_1, \vec{v}_2, \cdots, \vec{v}_r\}$ is called the **Gram-Schmidt Process**. In addition, if each $\vec{v}_j, j = 1, 2, \ldots, r$ is replaced by the unit vector $\vec{u}_j = \dfrac{\vec{v}_j}{||\vec{v}_j||}, j = 1, 2, \ldots, r$ then the original base for $\mathcal{V}$ has been replaced by the pairwise orthogonal unit vectors $\{\vec{u}_1, \vec{u}_2, \ldots, \vec{u}_r\}$. Any such base for a vector space is called an **orthonormal basis** for $\mathcal{V}$.

3. Define the two-dimensional vector space $\mathcal{V}_2 = \text{span}\{\vec{v}_1, \vec{v}_2\}$ where $\vec{v}_1$ and $\vec{v}_2$ are defined in (4.45) and set

$$
\text{proj}_{\mathcal{V}_2}(\vec{w}_3) = \left(\frac{\vec{w}_3 \cdot \vec{v}_1}{||\vec{v}_1||^2} \right) \vec{v}_1 + \left(\frac{\vec{w}_3 \cdot \vec{v}_2}{||\vec{v}_2||^2} \right) \vec{v}_2 \tag{4.47}
$$

The definition in (4.47) is the linear combination of the vectors $\vec{v}_1$ and $\vec{v}_2$ so that $\vec{w}_3 - \text{proj}_{\mathcal{V}_2}(\vec{w}_3)$ is perpendicular to both $\vec{v}_1$ and $\vec{v}_2$ and therefore to any linear combination of $\vec{v}_1$ and $\vec{v}_2$, that is, the vector $\vec{w}_3 - \text{proj}_{\mathcal{V}_2}(\vec{w}_3)$ is orthogonal to the subspace $\mathcal{V}_2$. Hence, $\text{proj}_{\mathcal{V}_2}(\vec{w}_3)$ is called the **projection of $\vec{w}_3$ onto the subspace $\mathcal{V}_2$**. More generally, let the vectors $\vec{v}_j, j = 1, 2, \ldots, r$ be constructed from $\vec{w}_j, j = 1, 2, \ldots, r$ as in equations (4.45) and (4.46) and define the vector

$$
\text{proj}_{\mathcal{V}_{r-1}}(\vec{w}_r) = \left(\frac{\vec{w}_r \cdot \vec{v}_1}{||\vec{v}_1||^2} \right) \vec{v}_1 + \left(\frac{\vec{w}_r \cdot \vec{v}_2}{||\vec{v}_2||^2} \right) \vec{v}_2 + \cdots + \left(\frac{\vec{w}_r \cdot \vec{v}_{r-1}}{||\vec{v}_{r-1}||^2} \right) \vec{v}_{r-1}. \tag{4.48}
$$

The vector $\text{proj}_{\mathcal{V}_{r-1}}(\vec{w}_r)$ is called **the projection of $\vec{w}_r$ onto the $(r-1)-$dimensional subspace $\mathcal{V}_{r-1} = \text{span}\{\vec{v}_1, \vec{v}_2, \ldots, \vec{v}_{r-1}\}$**.

4. The two independent vectors $\vec{w}_1 = \begin{bmatrix} 0 \\ 1 \\ 1 \end{bmatrix}$ and $\vec{w}_2 = \begin{bmatrix} 1 \\ 0 \\ 1 \end{bmatrix}$ span a two-dimensional subspace of $\mathcal{R}^3$. Apply the Gram-Schmidt to the two vectors to find the two orthogonal vectors $\vec{v}_1 = \begin{bmatrix} 0 \\ 1 \\ 1 \end{bmatrix}$ and $\vec{v}_2 = \dfrac{1}{2} \begin{bmatrix} 2 \\ -1 \\ 1 \end{bmatrix}$ and define $\mathcal{V}_2 = \text{span}\{\vec{v}_1, \vec{v}_2\}$. This

replacement of $\{\vec{w}_1, \vec{w}_2\}$ by the orthogonal pair $\{\vec{v}_1, \vec{v}_2\}$ plays an important role in part 2 of Example(5.14). Continue the Gram-Schmidt process with $\vec{w}_3 = \begin{bmatrix} 2 \\ 3 \\ 1 \end{bmatrix}$ and calculate

$$
\begin{aligned}
\vec{v}_3 &= \vec{w}_3 - \left[\left(\frac{\vec{w}_3 \cdot \vec{v}_1}{||\vec{v}_1||^2} \right) \vec{v}_1 + \left(\frac{\vec{w}_3 \cdot \vec{v}_2}{||\vec{v}_2||^2} \right) \vec{v}_2 \right] = \begin{bmatrix} 2 \\ 3 \\ 1 \end{bmatrix} - \left(\frac{4}{2} \begin{bmatrix} 0 \\ 1 \\ 1 \end{bmatrix} + \frac{1}{3} \begin{bmatrix} 2 \\ -1 \\ 1 \end{bmatrix} \right) \\
&= \vec{w}_3 - \text{proj}_{\mathcal{V}_2}(\vec{w}_3) = \begin{bmatrix} 2 \\ 3 \\ 1 \end{bmatrix} - \left(\frac{1}{3} \begin{bmatrix} 2 \\ 5 \\ 7 \end{bmatrix} \right) = \frac{4}{3} \begin{bmatrix} 1 \\ 1 \\ -1 \end{bmatrix}.
\end{aligned}
$$

So the independent basis $\{\vec{w}_1, \vec{w}_2, \vec{w}_3\}$ for $\mathcal{R}^3$ has been replaced by the orthogonal basis $\{\vec{v}_1, \vec{v}_2, \vec{v}_3\}$. Another way to think of this example is to write

$$\mathcal{R}^3 = \mathcal{V}_2 \oplus \mathcal{V}_2^{\perp} \quad \text{so from the above} \quad \mathcal{V}_2^{\perp} = \text{span}\{\vec{v}_3\}.$$

Let $\vec{w} \in \mathcal{R}^3$ be arbitrary and write

$$\vec{w} = \text{proj}_{\mathcal{V}_2}(\vec{w}) + (\vec{w} - \text{proj}_{\mathcal{V}_2}(\vec{w}))$$

where $\text{proj}_{\mathcal{V}_2}(\vec{w}) \in \mathcal{V}_2$ and $\vec{w} - \text{proj}_{\mathcal{V}_2}(\vec{w}) \in \mathcal{V}_2^{\perp}$. This is the decomposition mentioned in Theorem(4.26) and illustrated in equation (4.41) in Example(4.27).

Exercise 4.17 Least Squares Solutions: Define the 3×2 matrix system

$$A\vec{x} = [\, \vec{w}_1 \ \vec{w}_2 \,]\vec{x} = \begin{bmatrix} 0 & 1 \\ 1 & 0 \\ 1 & 1 \end{bmatrix} \begin{bmatrix} x_1 \\ x_2 \end{bmatrix} = \begin{bmatrix} 2 \\ 3 \\ 1 \end{bmatrix} = \vec{w}_3 \equiv \vec{b} \tag{4.49}$$

where the vectors $\vec{w}_j, j = 1, 2, 3$ are the vectors in part 4 of Exercise(4.16). It is straightforward to check that this system is inconsistent. Here is an alternative exploration for a vector $\vec{x}$ that "satisfies" equation (4.49).

1. Multiply equation (4.49) by A^T to find the matrix system

$$(A^T A)\vec{x} = \begin{bmatrix} 2 & 1 \\ 1 & 2 \end{bmatrix} \vec{x} = A^T \vec{b} = \begin{bmatrix} 4 \\ 3 \end{bmatrix}. \tag{4.50}$$

Find the unique solution $\vec{x} = \vec{x}_{ls}$ of the system $(A^T A)\vec{x} = A^T \vec{b}$. Since the columns of A are independent, Exercise(4.15) implies the matrix $A^T A$ is invertible so the solution is unique.

2. Write out $A\vec{x}_{ls} = x_1 \vec{w}_1 + x_2 \vec{w}_2$ where $\vec{x}_{ls} = \begin{bmatrix} x_1 \\ x_2 \end{bmatrix}$ is the unique solution found in part 1. Compare $A\vec{x}_{ls}$ to the vector $\text{proj}_{\mathcal{C}_A}(\vec{b}) = \text{proj}_{\mathcal{V}_2}(\vec{w}_3)$ in part 4 of Exercise(4.16). In

words, the problem $A\vec{x} = \vec{b}$ has been replaced with the problem $A\vec{x}_{ls} = \text{proj}_{\mathcal{C}_A}(\vec{b})$. This problem is consistent since $\vec{b}$ has been replaced by its projection onto the subspace $\mathcal{C}_A$. To check the consistency of the problem, row reduce the augmented system

$$[\, A \mid \text{proj}_{\mathcal{C}_A}(\vec{b}) \,] = \begin{bmatrix} 0 & 1 & 2/3 \\ 1 & 0 & 5/3 \\ 1 & 1 & 7/3 \end{bmatrix}.$$

3. Suppose the matrix A is $m \times n$, the vector $\vec{b}$ is $m \times 1$ and it is required to solve $A\vec{x} = \vec{b}$. If $\vec{b} \in \mathcal{C}_A$ this is a problem from Chapter Two. If not replace the system $A\vec{x} = \vec{b}$ by

$$(A^T A)\vec{x} = A^T \vec{b} \qquad \textbf{(Normal equations)} \tag{4.51}$$

and solve this for $\vec{x} = \vec{x}_{ls}$ which is called **a least squares solution** of the normal equations. This is always solvable since,

if $A\vec{x} = \vec{b}$ then $A^T(A\vec{x}) = (A^T A)\vec{x} = A^T \vec{b}$ or in terms of subspaces: $A^T \vec{b} \in \mathcal{C}_{A^T A}$.

If the columns of A are independent then as in part 1, the solution

$$\vec{x}_{ls} = (A^T A)^{-1} A^T \vec{b} \tag{4.52}$$

is unique and is called **the least squares solution** to the problem (4.51). The reason for this name is due to the inequality

$$||A\vec{x}_{ls} - \vec{b}||^2 \leq ||A\vec{x} - \vec{b}||^2 \text{ for every } \vec{x} \in \mathcal{R}^n. \tag{4.53}$$

The vector in the column space of A given by $\vec{c}_A = A\vec{x} - A\vec{x}_{ls} = A(\vec{x} - \vec{x}_{ls})$ is orthogonal to the error vector $\vec{r} = A\vec{x}_{ls} - \vec{b}$. Fill in the steps to understand the calculation of the dot product

$$\begin{aligned} \vec{c}_A \cdot \vec{r}_{ls} &= (A\vec{x} - A\vec{x}_{ls})^T \cdot (A\vec{x}_{ls} - \vec{b}) \\ &= (\vec{x} - \vec{x}_{ls})^T (A^T A\vec{x}_{ls} - A^T \vec{b}) = 0. \end{aligned}$$

since $\vec{x}_{ls}$ is a least squares solution it satisfies equation(4.51). Geometrically, the triangle with sides $\vec{c}_A$, $\vec{r}_{ls}$ and hypotenuse $A\vec{x} - \vec{b}$ is a right triangle so

$$||A\vec{x} - \vec{b}||^2 = ||A\vec{x}_{ls} - \vec{b}||^2 + ||A\vec{x} - A\vec{x}_{ls}||^2 \geq ||A\vec{x}_{ls} - \vec{b}||^2 \equiv ||\vec{r}_{ls}||^2$$

where the inequality follows since $||A\vec{x} - A\vec{x}_{ls}||^2 \geq 0$. The quantity $||\vec{r}_{ls}||$ is called **least squares error** in the approximation.

4. Find the least squares solution to the problem $A\vec{x} = \begin{bmatrix} 1 & 1 \\ 1 & 2 \\ 1 & 3 \end{bmatrix} \vec{x} = \begin{bmatrix} 1 \\ 3 \\ 5 \end{bmatrix}$. This problem is analogous to the situation from Example(2.5) of Chapter Two where the three equations in two unknowns have a unique solution (See Figure 2.5). This is

an illustration of an example where the given system is consistent $\vec{b} = \begin{bmatrix} 1 \\ 3 \\ 5 \end{bmatrix} \in \mathcal{C}_A$

and the least squares solution is the "traditional" solution. This is always the case. Reason: If $\vec{b} \in \mathcal{C}_A$ for the problem $A\vec{x} = \vec{b}$ what and where is $\text{proj}_{\mathcal{C}_A}(\vec{b})$?

5. Find the least squares solution to the problem to $A = \begin{bmatrix} 1 & 1 \\ 1 & 2 \\ 1 & 3 \end{bmatrix}$ $\vec{x} = \begin{bmatrix} 0 \\ 3 \\ 4 \end{bmatrix}$. The

matrix $A^T A$ is the same as in part 4. To see a geometric interpretation of the least squares error plot on the $x_1 - x_2$ axis the three ordered pairs $(1,0), (2,3)$ and $(3,4)$. Suppose it is required to pass a straight line $x_2 = b + m x_1$, "as best you can" through these three points. Substitute each of these points in the equation $y(x_1) \equiv x_2 = b + m x_1$ (for example, the first point gives $x_2 = 0 = b + m 1$). One finds three equations in the two unknowns b and m. The system is the same as the system in the first sentence so its solution for b and m is the same as what was found there. Define the three distances $d_j = \begin{cases} 0 - y(1), & j = 1 \\ 3 - y(2), & j = 2 \\ 4 - y(3), & j = 3 \end{cases}$. Compare $||\vec{r}_{ls}||^2$ (see part 3) to the quantity $q^2 = d_1^2 + d_2^2 + d_3^2$. (Hint: $||\vec{r}_{ls}||^2 = q^2$).

6. If the columns of A are dependent, then the system in (4.51) is consistent but there are infinitely many least squares solutions. Illustrate this sentence with the system $A\vec{x} = \begin{bmatrix} 1 & 1 \\ 1 & 1 \\ 1 & 1 \end{bmatrix}$ $\vec{x} = \begin{bmatrix} 1 \\ 3 \\ 5 \end{bmatrix}$. The solution of the normal equations (4.51), with x_2

selected as the free variable, can be written $\vec{x}_{ls}(x_2) = \begin{bmatrix} 3 - x_2 \\ x_2 \end{bmatrix}$. The squared length

of $\vec{x}_{ls}(x_2)$ is $||\vec{x}_{ls}(x_2)||^2 = (3 - x_2)^2 + x_2^2$ and is minimized at $x_2 = \dfrac{3}{2}$ (draw a graph of the

parabola $||\vec{x}_{ls}(x_2)||^2 = (3 - x_2)^2 + x_2^2$ to see this). Hence $\vec{x}_{ls}(3/2) = \begin{bmatrix} 3/2 \\ 3/2 \end{bmatrix}$ is, in the

family of least squared solutions, the solution of minimum norm. Finally, show that

the row space $R_A = \text{span}\left\{ \begin{bmatrix} 1 \\ 1 \end{bmatrix} \right\}$ so that the null space $\mathcal{N}(A) = \text{span}\left\{ \begin{bmatrix} 1 \\ -1 \end{bmatrix} \right\}$.

Find x_2 so that $\vec{x}_{ls}(x_2) = \begin{bmatrix} 3 - x_2 \\ x_2 \end{bmatrix}$ is orthogonal to $\mathcal{N}(A)$. This is always the

case. If the normal equations (4.51) have infinitely many solutions then the solution of minimum norm is orthogonal to the null space of A. This is the unique $\vec{x}_{ls}$ in the row space of $A^T A$. See the discussion following (4.44).

4.13 Sample Tests

4.13.1 Sample Test 1

Name_____   Date_____

1. For the matrix $A = \begin{bmatrix} 1 & 2 & 0 & 3 \\ 2 & 1 & 1 & 1 \\ 1 & -1 & 1 & -2 \end{bmatrix}$ the $\mathcal{C}_A = \text{span} \left\{ \begin{bmatrix} 1 \\ 0 \\ -1 \end{bmatrix}, \begin{bmatrix} 0 \\ 1 \\ 1 \end{bmatrix} \right\}$.

(a) Is the vector $\vec{b} = \begin{bmatrix} 1 \\ 1 \\ 1 \end{bmatrix} \in \mathcal{C}_A$? (justify your answer).

(b) Is the vector $\vec{b} = \begin{bmatrix} 2 \\ 1 \\ -1 \end{bmatrix} \in \mathcal{C}_A$? (justify your answer).

(c) Find $\mathcal{N}(A^T)$. (Every vector in $\mathcal{N}(A^T)$ is orthogonal to every vector in $\mathcal{C}_A$).

2. Find an orthonormal basis for the vector space $\mathcal{H} = \text{span} \left\{ \begin{bmatrix} a \\ a+b \\ b \end{bmatrix} \in \mathcal{R}^3, a, b \in \mathcal{R} \right\}$.

That is, find vectors $\vec{q}_1$ and $\vec{q}_2$ such that $\vec{q}_1 \perp \vec{q}_2$ ($\vec{q}_1$ and $\vec{q}_2$ are perpendicular), $\|\vec{q}_1\| = \|\vec{q}_2\| = 1$ and $\mathcal{H} = \text{span}\{\vec{q}_1, \vec{q}_2\}$. Hint: The vectors $\vec{v}_1 = \begin{bmatrix} 1 \\ 1 \\ 0 \end{bmatrix}$ and $\vec{v}_2 = \begin{bmatrix} 0 \\ 1 \\ 1 \end{bmatrix}$ are a

basis for $\mathcal{H}$ and define $\vec{q}_1 = \dfrac{\vec{v}_1}{\|\vec{v}_1\|}$.

3. Answer each of the following either True T or false F (circle one) where A is a 3×4 matrix, $\mathcal{N}(A)$ is the null space of A and R_A is the row space of A.

   (a) __T__F__ If the dimension of the $\mathcal{N}(A) = 2$, then the dimension of $R_A = 2$.

   (b) __T__F__ If the dimension of the $\mathcal{N}(A) = 2$, then the dimension of $R_A = 1$.

   (c) __T__F__ If the dimension of the $\mathcal{N}(A) = 1$, then the problem $A\vec{x} = \vec{b}$ is solvable.

   (d) __T__F__ If the dimension of $N(A^T) = 1$ then the rank of A is 2.

   (e) __T__F__ The rank of A could be 4.

4. Let the A be the 2×3 matrix $A = \begin{bmatrix} 1 & 3 & 5 \\ 2 & 6 & 10 \end{bmatrix}$

   (a) Find the null space $\mathcal{N}(A)$ and row space R_A of A. ($\mathcal{N}(A) \perp R_A$).

   (b) Find the column space $\mathcal{C}_A$ of A and the null space $\mathcal{N}(A^T)$ of A^T. ($\mathcal{N}(A^T) \perp \mathcal{C}_A$).

4.13.2 Sample Test 2

Name_____   Date_____

1. Find a basis for the vector space defined by $\mathcal{V} = \left\{ \begin{bmatrix} x_1 \\ x_2 \\ x_3 \end{bmatrix} : x_1 + x_2 = 0, x_3 \in \mathcal{R} \right\}$.

2. Short Answer (fill in the blank). Let

$$\vec{v}_1 = \begin{bmatrix} 1 \\ 2 \\ 1 \end{bmatrix}, \ \vec{v}_2 = \begin{bmatrix} 2 \\ 1 \\ -1 \end{bmatrix} \in \mathcal{R}^3 \ \text{ and } \ \vec{w}_1 = \begin{bmatrix} -2 \\ 1 \\ 3 \\ 0 \end{bmatrix}, \ \vec{w}_2 = \begin{bmatrix} 1 \\ -5 \\ 0 \\ 3 \end{bmatrix} \in \mathcal{R}^4.$$

Suppose that A is a matrix and that

$$\mathcal{C}_A = \text{span}\left\{\vec{v}_1, \vec{v}_2\right\} \ \text{and} \ \mathcal{N}(A) = \text{span}\left\{\vec{w}_1, \vec{w}_2\right\}.$$

(a) The size of the matrix A is _____.

(b) The dimension of $\mathcal{N}(A)$ is _____.

(c) The rank of the matrix A is _____.

(d) The dimension of $\mathcal{C}_A$ is _____.

(e) The problem $A\vec{x} = \vec{b}$ is solvable for all $\vec{b} \in \mathcal{R}^3$. _____ (True or False)

(f) The dimension of $\mathcal{N}(A^T)$ is _____.

(g) The rank of the matrix A^T is _____.

(h) The dimension of $\mathcal{C}_{A^T} = R_A$ is _____.

(i) There are **nonzero** solutions of $A^T \vec{w} = \vec{0}$. _____ (True or False)

3. Consider the problem $A\vec{x} = \begin{bmatrix} 1 & 2 & 3 \\ 2 & 5 & 4 \end{bmatrix} \begin{bmatrix} x_1 \\ x_2 \\ x_3 \end{bmatrix} = \begin{bmatrix} b_1 \\ b_2 \end{bmatrix}$.

(a) Find the general solution to the problem $A\vec{x} = \vec{b}$. Write $\vec{x} = \vec{x}_h + \vec{x}_p$ where $\vec{x}_h$ is the homogeneous solution and $\vec{x}_p$ is a particular solution.

(b) Write down a basis for $\mathcal{N}(A)$ (Using (a) is the easiest way to do this).

(c) Write down a basis for $\mathcal{C}_A$ (Think).

(d) Write down a basis for $\mathcal{C}_{A^T} = R_A$ (Think).

4. Write down the equation to check to see whether the set of vectors in

$$S = \left\{ \begin{bmatrix} 1 \\ 2 \end{bmatrix}, \begin{bmatrix} 2 \\ 5 \end{bmatrix}, \begin{bmatrix} 3 \\ 4 \end{bmatrix} \right\}$$

is a linearly dependent or independent set. Decide which it is and verify your result. You can use Part (b) of Problem 3.

5. The matrix $A = \begin{bmatrix} 1 & 2 & 0 & 3 \\ 2 & 1 & 1 & 1 \\ 1 & -1 & 1 & -2 \end{bmatrix}$ has the row echelon form

$$[A] = \begin{bmatrix} 1 & 2 & 0 & 3 \\ 2 & 1 & 1 & 1 \\ 1 & -1 & 1 & -2 \end{bmatrix} \sim \begin{bmatrix} 1 & 2 & 0 & 3 \\ 0 & -3 & 1 & -5 \\ 0 & 0 & 0 & 0 \end{bmatrix}.$$

(a) The matrix A has _____ pivots so the rank of A is _____. It follows that the dimension of $\mathcal{C}_A$ is _____ and the dimension of $\mathcal{C}_{A^T}$ is _____.

(b) It follows from work in class that $\mathcal{C}_A = \text{span} \left\{ \begin{bmatrix} 1 \\ 2 \\ 1 \end{bmatrix}, \begin{bmatrix} 2 \\ 1 \\ -1 \end{bmatrix} \right\}$ (the columns of A corresponding to the pivot columns). This is given. Find a basis for the $\mathcal{N}(A^T)$. You can find this directly (use the definition). Another way is to use the fact that if $\vec{\eta} \in \mathcal{N}(A^T)$ then $\vec{\eta} \cdot \vec{v} = 0$ for every $\vec{v} \in \mathcal{C}_A$.

Chapter 5

The Eigenvalue Problem

The main goal of this chapter is the orthogonal diagonalization of symmetric matrices in Theorem(5.28). This is the second of the "Big Two" and is among the prettiest results in matrix theory. It not only has an intrinsic aesthetic value but also has numerous practical applications. The catalyst for a reason to believe the theorem is provided by introducing the complex number system and using a result known as Schur's Lemma. Introduction of the complex numbers requires a generalization of the dot product from Chapter One, which is the content of Definition(5.17). Schur's Lemma seems to be undervalued if not overlooked in introductory matrix theory courses. This is a mystery as the result is simply stated, elegant, and useful. From the perspective in this chapter, the lemma is an iterative application of the Gram-Schmidt procedure from Exercise(4.16). The fourteen exercises (5.1) through (5.14) are all computational and designed to illustrate and reinforce the ideas of this chapter. Exercise(5.15) and (5.16) give a reason to believe the result that the geometric multiplicity of an eigenvalue is always less than or equal to its algebraic multiplicity (Theorem(5.33)). Exercise(5.17) provides some practice with quadratic forms and leads naturally to the min-max theorem in Exercise(5.18). Exercises (5.19) and (5.20) illustrates the use of the diagonalization Theorem(5.28) in the derivation of two important examples of orthogonal matrices: projections and reflections, respectively. The final Exercise(5.22) uses the result of Exercise(5.21) (the exponential of a matrix) to reveal the close connection between the difference equation in Exercise(5.3) and a differential equation.

5.1   A Redneck Sequence

Throughout Chapter Four the problem studied was defined by the linear system $A\vec{x} = \vec{b}$ where A is an $m \times n$ matrix, $\vec{x}$ is an $n \times 1$ vector and the vector $\vec{b}$ is a $m \times 1$ vector. In this chapter the matrix A is always square $(m = n)$ so that the vector $\vec{b}$ is $n \times 1$. The definition of the eigenproblem requires the vector $\vec{b}$ to have a special form. To motivate the material of this chapter consider the 2×2 linear system

$$A\vec{x} = \begin{bmatrix} -1 & 2 \\ 1 & 0 \end{bmatrix} \vec{x} = \begin{bmatrix} 1 \\ 1 \end{bmatrix} = \vec{b}.$$

The inverse of the matrix A is given by

$$A^{-1} = \frac{-1}{2} \begin{bmatrix} 0 & -2 \\ -1 & -1 \end{bmatrix} = \frac{1}{2} \begin{bmatrix} 0 & 2 \\ 1 & 1 \end{bmatrix},$$

so the solution vector $\vec{x}$ is

$$\vec{x} = A^{-1} \begin{bmatrix} 1 \\ 1 \end{bmatrix} = \frac{1}{2} \begin{bmatrix} 0 & 2 \\ 1 & 1 \end{bmatrix} \begin{bmatrix} 1 \\ 1 \end{bmatrix} = \begin{bmatrix} 1 \\ 1 \end{bmatrix}.$$

Label this solution $\vec{x} = \vec{p}_1$ and rewrite the original system in the form

$$A\vec{p}_1 = \begin{bmatrix} -1 & 2 \\ 1 & 0 \end{bmatrix} \vec{p}_1 = \begin{bmatrix} -1 & 2 \\ 1 & 0 \end{bmatrix} \begin{bmatrix} 1 \\ 1 \end{bmatrix} = \begin{bmatrix} 1 \\ 1 \end{bmatrix} = \vec{b} = (1)\vec{p}_1.$$

The solution vector $\vec{p}_1$ is a scalar multiple (in this case the scalar multiple is one) of the right-hand side $\vec{b}$. This motivates the query as to whether there are any other such right hand sides $\vec{b}$ so that the solution vector to $\vec{x}$ is a multiple of $\vec{b}$. Change the vector $\vec{b}$ to $\vec{b} = \begin{bmatrix} -4 \\ 2 \end{bmatrix}$ so the system reads

$$A\vec{x} = \begin{bmatrix} -1 & 2 \\ 1 & 0 \end{bmatrix} \vec{x} = \begin{bmatrix} -4 \\ 2 \end{bmatrix} = \vec{b}.$$

Multiplying both sides of the equation by A^{-1} yields

$$\vec{x} = A^{-1} \begin{bmatrix} -4 \\ 2 \end{bmatrix} = \frac{1}{2} \begin{bmatrix} 0 & 2 \\ 1 & 1 \end{bmatrix} \begin{bmatrix} -4 \\ 2 \end{bmatrix} = \begin{bmatrix} 2 \\ -1 \end{bmatrix} \equiv \vec{p}_2,$$

so the vector $\vec{b}$ is a scalar multiple of the solution vector. With this labeling the equation reads

$$A\vec{p}_2 = \begin{bmatrix} -1 & 2 \\ 1 & 0 \end{bmatrix} \vec{p}_2 = \begin{bmatrix} -1 & 2 \\ 1 & 0 \end{bmatrix} \begin{bmatrix} 2 \\ -1 \end{bmatrix} = \begin{bmatrix} -4 \\ 2 \end{bmatrix} = \vec{b} = (-2)\vec{p}_2.$$

Using the two special vectors just found define the 2×2 matrix

$$P = [\vec{p}_1 \ \vec{p}_2] = \begin{bmatrix} 1 & 2 \\ 1 & -1 \end{bmatrix}$$

whose inverse is given by

$$P^{-1} = \frac{-1}{3} \begin{bmatrix} -1 & -2 \\ -1 & 1 \end{bmatrix} = \frac{1}{3} \begin{bmatrix} 1 & 2 \\ 1 & -1 \end{bmatrix}.$$

The product has the property

$$P^{-1}AP = \frac{1}{3} \begin{bmatrix} 1 & 2 \\ 1 & -1 \end{bmatrix} \begin{bmatrix} -1 & 2 \\ 1 & 0 \end{bmatrix} \begin{bmatrix} 1 & 2 \\ 1 & -1 \end{bmatrix} = \begin{bmatrix} 1 & 0 \\ 0 & -2 \end{bmatrix} \equiv \Lambda, \qquad (5.1)$$

which is a diagonal matrix containing the two multiples 1 and -2 of the solution vectors. Assuming there are always such multiples and vectors $\vec{p}_1$ and $\vec{p}_2$ for a given matrix A it is a fair question to ask how one finds them. First notice that each of the vectors $\vec{p}_1$ and $\vec{p}_2$ has the property that

$$A\vec{p}_1 = \lambda_1 \vec{p}_1 \quad \text{and} \quad A\vec{p}_2 = \lambda_2 \vec{p}_2,$$

which is equivalent to

$$(A - \lambda_1 I)\vec{p}_1 = \vec{0} \quad \text{and} \quad (A - \lambda_2 I)\vec{p}_2 = \vec{0}$$

where $\lambda_1 = 1$ and $\lambda_2 = -2$. In either case there is a non-zero vector $\vec{p}$ and a corresponding scalar λ so that $A\vec{p} = \lambda\vec{p}$. From Theorem(3.28) the homogeneous system $(A - \lambda I)\vec{p} = \vec{0}$ has a non-trivial solution if there is a non-zero vector $\vec{p} \in \mathcal{N}(A - \lambda I)$ and the same theorem gives the alternative equivalence $\det(A - \lambda I) = 0$. The determinant statement provides the computational procedure

$$\det(A - \lambda I)) = \det\left(\begin{bmatrix} -1 & 2 \\ 1 & 0 \end{bmatrix} - \lambda \begin{bmatrix} 1 & 0 \\ 0 & 1 \end{bmatrix} \right) = \det\left(\begin{bmatrix} -1 & 2 \\ 1 & 0 \end{bmatrix} - \begin{bmatrix} \lambda & 0 \\ 0 & \lambda \end{bmatrix} \right)$$

$$= \det\left(\begin{bmatrix} -1 - \lambda & 2 \\ 1 & -\lambda \end{bmatrix} \right) = (-1 - \lambda)(-\lambda) - (2)(1)$$

$$= \lambda^2 + \lambda - 2 = (\lambda - 1)(\lambda + 2) = 0$$

so that $\lambda_1 = 1$ and $\lambda_2 = -2$ are solutions to this quadratic equation. Hence the two matrices $(A - \lambda_j I)$, $j = 1, 2$ are singular so the homogeneous problems $(A - \lambda_j I)\vec{p}_j = \vec{0}$ $j = 1, 2$ have non-zero solutions. In order to find vectors $\vec{p}_j, j = 1, 2$ satisfying $A\vec{p}_j = \lambda_j \vec{p}_j$ proceed as follows: with $\lambda_1 = 1$ solve for $\vec{p}_1$ in

$$(A - \lambda_1 I)\vec{p}_1 = (A - I)\vec{p}_1 = \left(\begin{bmatrix} -2 & 2 \\ 1 & -1 \end{bmatrix} \right) \vec{p}_1 = \begin{bmatrix} 0 \\ 0 \end{bmatrix}$$

to find that $\vec{p}_1 = \begin{bmatrix} 1 \\ 1 \end{bmatrix}$ is a solution. In the notation of Definition(4.11)

$$\mathcal{N}(A - \lambda_1 I) = \mathcal{N}(A - I) = \text{span}\left\{ \begin{bmatrix} 1 \\ 1 \end{bmatrix} \right\}.$$

Repeat this process with $\lambda_2 = -2$ to find

$$(A - \lambda_2 I)\vec{p}_2 = (A + 2I)\vec{p}_2 = \left(\begin{bmatrix} 1 & 2 \\ 1 & 2 \end{bmatrix} \right)\vec{p}_2 = \begin{bmatrix} 0 \\ 0 \end{bmatrix}$$

and $\vec{p}_2 = \begin{bmatrix} 2 \\ -1 \end{bmatrix}$ is a solution and

$$\mathcal{N}(A - \lambda_2 I) = \mathcal{N}(A + 2I) = \text{span}\left\{ \begin{bmatrix} 2 \\ -1 \end{bmatrix} \right\}.$$

Since the vector $\vec{p}_1$ is not a multiple of $\vec{p}_2$ the two vectors are linearly independent so that the matrix $P \equiv [\vec{p}_1\ \vec{p}_2]$ is invertible. Recall the special case of Theorem(4.22).

Given a matrix A the above discussion provides an algorithmic procedure to find numbers λ and vectors $\vec{p}$ so that $A\vec{p} = \lambda\vec{p}$. First find numbers λ from the determinant equation $\det(A - \lambda I) = 0$. Once these numbers are found find the null space $\mathcal{N}(A - \lambda I)$. This algorithm is not hard to follow but there is a question: why would anyone care about finding such λ and $\vec{p}$? Here is a reason to believe.

Example 5.1 The following problem is very important to a number of Rednecks in remote areas of East Tennessee. Given two integers α_0 and α_1 define the redneck sequence

$$\alpha_{n+1} = -\alpha_n + 2\alpha_{n-1}. \tag{5.2}$$

If $\alpha_0 = 1$ and $\alpha_1 = 2$ then direct calculation gives

$$\begin{aligned}
\alpha_2 &= -\alpha_1 + 2\alpha_0 = -2 + 2(1) = 0 \\
\alpha_3 &= -\alpha_2 + 2\alpha_1 = 0 + 2(2) = 4 \\
\alpha_4 &= -\alpha_3 + 2\alpha_2 = -4 + 2(0) = -4 \\
\alpha_5 &= -\alpha_4 + 2\alpha_3 = 4 + 2(4) = 12.
\end{aligned}$$

With a little patience one finds $\alpha_{11} = 684$. However to find this value one needs to find the values $\alpha_{10} = -340$ and $\alpha_9 = 172$. But to find α_9 one needs to find α_8 and α_7 and so on back to α_1 and α_0, What would be desirable is a formula for the quantity α_{n+1} which only involves n and the initial values α_0 and α_1. To pursue the development of such a formula define the change of variable

$$u_n = \alpha_n \quad \text{and} \quad v_n = \alpha_{n-1} \tag{5.3}$$

and rewrite the difference equation in (5.2) as

$$u_{n+1} = \alpha_{n+1} = -\alpha_n + 2\alpha_{n-1} = -u_n + 2v_n$$
$$v_{n+1} = \alpha_n = u_n \ .$$

Define the vector $\vec{w}_n = \begin{bmatrix} u_n \\ v_n \end{bmatrix}$ so that

$$\vec{w}_{n+1} = \begin{bmatrix} u_{n+1} \\ v_{n+1} \end{bmatrix} = \begin{bmatrix} -1 & 2 \\ 1 & 0 \end{bmatrix} \begin{bmatrix} u_n \\ v_n \end{bmatrix} = A\vec{w}_n \tag{5.4}$$

where A is the matrix in Example(5.1). From (5.4), write

$$\vec{w}_{n+1} = A\vec{w}_n = A^2\vec{w}_{n-1} = A^3\vec{w}_{n-2} = \cdots = A^{n-1}\vec{w}_2 = A^n\vec{w}_1 \tag{5.5}$$

so to find $u_{n+1} = \alpha_{n+1}$ one only needs to find the powers A^n. A little reflection on computing matrix products reveals all that has been done is exchange one sort of difficulty [iterate using (5.2)] for a different sort of difficulty (calculate the powers A^n). It is time to look for a different approach. The hint is provided by (5.1). Rewrite that equation in the form $A = P\Lambda P^{-1}$ and calculate

$$A^2 = \left(P\Lambda P^{-1}\right)\left(P\Lambda P^{-1}\right) = P\Lambda \left(P^{-1}P\right)\Lambda P^{-1} = P\Lambda^2 P^{-1},$$

which, upon repeated applications, gives

$$A^n = P\Lambda^n P^{-1} = P\begin{bmatrix} 1 & 0 \\ 0 & -2 \end{bmatrix}^n P^{-1} = P\begin{bmatrix} 1 & 0 \\ 0 & (-2)^n \end{bmatrix} P^{-1}. \tag{5.6}$$

Substitute this result in (5.5) to find

$$\vec{w}_{n+1} = \begin{bmatrix} u_{n+1} \\ v_{n+1} \end{bmatrix} = A^n\vec{w}_1 = P\begin{bmatrix} 1 & 0 \\ 0 & (-2)^n \end{bmatrix} P^{-1}\begin{bmatrix} u_1 \\ v_1 \end{bmatrix}$$

$$\tag{5.7}$$

$$= \frac{1}{3}\begin{bmatrix} u_1 + 2v_1 + 2(-2)^n \left[u_1 - v_1\right] \\ u_1 + 2v_1 + (-2)^n \left[-u_1 + v_1\right] \end{bmatrix}.$$

The first component of (5.7) reads

$$u_{n+1} = \alpha_{n+1} = \frac{1}{3}\left(u_1 + 2v_1 + 2(-2)^n \left[u_1 - v_1\right]\right) \tag{5.8}$$

$$= \frac{1}{3}\left(\alpha_1 + 2\alpha_0 + 2(-2)^n \left[\alpha_1 - \alpha_0\right]\right)$$

where the second equality follows from the definitions $u_1 = \alpha_1$ and $v_1 = \alpha_0$. Set $\alpha_1 = 2\alpha_0$ in (5.8) to find

$$\alpha_{n+1} = \frac{2\alpha_0}{3}\left(2 + (-2)^n\right). \tag{5.9}$$

The specific conditions $\alpha_0 = 1$ and $n = 10$ give

$$\alpha_{11} = \frac{2}{3}\left(2 + (-2)^{10}\right) = \frac{2}{3}\left(2 + 1024\right) = \frac{2052}{3} = 684,$$

which agrees with the value found iterating formula (5.2). It is clear from the iteration in (5.2) that if α_0 and α_1 are integers then α_n is an integer for all n. In the case that $\alpha_1 = 2\alpha_0$ the formula in (5.9) can be written in the form

$$\alpha_{n+1} = \frac{2\alpha_0}{3}\left(2 + (-2)^n\right) = 4\alpha_0\left(\frac{1 - (-2)^{n-1}}{3}\right), \quad n = 1, 2, 3, \ldots$$

and perhaps the most amazing thing about this formula is that the quantity in parenthesis is always an integer.

5.2   Eigenpairs and the Characteristic Equation

The Redneck sequence in Equation(5.2) is called a second-order linear difference equation and can always be transformed, using the definition in (5.3), to the matrix equation (5.4) for an appropriate matrix A. If the matrix A can be written as in (5.6), that is, there is a matrix P such that $P^{-1}AP = \Lambda$, then the difference equation can always be solved using (5.7). This is the heart of the matter as well as the subject of this chapter: given a matrix A, when is there an invertible matrix P so that

$$P^{-1}AP = \begin{bmatrix} \lambda_1 & 0 \\ 0 & \lambda_2 \end{bmatrix} \equiv \Lambda? \tag{5.10}$$

Although the importance of Example(5.2) in Redneck circles in East Tennessee may not carry broad world-wide interest Exercise(5.5) finds an explicit representation for the Fibonacci numbers. Exercises(5.3) ($\lambda_1 \neq \lambda_2$) and (5.4) ($\lambda_1 = \lambda_2$) handle the general second-order difference equation. The procedure for finding scalars λ and vectors $\vec{p}$ in (5.10) for the 2×2 matrix in Example(5.1) is the same procedure for a general $n \times n$ matrix A. The numbers λ and the vectors $\vec{p}$ have special names.

Definition 5.2 Eigenvalue, Eigenvector, Eigenpair, Characteristic Equation and the Spectrum: Define the $n \times n$ matrix

$$A = \begin{bmatrix} a_{11} & a_{12} & \cdots & a_{1n} \\ a_{21} & a_{22} & \vdots & a_{2n} \\ \vdots & \vdots & \ddots & \vdots \\ a_{n1} & a_{n2} & \cdots & a_{nn} \end{bmatrix}$$

and search for non-zero vectors $\vec{p}$ and scalars λ, so that

$$A\vec{p} = \lambda\vec{p} = \lambda I\vec{p} \tag{5.11}$$

where I is the $n \times n$ identity matrix. If $\vec{p} = \vec{0}$, then any number λ satisfies (5.11) so that the equation is true, but uninformative. Hence only non-zero vectors are sought. Upon subtracting the right-hand side from the left-hand side of (5.11) results in the homogeneous system of equations

$$A\vec{p} - \lambda I \vec{p} = (A - \lambda I)\vec{p} = \vec{0} \ . \tag{5.12}$$

The $n \times n$ matrix I was inserted in (5.11) so that the matrix $A - \lambda I$ could be formed. The symbol $A - \lambda$ is meaningless. The pair consisting of the scalar λ and the non-zero vector $\vec{p}$ satisfying (5.11) is called an **eigenpair** for the matrix A. If $A\vec{p} = \lambda\vec{p}$ and α is a non-zero scalar then $\alpha\vec{p}$ is also an eigenvector for A since $A(\alpha\vec{p}) = \lambda(\alpha\vec{p})$. That is, any non-zero multiple for an eigenvector of A is also an eigenvector for A. Using the language from Chapter Four the vector $\vec{p}$ is in the null space $\mathcal{N}(A - \lambda I)$. The number λ is called an **eigenvalue** of A and the non-zero vector $\vec{p}$ is called the **eigenvector** of A associated with the eigenvalue λ. The equation in (5.12) has non-zero solutions if and only if

$$0 = \rho_A(\lambda) \equiv \det(A - \lambda I) = \begin{vmatrix} a_{11} - \lambda & a_{12} & \cdots & a_{1n} \\ a_{21} & a_{22} - \lambda & & a_{2n} \\ \vdots & & \ddots & \vdots \\ a_{n1} & a_{n2} & & a_{nn} - \lambda \end{vmatrix} . \tag{5.13}$$

The nth degree polynomial equation $\rho_A(\lambda)$ is called the **characteristic equation** of the matrix A. The eigenvalues of A are the roots of this n^{th} degree polynomial. The Fundamental Theorem of Algebra guarantees that these roots consist of n real and/or complex numbers λ_j , $j = 1, 2, \ldots, n$ so that $\rho_A(\lambda_j) = 0$. This set is called the **spectrum** of the matrix A and is denoted by

$$\sigma(A) = \{\lambda_1, \lambda_2, \ldots, \lambda_n\} \ .$$

Upon factoring $\rho_A(\lambda)$ one finds

$$\rho_A(\lambda) = (-1)^n (\lambda - \lambda_1)(\lambda - \lambda_2) \cdots (\lambda - \lambda_n). \tag{5.14}$$

The eigenvector $\vec{p}_j$ associated with λ_j is found by substituting λ_j, $j = 1, 2, \cdots n$ in (5.12) and solving the resulting homogeneous system $(A - \lambda_j I)\vec{p}_j = \vec{0}$. Equivalently, find $\mathcal{N}(A - \lambda_j I)$.

It is not hard to find or "stumble on" examples where the identity in (5.10) does not occur. This is illustrated by another difference equation example.

Example 5.3 A difference equation that does not look too different from the difference equation in (5.2) is given by

$$\alpha_{n+1} = 2\alpha_n - \alpha_{n-1}. \tag{5.15}$$

If $\alpha_0 = 1$ and $\alpha_1 = 2$ then direct calculation shows that

$$\alpha_2 = 2(2) - 1 = 3, \quad \alpha_3 = 2(3) - 2 = 4, \quad \alpha_4 = 2(4) - 3 = 5, \quad \alpha_5 = 2(5) - 4 = 6$$

and one may be tempted to conclude that $\alpha_n = n + 1$. To try to establish this identity, use the change of variable in (5.3) to find the analogue of (5.4)

$$\vec{w}_{n+1} = \begin{bmatrix} u_{n+1} \\ v_{n+1} \end{bmatrix} = \begin{bmatrix} 2 & -1 \\ 1 & 0 \end{bmatrix} \begin{bmatrix} u_n \\ v_n \end{bmatrix} = A\vec{w}_n. \tag{5.16}$$

Using the matrix $A = \begin{bmatrix} 2 & -1 \\ 1 & 0 \end{bmatrix}$ in equation (5.13) shows that the characteristic equation for A is

$$0 = \rho_A(\lambda) \equiv \det(A - \lambda I) = \begin{vmatrix} 2 - \lambda & -1 \\ 1 & -\lambda \end{vmatrix} = (2 - \lambda)(-\lambda) + 1 = (\lambda - 1)^2$$

so $\lambda_1 = \lambda_2 = 1$. For this example there is only one (distinct) eigenvalue for A. An eigenvector is found by solving the homogeneous system

$$(A - \lambda_1 I)\vec{p}_1 = (A - (1)I)\vec{p}_1 = \begin{pmatrix} 1 & -1 \\ 1 & -1 \end{pmatrix} \vec{p}_1 = \begin{pmatrix} 0 \\ 0 \end{pmatrix}.$$

The vector $\vec{p}_1 = \begin{pmatrix} 1 \\ 1 \end{pmatrix}$, or any multiple of $\vec{p}_1$, is an eigenvector of A corresponding to $\lambda_1 = 1$. Since the rank of

$$(A - (1)I) \sim \begin{pmatrix} 1 & -1 \\ 0 & 0 \end{pmatrix}$$

is one, it follows from the dimension theorem(4.22) that dim $\mathcal{N}(A - (1)I) = 1$ so there is not a second (independent) eigenvector for A. Hence there is not a matrix P so that equation (5.10) is true. To find the nth term α_n for this sequence one must proceed in a different fashion than the procedure used in Example(5.1). This will require more tools than presently available, but will be revisited in Exercise(5.4).

In the previous discussion the 2×2 matrix in (5.4) satisfies (5.10) and the 2×2 matrix in (5.16) fails to satisfy (5.10). In the former case there were two independent eigenvectors, but this was not the case in the latter. The following more comprehensive example reinforces this result while illustrating every possible scenario that can occur for a 2×2 matrix.

Example 5.4 Let $A = \begin{bmatrix} 2 & \alpha \\ 4 & \beta \end{bmatrix}$ where α and β are arbitrary. Using (5.13) the characteristic equation for A is

$$\begin{aligned} \rho_A(\lambda) &= \det(A - \lambda I)) = \det\left(\begin{bmatrix} 2 & \alpha \\ 4 & \beta \end{bmatrix} - \lambda \begin{bmatrix} 1 & 0 \\ 0 & 1 \end{bmatrix} \right) \\ &= \det\left(\begin{bmatrix} 2 - \lambda & \alpha \\ 4 & \beta - \lambda \end{bmatrix} \right) = (2 - \lambda)(\beta - \lambda) - 4\alpha \tag{5.17} \\ &= \lambda^2 - (\beta + 2)\lambda + (2\beta - 4\alpha) = 0. \end{aligned}$$

The determinant of the matrix A is $\det(A) = 2\beta - 4\alpha$.

1. Let $\alpha = 4$ and $\beta = 2$ so that $A = \begin{bmatrix} 2 & 4 \\ 4 & 2 \end{bmatrix}$ and

$$\rho_A(\lambda) = \lambda^2 - 4\lambda - 12 = (\lambda + 2)(\lambda - 6) = 0.$$

The eigenvalues are $\lambda_1 = -2$ and $\lambda_2 = 6$. The corresponding eigenvectors are found from (5.13) by solving

$$(A - (-2)I)\vec{p}_1 = \begin{bmatrix} 4 & 4 \\ 4 & 4 \end{bmatrix} \vec{p}_1 = \begin{bmatrix} 0 \\ 0 \end{bmatrix}$$

and

$$(A - 6I)\vec{p}_2 = \begin{bmatrix} -4 & 4 \\ 4 & -4 \end{bmatrix} \vec{p}_2 = \begin{bmatrix} 0 \\ 0 \end{bmatrix}$$

which give $\vec{p}_1 = \begin{bmatrix} 1 \\ -1 \end{bmatrix}$ and $\vec{p}_2 = \begin{bmatrix} 1 \\ 1 \end{bmatrix}$. Define the matrix

$$P = [\vec{p}_1 \ \vec{p}_2] = \begin{bmatrix} 1 & 1 \\ -1 & 1 \end{bmatrix} \quad \text{so that} \quad P^{-1} = \frac{1}{2}\begin{bmatrix} 1 & -1 \\ 1 & 1 \end{bmatrix}$$

and

$$P^{-1}AP = P^{-1}\begin{bmatrix} 2 & 4 \\ 4 & 2 \end{bmatrix} P = \begin{bmatrix} -2 & 0 \\ 0 & 6 \end{bmatrix} = \begin{bmatrix} \lambda_1 & 0 \\ 0 & \lambda_2 \end{bmatrix} = \Lambda.$$

This is a specific case of (5.10) and

$$\det(A) = 2\beta - 4\alpha = 2(2) - 4(4) = -12 = \lambda_1\lambda_2 = (-2)(6).$$

One other note for this particular matrix A is that the matrix P has the following interesting property $\frac{1}{2}P^T = \frac{1}{2}\begin{bmatrix} 1 & -1 \\ 1 & 1 \end{bmatrix} = P^{-1}$ or

$$QQ^T \equiv \left(\frac{1}{\sqrt{2}}P\right)\left(\frac{1}{\sqrt{2}}P^T\right) = \begin{bmatrix} 1 & 0 \\ 0 & 1 \end{bmatrix} = I. \tag{5.18}$$

Using the language introduced in Exercise(3.17), the matrix P can be replaced by the orthogonal matrix Q. Orthogonal matrices will play an important role later in this chapter and this particular example will be revisited in Example(5.12).

2. Let $\alpha = 0$ and $\beta = -2$ so that $A = \begin{bmatrix} 2 & 0 \\ 4 & -2 \end{bmatrix}$ and $\rho_A(\lambda) = \lambda^2 - 4 = 0$. The eigenvalues are $\lambda_1 = -2$ and $\lambda_2 = 2$. The corresponding eigenvectors are found by solving

$$(A - (-2)I)\vec{p}_1 = \begin{bmatrix} 4 & 0 \\ 4 & 0 \end{bmatrix} \vec{p}_1 = \begin{bmatrix} 0 \\ 0 \end{bmatrix}$$

and

$$(A - 2I)\vec{p}_2 = \begin{bmatrix} 0 & 0 \\ 4 & -4 \end{bmatrix} \vec{p}_2 = \begin{bmatrix} 0 \\ 0 \end{bmatrix}$$

which give $\vec{p}_1 = \begin{bmatrix} 0 \\ 1 \end{bmatrix}$ and $\vec{p}_2 = \begin{bmatrix} 1 \\ 1 \end{bmatrix}$. Define the matrix $P = [\vec{p}_1 \ \vec{p}_2] = \begin{bmatrix} 0 & 1 \\ 1 & 1 \end{bmatrix}$ so

that $P^{-1} = \begin{bmatrix} -1 & 1 \\ 1 & 0 \end{bmatrix}$ and

$$P^{-1}AP = P^{-1} \begin{bmatrix} 2 & 0 \\ 4 & -2 \end{bmatrix} P = \begin{bmatrix} -2 & 0 \\ 0 & 2 \end{bmatrix} = \begin{bmatrix} \lambda_1 & 0 \\ 0 & \lambda_2 \end{bmatrix} = \Lambda. \qquad (5.19)$$

Notice that the matrix A is lower triangular and the eigenvalues are on the diagonal of the matrix A. Also $\det(A) = 2(-2) - 4(0) = -4 = \lambda_1\lambda_2 = (-2)(2)$. Further since

$$P = \begin{bmatrix} 0 & 1 \\ 1 & 1 \end{bmatrix} = P^T \text{ it is impossible for } P^{-1} = \begin{bmatrix} -1 & 1 \\ 1 & 1 \end{bmatrix} = \alpha P^T$$

for any scalar multiple α. No analogue of (5.18) is available for this example. This will also be revisited in Example(5.12).

3. If $\alpha = 2$ and $\beta = 4$ then $A = \begin{bmatrix} 2 & 2 \\ 4 & 4 \end{bmatrix}$ and (5.17) gives

$$\rho_A(\lambda) = \lambda^2 - 6\lambda = \lambda(\lambda - 6) = 0$$

and the eigenvalues are $\lambda_1 = 0$ and $\lambda_2 = 6$. The corresponding eigenvectors are found by solving

$$(A - 0I)\vec{p}_1 = \begin{bmatrix} 2 & 2 \\ 4 & 4 \end{bmatrix} \vec{p}_1 = \begin{bmatrix} 0 \\ 0 \end{bmatrix}$$

and

$$(A - 6I)\vec{p}_2 = \begin{bmatrix} -4 & 2 \\ 4 & -2 \end{bmatrix} \vec{p}_2 = \begin{bmatrix} 0 \\ 0 \end{bmatrix}$$

which gives $\vec{p}_1 = \begin{bmatrix} 1 \\ -1 \end{bmatrix}$ and $\vec{p}_2 = \begin{bmatrix} 1 \\ 2 \end{bmatrix}$. Define the matrix

$$P = [\vec{p}_1 \ \vec{p}_2] = \begin{bmatrix} 1 & 1 \\ -1 & 2 \end{bmatrix} \text{ so that } P^{-1} = \frac{1}{3} \begin{bmatrix} 2 & -1 \\ 1 & 1 \end{bmatrix}$$

and

$$P^{-1}AP = P^{-1} \begin{bmatrix} 2 & 2 \\ 4 & 4 \end{bmatrix} P = \begin{bmatrix} 0 & 0 \\ 0 & 6 \end{bmatrix} = \begin{bmatrix} \lambda_1 & 0 \\ 0 & \lambda_2 \end{bmatrix} = \Lambda. \qquad (5.20)$$

The matrix A is not invertible ($\det(A) = 0$) and the number $\lambda_1 = 0$ is an eigenvalue for A. As it turns out (see Theorem(5.5)) this is always the case: a square matrix A is not invertible if and only if $\lambda = 0$ is an eigenvalue of A.

4. If $\alpha = -1$ and $\beta = 6$ then $A = \begin{bmatrix} 2 & -1 \\ 4 & 6 \end{bmatrix}$ and (5.17) gives

$$\rho_A(\lambda) = \lambda^2 - 8\lambda + 16 = (\lambda - 4)^2 = 0.$$

There is a repeated eigenvalue $\lambda_1 = \lambda_2 = 4$. Using (5.12) with $\lambda_1 = 4$ gives

$$(A - 4I)\vec{p}_1 = \begin{bmatrix} -2 & -1 \\ 4 & 2 \end{bmatrix} \vec{p}_1 = \begin{bmatrix} 0 \\ 0 \end{bmatrix}$$

which has $\vec{p}_1 = \begin{bmatrix} 1 \\ -2 \end{bmatrix}$ as an eigenvector. The row reduction

$$(A - 4I) = \begin{bmatrix} -2 & -1 \\ 4 & 2 \end{bmatrix} \sim \begin{bmatrix} -2 & -1 \\ 0 & 0 \end{bmatrix}$$

shows that the rank of the matrix $(A - 4I)$ is one so, by the dimension theorem(4.22) the dimension of $\mathcal{N}(A - 4I)$ is one. This means that the vector $\vec{p}_1$ spans the null space of $(A - 4I)$. There is not another eigenvalue besides the number $\lambda_1 = 4$ so there is not a second (independent) eigenvector for the matrix A and therefore no matrix P satisfying (5.10). This is the same situation as was illustrated in the difference equation in (5.15). It is true that if $\sigma(A) = \{\lambda_1, \lambda_2\} = \{4, 4\}$ and $\vec{p}_1 = \begin{bmatrix} 1 \\ -2 \end{bmatrix}$ then $A\vec{p}_1 = \lambda_1\vec{p}_1$. Set $\vec{p}_2 = \alpha\vec{p}_1$ where α is a non-zero scalar. Notice that

$$A\vec{p}_2 = A(\alpha\vec{p}_1) = \alpha(A\vec{p}_1) = \alpha(\lambda_1\vec{p}_1) = \lambda_1(\alpha\vec{p}_1) = \lambda_1\vec{p}_2$$

so that $\vec{p}_2$ is also an eigenvector for λ_1. Define the matrix $P = [\vec{p}_1\ \vec{p}_2]$ so that

$$\begin{aligned} AP &= \begin{bmatrix} 2 & -1 \\ 4 & 6 \end{bmatrix} \begin{bmatrix} 1 & \alpha \\ -2 & -2\alpha \end{bmatrix} = \begin{bmatrix} 4 & 4\alpha \\ -8 & -8\alpha \end{bmatrix} \\ &= [4\vec{p}_1\ 4\alpha\vec{p}_1] = [4\vec{p}_1\ 4\vec{p}_2] \\ &= \begin{bmatrix} 1 & \alpha \\ -2 & -2\alpha \end{bmatrix} \begin{bmatrix} 4 & 0 \\ 0 & 4 \end{bmatrix} = P\Lambda \end{aligned}$$

but the identity in (5.10) does not follow since P is not invertible. However it is the case that $\det(A) = 2(6) - 4(-1) = 16 = \lambda_1\lambda_2 = (4)(4)$.

Many of the properties outlined for the 2×2 matrices in Example(5.4) are true for general $n \times n$ matrices. Before proceeding to these examples, there are some special matrices whose eigenvalues can be found by inspection. In addition, due to the definition of the characteristic equation for A in (5.13), a connection between the determinant of A and the eigenvalues of A is to be expected. This connection as well as the eigenvalues of the special matrices is included in the following theorem.

5.3   Properties of Eigenvalues and Determinants

Theorem 5.5 Let A be an $n \times n$ matrix with spectrum $\sigma(A) = \{\lambda_1, \lambda_2, \ldots, \lambda_n\}$.

1. $\det(A) = \lambda_1 \lambda_2 \cdots \lambda_n$.

    Put $\lambda = 0$ in (5.13) and (5.14) so that

    $$
    \begin{aligned}
    \det(A) &= \rho_A(0) = (-1)^n (-\lambda_1)(-\lambda_2) \cdots (-\lambda_n) \\
    &= (-1)^n \left[(-1)(\lambda_1)(-1)(\lambda_2) \cdots (-1)(\lambda_n) \right] \\
    &= (-1)^n (-1)^n \left[(\lambda_1)(\lambda_2) \cdots (\lambda_n) \right] \\
    &= (-1)^{2n} \left[(\lambda_1)(\lambda_2) \cdots (\lambda_n) \right] \\
    &= \lambda_1 \lambda_2 \cdots \lambda_n \ .
    \end{aligned}
    $$

    This was illustrated for all parts of Example(5.4).

2. The $\det(A) = 0$ if and only if some $\lambda_j = 0$ if and only if the matrix A is not invertible.

    For the first part of the statement use part 1 to see that $\lambda = \lambda_j = 0$ if and only if $\det(A) = 0$. The second part of the statement connects the condition $\lambda = 0$ to Theorem(3.26). This was illustrated in part 3 of Example(5.4).

3. The eigenvalues of A and A^T are the same.

    The equalities

    $$
    \det(A - \lambda I) = \det(A - \lambda I)^T = \det(A^T - \lambda I^T) = \det(A^T - \lambda I)
    $$

    follow from part 4 of Theorem(3.20) which guarantees that the determinant of a matrix is equal to the determinant of its transpose.

4. If A is a diagonal, an upper triangular or a lower triangular matrix then the eigenvalues of A are the diagonal entries of A.

    Let $A = R$ be an $n \times n$ upper triangular matrix so that

    $$
    0 = \rho_R(\lambda) = \det(R - \lambda I) = \begin{vmatrix} r_{11} - \lambda & r_{12} & \cdots & r_{1n} \\ 0 & r_{22} - \lambda & & r_{2n} \\ \vdots & \vdots & \ddots & \vdots \\ 0 & 0 & \cdots & r_{nn} - \lambda \end{vmatrix}
    $$

    $$
    = (r_{11} - \lambda)(r_{22} - \lambda) \cdots (r_{nn} - \lambda)
    $$

    by successively expanding around the first column. Hence, $\rho_R(r_{ii}) = 0$ for $i = 1, 2, \ldots, n$ and $\sigma(R) = \{r_{11}, r_{22}, \ldots, r_{nn}\}$. If $A = L$ is lower triangular, the result follows by using part 3 above and the fact that $L^T = R$. A diagonal matrix A is a special case of the upper (or lower) triangular case by taking $r_{ij} = 0$ if $i > j$ (or $i < j$). This is illustrated in part 2 of Example(5.4).

In Example(5.4) the first three parts illustrate matrices A for which there is a matrix P so that $P^{-1}AP = \Lambda$. In the fourth part of Example(5.4) there is not a matrix P so that (5.10) holds. This language "there is a matrix P so that $P^{-1}AP = \Lambda$" or "there is no matrix P so that $P^{-1}AP = \Lambda$" becomes cumbersome. It is given its own definition.

Definition 5.6 Similar Matrices and Diagonalization: Let A and B be $n \times n$ matrices. If there is an invertible matrix P so that

$$P^{-1}AP = B$$

the matrix A is said to be **similar** to the matrix B. Since the relation also implies that $Q^{-1}BQ = A$ with $Q = P^{-1}$ the matrix B is **similar** to A. When there exists an invertible matrix P such that $P^{-1}AP = B$ the matrices A and B are called **similar**. If the matrix $B = \Lambda$ is a diagonal matrix

$$P^{-1}AP = \begin{bmatrix} \lambda_1 & 0 & \cdots & 0 \\ 0 & \lambda_2 & & \vdots \\ \vdots & \vdots & \ddots & 0 \\ 0 & 0 & \cdots 0 & \lambda_n \end{bmatrix} \equiv \Lambda \tag{5.21}$$

then the matrix A is similar to a diagonal matrix. In this important case the matrix A is called **diagonalizable**. The matrix P is called the **diagonalizer** of A. If the eigenvalues of A are listed as the spectrum $\sigma(A) = \{\lambda_1, \lambda_2, \ldots, \lambda_n\}$ then there are potentially repetitions in the list (end of part 4 in Example(5.4)). Whether there are repetitions in the list or not it is the case that for each λ_j there is at least one vector $\vec{p}_j$ so that $A\vec{p}_j = \lambda_j\vec{p}_j$, $j = 1, 2, \ldots, n$. As was the case in part 4 of Example(5.4) some $\vec{p}_j$ may be a multiple of $\vec{p}_k$ if $\lambda_j = \lambda_k$. At any rate, define the matrix $P = [\vec{p}_1 \ \vec{p}_2 \ \cdots \ \vec{p}_n]$ and write the $n-$equations in the matrix form

$$AP = [A\vec{p}_1 \ A\vec{p}_2 \ \cdots \ A\vec{p}_n] = [\lambda_1\vec{p}_1 \ \lambda_2\vec{p}_2 \ \cdots \ \lambda_n\vec{p}_n]$$

$$= [\vec{p}_1 \ \vec{p}_2 \ \cdots \ \vec{p}_n] \begin{bmatrix} \lambda_1 & 0 & \cdots & 0 \\ 0 & \lambda_2 & \ddots & \vdots \\ \vdots & \ddots & \ddots & 0 \\ 0 & \cdots & 0 & \lambda_n \end{bmatrix} = P\Lambda. \tag{5.22}$$

This identity is true whether the matrix P is invertible or not. It is just the statement that λ_j and $\vec{p}_j, j = 1, 2, \ldots, n$ are eigenpairs for A written in matrix form. If the matrix P is invertible then (5.21) follows from (5.22). Recall from the special case of the dimension theorem(4.22) that the matrix P is invertible if and only if the columns of P form a linearly independent set of vectors.

From the matrix for the difference equation in (5.15) or part 4 of Example(5.4) one may be led to believe that the double root for the characteristic equation for the matrix A is the reason why there is no matrix P such that $P^{-1}AP = \Lambda$. Although this is part of the reason, it is not the whole story. The next example sheds light on this situation.

Example 5.7 Let α and β be arbitrary and define the matrix

$$A = \begin{bmatrix} \alpha & 1 & 0 \\ 0 & 2 & 0 \\ \beta & -2 & 3 \end{bmatrix}.$$

The eigenvalues of A are found by solving the cubic equation

$$0 = \rho_A(\lambda) = |A - \lambda I| = \begin{vmatrix} \alpha - \lambda & 1 & 0 \\ 0 & 2 - \lambda & 0 \\ \beta & -2 & 3 - \lambda \end{vmatrix} = (\alpha - \lambda)(2 - \lambda)(3 - \lambda)$$

where the characteristic equation is found by expanding the determinant around either the second row or the third column. The eigenvalues of A are $\lambda_1 = \alpha$, $\lambda_2 = 2$ and $\lambda_3 = 3$ so the spectrum of A is $\sigma(A) = \{\alpha, 2, 3\}$. There are a few cases here. Case one is the situation in which the parameter α is neither of the values 2 or 3. Case two sets $\alpha = 3$. The final case considered is $\alpha = 2$. It may seem, from an inspection of $\rho_A(\lambda)$, that the cases $\alpha = 2$ or $\alpha = 3$ are interchangeable. Compare the case $\alpha = 3$ below with the case $\alpha = 2$ which is Exercise(5.8).

1. If $\alpha = 1$ the characteristic equation $\rho_A(\lambda)$ has the three distinct roots $\lambda_1 = 1, \lambda_2 = 2$ and $\lambda_3 = 3$ and therefore the matrix A has three distinct eigenvalues. If $\lambda_1 = 1$ then the row reduction

$$(A - 1I) = \begin{bmatrix} 0 & 1 & 0 \\ 0 & 1 & 0 \\ \beta & -2 & 2 \end{bmatrix} \sim \begin{bmatrix} \beta & -2 & 2 \\ 0 & 1 & 0 \\ 0 & 0 & 0 \end{bmatrix}$$

has the non-zero solution $\vec{p}_1 = \begin{bmatrix} -1 \\ 0 \\ \beta/2 \end{bmatrix}$ so that $\vec{p}_1$ or any multiple of $\vec{p}_1$ is a solution of

the homogeneous system $(A - 1I)\vec{p}_1 = \vec{0}$. Hence $\vec{p}_1$ is an eigenvector for A associated with the eigenvalue $\lambda_1 = 1$. In a similar fashion the eigenvectors for eigenvalues $\lambda_2 = 2$ and $\lambda_3 = 3$ are given by

$$\vec{p}_2 = \begin{bmatrix} 1 \\ 1 \\ 2 - \beta \end{bmatrix} \quad \text{and} \quad \vec{p}_3 = \begin{bmatrix} 0 \\ 0 \\ 1 \end{bmatrix}.$$

A little work (row reduce $[\, P \mid I \,] \sim [\, I \mid P^{-1} \,]$) shows that if

$$P = [\vec{p}_1 \ \vec{p}_2 \ \vec{p}_3] = \begin{bmatrix} -1 & 1 & 0 \\ 0 & 1 & 0 \\ \dfrac{\beta}{2} & 2 - \beta & 1 \end{bmatrix} \quad \text{then} \quad P^{-1} = \begin{bmatrix} -1 & 1 & 0 \\ 0 & 1 & 0 \\ \dfrac{\beta}{2} & \dfrac{\beta - 4}{2} & 1 \end{bmatrix}.$$

It is straightforward to check that

$$
AP = \begin{bmatrix} 1 & 1 & 0 \\ 0 & 2 & 0 \\ \beta & -2 & 3 \end{bmatrix} \begin{bmatrix} -1 & 1 & 0 \\ 0 & 1 & 0 \\ \dfrac{\beta}{2} & 2-\beta & 1 \end{bmatrix}
$$

$$
= \begin{bmatrix} -1 & 1 & 0 \\ 0 & 1 & 0 \\ \dfrac{\beta}{2} & 2-\beta & 1 \end{bmatrix} \begin{bmatrix} 1 & 0 & 0 \\ 0 & 2 & 0 \\ 0 & 0 & 3 \end{bmatrix} = P\Lambda.
$$

which is (5.22) but, since P is invertible, the more important relation

$$
P^{-1}AP = \begin{bmatrix} -1 & 1 & 0 \\ 0 & 1 & 0 \\ \dfrac{\beta}{2} & \dfrac{\beta-4}{2} & 1 \end{bmatrix} \begin{bmatrix} 1 & 1 & 0 \\ 0 & 2 & 0 \\ \beta & -2 & 3 \end{bmatrix} \begin{bmatrix} -1 & 1 & 0 \\ 0 & 1 & 0 \\ \dfrac{\beta}{2} & 2-\beta & 1 \end{bmatrix}
$$

$$
= \begin{bmatrix} -1 & 1 & 0 \\ 0 & 1 & 0 \\ \dfrac{\beta}{2} & \dfrac{\beta-4}{2} & 1 \end{bmatrix} \begin{bmatrix} -1 & 2 & 0 \\ 0 & 2 & 0 \\ \dfrac{\beta}{2} & 4-2\beta & 3 \end{bmatrix} \tag{5.23}
$$

$$
= \begin{bmatrix} 1 & 0 & 0 \\ 0 & 2 & 0 \\ 0 & 0 & 3 \end{bmatrix}
$$

follows and illustrates the similarity in (5.21).

2. Let $\alpha = 3$ in the matrix A so that the eigenvalues of A are $\lambda_1 = 2$, $\lambda_2 = \lambda_3 = 3$. For $\lambda_1 = 2$ the eigenvector $\vec{p}_1 = \begin{bmatrix} -1 \\ 1 \\ 2+\beta \end{bmatrix}$ is found by solving $(A - 2I)\vec{p}_1 = \vec{0}$. For the eigenvalue $\lambda_2 = 3$, consider the row reduction

$$
(A - 3I) = \begin{bmatrix} 0 & 1 & 0 \\ 0 & -1 & 0 \\ \beta & -2 & 0 \end{bmatrix} \sim \begin{bmatrix} \beta & -2 & 0 \\ 0 & 1 & 0 \\ 0 & 0 & 0 \end{bmatrix}. \tag{5.24}
$$

This yields two other possibilities. If $\beta = 0$, the two vectors

$$
\vec{p}_2 = \begin{bmatrix} 1 \\ 0 \\ 0 \end{bmatrix} \quad \text{and} \quad \vec{p}_3 = \begin{bmatrix} 0 \\ 0 \\ 1 \end{bmatrix}
$$

are independent eigenvectors for the double root $\lambda_2 = 3$. Hence the matrix

$$
P = [\vec{p}_1 \ \vec{p}_2 \ \vec{p}_3] = \begin{bmatrix} -1 & 1 & 0 \\ 1 & 0 & 0 \\ 2 & 0 & 1 \end{bmatrix}
$$

is invertible and the multiplication

$$P^{-1}AP = \begin{bmatrix} 0 & 1 & 0 \\ 1 & 1 & 0 \\ 0 & -2 & 1 \end{bmatrix} \begin{bmatrix} 3 & 1 & 0 \\ 0 & 2 & 0 \\ 0 & -2 & 3 \end{bmatrix} \begin{bmatrix} -1 & 1 & 0 \\ 1 & 0 & 0 \\ 2 & 0 & 1 \end{bmatrix} = \begin{bmatrix} 2 & 0 & 0 \\ 0 & 3 & 0 \\ 0 & 0 & 3 \end{bmatrix}$$

again illustrates (5.21). If $\beta \neq 0$ in (5.24) then the vector $\vec{p}_3$ above is the only eigenvector for the double root $\lambda_2 = 3$. This is because the rank of $(A - 3I)$ in (5.24) is two so by the dimension theorem(4.22) dim $\mathcal{N}(A - 3I) = 3 - 2 = 1$. This dimension statement is equivalent to the statement that there is only one independent eigenvector corresponding to the eigenvalue $\lambda_2 = 3$.

Recapping the case when $\alpha = 3$ the matrix $A = \begin{bmatrix} 3 & 1 & 0 \\ 0 & 2 & 0 \\ \beta & -2 & 3 \end{bmatrix}$ has the spectrum

$\sigma(A) = \{2, 3, 3\}$. The eigenvalue $\lambda_2 = 3$ is a double root of the characteristic equation. From the row reduction of $(A - 3I)$ in (5.24) the

$$\text{rank of } (A - 3I) = \begin{cases} 1 & \text{if} \quad \beta = 0 \\ 2 & \text{if} \quad \beta \neq 0 \end{cases}$$

so it follows from the dimension theorem that

$$\dim(\mathcal{N}(A - 3I)) = 3 - \begin{cases} 1 & \text{if} \quad \beta = 0 \\ 2 & \text{if} \quad \beta \neq 0 \end{cases} = \begin{cases} 2 & \text{if} \quad \beta = 0 \\ 1 & \text{if} \quad \beta \neq 0 \end{cases}.$$

Geometrically, the space of eigenvectors associated with the eigenvalue $\lambda_2 = 3$ is two dimensional if $\beta = 0$ and is one dimensional if $(\beta \neq 0)$. In the first case A is diagonalizable and in the second case it is not diagonalizable. Hence the eigenvalue $\lambda = 3$ is a double root of the characteristic equation (an algebraic condition) for all values of β but the dimension of its associated null space (a geometric condition) is one or two depending on the value of β.

5.4   Eigenvalue Multiplicities

Definition 5.8 The Algebraic and Geometric Multiplicity of an Eigenvalue and the Eigenspace: Assume that λ_f is an eigenvalue of A so that $\lambda_f \in \sigma(A)$. This means that λ_f is a root of the characteristic equation of A, that is, $\rho_A(\lambda_f) = 0$. This is equivalent to saying that the nth degree polynomial $\rho_A(\lambda)$ can be factored

$$\rho_A(\lambda) = (\lambda - \lambda_f)^a q(\lambda), \qquad a \geq 1$$

where the polynomial $q(\lambda)$ has degree $n - a$ and $q(\lambda_f) \neq 0$. Another way to say this is to say that $(\lambda - \lambda_f)^a$ is a factor of $\rho_A(\lambda)$ and $(\lambda - \lambda_f)^{a+1}$ is not a factor of $\rho_A(\lambda)$. The integer a is called the **algebraic multiplicity** of the eigenvalue λ_f. If $a = 1$ the eigenvalue λ_f is called a **simple eigenvalue**. Since λ_f is an eigenvalue of A, there is at least one non-zero vector $\vec{p}$ such that $A\vec{p} = \lambda_f\vec{p}$ or $(A - \lambda_f I)\vec{p} = \vec{0}$. The subspace of $\mathcal{R}^n$ defined by $\mathcal{N}(A - \lambda_f I)$ has dimension greater than or equal to one. The subspace $\mathcal{N}(A - \lambda_f I)$ is called the **eigenspace of A associated with the eigenvalue λ_f**. When the context is clear the subspace $\mathcal{N}(A - \lambda_f I)$ is called an **eigenspace of A**. Denote this dimension by the positive integer $g = \dim \mathcal{N}(A - \lambda_f I)$. This positive integer is called the **geometric multiplicity** of the eigenvalue λ_f. Assume that the rank of the matrix $A - \lambda_f I$ is the number r. The dimension of the null space $\mathcal{N}(A - \lambda_f I) = n - r$. Hence, the geometric multiplicity of λ_f satisfies $g = n - r$.

Example 5.9 For any of the matrices $A = \begin{bmatrix} 2 & \alpha \\ 4 & \beta \end{bmatrix}$ in parts 1, 2 and 3 of Example(5.4) corresponding to each simple eigenvalue $\lambda_j, j = 1, 2$ there is one eigenvector $\vec{p}_j$ and the two eigenvectors $\vec{p}_1$ and $\vec{p}_2$ are independent. Specifically, in part 1 of Example(5.4) where $\alpha = 4$ and $\beta = 2$ corresponding to the eigenvalue $\lambda_1 = -2$ is the eigenvector $\vec{p}_1 = \begin{bmatrix} 1 \\ -1 \end{bmatrix}$ and corresponding to $\lambda_2 = 6$ is $\vec{p}_2 = \begin{bmatrix} 1 \\ 1 \end{bmatrix}$ which are linearly independent. In the case $\alpha = -1$ and $\beta = 6$ the matrix A has the eigenvalue $\lambda = 4$ with algebraic multiplicity two. Since

$$\text{rank}(A - 4I) = \text{rank}\left(\begin{bmatrix} -2 & -1 \\ 4 & 2 \end{bmatrix}\right) = \text{rank}\left(\begin{bmatrix} -2 & -1 \\ 0 & 0 \end{bmatrix}\right) = 1$$

it follows that $\dim \mathcal{N}(A - 4I) = 1$. The subspace $\mathcal{N}(A - 4I)$ of $\mathcal{R}^2$ is spanned by the single eigenvector $\vec{p} = \begin{bmatrix} 1 \\ -2 \end{bmatrix}$ so that the geometric multiplicity of $\lambda = 4$ is one. Hence, the geometric multiplicity of $\lambda = 4$ is less than the algebraic multiplicity of $\lambda = 4$. In this case the matrix A is not diagonalizable.

For arbitrary values of β the characteristic equation for the matrix $A = \begin{bmatrix} 3 & 1 & 0 \\ 0 & 2 & 0 \\ \beta & -2 & 3 \end{bmatrix}$ of Example(5.7) is given by $\rho_A(\lambda) = (2 - \lambda)(3 - \lambda)^2$. Corresponding to the simple eigenvalue $\lambda = 2$ is the single eigenvector $\vec{p} = \begin{bmatrix} -1 \\ 1 \\ \beta + 2 \end{bmatrix}$ since the matrix

$$(A - 2I) = \begin{bmatrix} 1 & 1 & 0 \\ 0 & 0 & 0 \\ \beta & -2 & 1 \end{bmatrix} \sim \begin{bmatrix} 1 & 1 & 0 \\ 0 & 0 & 0 \\ 0 & -\beta - 2 & 1 \end{bmatrix} \sim \begin{bmatrix} 1 & 1 & 0 \\ 0 & -\beta - 2 & 1 \\ 0 & 0 & 0 \end{bmatrix}$$

has rank two. Hence, the $\dim \mathcal{N}(A - 2I) = 1$ so the geometric multiplicity of $\lambda = 2$ is one. The simple eigenvalue $\lambda = 2$ has the one dimensional subspace $\mathcal{N}(A - 2I)$.

From Example(5.7) the eigenvalue $\lambda = 3$ has algebraic multiplicity two and

$$\dim \left(\mathcal{N}(A - 3I)\right) = 3 - \begin{cases} 1 & \text{if} \quad \beta = 0 \\ 2 & \text{if} \quad \beta \neq 0 \end{cases} = \begin{cases} 2 & \text{if} \quad \beta = 0 \\ 1 & \text{if} \quad \beta \neq 0 \end{cases}.$$

In the language of Definition(5.8) the geometric multiplicity of $\lambda = 3$ is one if $\beta \neq 0$ and is two if $\beta = 0$. In either case the geometric multiplicity of $\lambda = 3$ is less than or equal to the algebraic multiplicity $\lambda = 3$. This inequality between the geometric and the algebraic multiplicity of the eigenvalue was also noted in the 2×2 case opening this example. Finally, in the case that the algebraic and the geometric multiplicity are the same ($\beta = 0$), the matrix A is diagonalizable (part 2 of Example(5.7)).

A general way to state the result in the last example is that if an eigenvalue λ of the matrix A has algebraic multiplicity a and geometric multiplicity g and if $a = g$, then the matrix A has a independent eigenvectors corresponding to the one eigenvalue λ. Further, if this equality of algebraic and geometric multiplicity persists for every eigenvalue of A then there are $n-$independent eigenvectors for the matrix A. In this event the matrix A is diagonalizable. This is a true statement, but to show it is true requires a bit more machinery than presently available. After building this machinery this result will be addressed. Another constant in all of the previous examples is that corresponding to a simple eigenvalue is a one-dimensional eigenspace and the eigenvectors corresponding to different eigenvalues are independent. This was the situation for parts 1, 2, and 3 of Example(5.4) and for parts 1 and 2 of Example(5.7). This is always the case.

5.5   Simple Eigenvalues and Independent Eigenvectors

Theorem 5.10 Distinct Eigenvalues and Independent Eigenvectors: Assume A is $n \times n$ and that $\lambda_1, \lambda_2, \ldots, \lambda_k$ are distinct eigenvalues of A, $\lambda_i \neq \lambda_j$, if $i \neq j$. Set $A\vec{p}_j = \lambda_j \vec{p}_j$, $j = 1, 2 \ldots, k$. The set of eigenvectors $\{\vec{p}_1, \vec{p}_2, \ldots, \vec{p}_k\}$ is a linearly independent set. If $k = n$ then $P \equiv [\vec{p}_1 \ \vec{p}_2 \ \ldots \ \vec{p}_n]$ is invertible and A is diagonalizable

$$
P^{-1}AP = \begin{bmatrix} \lambda_1 & 0 & \cdots & 0 \\ 0 & \lambda_2 & \cdots & 0 \\ \vdots & \vdots & \ddots & \vdots \\ 0 & 0 & \cdots & \lambda_n \end{bmatrix}.
$$

Assume that $k = 2$, $\lambda_1 \neq \lambda_2$ and $A\vec{p}_1 = \lambda_1 \vec{p}_1$ and $A\vec{p}_2 = \lambda_2 \vec{p}_2$. To see that the vectors $\vec{p}_1$ and $\vec{p}_2$ are linearly independent begin with the equation

$$c_1 \vec{p}_1 + c_2 \vec{p}_2 = 0 \tag{5.25}$$

and show that $c_1 = c_2 = 0$. Multiply (5.25) by λ_1 to get

$$c_1 \lambda_1 \vec{p}_1 + c_2 \lambda_1 \vec{p}_2 = 0.$$

Now multiply equation (5.25) by A and use the fact that $\vec{p}_1$ and $\vec{p}_2$ are eigenvectors to see

$$\vec{0} = A(c_1 \vec{p}_1 + c_2 \vec{p}_2) = c_1 A\vec{p}_1 + c_2 A\vec{p}_2 = c_1 \lambda_1 \vec{p}_1 + c_2 \lambda_2 \vec{p}_2 \ .$$

Subtract the last two lines to find

$$c_2 \lambda_1 \vec{p}_2 - c_2 \lambda_2 \vec{p}_2 = c_2 (\lambda_1 - \lambda_2) \vec{p}_2 = \vec{0} \ .$$

The last line implies $c_2 = 0$ since $\lambda_1 \neq \lambda_2$ and $\vec{p}_2 \neq \vec{0}$ is an eigenvector. Substitute $c_2 = 0$ in (5.25) to get $c_1 \vec{p}_1 = \vec{0}$ which implies that $c_1 = 0$ since $\vec{p}_1 \neq \vec{0}$ is an eigenvector. Since (5.25) implies that $c_1 = c_2 = 0$ the two eigenvectors are independent.

For the inductive step, assume that the set $\{\vec{p}_1, \vec{p}_2, \ldots, \vec{p}_{k-1}\}$ is an independent set and use this assumption to show that the set $\{\vec{p}_1, \vec{p}_2, \ldots, \vec{p}_{k-1}, \vec{p}_k\}$ is an independent set. Begin with the equation

$$c_1 \vec{p}_1 + c_2 \vec{p}_2 + \cdots + c_{k-1} \vec{p}_{k-1} + c_k \vec{p}_k = \vec{0} \tag{5.26}$$

and apply the matrix A to the equation in (5.26) to get

$$\begin{aligned}
\vec{0} &= A \left(c_1 \vec{p}_1 + c_2 \vec{p}_2 + \cdots + c_{k-1} \vec{p}_{k-1} + c_k \vec{p}_k \right) \\[2mm]
&= c_1 A \vec{p}_1 + c_2 A \vec{p}_2 + \cdots + c_{k-1} A \vec{p}_{k-1} + c_k A \vec{p}_k \\[2mm]
&= c_1 \lambda_1 \vec{p}_1 + c_2 \lambda_2 \vec{p}_2 + \cdots + \lambda_{k-1} c_{k-1} \vec{p}_{k-1} + \lambda_k c_k \vec{p}_k \ .
\end{aligned}$$

These are exactly the previous lines if $k = 2$. Multiply (5.26) by λ_k and subtract the last line from this product to obtain

$$c_1 (\lambda_k - \lambda_1) \vec{p}_1 + c_2 (\lambda_k - \lambda_2) \vec{p}_2 + \cdots + (\lambda_k - \lambda_{k-1}) c_{k-1} \vec{p}_{k-1} = \vec{0} \ .$$

Since $\lambda_k \neq \lambda_j$ $j = 1, 2, \ldots, k - 1$ and $\{\vec{p}_1, \vec{p}_2, \ldots, \vec{p}_{k-1}\}$ is a linearly independent set of eigenvectors $(\vec{p}_j \neq \vec{0})$, the last line implies that

$$c_1 = c_2 = \cdots c_{k-1} = 0.$$

Substituting these into (5.26) and using $\vec{p}_k \neq \vec{0}$ gives $c_k = 0$ so that the set of k vectors $\{\vec{p}_1, \vec{p}_2, \ldots, \vec{p}_{k-1}, \ \vec{p}_k\}$ is linearly independent. If in (5.26) $k = n$ then A has n distinct eigenvalues, λ_j, $j = 1, 2, \ldots, n$. The last line of the theorem follows since the columns of the matrix P consists of the n independent eigenvectors $\vec{p}_j$, $j = 1, 2, \ldots, n$ and, due to the independence, the matrix P is invertible. This is the special case of the dimension theorem(4.22).

If an eigenvalue λ is simple then its algebraic multiplicity $a = 1$ has the property that its geometric multiplicity $g = 1$ so the the inequality $g \leq a$ is true. If an eigenvalue λ has algebraic multiplicity a (not necessarily simple) and its geometric multiplicity is g, then in all of the preceding examples the inequality $g \leq a$ is satisfied. See part 4 of Example(5.4) and parts 2 and 3 of Example(5.7). This inequality is true in general and is further reinforced in the following example.

Example 5.11 Define the 4×4 matrix $A = \begin{bmatrix} & & & 0 \\ & B & & 0 \\ & & & 0 \\ 0 & 1 & 0 & 3 \end{bmatrix}$ where the 3×3 matrix B is

defined by $B = \begin{bmatrix} 3 & 1 & 0 \\ 0 & 2 & 0 \\ \beta & -2 & 3 \end{bmatrix}$. From Example(5.7) the characteristic equation for B is

$$\rho_B(\lambda) = \det\left(B - \lambda I\right)) = (2 - \lambda)(3 - \lambda)^2.$$

Expanding the $\det(A - \lambda I)$ around the fourth column gives the characteristic equation

$$\begin{aligned} \rho_A(\lambda) = |A - \lambda I| &= \det\left(\begin{bmatrix} & & & 0 \\ & B - \lambda I & & 0 \\ & & & 0 \\ 0 & 1 & 0 & 3 - \lambda \end{bmatrix}\right) \\ &= (3 - \lambda)\det\left(B - \lambda I\right)) \\ &= (3 - \lambda)\rho_B(\lambda) = (2 - \lambda)(3 - \lambda)^3. \end{aligned}$$

The notation I for both the 4×4 and 3×3 identity matrix is a minor abuse of notation but should not create any confusion. From $\rho_A(\lambda) = 0$ it follows that $\lambda_1 = 2$ is a simple eigenvalue of A and a straightforward calculation shows that

$$\begin{aligned} \operatorname{rank}(A - 2I) &= \operatorname{rank}\left(\begin{bmatrix} 1 & 1 & 0 & 0 \\ 0 & 0 & 0 & 0 \\ \beta & -2 & 1 & 0 \\ 0 & 1 & 0 & 1 \end{bmatrix}\right) = \operatorname{rank}\left(\begin{bmatrix} 1 & 1 & 0 & 0 \\ 0 & 1 & 0 & 1 \\ \beta & -2 & 1 & 0 \\ 0 & 0 & 0 & 0 \end{bmatrix}\right) \\ &= \operatorname{rank}\left(\begin{bmatrix} 1 & 1 & 0 & 0 \\ 0 & 1 & 0 & 1 \\ 0 & -2 - \beta & 1 & 0 \\ 0 & 0 & 0 & 0 \end{bmatrix}\right) \\ &= \operatorname{rank}\left(\begin{bmatrix} 1 & 1 & 0 & 0 \\ 0 & 1 & 0 & 1 \\ 0 & 0 & 1 & 2 + \beta \\ 0 & 0 & 0 & 0 \end{bmatrix}\right) = 3 \end{aligned}$$

for all β. Application of the dimension theorem guarantees that

$$\dim\left(\mathcal{N}(A - 2I)\right) = \dim(\mathcal{R}^4) - \operatorname{rank}(A - 2I) = 4 - 3 = 1$$

for all β. The equation

$$A\vec{p}_1 = A \begin{bmatrix} 1 \\ -1 \\ -\beta - 2 \\ 1 \end{bmatrix} = \begin{bmatrix} 3 & 1 & 0 & 0 \\ 0 & 2 & 0 & 0 \\ \beta & -2 & 3 & 0 \\ 0 & 1 & 0 & 3 \end{bmatrix} \begin{bmatrix} 1 \\ -1 \\ -\beta - 2 \\ 1 \end{bmatrix}$$

$$= \begin{bmatrix} 2 \\ -2 \\ -2\beta - 4 \\ 2 \end{bmatrix} = 2 \begin{bmatrix} 1 \\ -1 \\ -\beta - 2 \\ 1 \end{bmatrix} = 2\vec{p}_1 \tag{5.27}$$

shows that $\vec{p}_1$ is the single eigenvector corresponding to $\lambda_1 = 2$. The eigenvalue $\lambda_2 = 3$ has algebraic multiplicity $a = 3$ and the row reduction

$$(A - 3I) = \begin{bmatrix} 0 & 1 & 0 & 0 \\ 0 & -1 & 0 & 0 \\ \beta & -2 & 0 & 0 \\ 0 & 1 & 0 & 0 \end{bmatrix} \sim \begin{bmatrix} \beta & -2 & 0 & 0 \\ 0 & 1 & 0 & 0 \\ 0 & 0 & 0 & 0 \\ 0 & 0 & 0 & 0 \end{bmatrix}$$

shows that the

$$\text{rank of } (A - 3I) = \begin{cases} 2 & \text{if } \beta \neq 0 \\ 1 & \text{if } \beta = 0 \end{cases}.$$

The dimension theorem(4.22) shows that the geometric multiplicity is given by

$$g = \dim \mathcal{N}(A - 3I) = 4 - \begin{cases} 2 & \text{if } \beta \neq 0 \\ 1 & \text{if } \beta = 0 \end{cases} = \begin{cases} 2 & \text{if } \beta \neq 0 \\ 3 & \text{if } \beta = 0 \end{cases} \leq a = 3.$$

In the case that $\beta \neq 0$ the two vectors $\vec{e}_3 = \begin{bmatrix} 0 \\ 0 \\ 1 \\ 0 \end{bmatrix}$ and $\vec{e}_4 = \begin{bmatrix} 0 \\ 0 \\ 0 \\ 1 \end{bmatrix}$ are a basis for two

dimensional eigenspace $\mathcal{N}(A - 3I)$. If $\beta \neq 0$ the matrix A has only the three independent eigenvectors $\{\vec{p}_1, \vec{e}_3, \vec{e}_4\}$ and the matrix A is not diagonalizable. However if $\beta = 0$ the vector

$\vec{e}_1 = \begin{bmatrix} 1 \\ 0 \\ 0 \\ 0 \end{bmatrix}$ along with $\vec{e}_3$ and $\vec{e}_4$ are independent eigenvectors for $\lambda_2 = 3$. In this case the

dimension of the eigenspace $\mathcal{N}(A - 3I)$ is three. If $\beta = 0$ in the vector $\vec{p}_1$ in (5.27) then that equation shows that $\vec{p}_1$ is an eigenvector for $\lambda_1 = 2$ so the matrix $P = [\vec{p}_1 \ \vec{e}_1 \ \vec{e}_3 \ \vec{e}_4]$ diagonalizes the matrix A

$$P^{-1}AP = \begin{bmatrix} 0 & -1 & 0 & 0 \\ 1 & 1 & 0 & 0 \\ 0 & -2 & 1 & 0 \\ 0 & 1 & 0 & 1 \end{bmatrix} \begin{bmatrix} 3 & 1 & 0 & 0 \\ 0 & 2 & 0 & 0 \\ 0 & -2 & 3 & 0 \\ 0 & 1 & 0 & 3 \end{bmatrix} \begin{bmatrix} 1 & 1 & 0 & 0 \\ -1 & 0 & 0 & 0 \\ -2 & 0 & 1 & 0 \\ 1 & 0 & 0 & 1 \end{bmatrix}$$

$$= \begin{bmatrix} 0 & -1 & 0 & 0 \\ 1 & 1 & 0 & 0 \\ 0 & -2 & 1 & 0 \\ 0 & 1 & 0 & 1 \end{bmatrix} \begin{bmatrix} 2 & 3 & 0 & 0 \\ -2 & 0 & 0 & 0 \\ -4 & 0 & 3 & 0 \\ 2 & 0 & 0 & 3 \end{bmatrix} = \begin{bmatrix} 2 & 0 & 0 & 0 \\ 0 & 3 & 0 & 0 \\ 0 & 0 & 3 & 0 \\ 0 & 0 & 0 & 3 \end{bmatrix}.$$

The next example is a revisit and review of part 1 of Example(5.4). It advertises a direction for the rest of this chapter.

Example 5.12 The eigenvectors for $A = \begin{bmatrix} 2 & 4 \\ 4 & 2 \end{bmatrix}$ are

$$\vec{p}_1 = \begin{bmatrix} 1 \\ -1 \end{bmatrix} \text{ and } \vec{p}_2 = \begin{bmatrix} 1 \\ 1 \end{bmatrix}.$$

These vectors are orthogonal, $\vec{p}_1 \cdot \vec{p}_2 = \vec{p}_1^T \vec{p}_2 = 0$. In matrix form this orthogonality reads

$$P^T P = \begin{bmatrix} \vec{p}_1^T \\ \vec{p}_2^T \end{bmatrix} \begin{bmatrix} \vec{p}_1 & \vec{p}_2 \end{bmatrix} = \begin{bmatrix} 1 & -1 \\ 1 & 1 \end{bmatrix} \begin{bmatrix} 1 & 1 \\ -1 & 1 \end{bmatrix}$$

$$= \begin{bmatrix} 2 & 0 \\ 0 & 2 \end{bmatrix} = 2 \begin{bmatrix} 1 & 0 \\ 0 & 1 \end{bmatrix}.$$

Multiply on the right by P^{-1} and on the left by $1/2$ to see that

$$\frac{1}{2} P^T = \frac{1}{2} \begin{bmatrix} 1 & -1 \\ 1 & 1 \end{bmatrix} = P^{-1},$$

which is the identity advertised in (5.18). Since any scalar multiple of an eigenvector is an eigenvector replace $\vec{p}_1$ and $\vec{p}_2$ with

$$\vec{q}_1 = \frac{\vec{p}_1}{\|\vec{p}_1\|} = \frac{1}{\sqrt{2}} \begin{bmatrix} 1 \\ -1 \end{bmatrix} \text{ and } \vec{q}_2 = \frac{\vec{p}_2}{\|\vec{p}_2\|} = \frac{1}{\sqrt{2}} \begin{bmatrix} 1 \\ 1 \end{bmatrix}$$

which are eigenvectors with unit length. These vectors are also orthogonal, since the dot product $\vec{q}_1 \cdot \vec{q}_2 = \vec{q}_1^T \vec{q}_2 = 0$. As in (5.18) define

$$Q = [\vec{q}_1 \ \vec{q}_2] = \frac{1}{\sqrt{2}} \begin{bmatrix} 1 & 1 \\ -1 & 1 \end{bmatrix} \text{ has the inverse } Q^{-1} = \frac{1}{\sqrt{2}} \begin{bmatrix} 1 & -1 \\ 1 & 1 \end{bmatrix} \quad (5.28)$$

which has the property $Q^T = Q^{-1}$ or $Q^T Q = I$. In words this property states that the columns (or the rows) of Q are orthogonal and have unit length. Moreover

$$Q^{-1}AQ = Q^T A Q = \left(\frac{1}{\sqrt{2}} \begin{bmatrix} 1 & 1 \\ -1 & 1 \end{bmatrix} \right) \begin{bmatrix} 2 & 4 \\ 4 & 2 \end{bmatrix} \left(\frac{1}{\sqrt{2}} \begin{bmatrix} 1 & -1 \\ 1 & 1 \end{bmatrix} \right)$$

$$= \begin{bmatrix} -2 & 0 \\ 0 & 6 \end{bmatrix} = \Lambda.$$

so the orthogonal matrix Q is also a diagonalizer of the matrix A. This is equivalent to the diagonalization $P^{-1}AP = \Lambda$. The important part of this example is that the eigenvectors of A are orthogonal. To highlight this last statement, recall that the matrix $A = \begin{bmatrix} 2 & 0 \\ 4 & -2 \end{bmatrix}$ from part 2 of Example(5.4) is diagonalized by $P = \begin{bmatrix} 0 & 1 \\ 1 & 1 \end{bmatrix}$ and

$$P^{-1}AP = \begin{bmatrix} -1 & 1 \\ 1 & 0 \end{bmatrix} \begin{bmatrix} 2 & 0 \\ 4 & -2 \end{bmatrix} \begin{bmatrix} 0 & 1 \\ 1 & 1 \end{bmatrix} = \begin{bmatrix} -2 & 0 \\ 0 & 2 \end{bmatrix} = \Lambda.$$

If it were possible to find an α so that

$$P^{-1} = \begin{bmatrix} -1 & 1 \\ 1 & 0 \end{bmatrix} = \alpha \begin{bmatrix} 0 & 1 \\ 1 & 1 \end{bmatrix} = \alpha P^T$$

then this would require $-1 = \alpha 0 = 0$, which is impossible. Since the eigenvectors of A are not orthogonal, the matrix P cannot be replaced by an orthogonal matrix Q as in (5.28).

5.6 Orthogonal Matrices

Definition 5.13 Orthogonal Matrix and Orthogonal Diagonalization: Let Q be an $n \times n$ matrix with columns $\vec{q}_j, j = 1, 2, \ldots, n$. If the columns satisfy

$$\vec{q}_i \cdot \vec{q}_j = \vec{q}_i^T \vec{q}_j = \begin{cases} 1, & i = j \\ 0, & i \neq j \end{cases} \qquad i, j = 1, 2, \ldots, n \tag{5.29}$$

then the matrix Q is called an **orthogonal matrix**. The equality $(i = j)$ says that each of the columns $\vec{q}_j, j = 1, 2, \cdots, n$ is a unit vector and the inequality $(i \neq j)$ says the columns form an orthogonal (perpendicular) set of vectors. A matrix statement for (5.29) reads

$$Q^T Q = \begin{bmatrix} \vec{q}_1^T \\ \vec{q}_2^T \\ \vdots \\ \vec{q}_n^T \end{bmatrix} [\, \vec{q}_1 \; \vec{q}_2 \; \cdots \; \vec{q}_n \,] = \begin{bmatrix} \vec{q}_1^T \vec{q}_1 & \vec{q}_1^T \vec{q}_2 & \cdots & \vec{q}_1^T \vec{q}_n \\ \vec{q}_2^T \vec{q}_1 & \vec{q}_2^T \vec{q}_2 & \cdots & \vec{q}_2^T \vec{q}_n \\ \vdots & \vdots & \ddots & \vdots \\ \vec{q}_3^T \vec{q}_1 & \vec{q}_3^T \vec{q}_2 & \cdots & \vec{q}_n^T \vec{q}_n \end{bmatrix}$$

$$= \begin{bmatrix} 1 & 0 & \cdots & 0 \\ 0 & 1 & \cdots & 0 \\ \vdots & \vdots & \ddots & \vdots \\ 0 & 0 & \cdots & 1 \end{bmatrix}.$$

This shows that $Q^T = Q^{-1}$. The rows as well as the columns form an orthogonal set. If the matrix A can be diagonalized by an orthogonal matrix Q then A is said to be **orthogonally diagonalizable**, which in symbols reads $Q^T A Q = \Lambda$. Suppose the vectors in the matrix $P = [\, \vec{p}_1 \; \vec{p}_2 \; \cdots \; \vec{p}_n \,]$ satisfy

$$\vec{p}_i \cdot \vec{p}_j = \vec{p}_i^T \vec{p}_j = \begin{cases} \|\vec{p}_i\|^2, & i = j \\ 0, & i \neq j \end{cases} \qquad i, j = 1, 2, \ldots, n.$$

Replacing each $\vec{p}_i$ with $\vec{q}_i = \dfrac{\vec{p}_i}{\|\vec{p}_i\|}$ produces an orthogonal matrix Q.

Example 5.14 Define the matrix $A = \begin{bmatrix} 1 & -2 & 2 \\ -2 & \alpha & \beta \\ 2 & \beta & \alpha \end{bmatrix}$ and calculate

$$\rho_A(\lambda) = \det(A - \lambda I) = \begin{vmatrix} 1 - \lambda & -2 & 2 \\ -2 & \alpha - \lambda & \beta \\ 2 & \beta & \alpha - \lambda \end{vmatrix}$$

$$= [\alpha + \beta - \lambda] \{(1 - \lambda)(\alpha - \beta - \lambda) - 8\}.$$

Here are two cases of interest.

1. If $\alpha = 0$ and $\beta = 1$, a straightforward calculation shows that

$$\rho_A(\lambda) = (1 - \lambda)(\lambda^2 - 9) = (\lambda + 3)(1 - \lambda)(\lambda - 3)$$

so that $\sigma(A) = \{-3, 1, 3\}$. The three independent eigenvectors are $P = [\vec{p}_1\ \vec{p}_2\ \vec{p}_3]$ so the diagonalization of A reads

$$P^{-1}AP = \frac{1}{6} \begin{bmatrix} 2 & 2 & -2 \\ 0 & 3 & 3 \\ 2 & -1 & 1 \end{bmatrix} \begin{bmatrix} 1 & -2 & 2 \\ -2 & 0 & 1 \\ 2 & 1 & 0 \end{bmatrix} \begin{bmatrix} 1 & 0 & 2 \\ 1 & 1 & -1 \\ -1 & 1 & 1 \end{bmatrix}$$

$$= \frac{1}{6} \begin{bmatrix} 2 & 2 & -2 \\ 0 & 3 & 3 \\ 2 & -1 & 1 \end{bmatrix} \begin{bmatrix} -3 & 0 & 6 \\ -3 & 1 & -3 \\ 3 & 1 & 3 \end{bmatrix} = \begin{bmatrix} -3 & 0 & 0 \\ 0 & 1 & 0 \\ 0 & 0 & 3 \end{bmatrix}.$$

Theorem(5.10) guarantees that this matrix A is diagonalizable, since the eigenvalues are all simple. The matrix A has a further property. The eigenvectors of A which are the columns of P are perpendicular to each other $\vec{p}_i \cdot \vec{p}_j = 0$ for $i \neq j$. As in the end of Definition(5.13) set

$$\vec{q}_1 \equiv \frac{\vec{p}_1}{\|\vec{p}_1\|} = \frac{1}{\sqrt{3}} \begin{bmatrix} 1 \\ 1 \\ -1 \end{bmatrix}, \quad \vec{q}_2 \equiv \frac{\vec{p}_2}{\|\vec{p}_2\|} = \frac{1}{\sqrt{2}} \begin{bmatrix} 0 \\ 1 \\ 1 \end{bmatrix}$$

and

$$\vec{q}_3 \equiv \frac{\vec{p}_3}{\|\vec{p}_3\|} = \frac{1}{\sqrt{6}} \begin{bmatrix} 2 \\ -1 \\ 1 \end{bmatrix}.$$

The matrix

$$Q = \begin{bmatrix} \dfrac{\vec{p}_1}{\|\vec{p}_1\|} & \dfrac{\vec{p}_2}{\|\vec{p}_2\|} & \dfrac{\vec{p}_3}{\|\vec{p}_3\|} \end{bmatrix} = \begin{bmatrix} \dfrac{1}{\sqrt{3}} & 0 & \dfrac{2}{\sqrt{6}} \\ \dfrac{1}{\sqrt{3}} & \dfrac{1}{\sqrt{2}} & \dfrac{-1}{\sqrt{6}} \\ \dfrac{-1}{\sqrt{3}} & \dfrac{1}{\sqrt{2}} & \dfrac{1}{\sqrt{6}} \end{bmatrix} \tag{5.30}$$

is an orthogonal matrix and since its columns are eigenvectors for A, the matrix Q diagonalizes A:

$$Q^{-1}AQ = Q^T AQ = \begin{bmatrix} -3 & 0 & 0 \\ 0 & 1 & 0 \\ 0 & 0 & 3 \end{bmatrix}.$$

2. If $\alpha = 1$ and $\beta = 2$ then $A = \begin{bmatrix} 1 & -2 & 2 \\ -2 & 1 & 2 \\ 2 & 2 & 1 \end{bmatrix}$ and the characteristic equation for A is

$$\rho_A(\lambda) = |A - \lambda I| = \begin{bmatrix} 1-\lambda & -2 & 2 \\ -2 & 1-\lambda & 2 \\ 2 & 2 & 1-\lambda \end{bmatrix} = -(\lambda+3)(\lambda-3)^2.$$

Hence $\lambda_1 = -3$ is a simple eigenvalue and $\lambda_2 = 3$ is an eigenvalue with algebraic multiplicity $a = 2$. To find the eigenvector associated with $\lambda_1 = -3$, solve the equation $(A + 3I)\vec{p}_1 = \vec{0}$ using the row reduction

$$(A + 3I)\vec{p}_1 = \begin{bmatrix} 4 & -2 & 2 \\ -2 & 4 & 2 \\ 2 & 2 & 4 \end{bmatrix} \sim \begin{bmatrix} 4 & -2 & 2 \\ 0 & 3 & 3 \\ 0 & 0 & 0 \end{bmatrix}$$

to find $\vec{p}_1 = \begin{bmatrix} 1 \\ 1 \\ -1 \end{bmatrix}$. Further, the last display shows that the rank of $A + 3I$ is two so the dim $\mathcal{N}(A+3I) = 1$. The row reduction for the homogeneous system corresponding to the eigenvalue $\lambda_2 = \lambda_3 = 3$ is given by

$$[A - 3I] = \begin{bmatrix} -2 & -2 & 2 \\ -2 & -2 & 2 \\ 2 & 2 & -2 \end{bmatrix} \sim \begin{bmatrix} -2 & -2 & 2 \\ 0 & 0 & 0 \\ 0 & 0 & 0 \end{bmatrix}.$$

The matrix A has two independent eigenvectors $\vec{p}_2 = \begin{bmatrix} 0 \\ 1 \\ 1 \end{bmatrix}$ and $\vec{p}_3 = \begin{bmatrix} 2 \\ -1 \\ 1 \end{bmatrix}$ corresponding to the eigenvalue $\lambda_2 = 3$ so the geometric multiplicity of $\lambda_2 = 3$ is two. In symbols this reads dim $\mathcal{N}(A - 3I) = 2$. One could also take the two independent eigenvectors

$$\vec{\hat{p}}_2 = \vec{p}_2 = \begin{bmatrix} 0 \\ 1 \\ 1 \end{bmatrix} \quad \text{and} \quad \vec{\hat{p}}_3 = \begin{bmatrix} 1 \\ 0 \\ 1 \end{bmatrix}$$

as a basis for null space $\mathcal{N}(A - 3I)$. The base with $\vec{p}_2$ and $\vec{p}_3$ is preferred since these two eigenvectors vectors are orthogonal. If one had selected $\vec{\hat{p}}_2$ and $\vec{\hat{p}}_3$ as the eigenvectors for $\lambda_2 = 3$ then the Gram-Schmidt process (Exercise(4.16)) gives an algorithmic procedure to obtain the orthogonal set $\vec{p}_2$ and $\vec{p}_3$ from the set $\vec{p}_2$ and $\vec{p}_3$. The second equation in (4.45) (the Gram-Schmidt process) will produce $\vec{p}_2$ and $\vec{p}_3$ from $\vec{p}_2$ and $\vec{p}_3$. Notice that the three vectors $\{\vec{p}_1\ \vec{p}_2\ \vec{p}_3\}$ are the same as the three independent vectors for the matrix A in part 1 (See Exercise(5.6), part 8, for what this implies). For now, the matrix $P = [\vec{p}_1\ \vec{p}_2\ \vec{p}_3]$ as well as the matrix Q in (5.30) diagonalize this matrix A:

$$P^{-1}AP = Q^T AQ = \begin{bmatrix} -3 & 0 & 0 \\ 0 & 3 & 0 \\ 0 & 0 & 3 \end{bmatrix} = \Lambda.$$

The present example and part 2 of Example(5.7) both have an eigenvalue with algebraic multiplicity two and corresponding two-dimensional eigenspaces. In each case there is an invertible matrix P so that the corresponding matrix is diagonalizable. A point of departure then occurs. In the present example the diagonalizer P was exchanged for an orthogonal matrix Q. However in part 2 of Example(5.7) it is impossible to select the eigenvector $\vec{p}_1$ so that it is orthogonal to either of the eigenvectors $\vec{p}_2$ or $\vec{p}_3$. Hence there is no orthogonal matrix Q which will diagonalize the matrix A in part 2 of Example(5.7).

5.7   Complex Dot Products

The diagonalization that occurred in the last example is not just a fortunate turn of events or a piece of luck. It is a part of a very general and pretty matrix result. On the road to this result it will be discovered that the real numbers are not rich enough in structure to reveal the whole story. The following example shows that even with real entries for the matrix A, the complex numbers enter the discussion.

Example 5.15 The characteristic equation for the matrix $A = \begin{bmatrix} 1 & 1 \\ -1 & 1 \end{bmatrix}$ is given by

$$\rho_A(\lambda) = |A - \lambda I| = \begin{vmatrix} 1-\lambda & 1 \\ -1 & 1-\lambda \end{vmatrix} = \lambda^2 - 2\lambda + 2 = 0.$$

The eigenvalues are obtained from the quadratic formula

$$\lambda_\pm = \frac{-(-2) \pm \sqrt{(-2)^2 - 4(1)(2)}}{2} = \frac{2 \pm \sqrt{-4}}{2} = 1 \pm i$$

where $i = \sqrt{-1}$ is called the complex or imaginary unit. The real matrix A has eigenvalues which are the complex numbers $\lambda_\pm = 1 \pm i$. The eigenvector corresponding to the eigenvalue $\lambda_+ = 1 + i$ is computed from the equation

$$(A - \lambda_+ I)\vec{p}_1 = \begin{bmatrix} -i & 1 \\ -1 & -i \end{bmatrix} \vec{p}_1 = \begin{bmatrix} 0 \\ 0 \end{bmatrix}.$$

A vector satisfying this equation is given by $\vec{p_1} = \begin{bmatrix} i \\ -1 \end{bmatrix}$ so that

$$A\vec{p_1} = \begin{bmatrix} 1 & 1 \\ -1 & 1 \end{bmatrix} \begin{bmatrix} i \\ -1 \end{bmatrix} = \begin{bmatrix} -1+i \\ -1-i \end{bmatrix} = (1+i) \begin{bmatrix} i \\ -1 \end{bmatrix}.$$

Similarly if $\lambda_- = 1 - i$ the vector $\vec{p_2} = \begin{bmatrix} i \\ 1 \end{bmatrix}$ satisfies $(A - \lambda_- I)\vec{p_2} = \vec{0}$ so that

$$A\vec{p_2} = \begin{bmatrix} 1 & 1 \\ -1 & 1 \end{bmatrix} \begin{bmatrix} i \\ 1 \end{bmatrix} = \begin{bmatrix} 1+i \\ 1-i \end{bmatrix} = (1-i) \begin{bmatrix} i \\ 1 \end{bmatrix}.$$

The vectors $\vec{p_1}$ and $\vec{p_2}$ are linearly independent [Definition(4.8) is the same], since

$$c_1\vec{p_1} + c_2\vec{p_2} = c_1 \begin{bmatrix} i \\ -1 \end{bmatrix} + c_2 \begin{bmatrix} i \\ 1 \end{bmatrix} = \begin{bmatrix} i(c_1 + c_2) \\ (-c_1 + c_2) \end{bmatrix} = \begin{bmatrix} 0 \\ 0 \end{bmatrix}$$

shows $c_1 = c_2 = 0$. This independence also follows from Theorem(5.10), since that theorem is valid whether the eigenvectors are real or complex. The matrix

$$P = [\vec{p_1} \ \vec{p_2}] = \begin{bmatrix} i & i \\ -1 & 1 \end{bmatrix} \text{ is invertible with inverse } P^{-1} = \frac{1}{2i} \begin{bmatrix} 1 & -i \\ 1 & i \end{bmatrix}.$$

Hence the matrix A is diagonalizable and

$$P^{-1}AP = \frac{1}{2i} \begin{bmatrix} 1 & -i \\ 1 & i \end{bmatrix} \begin{bmatrix} 1 & 1 \\ -1 & 1 \end{bmatrix} \begin{bmatrix} i & i \\ -1 & 1 \end{bmatrix} = \Lambda = \begin{bmatrix} 1+i & 0 \\ 0 & 1-i \end{bmatrix}.$$

The matrix in this example and the matrix A in parts 1, 2 and 3 of Example(5.4) have the following property in common: two distinct eigenvalues with two independent eigenvectors. The only change is that this example required some complex arithmetic.

When the entries of some n−vector $\vec{x}$ have complex entries all of the standard laws of the arithmetic for vectors discussed in Theorem(1.5) from Chapter One remain valid. However, the dot product needs a minor modification. To see why such a modification is introduced, consider calculating the vector product

$$\vec{p_1}^T \vec{p_1} = [\, i \ -1 \,] \begin{bmatrix} i \\ -1 \end{bmatrix} = i(i) + (-1)(-1) = i^2 + 1 = -1 + 1 = 0.$$

When the entries in the vector $\vec{p_1}$ are real this product is the dot product of $\vec{p_1}$ with itself which from Definition(1.8) gives the square of the length of the vector $\vec{p_1}$. It would be nice to maintain a notion of length (a non-negative quantity) even if the entries of $\vec{p_1}$ are complex. All that is needed is a broader definition of the dot product which reduces to the original definition when the entries are real. A clue is provided from complex numbers.

Definition 5.16 Complex Number, Complex Conjugates and the Length of a Complex Number: Let a and b be real numbers and set $x = a + bi$ where $i^2 = -1$ is called the complex unit. The number a is called the real part of the complex number x and b is called the imaginary part of x. The **complex conjugate** of x is defined by $\bar{x} = \overline{a + bi} = a - bi$ and is read x–bar. The operation **bar** changes the sign of the imaginary part of a complex number. If $x = a$ is a real number then $\bar{x} = \bar{a} = a$. Notice that

$$\bar{\bar{x}} = \overline{\overline{a + bi}} = \overline{a - bi} = a + bi = x.$$

The product

$$x\bar{x} = (a + bi)(a - bi) = a^2 + abi - abi - (bi)(bi) = a^2 - b^2(i)^2 = a^2 + b^2$$

is always a non-negative real number. The quantity $|x| = \sqrt{a^2 + b^2}$ is called the **length** of x since the complex number x is often associated with the ordered pair (a, b). In this notation $x\bar{x} = |x|^2 = a^2 + b^2$ is the square of the length of x. Let a_j and b_j, $j = 1, 2, \ldots, n$ be real numbers and define the complex numbers $x_j = a_j + b_j i$. Define the two vectors

$$\vec{x} = \begin{bmatrix} x_1 \\ x_2 \\ \vdots \\ x_n \end{bmatrix} = \begin{bmatrix} a_1 + b_1 i \\ a_2 + b_2 i \\ \vdots \\ a_n + b_n i \end{bmatrix} \quad \text{and} \quad \bar{\vec{x}} = \begin{bmatrix} \bar{x}_1 \\ \bar{x}_2 \\ \vdots \\ \bar{x}_n \end{bmatrix} = \begin{bmatrix} a_1 - b_1 i \\ a_2 - b_2 i \\ \vdots \\ a_n - b_n i \end{bmatrix}.$$

Calculate the product

$$\begin{aligned} \bar{\vec{x}}^{\,T} \vec{x} &= \begin{bmatrix} \bar{x}_1 & \bar{x}_2 & \cdots & \bar{x}_n \end{bmatrix} \begin{bmatrix} x_1 \\ x_2 \\ \vdots \\ x_n \end{bmatrix} = \sum_{j=1}^{n} \bar{x}_j x_j = \sum_{j=1}^{n} |x_j|^2 \\ &= \sum_{j=1}^{n} \left(\sqrt{a_j^2 + b_j^2}\right)^2 = \sum_{j=1}^{n} (a_j^2 + b_j^2) \geq 0. \end{aligned}$$

If $b_j = 0$, $j = 1, 2, \ldots, n$ the previous display is $||\vec{x}||^2$ as given in Definition(1.1). Since this is the real vector product it seems reasonable to continue this notation. The symbol $\bar{\vec{x}}^{\,T}$ is cumbersome to write, so the following definition is employed.

Definition 5.17 Conjugate Transpose, the Dot Product, Orthogonal Vectors and the Length of a Vector: If $\vec{x} = \begin{bmatrix} x_1 \\ x_2 \\ \vdots \\ x_n \end{bmatrix}$ then its **conjugate transpose** is the row

vector

$$\vec{x}^{\,*} \equiv \bar{\vec{x}}^{\,T} = \begin{bmatrix} \bar{x}_1 & \bar{x}_2 & \cdots & \bar{x}_n \end{bmatrix}.$$

If $\vec{y}$ is another $n-$vector then the **dot or scalar product** is defined by

$$\vec{x} \cdot \vec{y} \equiv \vec{x}^{\,*}\vec{y} \equiv \bar{\vec{x}}^{\,T}\vec{y} = \sum_{j=1}^{n} \bar{x}_j y_j. \tag{5.31}$$

If $\vec{x}^{\,*}\vec{y} = 0$ the vectors are still called **orthogonal** and the notation remains $\vec{x} \perp \vec{y}$. The one change in passing from vectors with real entries to vectors with complex entries is that the dot product is not commutative

$$\vec{y} \cdot \vec{x} \equiv \vec{y}^{\,*}\vec{x} = \sum_{j=1}^{n} \bar{y}_j x_j = \overline{\sum_{j=1}^{n} y_j \bar{x}_j} = \overline{\sum_{j=1}^{n} \bar{x}_j y_j} = \overline{\vec{x}^{\,*}\vec{y}} = \overline{\vec{x} \cdot \vec{y}}. \tag{5.32}$$

If $\vec{x} = \vec{y}$ in (5.32) then the non-negative quantity

$$\vec{x} \cdot \vec{x} \equiv \vec{x}^{\,*}\vec{x} = \sum_{j=1}^{n} \bar{x}_j x_j = \sum_{j=1}^{n} |x_j|^2$$

is called the **length** of $\vec{x}$. The notation is the same as in the real case so

$$\|\vec{x}\| = \sqrt{\vec{x} \cdot \vec{x}} = \sqrt{\vec{x}^{\,*}\vec{x}}$$

is the length of $\vec{x}$. If the entries of $\vec{x}$ and $\vec{y}$ are real then $\vec{x} \cdot \vec{y} = \overline{\vec{y} \cdot \vec{x}} = \vec{y} \cdot \vec{x}$ since the conjugate of a real number is itself and the dot product here is the original dot product.

Example 5.18 Returning to the vectors from Example(5.15) if $\vec{p}_1 = \begin{bmatrix} i \\ -1 \end{bmatrix}$ the square of its length is

$$\begin{aligned}
\|\vec{p}_1\|^2 &= \vec{p}_1 \cdot \vec{p}_1 = \vec{p}_1^{\,*} \begin{bmatrix} i \\ -1 \end{bmatrix} = \overline{[\, i \;\; -1\,]} \begin{bmatrix} i \\ -1 \end{bmatrix} \\
&= [\,-i \;\; -1\,] \begin{bmatrix} i \\ -1 \end{bmatrix} = -i^2 + (-1)(-1) = 2.
\end{aligned}$$

If $\vec{p}_2 = \begin{bmatrix} i \\ 1 \end{bmatrix}$ the calculation

$$\vec{p}_1 \cdot \vec{p}_2 = \vec{p}_1^{\,*}\vec{p}_2 = \overline{[\, i \;\; -1\,]} \begin{bmatrix} i \\ 1 \end{bmatrix} = [\,-i \;\; -1\,] \begin{bmatrix} i \\ 1 \end{bmatrix} = -i^2 - 1 = 0$$

shows that $\vec{p}_1$ and $\vec{p}_2$ are orthogonal. Further, if $\vec{q} = \begin{bmatrix} 1 \\ i \end{bmatrix}$ then

$$\vec{p}_1 \cdot \vec{q} = \vec{p}_1^{\,*}\vec{p}_2 = \overline{[\, i \;\; -1\,]} \begin{bmatrix} 1 \\ i \end{bmatrix} = [\,-i \;\; -1\,] \begin{bmatrix} 1 \\ i \end{bmatrix} = -i - i = -2i$$

and

$$\vec{q} \cdot \vec{p_1} = \vec{q}^* \vec{p_1} = \overline{[1\ i]} \begin{bmatrix} i \\ -1 \end{bmatrix} = [1\ -i] \begin{bmatrix} i \\ -1 \end{bmatrix} = i + i = 2i$$

which illustrates a special case of (5.32): $\overline{\vec{p_1} \cdot \vec{q}} = \overline{-2i} = 2i = \vec{q} \cdot \vec{p_1}$.

There are occasions when, even though the entries in the matrix A are complex, the eigenvalues of the matrix are real. The following example is an illustration of this situation.

Example 5.19 The characteristic equation for $A = \begin{bmatrix} 2 & 3-3i \\ 3+3i & 5 \end{bmatrix}$ is given by

$$\rho_A(\lambda) = |A - \lambda I| = \begin{vmatrix} 2-\lambda & 3-3i \\ 3+3i & 5-\lambda \end{vmatrix} = \lambda^2 - 7\lambda - 8 = (\lambda+1)(\lambda-8).$$

The eigenvalues of A are the real numbers $\lambda_1 = -1$ and $\lambda_2 = 8$. The eigenvector corresponding to the eigenvalue $\lambda_1 = -1$ is any non-zero solution to the equation

$$(A - (-1)I)\vec{p_1} = (A + I)\vec{p_1} = \begin{bmatrix} 3 & 3-3i \\ 3+3i & 6 \end{bmatrix} \vec{p_1} = \vec{0}\ .$$

A vector satisfying this equation is given by $\vec{p_1} = \begin{bmatrix} 1-i \\ -1 \end{bmatrix}$ so $\lambda_1 = -1$ and $\vec{p_1}$ satisfies the equation

$$\begin{bmatrix} 2 & 3-3i \\ 3+3i & 5 \end{bmatrix} \begin{bmatrix} 1-i \\ -1 \end{bmatrix} = \begin{bmatrix} 2-2i-3+3i \\ 3-3i+3i+3-5 \end{bmatrix} = (-1) \begin{bmatrix} 1-i \\ -1 \end{bmatrix}.$$

Similarly $\lambda_2 = 8$ and $\vec{p_2} = \begin{bmatrix} 1 \\ 1+i \end{bmatrix}$ satisfies

$$\begin{bmatrix} 2 & 3-3i \\ 3+3i & 5 \end{bmatrix} \begin{bmatrix} 1 \\ 1+i \end{bmatrix} = \begin{bmatrix} 2+3-3i+3i+3 \\ 3+3i+5+5i \end{bmatrix} \begin{bmatrix} 8 \\ 8+8i \end{bmatrix} = 8 \begin{bmatrix} 1 \\ 1+i \end{bmatrix}.$$

The two vectors are linearly independent, since $\lambda_1 \neq \lambda_2$ and, as noted in Example(5.15), Theorem(5.10) still applies. The matrix

$$P = [\vec{p_1}\ \vec{p_2}] = \begin{bmatrix} 1-i & 1 \\ -1 & 1+i \end{bmatrix}$$

is invertible since $\det(P) = (1-i)(1+i) + 1 = 1 - i + i + 1 + 1 = 3 \neq 0$. The inverse of P can be found using formula (3.14) in Theorem(3.14) and this formula gives

$$P^{-1} = \frac{1}{\det(P)} \begin{bmatrix} 1+i & -1 \\ 1 & 1-i \end{bmatrix} = \frac{1}{3} \begin{bmatrix} 1+i & -1 \\ 1 & 1-i \end{bmatrix}.$$

Hence the matrix A is diagonalizable and

$$P^{-1}AP = \frac{1}{3}\begin{bmatrix} 1+i & -1 \\ 1 & 1-i \end{bmatrix}\begin{bmatrix} 2 & 3-3i \\ 3+3i & 5 \end{bmatrix}\begin{bmatrix} 1-i & 1 \\ -1 & 1+i \end{bmatrix}$$

$$= \frac{1}{3}\begin{bmatrix} 1+i & -1 \\ 1 & 1-i \end{bmatrix}\begin{bmatrix} -1+i & 8 \\ 1 & 8+8i \end{bmatrix}$$

$$= \frac{1}{3}\begin{bmatrix} (1+i)(-1+i)-1 & 8(1+i)-(8+8i) \\ -1+i+1-i & 8+(1-i)(8+8i) \end{bmatrix}$$

$$= \frac{1}{3}\begin{bmatrix} -1-1-1 & 0 \\ 0 & 8+8+8 \end{bmatrix} = \begin{bmatrix} -1 & 0 \\ 0 & 8 \end{bmatrix} = \Lambda.$$

The dot product of the vectors $\vec{p}_1$ and $\vec{p}_2$ satisfies

$$\vec{p}_1{}^*\vec{p}_2 = \overline{[1-i \quad -1]}\begin{bmatrix} 1 \\ 1+i \end{bmatrix} = [1+i \quad -1]\begin{bmatrix} 1 \\ 1+i \end{bmatrix} = 0$$

so that $\vec{p}_1 \perp \vec{p}_2$. The calculation

$$\|\vec{p}_1\|^2 = \vec{p}_1{}^*\vec{p}_1 = [1+i \quad -1]\begin{bmatrix} 1-i \\ -1 \end{bmatrix} = (1+i)(1-i)+1 = 3$$

shows that the length of $\vec{p}_1$ is $\|\vec{p}_1\| = \sqrt{3}$. The length of $\vec{p}_2$ is the same. The unit vectors defined by

$$\vec{q}_1 = \frac{1}{\sqrt{3}}\begin{bmatrix} 1-i \\ -1 \end{bmatrix} \text{ and } \vec{q}_2 = \frac{1}{\sqrt{3}}\begin{bmatrix} 1 \\ 1+i \end{bmatrix},$$

are orthogonal. The matrix $Q = [\vec{q}_1 \ \vec{q}_2]$ has the property

$$\bar{Q}^T Q \equiv \frac{1}{\sqrt{3}}\begin{bmatrix} 1+i & -1 \\ 1 & 1-i \end{bmatrix}\frac{1}{\sqrt{3}}\begin{bmatrix} 1-i & 1 \\ -1 & 1+i \end{bmatrix} = \begin{bmatrix} 1 & 0 \\ 0 & 1 \end{bmatrix}. \tag{5.33}$$

The equation in (5.33) shows that $\bar{Q}^T = Q^{-1}$ so that

$$\bar{Q}^T A Q = \Lambda = \begin{bmatrix} -1 & 0 \\ 0 & 8 \end{bmatrix}.$$

This example has a number of properties that mimic properties of the symmetric matrices in Examples(5.12) and (5.14). In contrast to those two examples, however, the matrix

$$A = \begin{bmatrix} 2 & 3-3i \\ 3+3i & 5 \end{bmatrix} \neq \begin{bmatrix} 2 & 3+3i \\ 3-3i & 5 \end{bmatrix} = A^T \tag{5.34}$$

is not symmetric. Definition(3.8) called a square matrix symmetric if $A = A^T$. At that point the matrix entries were from the real numbers. This definition is now stated as follows:

a real square matrix A is symmetric if $A = A^T$. However the matrix A does satisfies

$$\overline{A^T} = \bar{A}\,^T = \overline{\begin{bmatrix} 2 & 3-3i \\ 3+3i & 5 \end{bmatrix}}^T = \begin{bmatrix} \bar{2} & \overline{3-3i} \\ \overline{3+3i} & \bar{5} \end{bmatrix}^T$$

$$= \begin{bmatrix} 2 & 3+3i \\ 3-3i & 5 \end{bmatrix}^T = A.$$

Just as Definition(5.17) provided a broader definition of the vector transpose, the previous display motivates a broader definition of the matrix transpose.

5.8   Hermitian and Unitary Matrices

Definition 5.20 Hermitian Matrices: The $n \times n$ matrix A is called a **Hermitian matrix** if it is equal to its conjugate transpose,

$$A^* = [a_{ij}]^* = [\bar{a}_{ij}]^T = [\bar{a}_{ji}] = [a_{ij}] = A \ . \tag{5.35}$$

If $i = j$ then (5.35) shows that the diagonal entries satisfy $\overline{a_{jj}} = a_{jj}$ so that if A is Hermitian then the diagonal entries are real numbers. If all of the entries in A are real numbers ($\overline{a_{ij}} = a_{ij}$) then a Hermitian matrix A is a symmetric matrix.

Theorem 5.21 The Eigenvalues of a Hermitian Matrix are real: If λ and $\vec{p}$ are an eigenpair for the Hermitian matrix A then λ is a real number.

Multiply each side of the equation $A\vec{p} = \lambda\vec{p}$ by $\vec{p}^{\,*}$ to find

$$\vec{p}^{\,*}A\vec{p} = \lambda\vec{p}^{\,*}\vec{p} = \lambda||\vec{p}\,||^2.$$

Take the conjugate transpose of the left hand side to see $(\vec{p}^{\,*}A\vec{p})^* = \vec{p}^{\,*}A^*\vec{p} = \vec{p}^{\,*}A\vec{p}$ since $(\vec{p}^{\,*})^* = \vec{p}$ and $A^* = A$. Take the conjugate transpose on the right hand side to get $(\lambda||\vec{p}\,||^2)^* = \bar{\lambda}||\vec{p}\,||^2$ so that

$$\vec{p}^{\,*}A\vec{p} = (\vec{p}^{\,*}A\vec{p})^* = \vec{p}^{\,*}A^*\vec{p} = \bar{\lambda}||\vec{p}\,||^2 \ .$$

Subtract the second displayed equation from the first to find

$$\lambda||\vec{p}\,||^2 - \bar{\lambda}||\vec{p}\,||^2|| = (\lambda - \bar{\lambda})||\vec{p}\,||^2 = 0.$$

Since $\vec{p}$ is an eigenvector, $||\vec{p}||^2 \neq 0$ so that $\lambda = \bar{\lambda}$, or λ is a real number.

Theorem 5.22 Orthogonal Eigenvectors of a Hermitian Matrix: Assume $A = A^*$, $A\vec{p_1} = \lambda_1\vec{p_1}$, $A\vec{p_2} = \lambda_2\vec{p_2}$ and $\lambda_1 \neq \lambda_2$. The eigenvectors $\vec{p_1}$ and $\vec{p_2}$ corresponding to distinct eigenvalues are orthogonal, $\vec{p_1}^*\vec{p_2} = 0$.

Multiply $A\vec{p}_1 = \lambda_1 \vec{p}_1$ by $\vec{p}_2^{\,*}$ to get

$$\vec{p}_2^{\,*} A \vec{p}_1 = \vec{p}_2^{\,*} \lambda_1 \vec{p}_1 = \lambda_1 \vec{p}_2^{\,*} \vec{p}_1 \tag{5.36}$$

and $A\vec{p}_2 = \lambda_2 \vec{p}_2$ by $\vec{p}_1^{\,*}$ to find

$$\vec{p}_1^{\,*} A \vec{p}_2 = \vec{p}_1^{\,*} \lambda_2 \vec{p}_2 = \lambda_2 \vec{p}_1^{\,*} \vec{p}_2. \tag{5.37}$$

Take the conjugate transpose of (5.37) to find

$$\vec{p}_2^{\,*} A^* \vec{p}_1 = \vec{p}_2^{\,*} A \vec{p}_1 = \lambda_2 \vec{p}_2^{\,*} \vec{p}_1$$

since $A = A^*$ and λ_2 is real. Subtract the last line from the identity in (5.36) to find

$$(\lambda_1 - \lambda_2) \vec{p}_2^{\,*} \vec{p}_1 = 0.$$

Since $\lambda_1 \neq \lambda_2$ the scalar product $\vec{p}_2^{\,*} \vec{p}_1 = 0$ so that $\vec{p}_1$ and $\vec{p}_2$ are orthogonal.

A real symmetric matrix A is Hermitian, so it follows from the above that the eigenvalues of A are real and the eigenvectors corresponding to distinct eigenvalues are orthogonal. Example(5.14) illustrates a case when the diagonalizer Q is an orthogonal matrix ($Q^T = Q^{-1}$). The matrix A in Example(5.19) is Hermitian and this example illustrates a case where the matrix of eigenvectors has the property $Q^* A Q = \Lambda$. This class of matrices plays the role in Hermitian matrices that orthogonal matrices play for symmetric matrices.

Definition 5.23 Unitary Matrices: Matrices satisfying $Q^* = Q^{-1}$ are called **Unitary Matrices**. If Q is unitary with real entries then Q is an orthogonal matrix.

One may conjecture that all Hermitian matrices are diagonalizable and to show this is a goal of this chapter. As it turns out if one focuses to closely on this goal one may miss the heart of the matter. The next example relaxes the diagonalization requirement a bit.

Example 5.24 The matrix $A = \begin{bmatrix} 2 & -1 \\ 4 & 6 \end{bmatrix}$ from part 4 of Example(5.4) has $\lambda = 4$ as an eigenvalue with algebraic multiplicity two and corresponding eigenvector

$$\vec{p}_1 = \begin{bmatrix} 1 \\ -2 \end{bmatrix}$$

with geometric multiplicity one. Hence this matrix is not diagonalizable. However, define the unit eigenvector

$$\vec{q}_1 = \frac{\vec{p}_1}{||\vec{p}_1||} = \frac{1}{\sqrt{5}} \begin{bmatrix} 1 \\ -2 \end{bmatrix}.$$

Select any unit vector orthogonal to $\vec{q_1}$, say $\vec{q_2} = \dfrac{1}{\sqrt{5}} \begin{bmatrix} 2 \\ 1 \end{bmatrix}$. This selection guarantees that the matrix $Q = [\vec{q_1}\ \vec{q_2}]$ is an orthogonal matrix. The matrix multiplication gives

$$
\begin{aligned}
Q^*AQ = Q^TAQ &= \frac{1}{\sqrt{5}} \begin{bmatrix} 1 & -2 \\ 2 & 1 \end{bmatrix} \begin{bmatrix} 2 & -1 \\ 4 & 6 \end{bmatrix} \frac{1}{\sqrt{5}} \begin{bmatrix} 1 & 2 \\ -2 & 1 \end{bmatrix} \\
&= \frac{1}{5} \begin{bmatrix} 1 & -2 \\ 2 & 1 \end{bmatrix} \begin{bmatrix} 4 & 3 \\ -8 & 14 \end{bmatrix} = \begin{bmatrix} 4 & -5 \\ 0 & 4 \end{bmatrix} = R.
\end{aligned}
$$

An upper triangular factorization is better than nothing! Note that the eigenvalues of A are on the diagonal of R.

5.9   Triangular Factorization and Schur's Lemma

Theorem 5.25 Schur's Lemma or the Triangular Factorization of A: Let A be an arbitrary $n \times n$ matrix. There is a unitary matrix Q ($Q^* = Q^{-1}$) and an upper triangular matrix R so that

$$
Q^*AQ = R = \begin{bmatrix} r_{11} & r_{12} & \cdots & r_{1n} \\ 0 & r_{22} & \cdots & r_{2n} \\ \vdots & \ddots & \ddots & \vdots \\ 0 & 0 & \cdots & r_{nn} \end{bmatrix} = \begin{bmatrix} \lambda_1 & r_{12} & \cdots & r_{1n} \\ 0 & \lambda_2 & \cdots & r_{2n} \\ \vdots & \ddots & \ddots & \vdots \\ 0 & 0 & \cdots & \lambda_n \end{bmatrix}.
$$

Let A be a 2×2 matrix. Every matrix has at least one eigenpair λ and $\vec{q_1}$ where the eigenvector has unit length, $\vec{q_1}^{\,*}\vec{q_1} = 1$. Select any unit vector $\vec{q_2}$ orthogonal to $\vec{q_1}$ and define

$$
Q = \begin{bmatrix} \vec{q_1} & \vec{q_2} \end{bmatrix} \quad \text{so that} \quad Q^* = \begin{bmatrix} \vec{q_1}^{\,*} \\ \vec{q_2}^{\,*} \end{bmatrix}.
$$

By definition Q is a unitary matrix so that $Q^{-1} = Q^*$. The calculation

$$
\begin{aligned}
Q^*AQ &= \begin{bmatrix} \vec{q_1}^{\,*} \\ \vec{q_2}^{\,*} \end{bmatrix} A \begin{bmatrix} \vec{q_1} & \vec{q_2} \end{bmatrix} = \begin{bmatrix} \vec{q_1}^{\,*} \\ \vec{q_2}^{\,*} \end{bmatrix} \begin{bmatrix} A\vec{q_1} & A\vec{q_2} \end{bmatrix} \\
&= \begin{bmatrix} \vec{q_1}^{\,*} \\ \vec{q_2}^{\,*} \end{bmatrix} \begin{bmatrix} \lambda\vec{q_1} & A\vec{q_2} \end{bmatrix} = \begin{bmatrix} \lambda\vec{q_1}^{\,*}\vec{q_1} & \vec{q_1}^{\,*}A\vec{q_2} \\ \lambda\vec{q_2}^{\,*}\vec{q_1} & \vec{q_2}^{\,*}A\vec{q_2} \end{bmatrix} \\
&= \begin{bmatrix} \lambda & \vec{q_1}^{\,*}A\vec{q_2} \\ 0 & \vec{q_2}^{\,*}A\vec{q_2} \end{bmatrix} = R
\end{aligned}
\tag{5.38}
$$

shows that every 2×2 matrix A is unitarily similar to an upper triangular matrix.

Assume that $\vec{q_1}$ is a unit vector for the 3×3 matrix B and $B\vec{q_1} = \mu\vec{q_1}$ $\vec{q_1} \neq \vec{0}$ so μ and $\vec{q_1}$ is an eigenpair for B. Select any two unit vectors $\vec{q_2}$ and $\vec{q_3}$ so that the set $\{\vec{q_1}, \vec{q_2}, \vec{q_3}\}$

is an orthogonal set. The Gram-Schmidt process in Exercise(4.16) gives an algorithmic procedure for selecting $\vec{q}_2$ and $\vec{q}_3$. Note that the dot products in the Gram-Schmidt process can be defined by Definition(1.8) or by Definition(5.17). This means that the matrix $\tilde{Q} = \begin{bmatrix} \vec{q}_1 & \vec{q}_2 & \vec{q}_3 \end{bmatrix}$ is a unitary matrix:

$$\tilde{Q}^*\tilde{Q} = \begin{bmatrix} 1 & 0 & 0 \\ 0 & 1 & 0 \\ 0 & 0 & 1 \end{bmatrix}.$$

As in the 2×2 factorization leading to (5.38) calculate

$$
\begin{aligned}
\tilde{Q}^*B\tilde{Q} &= \begin{bmatrix} \vec{q}_1^{\,*} \\ \vec{q}_2^{\,*} \\ \vec{q}_3^{\,*} \end{bmatrix} \begin{bmatrix} B\vec{q}_1 & B\vec{q}_2 & B\vec{q}_3 \end{bmatrix} = \begin{bmatrix} \vec{q}_1^{\,*} \\ \vec{q}_2^{\,*} \\ \vec{q}_3^{\,*} \end{bmatrix} \begin{bmatrix} \mu\vec{q}_1 & B\vec{q}_2 & B\vec{q}_3 \end{bmatrix} \\[2mm]
&= \begin{bmatrix} \mu\vec{q}_1^{\,*}\vec{q}_1 & \vec{q}_1^{\,*}B\vec{q}_2 & \vec{q}_1^{\,*}B\vec{q}_3 \\ \mu\vec{q}_2^{\,*}\vec{q}_1 & \vec{q}_2^{\,*}B\vec{q}_2 & \vec{q}_2^{\,*}B\vec{q}_3 \\ \mu\vec{q}_3^{\,*}\vec{q}_1 & \vec{q}_3^{\,*}B\vec{q}_2 & \vec{q}_3^{\,*}B\vec{q}_3 \end{bmatrix} \\[2mm]
&= \begin{bmatrix} \mu & \vec{q}_1^{\,*}B\vec{q}_2 & \vec{q}_1^{\,*}B\vec{q}_3 \\ 0 & \vec{q}_2^{\,*}B\vec{q}_2 & \vec{q}_2^{\,*}B\vec{q}_3 \\ 0 & \vec{q}_3^{\,*}B\vec{q}_2 & \vec{q}_3^{\,*}B\vec{q}_3 \end{bmatrix} = \begin{bmatrix} \mu & \beta_{12} & \beta_{13} \\ 0 & & \\ 0 & & A \end{bmatrix}.
\end{aligned}
\qquad (5.39)
$$

The 2×2 matrix A in the lower right hand corner of (5.39) can be unitarily transformed to an upper triangular matrix R by (5.38), that is,

$$Q^*AQ = R = \begin{bmatrix} \lambda & \vec{q}_1^{\,*}A\vec{q}_2 \\ 0 & \vec{q}_2^{\,*}A\vec{q}_2 \end{bmatrix} \equiv \begin{bmatrix} \lambda & \alpha_{12} \\ 0 & \alpha_{22} \end{bmatrix}.$$

Now define the matrix $\hat{Q} = \begin{bmatrix} 1 & 0 & 0 \\ 0 & & \\ 0 & & Q \end{bmatrix}$ so that $\hat{Q}^* = \begin{bmatrix} 1 & 0 & 0 \\ 0 & & \\ 0 & & Q^* \end{bmatrix}$ and a simple

calculation shows that $\hat{Q}^*\hat{Q} = \begin{bmatrix} 1 & 0 & 0 \\ 0 & 1 & 0 \\ 0 & 0 & 1 \end{bmatrix} = I$ so that $\hat{Q}$ is a unitary matrix. Define the

matrix $P = \tilde{Q}\hat{Q}$ and calculate

$$
\begin{aligned}
P^*BP &= \hat{Q}^*\tilde{Q}^*B\tilde{Q}\hat{Q} = \hat{Q}^* \begin{bmatrix} \mu & \beta_{12} & \beta_{13} \\ 0 & & \\ 0 & & A \end{bmatrix} \hat{Q} = \begin{bmatrix} \mu & \beta_{12} & \beta_{13} \\ 0 & & \\ 0 & & \hat{Q}^*A\hat{Q} \end{bmatrix} \\[2mm]
&= \begin{bmatrix} \mu & \beta_{12} & \beta_{13} \\ 0 & & \\ 0 & & R \end{bmatrix} = \begin{bmatrix} \mu & \beta_{12} & \beta_{13} \\ 0 & \lambda & \alpha_{12} \\ 0 & 0 & \alpha_{22} \end{bmatrix} \equiv \bar{R}.
\end{aligned}
$$

Another matrix multiplication shows that the matrix $P = \tilde{Q}\hat{Q}$ is unitary and the previous calculation gives a unitary matrix so that $P^*BP = \bar{R}$ is upper triangular matrix.

Assume the matrix B is $n \times n$, $B\vec{q_1} = \mu\vec{q_1}$ and $\vec{q_1}$ is a unit vector. Select the $n-1$ unit vectors $\{\vec{q_2}, \vec{q_3}, \ldots, \vec{q_n}\}$ so that the set consisting of the n vectors $\{\vec{q_1}, \vec{q_2}, \ldots, \vec{q_n}\}$ is an orthonormal set. Here the Gram-Schmidt process is again used. Now the matrix A in (5.39) is an $n-1 \times n-1$ matrix. If it is assumed that A is unitarily similar to an upper triangular matrix, then the above provides the inductive step needed to obtain the statement of Schur's Lemma for $n \times n$ matrices. To write this proof out requires the production of a number of matrices like that found in equation (5.44). This is a more complicated typing problem than it is a difficult proof problem.

If A is real with real eigenvalues $\lambda_i, i = 1, 2, \ldots n$ then the word unitary can be replaced with orthogonal in Schur's Lemma so, in this case, the lemma reads: there is an orthogonal matrix Q so that

$$Q^*AQ = \begin{bmatrix} \lambda_1 & r_{12} & \cdots & r_{1n} \\ 0 & \lambda_2 & \cdots & r_{2n} \\ \vdots & \ddots & \ddots & \vdots \\ 0 & 0 & \cdots & \lambda_n \end{bmatrix}.$$

Here is an example of the construction in Schur's Lemma.

Example 5.26 The matrix $A = \begin{bmatrix} 3 & 1 & 0 \\ 0 & 2 & 0 \\ 1 & -2 & 3 \end{bmatrix}$ in Example(5.7) has $\sigma(A) = \{3, 3, 2\}$ with the eigenvector $\vec{p_1} = \begin{bmatrix} -1 \\ 1 \\ 3 \end{bmatrix}$ corresponding to $\lambda_3 = 2$. Hence, the vector

$$\vec{q_1} = \frac{\vec{p_1}}{\|\vec{p_1}\|} = \frac{1}{\sqrt{11}} \begin{bmatrix} -1 \\ 1 \\ 3 \end{bmatrix}$$

is a unit eigenvector in the direction of $\vec{p_1}$. The two unit vectors

$$\vec{q_2} = \frac{1}{\sqrt{2}} \begin{bmatrix} 1 \\ 1 \\ 0 \end{bmatrix} \text{ and } \vec{q_3} = \frac{1}{\sqrt{22}} \begin{bmatrix} 3 \\ -3 \\ 2 \end{bmatrix}$$

are orthogonal to each other and are orthogonal to $\vec{q_1}$. See equation (4.45) in part 2 of the Gram-Schmidt Exercise(4.16). The matrix

$$Q = [\vec{q_1} \ \vec{q_2} \ \vec{q_3}] = \begin{bmatrix} \dfrac{-1}{\sqrt{11}} & \dfrac{1}{\sqrt{2}} & \dfrac{3}{\sqrt{22}} \\ \dfrac{1}{\sqrt{11}} & \dfrac{1}{\sqrt{2}} & \dfrac{-3}{\sqrt{22}} \\ \dfrac{3}{\sqrt{11}} & 0 & \dfrac{2}{\sqrt{22}} \end{bmatrix}$$

has the property

$$Q^T A Q = Q^T \begin{bmatrix} 3 & 1 & 0 \\ 0 & 2 & 0 \\ 0 & -2 & 3 \end{bmatrix} Q$$

$$= \begin{bmatrix} 2 & \dfrac{-5}{\sqrt{22}} & \dfrac{3}{\sqrt{2}} \\ 0 & 3 & 0 \\ 0 & \dfrac{2}{\sqrt{11}} & 3 \end{bmatrix} \equiv \begin{bmatrix} 2 & \dfrac{-5}{\sqrt{22}} & \dfrac{3}{\sqrt{22}} \\ 0 & & \\ 0 & & A \end{bmatrix}.$$

The 2×2 matrix $A = \begin{bmatrix} 3 & 0 \\ \dfrac{2}{\sqrt{11}} & 3 \end{bmatrix}$ has $\lambda = 3$ as an eigenvalue with algebraic multiplicity

two with the single eigenvector $\vec{p}_1 = \begin{bmatrix} 0 \\ 1 \end{bmatrix}$. Select $\vec{q}_2 = \begin{bmatrix} 1 \\ 0 \end{bmatrix}$, which is a unit vector

orthogonal to the unit eigenvector $\vec{p}_1$, and define

$$Q_1 = \begin{bmatrix} 0 & 1 \\ 1 & 0 \end{bmatrix} \quad \text{and} \quad \hat{Q} = \begin{bmatrix} 1 & 0 & 0 \\ 0 & & \\ 0 & & Q_1 \end{bmatrix} = \begin{bmatrix} 1 & 0 & 0 \\ 0 & 0 & 1 \\ 0 & 1 & 0 \end{bmatrix}.$$

The calculation

$$\hat{Q}^T (Q^T A Q) \hat{Q} = \hat{Q}^T \begin{bmatrix} 2 & \dfrac{-5}{\sqrt{22}} & \dfrac{3}{\sqrt{2}} \\ 0 & 3 & 0 \\ 0 & \dfrac{2}{\sqrt{11}} & 3 \end{bmatrix} \hat{Q}$$

$$= \begin{bmatrix} 1 & 0 & 0 \\ 0 & 0 & 1 \\ 0 & 1 & 0 \end{bmatrix} \begin{bmatrix} 2 & \dfrac{-5}{\sqrt{22}} & \dfrac{3}{\sqrt{2}} \\ 0 & 3 & 0 \\ 0 & \dfrac{2}{\sqrt{11}} & 3 \end{bmatrix} \begin{bmatrix} 1 & 0 & 0 \\ 0 & 0 & 1 \\ 0 & 1 & 0 \end{bmatrix}$$

$$= \begin{bmatrix} 2 & \dfrac{3}{\sqrt{2}} & \dfrac{-5}{\sqrt{22}} \\ 0 & 3 & \dfrac{2}{\sqrt{11}} \\ 0 & 0 & 3 \end{bmatrix}$$

produces an upper triangular matrix for the conclusion of Schur's Lemma corresponding
to the selection of $\vec{q}_1$. Suppose instead of beginning with $\lambda_3 = 2$ and $\vec{q}_1$ above, the vector

$\vec{q}_1 = \begin{bmatrix} 0 \\ 0 \\ 1 \end{bmatrix}$ is selected which is an eigenvector corresponding to $\lambda_1 = 3$. Define the matrix

$$\hat{Q} = [\vec{q}_1 \ \vec{q}_2 \ \vec{q}_3] = \begin{bmatrix} 0 & 1 & 0 \\ 0 & 0 & 1 \\ 1 & 0 & 0 \end{bmatrix}$$

where the vectors $\vec{\hat{q}}_2$ and $\vec{\hat{q}}_3$ are chosen so that the set of vectors $\{\vec{\hat{q}}_1, \vec{\hat{q}}_2, \vec{\hat{q}}_3\}$ form an orthogonal set of vectors. The calculation

$$\hat{Q}^T A \hat{Q} = \begin{bmatrix} 0 & 0 & 1 \\ 1 & 0 & 0 \\ 0 & 1 & 0 \end{bmatrix} \begin{bmatrix} 3 & 1 & 0 \\ 0 & 2 & 0 \\ 1 & -2 & 3 \end{bmatrix} \begin{bmatrix} 0 & 1 & 0 \\ 0 & 0 & 1 \\ 1 & 0 & 0 \end{bmatrix} = \begin{bmatrix} 3 & 1 & -2 \\ 0 & 3 & 1 \\ 0 & 0 & 2 \end{bmatrix}.$$

directly produces the upper triangular matrix R in Schur's theorem corresponding to the selection of $\vec{\hat{q}}_1$.

5.10   Hermitian and Symmetric Matrix Diagonalization

Theorem 5.27 The Diagonalization of Hermitian Matrices: If the $n \times n$ matrix A is Hermitian $(A = A^*)$ then A is unitarily similar to the diagonal matrix of it's real eigenvalues $\{\lambda_j\}_{j=1}^n$. There is a unitary matrix Q $(Q^{-1} = Q^*)$ so that

$$Q^* A Q = \Lambda = \begin{bmatrix} \lambda_1 & 0 & \cdots & 0 \\ 0 & \lambda_2 & \ddots & 0 \\ \vdots & \ddots & \ddots & \vdots \\ 0 & \cdots & 0 & \lambda_n \end{bmatrix}. \tag{5.40}$$

By Schur's Lemma there is a unitary matrix Q and an upper triangular matrix R, so that $A = QRQ^*$. Taking the conjugate transpose of this expression gives $A^* = QR^*Q^*$. Since it is assumed that A is Hermitian, it follows that

$$QRQ^* = A = A^* = QR^*Q^*.$$

Multiply the left hand side of this equation by Q^* and the right hand side by Q to obtain $R = R^*$. Since R is upper triangular the matrix R^* is lower triangular and the equality of the two implies that R is diagonal. Indeed, the diagonal equality implies that $r_{jj} = \overline{r_{jj}}, j = 1, 2, \ldots, n$ so that not only is R diagonal but the diagonal entries (the eigenvalues of A) are real numbers.

There is a partial converse to Theorem(5.27). If $Q^* A Q = \Lambda$ and the λ_j are all real, then $A^* = A$. To see this write, $A = Q\Lambda Q^*$ followed by

$$A^* = (Q\Lambda Q^*)^* = Q\Lambda^* Q* = Q\Lambda Q* = A.$$

A specific example is given in the Example(5.19). The matrix A is Hermitian and a unitary diagonalizer is the matrix Q which is displayed in (5.33). A real number illustration of Theorem(5.27) is provided by Example(5.12). The matrix A in part 1 of Example(5.12) is a symmetric (Hermitian) matrix and the orthogonal (unitary) diagonalizer is the matrix Q displayed in (5.28).

Theorem 5.28 The Diagonalization of Symmetric Matrices: If the entries of the matrix A are real and A is symmetric ($A = A^T$) then A is orthogonally similar to the diagonal matrix of it's real eigenvalues $\{\lambda_j\}_{j=1}^n$. In symbols, there is an orthogonal matrix Q satisfying

$$Q^T A Q = \Lambda = \begin{bmatrix} \lambda_1 & 0 & \cdots & 0 \\ 0 & \lambda_2 & \ddots & 0 \\ \vdots & 0 & \ddots & 0 \\ 0 & \cdots & 0 & \lambda_n \end{bmatrix}.$$

Actually, the converse statement of Theorem(5.28) is true. If a real matrix A is orthogonally similar to a diagonal matrix then $A = A^T$. To see this let Q be the orthogonal diagonalizer of A and rewrite $Q^T A Q = \Lambda$ in the form $A = Q\Lambda Q^T$ (use $Q^T = Q^{-1}$). Taking the transpose of the last identity gives

$$A^T = (Q\Lambda Q^T)^T = (Q^T)^T (\Lambda)^T Q^T = Q\Lambda Q^T = A.$$

Hence the matrix A is symmetric. Since Theorem(5.28) is a "real" theorem it is fair question to ask why complex numbers were introduced in Example(5.15). What is meant by referring to Theorem(5.28) as a "real" theorem is that the entries in the matrix A are all real, the eigenvalues are real, and the eigenvectors have all real components. Why bring up Hermitian matrices to arrive at the diagonalization of real symmetric matrices? The reason complex numbers and Hermitian matrices were brought up is very simple: a proof of the result that a real symmetric matrix is diagonalizable based only on real number considerations is more difficult.

According to Definition(5.6) an $n \times n$ matrix A is diagonalizable if A is similar to a diagonal matrix, there is a matrix P so that $P^{-1}AP = \Lambda$. After the fact it follows that the columns of P are the eigenvectors of A and the entries on the diagonal of Λ are the eigenvalues of A. To decide whether a given matrix A is diagonalizable amounts to the question of whether the given matrix A has n-independent eigenvectors. If A has n distinct eigenvalues then A is diagonalizable (Theorem(5.10)). If the matrix A is real adding the assumption that A is symmetric played an important role.

As was pointed out this added assumption was easier to analyze if the matrix A is Hermitian. If A is Hermitian then A is unitarily diagonalizable (Theorem(5.27)). The result of Example(5.15) shows that there are unitarily diagonalizable matrices which are not Hermitian (symmetric). In that example the matrix A is not Hermitian but it is unitarily diagonalizable. This gap between arbitrary matrices and Hermitian matrices is filled by the following types of matrices.

5.11   Diagonalization of Normal Matrices

Theorem 5.29 Normal Matrices and the Diagonalization of Normal Matrices: A matrix A is called **normal** if $AA^* = A^*A$. The $n \times n$ matrix A is unitarily diagonalizable if and only if A is normal.

One direction of the proof is straightforward. If A is unitarily diagonalizable $Q^*AQ = \Lambda$ then A is normal because

$$
\begin{aligned}
AA^* &= (Q\Lambda Q^*)(Q\Lambda^* Q^*) = Q\Lambda\Lambda^* Q^* \quad \text{diagonal matrices commute} \\
&= Q\Lambda^*\Lambda Q^* = (Q\Lambda^* Q^*)(Q\Lambda Q^*) = A^*A \ .
\end{aligned}
$$

By Schur's Lemma there is a unitary Q so that $Q^*AQ = R$ where the matrix R is upper triangular. If A is normal then

$$
\begin{aligned}
RR^* &= (Q^*AQ)(Q^*A^*Q) = Q^*AA^*Q = Q^*A^*AQ \quad \text{since } QQ^* = I \\
&= (Q^*A^*Q)(Q^*AQ) = R^*R
\end{aligned}
$$

where normality $AA^* = A^*A$ is used in the third equality. The last displayed equation shows that the upper triangular matrix R of Schur's Lemma is normal. To finish the argument one must show that a normal upper triangular matrix is a diagonal matrix. This is carried out for a 3×3 matrix R. There is a computational argument for this result which begins by equating, entry by entry, the two products

$$
\begin{aligned}
RR^* &=
\begin{bmatrix}
r_{11} & r_{12} & r_{13} \\
0 & r_{22} & r_{23} \\
0 & 0 & r_{33}
\end{bmatrix}
\begin{bmatrix}
\bar{r}_{11} & 0 & 0 \\
\bar{r}_{12} & \bar{r}_{22} & 0 \\
\bar{r}_{13} & \bar{r}_{23} & \bar{r}_{33}
\end{bmatrix} \\
&=
\begin{bmatrix}
\bar{r}_{11} & 0 & 0 \\
\bar{r}_{12} & \bar{r}_{22} & 0 \\
\bar{r}_{13} & \bar{r}_{23} & \bar{r}_{33}
\end{bmatrix}
\begin{bmatrix}
r_{11} & r_{12} & r_{13} \\
0 & r_{22} & r_{23} \\
0 & 0 & r_{33}
\end{bmatrix}
= R^*R \ .
\end{aligned}
$$

Equate the one-one element of the first product to the one-one element of the second product to find

$$
r_{11}\bar{r}_{11} + r_{12}\bar{r}_{12} + r_{13}\bar{r}_{13} = |r_{11}|^2 + r_{12}\bar{r}_{12} + r_{13}\bar{r}_{13} = |r_{11}|^2
$$

which, upon canceling $|r_{11}|^2$, implies that $r_{12}\bar{r}_{12} + r_{13}\bar{r}_{13} = |r_{12}|^2 + |r_{13}|^2 = 0$ or $r_{12} = r_{13} = 0$. Repeating this with the two-two element of the first product and the two-two element of the second product gives

$$
r_{22}\bar{r}_{22} + r_{23}\bar{r}_{23} = \bar{r}_{12}r_{12} + \bar{r}_{22}r_{22}.
$$

Cancel $r_{22}\bar{r}_{22} = |r_{22}|^2$ from each side, substitute $r_{12} = 0$ to find $r_{23}\bar{r}_{23} = |r_{23}|^2 = 0$, which implies that $r_{23} = 0$. Hence

$$
R =
\begin{bmatrix}
r_{11} & r_{12} & r_{13} \\
0 & r_{22} & r_{23} \\
0 & 0 & r_{33}
\end{bmatrix}
=
\begin{bmatrix}
r_{11} & 0 & 0 \\
0 & r_{22} & 0 \\
0 & 0 & r_{33}
\end{bmatrix}
$$

so that the matrix R is diagonal.

Example 5.30 The matrix $A = \begin{bmatrix} 1 & 1 \\ -1 & 1 \end{bmatrix}$ in Example(5.15) has the property

$$AA^* = \begin{bmatrix} 1 & 1 \\ -1 & 1 \end{bmatrix}\begin{bmatrix} 1 & -1 \\ 1 & 1 \end{bmatrix} = \begin{bmatrix} 2 & 0 \\ 0 & 2 \end{bmatrix} = \begin{bmatrix} 1 & -1 \\ 1 & 1 \end{bmatrix}\begin{bmatrix} 1 & 1 \\ -1 & 1 \end{bmatrix} = A^*A$$

so that this matrix is normal. Neither Theorem(5.27) nor Theorem(5.28) apply to the matrix A since A is neither Hermitian nor symmetric. However, it was shown in Example(5.15) that the matrix $P = [\ \vec{p}_1\ \vec{p}_2\ ] = \begin{bmatrix} i & i \\ -1 & 1 \end{bmatrix}$ has the property

$$P^{-1}AP = \frac{1}{2i}\begin{bmatrix} 1 & -i \\ 1 & i \end{bmatrix}\begin{bmatrix} 1 & 1 \\ -1 & 1 \end{bmatrix}\begin{bmatrix} i & i \\ -1 & 1 \end{bmatrix} = \begin{bmatrix} 1+i & 0 \\ 0 & 1-i \end{bmatrix}$$

so the matrix P diagonalizes the matrix A. The square of the length of $\vec{p}_1$ is given by

$$||\vec{p}_1||^2 = \vec{p}_1{}^*\vec{p}_1 = [-i \ -1]\begin{bmatrix} i \\ -1 \end{bmatrix} = -i^2 + 1 = 2.$$

It is straightforward to check that the length $||\vec{p}_2||^2 = ||\vec{p}_1||^2$ and

$$\vec{p}_1{}^*\vec{p}_2 = [-i \ -1]\begin{bmatrix} i \\ 1 \end{bmatrix} = -i^2 - 1 = 0$$

so a unitary diagonalizer in Theorem(5.29) is given by $Q = \dfrac{1}{\sqrt{2}}\begin{bmatrix} i & i \\ -1 & 1 \end{bmatrix}$.

Example 5.31 Let a, b, c and d be real numbers and show that the most general non-symmetric 2×2 normal matrix $A = \begin{bmatrix} a & b \\ c & d \end{bmatrix} = \begin{bmatrix} a & b \\ -b & a \end{bmatrix}$. Begin with the calculation

$$AA^* = \begin{bmatrix} a & b \\ c & d \end{bmatrix}\begin{bmatrix} a & c \\ b & d \end{bmatrix} = \begin{bmatrix} a^2+b^2 & ac+bd \\ ac+bd & c^2+d^2 \end{bmatrix}$$

$$= \begin{bmatrix} a^2+c^2 & ab+cd \\ ab+cd & b^2+d^2 \end{bmatrix}$$

$$= \begin{bmatrix} a & c \\ b & d \end{bmatrix}\begin{bmatrix} a & b \\ c & d \end{bmatrix} = A^*A.$$

Equating the one-one component gives $b^2 = c^2$ or $b = \pm c$. Since A is not symmetric, $(b \neq c)$ the last equality reads $b = -c$. Equating the one-two component gives $ac+bd = ab+cd$ or $a(c-b) = d(c-b)$. Substituting $b = -c$ and assuming $b \neq 0$ (A is not symmetric) leads to

$a = d$. To check that $A = \begin{bmatrix} a & b \\ -b & a \end{bmatrix}$ is normal calculate

$$AA^* = \begin{bmatrix} a & b \\ -b & a \end{bmatrix} \begin{bmatrix} a & -b \\ b & a \end{bmatrix} = \begin{bmatrix} a^2 + b^2 & 0 \\ 0 & a^2 + b^2 \end{bmatrix}$$

$$= \begin{bmatrix} a & -b \\ b & a \end{bmatrix} \begin{bmatrix} a & b \\ -b & a \end{bmatrix} = A^*A.$$

If $a = b = 1$ then this is the matrix in Example(5.30).

5.12   Algebraic Multiplicity $\geq$ Geometric Multiplicity

Example 5.32 Let A be a 4×4 matrix and denote its eigenvalues by $\sigma(A) = \{\lambda_1, \lambda_2, \lambda_3, \lambda_4\}$. Assume that λ_1 and λ_2 are simple eigenvalues (each have algebraic multiplicity one) and $\lambda_3 = \lambda_4$ has algebraic multiplicity two. By Schur's lemma there is a unitary Q so that

$$Q^*AQ = \begin{bmatrix} \lambda_1 & r_{12} & r_{13} & r_{14} \\ 0 & \lambda_2 & r_{23} & r_{24} \\ 0 & 0 & \lambda_3 & r_{34} \\ 0 & 0 & 0 & \lambda_3 \end{bmatrix}.$$

Using $Q^*Q = I$ and

$$Q^*AQ - (\lambda I)Q^*Q = Q^*AQ - Q^*(\lambda I)Q = Q^*(A - \lambda I)Q$$

gives

$$Q^*(A - \lambda I)Q = \begin{bmatrix} \lambda_1 - \lambda & r_{12} & r_{13} & r_{14} \\ 0 & \lambda_2 - \lambda & r_{23} & r_{24} \\ 0 & 0 & \lambda_3 - \lambda & r_{34} \\ 0 & 0 & 0 & \lambda_3 - \lambda \end{bmatrix}. \tag{5.41}$$

The result in Exercise(5.15) guarantees that the rank of $(A - \lambda I)$ is the same as the rank of $Q^*(A - \lambda I)Q$, that is, the right hand side of (5.41). According to Theorem(5.11) there are at least three independent eigenvectors for A, namely, those corresponding to the distinct eigenvalues, λ_1, λ_2, and λ_3. Hence, the question of whether A is diagonalizable rests on the dimension of $\mathcal{N}(A - \lambda_3 I)$. From (5.41), the

$$\text{rank}\,(A - \lambda_3 I) = \text{rank}\left(\begin{bmatrix} \lambda_1 - \lambda_3 & r_{12} & r_{13} & r_{14} \\ 0 & \lambda_2 - \lambda_3 & r_{23} & r_{24} \\ 0 & 0 & 0 & r_{34} \\ 0 & 0 & 0 & 0 \end{bmatrix}\right) \tag{5.42}$$

is at least two since $\lambda_1 - \lambda_3 \neq 0$ and $\lambda_2 - \lambda_3 \neq 0$. It follows from the dimension theorem that

$$\begin{aligned}
\dim \mathcal{N}(A - \lambda_3 I) &= 4 - \text{rank}(A - \lambda_3 I) \\
&= 4 - \begin{cases} 2 & r_{34} = 0 \\ 3 & r_{34} \neq 0 \end{cases} = \begin{cases} 2 & r_{34} = 0 \\ 1 & r_{34} \neq 0 \end{cases}.
\end{aligned} \tag{5.43}$$

The geometric multiplicity of λ_3 is less than or equal to its algebraic multiplicity. If $r_{34} = 0$ this matrix is diagonalizable and if $r_{34} \neq 0$ then this matrix is not diagonalizable.

The previous steps can be modified to show that the geometric multiplicity of an eigenvalue is always less than or equal to the algebraic multiplicity of the eigenvalue. Assume that λ_f is an eigenvalue of the $n \times n$ matrix A and λ_f has algebraic multiplicity a. Denote the spectrum of A by $\sigma(A) = \{\lambda_1, \lambda_2, \cdots, \lambda_{n-a}, \lambda_f\}$ where λ_f occurs a times and $\lambda_j \neq \lambda_f, j = 1, 2, \cdots, n - a$. By Schur's Lemma write

$$Q^*AQ = \begin{bmatrix} \lambda_1 & \cdots & r_{1,\gamma} & r_{1,\gamma+1} & r_{1,\gamma+2} & \cdots & r_{1n} \\ \vdots & \ddots & \vdots & \cdots & \vdots & \cdots & \vdots \\ 0 & \cdots & \lambda_{n-a} & \ddots & \cdots & \cdots & r_{\gamma,n} \\ 0 & \cdots & \vdots & \lambda_f & r_{\gamma+1,\gamma+2} & \cdots & r_{\gamma+1,n} \\ \vdots & \vdots & \vdots & \vdots & \ddots & \ddots & \vdots \\ 0 & \cdots & \vdots & \vdots & \vdots & \ddots & r_{n-1,n} \\ 0 & \cdots & \cdots & \cdots & \cdots & \cdots & \lambda_f \end{bmatrix} \quad \text{where} \quad \gamma = n - a$$

since the last a rows have the eigenvalue λ_f on the diagonal. The analogue of (5.41) reads

$$Q^*(A - \lambda_f I)Q = Q^*AQ - Q^*\lambda_f I Q = Q^*AQ - \lambda_f I$$

$$= \begin{bmatrix} \lambda_1 - \lambda_f & \cdots & r_{1,\gamma} & r_{1,\gamma+1} & r_{1,\gamma+2} & \cdots & r_{1n} \\ \vdots & \ddots & \vdots & \cdots & \vdots & \cdots & \vdots \\ 0 & \cdots & \lambda_{n-a} - \lambda_f & \ddots & \cdots & \cdots & r_{\gamma,n} \\ 0 & \cdots & \vdots & 0 & r_{\gamma+1,\gamma+2} & \cdots & r_{\gamma+1,n} \\ \vdots & \vdots & \vdots & \vdots & \ddots & \ddots & \vdots \\ 0 & \cdots & \vdots & \vdots & \vdots & \ddots & r_{n-1,n} \\ 0 & \cdots & \cdots & \cdots & \cdots & \cdots & 0 \end{bmatrix}. \quad (5.44)$$

Since $\lambda_j - \lambda_f \neq 0$ and $j = 1, 2, \ldots, n - a$ from (5.44) $\operatorname{rank}(A - \lambda_f I) \geq n - a$. Set $\dim \mathcal{N}(A - \lambda_f I) = g$; use the last inequality and the dimension theorem(4.22) to write

$$n - a \leq \operatorname{rank}(A - \lambda_f I) = n - \dim \mathcal{N}(A - \lambda_f I) = n - g.$$

The last display shows that the inequality $g \leq a$ always holds.

Theorem 5.33 Geometric Multiplicity $\leq$ Algebraic Multiplicity Assume that A is $n \times n$ and λ_f is an eigenvalue of A with algebraic multiplicity a_f. If the geometric multiplicity of λ_f is $g_f = \dim \mathcal{N}(A - \lambda_f I)$ then $g_f \leq a_f$.

If an $n \times n$ matrix A has n linearly independent eigenvectors then from Theorem(5.11) the matrix A is diagonalizable. In conjunction with the previous theorem this can also be formulated as follows.

Theorem 5.34 Another Diagonalization Theorem Let A be an $n \times n$ matrix. Denote an eigenvalue of A by λ_f. Let a_f be the algebraic multiplicity of λ_f and let $g_f = \dim \mathcal{N}(A - \lambda_f I)$ be the geometric multiplicity of λ_f. A is diagonalizable if and only if $a_f = g_f$ for every eigenvalue $\lambda_f \in \sigma(A)$.

Example 5.35 Assume that the $n \times n$ matrix A has n distinct eigenvalues. That is, denote the spectrum of A by $\sigma(A) = \{\lambda_1, \lambda_2, \cdots, \lambda_n\}$ where the assumption is $\lambda_i \neq \lambda_j, i \neq j$. Use (5.44) to see that $\dim \mathcal{N}(A - \lambda_j I) = 1$ for $j = 1, 2, \ldots, n$. The distinct assumption implies that the algebraic multiplicity of each λ_j is one so that Theorem(5.34) implies that A is diagonalizable. This is different way to obtain Theorem(5.10).

5.13   Quadratic Forms

Example 5.36 Quadratic Forms: Let a_{11}, a_{12} and a_{22} real numbers and define the function of two variables

$$
\begin{aligned}
q(x_1, x_2) &\equiv [x_1, x_2] A \begin{bmatrix} x_1 \\ x_2 \end{bmatrix} = [x_1, x_2] \begin{bmatrix} a_{11} & a_{12} \\ a_{12} & a_{22} \end{bmatrix} A \begin{bmatrix} x_1 \\ x_2 \end{bmatrix} \\
&= a_{11}x_1^2 + a_{22}x_2^2 + 2a_{12}x_1 x_2.
\end{aligned} \tag{5.45}
$$

The function $q(x_1, x_2)$ is called a **quadratic form**. The problem is to graph the quadratic $q(x_1, x_2) = \kappa > 0$ a constant. If $a_{12} = 0$ this is a standard problem from geometry and the graph is a circle ($a_{11} = a_{12} > 0$), ellipse ($a_{11} \neq a_{22}, a_{11}a_{22} > 0$), or a hyperbola ($a_{11}a_{22} < 0$). Since A is symmetric, Theorem(5.28) gives an orthogonal Q such that

$$
Q^T A Q = \begin{bmatrix} \lambda_1 & 0 \\ 0 & \lambda_2 \end{bmatrix} = \Lambda \quad \text{or} \quad A = Q \begin{bmatrix} \lambda_1 & 0 \\ 0 & \lambda_2 \end{bmatrix} Q^T = Q\Lambda Q^T \tag{5.46}
$$

where the (real) eigenvalues of A are $\{\lambda_1, \lambda_2\}$. Define the change of variable

$$
\begin{bmatrix} u_1 \\ u_2 \end{bmatrix} = Q^T \begin{bmatrix} x_1 \\ x_2 \end{bmatrix} \quad \text{whose transpose is} \quad [u_1, u_2] = [x_1, x_2]Q \tag{5.47}
$$

and substitute (5.46) into (5.45) followed by change of variable in (5.47) to find

$$
\begin{aligned}
q(x_1, x_2) &\equiv [x_1, x_2] A \begin{bmatrix} x_1 \\ x_2 \end{bmatrix} = [x_1, x_2] \left(Q\Lambda Q^T \right) \begin{bmatrix} x_1 \\ x_2 \end{bmatrix} \\
&= ([x_1, x_2]) Q\Lambda \left(Q^T \begin{bmatrix} x_1 \\ x_2 \end{bmatrix} \right) \\
&= [u_1, u_2] \begin{bmatrix} \lambda_1 & 0 \\ 0 & \lambda_2 \end{bmatrix} \begin{bmatrix} u_1 \\ u_2 \end{bmatrix} \\
&\equiv \hat{q}(u_1, u_2) = \lambda_1 u_1^2 + \lambda_2 u_2^2 = \kappa.
\end{aligned} \tag{5.48}
$$

In the $u_1 - u_2$ plane the graph of $\hat{q}$ is a circle ($\lambda_1 = \lambda_2 > 0$), ellipse ($\lambda_1 \neq \lambda_2$ and both positive) or a hyperbola ($\lambda_1 \lambda_2 < 0$).

The matrix of the quadratic form

$$
\begin{aligned}
q(x_1, x_2) &= 2x_1^2 + 8x_1x_2 + 2x_2^2 \\
&= [x_1, x_2]A \begin{bmatrix} x_1 \\ x_2 \end{bmatrix} = [x_1, x_2] \begin{bmatrix} 2 & 4 \\ 4 & 2 \end{bmatrix} \begin{bmatrix} x_1 \\ x_2 \end{bmatrix}
\end{aligned}
$$

is given by $A = \begin{bmatrix} 2 & 4 \\ 4 & 2 \end{bmatrix}$. The eigenvalues of A are $\lambda_1 = -2$ and $\lambda_2 = 6$ and the orthogonal diagonalizer of A was computed in part 1 of Example(5.4) and is $Q = \dfrac{1}{\sqrt{2}} \begin{bmatrix} 1 & 1 \\ -1 & 1 \end{bmatrix}$.

Hence the right-hand side of (5.47) reads

$$
\hat{q}(u_1, u_2) = -2u_1^2 + 6u_2^2 = \kappa
$$

which is a hyperbola. The graph of $q(x_1, x_2)$ is the same hyperbola as $\hat{q}(u_1, u_2)$ where the $x_1 - x_2$ plane has been rotated $45°$ to obtain the $u_1 - u_2$ plane [see Exercise(5.10)].

More generally, let $a_{11}, a_{12}, a_{13}, a_{22}, a_{33}$ and a_{33} be real numbers and define the function of three variables

$$
\begin{aligned}
q(x_1, x_2, x_3) &\equiv [x_1, x_2, x_3]A \begin{bmatrix} x_1 \\ x_2 \\ x_3 \end{bmatrix} \\
&= [x_1, x_2, x_3] \begin{bmatrix} a_{11} & a_{12} & a_{13} \\ a_{12} & a_{22} & a_{23} \\ a_{13} & a_{23} & a_{33} \end{bmatrix} \begin{bmatrix} x_1 \\ x_2 \\ x_3 \end{bmatrix} \\
&= a_{11}x_1^2 + a_{22}x_2^2 + a_{33}x_3^2 + 2a_{12}x_1x_2 + 2a_{13}x_1x_3 + 2a_{23}x_2x_3.
\end{aligned} \tag{5.49}
$$

Proceeding as in (5.46) and the lines following them yields an orthogonal Q such that

$$
Q^T A Q = \begin{bmatrix} \lambda_1 & 0 & 0 \\ 0 & \lambda_2 & 0 \\ 0 & 0 & \lambda_3 \end{bmatrix} = \Lambda \text{ or } A = Q \begin{bmatrix} \lambda_1 & 0 & 0 \\ 0 & \lambda_2 & 0 \\ 0 & 0 & \lambda_3 \end{bmatrix} Q^T = Q\Lambda Q^T \tag{5.50}
$$

where the (real) eigenvalues of A are $\{\lambda_1, \lambda_2, \lambda_3\}$. Define the 3×3 change of variables $\begin{bmatrix} u_1 \\ u_2 \\ u_3 \end{bmatrix} = Q^T \begin{bmatrix} x_1 \\ x_2 \\ x_3 \end{bmatrix}$, as was done in (5.47), so that (5.49) can be rewritten

$$
q(x_1, x_2, x_3) \equiv [x_1, x_2, x_3]A \begin{bmatrix} x_1 \\ x_2 \\ x_3 \end{bmatrix} = ([x_1, x_2, x_3]Q) \Lambda \left(Q^T \begin{bmatrix} x_1 \\ x_2 \\ x_3 \end{bmatrix} \right)
$$

$$= [u_1, u_2, u_3] \begin{bmatrix} \lambda_1 & 0 & 0 \\ 0 & \lambda_2 & 0 \\ 0 & 0 & \lambda_3 \end{bmatrix} \begin{bmatrix} u_1 \\ u_2 \\ u_3 \end{bmatrix} \tag{5.51}$$

$$\equiv \hat{q}(u_1, u_2, u_3) = \lambda_1 u_1^2 + \lambda_2 u_2^2 + \lambda_3 u_3^2 = \kappa.$$

In the $u_1 - u_2 - u_3$ space the graph $\hat{q}$ takes on a number of different forms. These forms are called Quadric Surfaces. Some of them are familiar, say a sphere if $\lambda_1 = \lambda_2 = \lambda_3 > 0$, or an ellipsoid if $\lambda_1 \neq \lambda_2$ and all three $\lambda_j, j = 1, 2, 3$ are positive. The elliptic cone occurs if $\kappa = 0$ and λ_1 and λ_2 are positive and $\lambda_3 < 0$. Somewhat less familiar is the hyperboloid of one (two) sheet(s) which occurs if $\kappa = 1$ and λ_1 and λ_2 are positive (negative) and $\lambda_3 < 0(> 0)$. If any one of the $\lambda_j = 0$, $j = 1, 2, 3$ then the surface is called a cylinder. For example, if $\lambda_3 = 0$ and λ_1 and λ_2 are positive then $\hat{q}(u_1, u_2, u_3) = \lambda_1 u_1^2 + \lambda_2 u_2^2$ is a circle (ellipse) if $\lambda_1 = \lambda_2$ ($\lambda_1 \neq \lambda_2$) in the $u_1 - u_2$ plane with u_3 arbitrary. Geometrically in the first case this is a true cylinder and in the second case this is called an elliptic cylinder. Perhaps the most entertaining aspect of the subject is naming the various surfaces.

In part 2 of Example(5.14) it was shown that the matrix $A = \begin{bmatrix} 1 & -2 & 2 \\ -2 & 1 & 2 \\ 2 & 2 & 1 \end{bmatrix}$ is diagonalized

by the matrix $P = \begin{bmatrix} 0 & 2 & 1 \\ 1 & -1 & 1 \\ 1 & 1 & -1 \end{bmatrix}$. Since the columns of P are orthogonal the matrix

$$Q = \begin{bmatrix} 0 & \dfrac{2}{\sqrt{6}} & \dfrac{1}{\sqrt{3}} \\ \dfrac{1}{\sqrt{2}} & \dfrac{-1}{\sqrt{6}} & \dfrac{1}{\sqrt{3}} \\ \dfrac{1}{\sqrt{2}} & \dfrac{1}{\sqrt{6}} & \dfrac{-1}{\sqrt{3}} \end{bmatrix} \tag{5.52}$$

is orthogonal $(Q^{-1} = Q^T)$ and has the property

$$Q^T A Q = Q^T \begin{bmatrix} 1 & -2 & 2 \\ -2 & 1 & 2 \\ 2 & 2 & 1 \end{bmatrix} Q = \begin{bmatrix} 3 & 0 & 0 \\ 0 & 3 & 0 \\ 0 & 0 & -3 \end{bmatrix}.$$

Substitute the change of variable $\vec{u} = Q^T \vec{x}$ in the quadratic form associated with the matrix A to find

$$\begin{aligned} q(x_1, x_2, x_3) &\equiv [x_1, x_2, x_3] A \begin{bmatrix} x_1 \\ x_2 \\ x_3 \end{bmatrix} \\ &= x_1^2 + x_2^2 + x_3^2 - 4x_1 x_2 + 4x_1 x_3 + 4x_2 x_3 \\ &= [u_1, u_2, u_3] \begin{bmatrix} 3 & 0 & 0 \\ 0 & 3 & 0 \\ 0 & 0 & -3 \end{bmatrix} \begin{bmatrix} u_1 \\ u_2 \\ u_3 \end{bmatrix} \\ &\equiv \hat{q}(u_1, u_2, u_3) = 3u_1^2 + 3u_2^2 - 3u_3^2 = \kappa. \end{aligned} \tag{5.53}$$

In the words of the previous paragraph the quadric surface associated with $q(x_1, x_2, x_3)$ is a hyperboloid of one sheet if $\kappa = 1$. If $\kappa = -1$ write the last equation in the form $-3u_1^2 - 3u_2^2 + 3u_3^2 = -\kappa = 1$ to obtain a hyperboloid of two sheets.

If $A = \begin{bmatrix} 4 & -2 & 2 \\ -2 & 3 & 1 \\ 2 & 1 & 3 \end{bmatrix}$ then $\sigma(A) = \{4, 6, 0\}$ and the matrix Q in (5.52) orthogonally

diagonalizes A so that $Q^T A Q = \begin{bmatrix} 4 & 0 & 0 \\ 0 & 6 & 0 \\ 0 & 0 & 0 \end{bmatrix}$. The analogue of (5.53) reads

$$
\begin{aligned}
q(x_1, x_2, x_3) &= 4x_1^2 + 3x_2^2 + 3x_3^2 + -4x_1x_2 + 4x_1x_3 - 4x_2x_3 \\
&= [x_1, x_2, x_3] A \begin{bmatrix} x_1 \\ x_2 \\ x_3 \end{bmatrix} = [u_1, u_2, u_3] \begin{bmatrix} 4 & 0 & 0 \\ 0 & 6 & 0 \\ 0 & 0 & 0 \end{bmatrix} \begin{bmatrix} u_1 \\ u_2 \\ u_3 \end{bmatrix} \quad (5.54) \\
&\equiv \hat{q}(u_1, u_2, u_3) = 4u_1^2 + 6u_2^2 = \kappa
\end{aligned}
$$

and for $\kappa > 0$ this is an elliptic cylinder. See Exercise (5.18) for a different, but related, application of the diagonalization of a symmetric matrix.

5.14   Exercises

Exercise 5.1 Find the eigenvalues and eigenvectors for the following matrices.

(i) $A = \begin{bmatrix} 2 & -1 \\ -1 & 2 \end{bmatrix}$ $\qquad$ (ii) $A = \begin{bmatrix} 1 & 5 \\ 5 & 1 \end{bmatrix}$

(iii) $A = \begin{bmatrix} 2 & -2 \\ 1 & 5 \end{bmatrix}$ $\qquad$ (iv) $A = \begin{bmatrix} 6 & -2 \\ 2 & 2 \end{bmatrix}$

(v) $A = \begin{bmatrix} 0 & 1 \\ -1 & 0 \end{bmatrix}$ $\qquad$ (vi) $A = \begin{bmatrix} 2 & 1+i \\ 1-i & 3 \end{bmatrix}$

(vii) What are the algebraic and geometric multiplicities of the eigenvalues in the above problems. For the matrix in (iv) find a matrix P so that $P^{-1}AP = \Lambda$. What happens if you try to find such a P for the matrix in (iv)? For the matrices in parts (i), (ii), (v), and (vi) find an orthogonal (unitary) Q so that $Q^T AQ = \Lambda$ ($Q^* AQ = \Lambda$).

Exercise 5.2 Find the eigenvalues and eigenvectors for the following matrices.

(i) $A = \begin{bmatrix} 1 & -1 & -1 \\ -1 & 1 & -1 \\ -1 & -1 & 1 \end{bmatrix}$ $\qquad$ (ii) $A = \begin{bmatrix} 2 & -1 & -1 \\ -1 & 2 & -1 \\ -1 & -1 & 2 \end{bmatrix}$

(iii) $A = \begin{bmatrix} 1 & -1 & 1 \\ 2 & 4 & -1 \\ 2 & 2 & 1 \end{bmatrix}$ $\qquad$ (iv) $A = \begin{bmatrix} 3 & 1 & 3 \\ 0 & 3 & 0 \\ 0 & -1 & 3 \end{bmatrix}$

(v) What are the algebraic and geometric multiplicities of the eigenvalues in the above problems. For the matrix in (iii) find a matrix P so that $P^{-1}AP = \Lambda$. What happens if you try to find such a P for the matrix in (iv)? For the matrices in parts (i) and (ii) find an orthogonal Q so that $Q^T AQ = \Lambda$ ($Q^* AQ = \Lambda$).

Exercise 5.3 Let α_0 and α_1 be given and define the α_{n+1} by the difference equation

$$\alpha_{n+1} = a\alpha_n + b\alpha_{n-1}, \; n \geq 1$$

where a and b are given. The numbers α_0 and α_1 are called initial values. Make the change of variable in (5.3) and verify the following steps.

1. Show that $A = \begin{bmatrix} a & b \\ 1 & 0 \end{bmatrix}$ is the matrix for the difference equation (see (5.4)).

2. From the equation

$$\det (A - \lambda I)) \;=\; \det \left(\begin{bmatrix} a - \lambda & b \\ 1 & -\lambda \end{bmatrix} \right)$$

$$=\; (a - \lambda)(-\lambda) - b = \lambda^2 - a\lambda - b = 0$$

find the eigenvalues

$$\lambda_\pm = \frac{a \pm \sqrt{a^2 + 4b}}{2},$$

and show that

$$\lambda_+ \pm \lambda_- = \begin{cases} a \\ \sqrt{a^2 + 4b} \end{cases} \quad \text{and} \quad \lambda_+ \lambda_- = -b.$$

3. Assume that

$$\lambda_+ = \frac{a + \sqrt{a^2 + 4b}}{2} \neq \lambda_- = \frac{a - \sqrt{a^2 + 4b}}{2}.$$

Show that the corresponding eigenvectors are

$$\vec{p}_+ = \begin{bmatrix} \lambda_+ \\ 1 \end{bmatrix} \quad \text{and} \quad \vec{p}_- = \begin{bmatrix} \lambda_- \\ 1 \end{bmatrix}.$$

Hence the matrix

$$P = [\, \vec{p}_+ \ \vec{p}_- \,] = \begin{bmatrix} \lambda_+ & \lambda_- \\ 1 & 1 \end{bmatrix}$$

is invertible with

$$P^{-1} = \frac{1}{\lambda_+ - \lambda_-} \begin{bmatrix} 1 & -\lambda_- \\ -1 & \lambda_+ \end{bmatrix}$$

and, proceeding as in (5.5), gives

$$A^n = P\Lambda^n P^{-1} = P \begin{bmatrix} \lambda_+ & 0 \\ 0 & \lambda_- \end{bmatrix}^n P^{-1} = P \begin{bmatrix} \lambda_+^n & 0 \\ 0 & \lambda_-^n \end{bmatrix} P^{-1}.$$

4. Show that

$$\alpha_n = \frac{1}{\lambda_+ - \lambda_-} \left[\lambda_+^n (\alpha_1 - \alpha_0 \lambda_-) + \lambda_-^n (-\alpha_1 + \alpha_0 \lambda_+) \right], \quad n \geq 2$$

for the nth term of the sequence.

5. Replace $\lambda_+ = 1$, $\lambda_- = -2$, and n by $n + 1$ in part 4 to find the result in Equation (5.8).

Exercise 5.4 For the difference equation in Exercise(5.3) assume that the eigenvalues are equal so by part 2 of Exercise(5.3) $\lambda_+ = \lambda_- \equiv \lambda = \frac{a}{2}$ and by part 3 a unit eigenvector is given by $\vec{p} \equiv \frac{\vec{p}_+}{\|\vec{p}_+\|} = \frac{1}{\sqrt{\lambda^2 + 1}} \begin{bmatrix} \lambda \\ 1 \end{bmatrix}$. Since the algebraic multiplicity of λ is two and its geometric multiplicity is one the matrix A is not diagonalizable. The vector $\vec{q} = \frac{1}{\sqrt{\lambda^2 + 1}} \begin{bmatrix} -1 \\ \lambda \end{bmatrix}$ is a unit vector perpendicular to $\vec{p}$ so the matrix $Q = [\, \vec{p} \, \vec{q} \,]$ is an orthogonal matrix.

1. Show that

$$Q^T A Q = \begin{bmatrix} \vec{p}^{\,T} \\ \vec{q}^{\,T} \end{bmatrix} \{A[\,\vec{p}\,\vec{q}\,]\} = \begin{bmatrix} \lambda \vec{p}^{\,T}\vec{p} & \vec{p}^{\,T}A\vec{q} \\ \lambda \vec{q}^{\,T}\vec{p} & \vec{q}^{\,T}A\vec{q} \end{bmatrix} \qquad \begin{array}{c} \vec{p}^{\,T}\vec{p} = ||\vec{p}\,||^2 = 1 \\ \text{and } \vec{q}^{\,T}\vec{p} = 0 \end{array}$$

$$= \begin{bmatrix} \lambda & \vec{p}^{\,T}A\vec{q} \\ 0 & \vec{q}^{\,T}A\vec{q} \end{bmatrix} = \begin{bmatrix} \lambda & -(\lambda^2 + 1) \\ 0 & \lambda \end{bmatrix}.$$

The main thing to show here is that $\vec{p}^{\,T}A\vec{q} = -||\vec{p}\,||^2 = -(\lambda^2 + 1)$ and $\vec{q}^{\,T}A\vec{q} = \dfrac{a}{2} = \lambda$.

2. If $R = \begin{bmatrix} r_{11} & r_{12} \\ 0 & r_{11} \end{bmatrix}$ then

$$R^2 = \begin{bmatrix} r_{11} & r_{12} \\ 0 & r_{11} \end{bmatrix} \begin{bmatrix} r_{11} & r_{12} \\ 0 & r_{11} \end{bmatrix} = \begin{bmatrix} r_{11}^2 & 2r_{11}r_{12} \\ 0 & r_{11}^2 \end{bmatrix}.$$

Let $S(n)$ be the statement that $R^{n+1} = \begin{bmatrix} r_{11}^{n+1} & (n+1)r_{11}^n r_{12} \\ 0 & r_{11}^{n+1} \end{bmatrix}$. The validity of the statement $S(1)$ is the previous display. The general case follows by induction. So assume $S(k)$ is true and show that this implies the validity of $S(k+1)$. To see this

$$R^{k+2} = RR^{k+1} = \begin{bmatrix} r_{11} & r_{12} \\ 0 & r_{11} \end{bmatrix} \begin{bmatrix} r_{11}^{k+1} & (k+1)r_{11}^k r_{12} \\ 0 & r_{11}^{k+1} \end{bmatrix} \begin{array}{l} \text{inductive} \\ \text{hypothesis} \end{array}$$

$$= \begin{bmatrix} r_{11}r_{11}^{k+1} & r_{11}(k+1)r_{11}^k r_{12} + r_{12}r_{11}^{k+1} \\ 0 & r_{11}r_{11}^{k+1} \end{bmatrix}$$

$$= \begin{bmatrix} r_{11}^{k+2} & (k+1)r_{11}^{k+1}r_{12} + r_{11}^{k+1}r_{12} \\ 0 & r_{11}^{k+2} \end{bmatrix}$$

$$= \begin{bmatrix} r_{11}^{k+2} & (k+2)r_{11}^{k+1}r_{12} \\ 0 & r_{11}^{k+2} \end{bmatrix}$$

which establishes the validity of $S(k+1)$. Use the procedure outlined in equations (5.5) through (5.7) with Q replacing P and conclude that

$$\alpha_n = \left(\frac{1}{\lambda^2 + 1}\right)\left[\lambda^n\left(\lambda\alpha_1 + \alpha_0\right) + \left\{\lambda^{n+1} - n\lambda^{n-1}(\lambda^2 + 1)\right\}\left(-\alpha_1 + \lambda\alpha_0\right)\right]$$

$$= n\lambda^{n-1}\alpha_1 + \lambda^n(1 - n)\alpha_0$$

3. In Example(5.3) it was tempting to conclude that $\alpha_n = n + 1$ for the sequence

$$\alpha_{n+1} = 2\alpha_n - \alpha_{n-1}$$

equipped with initial values $\alpha_0 = 1$ and $\alpha_1 = 2$. Show that the matrix of the difference equation is $A = \begin{bmatrix} 2 & -1 \\ 1 & 0 \end{bmatrix}$. In Example(5.3) it was shown that A has the single eigenvalue $\lambda = 1$. Using the formula in part 2 gives

$$
\begin{aligned}
\alpha_n &= n\lambda^{n-1}\alpha_1 + \lambda^n(1-n)\alpha_0 & \lambda = 1 \\
&= n\alpha_1 + (1-n)\alpha_0 & \alpha_1 = 2 \quad \alpha_0 = 1 \\
&= 2n + (1-n) = n+1
\end{aligned}
$$

which verifies the temptation mentioned in Example(5.3). If α_n is replaced by the determinant $|T_n|$ of the matrix $T_n = \begin{bmatrix} 2 & -1 & 0 & \cdots & 0 \\ -1 & 2 & -1 & \vdots & 0 \\ \vdots & \ddots & \ddots & \ddots & \vdots \\ 0 & 0 & \ddots & 2 & -1 \\ 0 & 0 & \cdots & -1 & 2 \end{bmatrix}$ then this problem

gives another way to establish $|T_{n+1}| = n+2$. Compare to Exercise(3.7).

4. Find α_n in the sequence

$$
\alpha_{n+1} = 3\alpha_n - \frac{9}{4}\alpha_{n-1}, \quad \alpha_0 = 1 \text{ and } \alpha_1 = \frac{3}{2}.
$$

Exercise 5.5 The **Fibonacci Numbers** are the numbers defined recursively by the formula

$$
f_{n+1} = f_n + f_{n-1} \text{ for } n \geq 1
$$

and the recursion begins with the definition $f_0 = 0$ and $f_1 = 1$. Set $u_n = f_n$ and $v_n = f_{n-1}$ and rewrite the recursion as the equation

$$
\begin{aligned}
u_{n+1} &= f_n + f_{n-1} = u_n + v_n \\
v_{n+1} &= f_n = u_n
\end{aligned}
$$

and write these difference equations as the vector equation $\vec{z}_{n+1} = A\vec{z}_n$ where

$$
A = \begin{bmatrix} 1 & 1 \\ 1 & 0 \end{bmatrix} \text{ and } \vec{z}_n = \begin{bmatrix} u_n \\ v_n \end{bmatrix}.
$$

At this point one could appeal to Exercise(5.3) or proceed as follows.

1. Set $\vec{z}_1 = \begin{bmatrix} u_1 \\ v_1 \end{bmatrix} = \begin{bmatrix} f_1 \\ f_0 \end{bmatrix} = \begin{bmatrix} 1 \\ 0 \end{bmatrix}$ and show that $\vec{z}_{n+1} = A^n \vec{z}_1$.

2. Find a matrix P so that $P^{-1}AP = \Lambda = \begin{bmatrix} \dfrac{1+\sqrt{5}}{2} & 0 \\ 0 & \dfrac{1-\sqrt{5}}{2} \end{bmatrix}$.

3. Show that the nth Fibonacci number is

$$f_n = \frac{1}{\sqrt{5}}\left(\left[\frac{1+\sqrt{5}}{2}\right]^n - \left[\frac{1-\sqrt{5}}{2}\right]^n\right).$$

Once again, it is fairly amazing that the formula is always an integer.

Exercise 5.6 From Exercise(5.1) part (iii) the spectrum of $A = \begin{bmatrix} 2 & -2 \\ 1 & 5 \end{bmatrix}$ is $\sigma(A) = \{3, 4\}$

and the matrix $P_A = \begin{bmatrix} 2 & 1 \\ -1 & -1 \end{bmatrix}$ diagonalizes A,

$$P_A^{-1}AP_A = \begin{bmatrix} 1 & 1 \\ -1 & -2 \end{bmatrix}\begin{bmatrix} 2 & -2 \\ 1 & 5 \end{bmatrix}\begin{bmatrix} 2 & 1 \\ -1 & -1 \end{bmatrix} = \begin{bmatrix} 3 & 0 \\ 0 & 4 \end{bmatrix}.$$

By Theorem(5.5) (B is upper triangular) the spectrum of $B = \begin{bmatrix} 4 & -4 \\ 0 & 3 \end{bmatrix}$ is $\sigma(B) = \{3, 4\}$

and $P_B = \begin{bmatrix} 4 & 1 \\ 1 & 0 \end{bmatrix}$ diagonalizes B,

$$P_B^{-1}BP_B = \begin{bmatrix} 0 & 1 \\ 1 & -4 \end{bmatrix}\begin{bmatrix} 4 & -4 \\ 0 & 3 \end{bmatrix}\begin{bmatrix} 4 & 1 \\ 1 & 0 \end{bmatrix} = \begin{bmatrix} 3 & 0 \\ 0 & 4 \end{bmatrix}.$$

1. The previous calculations shows that $\sigma(A) = \sigma(B)$. Inspect the matrices P_A and P_B to conclude that, although the eigenvalues of the matrices A and B are the same, the eigenvectors are different.

2. Find a matrix P so that $P^{-1}AP = B$. Hint: It follows from part 1

$$P_A^{-1}AP_A = \begin{bmatrix} 3 & 0 \\ 0 & 4 \end{bmatrix} = P_B^{-1}BP_B.$$

According to Definition(5.6) the matrices A and B are similar.

3. Assume that $P^{-1}AP = B$ where A and B are $n \times n$ matrices. Use the identity

$$\rho_B(\lambda) = \det(B - \lambda I) = \det(P^{-1}AP - \lambda I)$$

and the fact that the determinant of a product is the product of the determinant [part 5 of Theorem(3.20)] to show that $\rho_A(\lambda) = \rho_B(\lambda)$. This shows that the eigenvalues of similar matrices are the same, $\sigma(A) = \sigma(B)$. Further, assume that $A\vec{v} = \lambda\vec{v}$. Can you conclude that $\vec{v}$ is also an eigenvector for B.

Commuting Matrices: In contrast to part 1, matrices that share common eigenvectors are very special matrices. Label the matrices from parts (i) and (ii) of Exercise(5.1)

$$A_1 = \begin{bmatrix} 2 & -1 \\ -1 & 2 \end{bmatrix} \text{ and } A_2 = \begin{bmatrix} 1 & 5 \\ 5 & 1 \end{bmatrix}.$$

4. Show that

$$A_1 A_2 = \begin{bmatrix} 2 & -1 \\ -1 & 2 \end{bmatrix} \begin{bmatrix} 1 & 5 \\ 5 & 1 \end{bmatrix} = \begin{bmatrix} -3 & 9 \\ 9 & -3 \end{bmatrix} = \begin{bmatrix} 1 & 5 \\ 5 & 1 \end{bmatrix} \begin{bmatrix} 2 & -1 \\ -1 & 2 \end{bmatrix} = A_2 A_1.$$

Show that $(A_1 + A_2)^2 = A_1^2 + 2A_1 A_2 + A_2^2$. Recall part 2 of Exercise(3.5).

5. From parts 1 and 2 of Exercise(5.1) the matrix $P = \begin{bmatrix} 1 & 1 \\ 1 & -1 \end{bmatrix}$ diagonalizes both A_1 and A_2, that is, $P^{-1} A_j P = \Lambda_j$ where $\Lambda_1 = \begin{bmatrix} 1 & 0 \\ 0 & 3 \end{bmatrix}$ and $\Lambda_2 = \begin{bmatrix} -4 & 0 \\ 0 & 6 \end{bmatrix}$. Write each of these in the form $A_j = P\Lambda_j P^{-1}$ and verify that $A_1 A_2 = A_2 A_1$.

6. Let $A_j, j = 1, 2$ be two $n \times n$ matrices and assume that each A_j is diagonalized by the matrix P, $P^{-1} A_j P = \Lambda_j, j = 1, 2$. Show that $A_1 A_2 = A_2 A_1$.

7. If $A\vec{v} = \lambda \vec{v}$ then $(-A)\vec{v} = (-\lambda)\vec{v}$ so if $\lambda \in \sigma(A)$ then $-\lambda \in \sigma(-A)$ and $\pm A$ share the same eigenvector. Further, assume that A is diagonalized by P. In the last part let $A_1 = A$ and $A_2 = -A$ since $A(-A) = -A^2 = (-A)A$ so that $P^{-1}(-A)P = -\Lambda$.

8. Let A_j be the 3×3 matrix from part $j, j = 1, 2$ in Example(5.14). Due to the discussion at the end of that example it follows that $A_1 A_2 = A_2 A_1$.

Exercise 5.7 Let $A(\alpha)$ be the matrix $A(\alpha) = \begin{bmatrix} 1 & 0 & 0 \\ \alpha & 1 & 0 \\ 0 & 1 & 1 \end{bmatrix}$.

1. Show that $\sigma(A(\alpha)) = \{1, 1, 1\}$ so that $[A(\alpha) - I] = \begin{bmatrix} 0 & 0 & 0 \\ \alpha & 0 & 0 \\ 0 & 1 & 0 \end{bmatrix}$.

2. What is the $\dim[\mathcal{N}(A(0) - I)]$? Find the eigenvectors for $A(0)$.

3. What is the $\dim[\mathcal{N}(A(1) - I)]$? Find the eigenvectors for $A(1)$.

4. Are there any α so that the matrix $A(\alpha)$ is diagonalizable.

Exercise 5.8 Assume that $\alpha = 2$ in the matrix A of Example(5.7), so that the characteristic equation reads

$$0 = |A - \lambda I| = \begin{vmatrix} 2 - \lambda & 1 & 0 \\ 0 & 2 - \lambda & 0 \\ \beta & -2 & 3 - \lambda \end{vmatrix}$$

and the eigenvalues of A are $\lambda_1 = \lambda_2 = 2$ and $\lambda_3 = 3$.

1. For the simple eigenvalue $\lambda_3 = 3$, find the eigenvector is $\vec{p}_3 = \begin{bmatrix} 0 \\ 0 \\ 1 \end{bmatrix}$.

2. What is the rank of

$$(A - 2I) = \begin{bmatrix} 0 & 1 & 0 \\ 0 & 0 & 0 \\ \beta & -2 & 1 \end{bmatrix} \sim \begin{bmatrix} \beta & 0 & 1 \\ 0 & 1 & 0 \\ 0 & 0 & 0 \end{bmatrix}?$$

What is the dimension of the null space of $A - 2I$? Does your answer depend on the value of β? Is this matrix A ever diagonalizable? Find an eigenvector for $\lambda_1 = 2$.

Exercise 5.9 For $A = \begin{bmatrix} 2 & 1 & 0 & 0 \\ 0 & 3 & 0 & 0 \\ \beta & -2 & 3 & 0 \\ 0 & 1 & 0 & 3 \end{bmatrix}$, the characteristic equation is

$$\rho_A(\lambda) = |A - \lambda I| = \begin{bmatrix} 2 - \lambda & 1 & 0 & 0 \\ 0 & 3 - \lambda & 0 & 0 \\ \beta & -2 & 3 - \lambda & 0 \\ 0 & 1 & 0 & 3 - \lambda \end{bmatrix}.$$

1. Show that $\rho_A(\lambda) = |A - \lambda I| = (2 - \lambda)(3 - \lambda)^3$.

2. Show that $\lambda_1 = 2$ and $\vec{p}_1 = \begin{bmatrix} 1 \\ 0 \\ -\beta \\ 0 \end{bmatrix}$ are an eigenpair for A.

3. Does the rank of $(A - 3I) = \begin{bmatrix} -1 & 1 & 0 & 0 \\ 0 & 0 & 0 & 0 \\ \beta & -2 & 0 & 0 \\ 0 & 1 & 0 & 0 \end{bmatrix}$ depend on the value of β.

4. Find a basis for $\mathcal{N}((A - 3I))$. Is the matrix A ever diagonalizable?

5. Change the matrix to $A = \begin{bmatrix} 3 & 1 & 0 & 0 \\ 0 & 3 & 0 & 0 \\ \beta & -2 & 3 & 0 \\ 0 & 1 & 0 & 3 \end{bmatrix}$ so that

$$\rho_A(\lambda) = |A - \lambda I| = \begin{bmatrix} 3 - \lambda & 1 & 0 & 0 \\ 0 & 3 - \lambda & 0 & 0 \\ \beta & -2 & 3 - \lambda & 0 \\ 0 & 1 & 0 & 3 - \lambda \end{bmatrix} = (3 - \lambda)^4.$$

Is this matrix ever diagonalizable?

Exercise 5.10 Let θ be an angle with the positive x–axis, and define $Q = \begin{bmatrix} \cos(\theta) & -\sin(\theta) \\ \sin(\theta) & \cos(\theta) \end{bmatrix}$. Show that (see part 2 of Exercise(3.18))

$$Q^T Q = \begin{bmatrix} \cos(\theta) & \sin(\theta) \\ -\sin(\theta) & \cos(\theta) \end{bmatrix} \begin{bmatrix} \cos(\theta) & -\sin(\theta) \\ \sin(\theta) & \cos(\theta) \end{bmatrix} = \begin{bmatrix} 1 & 0 \\ 0 & 1 \end{bmatrix}$$

so that $Q^T = Q^{-1}$. Now set

$$\vec{y} = \begin{bmatrix} y_1 \\ y_2 \end{bmatrix} = Q\vec{x} = Q \begin{bmatrix} x_1 \\ x_2 \end{bmatrix} = \begin{bmatrix} x_1 \cos(\theta) - x_2 \sin(\theta) \\ x_1 \sin(\theta) + x_2 \cos(\theta) \end{bmatrix}.$$

From the two triangles in the figure note that

$$\cos(\alpha) = \frac{x_1}{||\vec{x}||} \quad \sin(\alpha) = \frac{x_2}{||\vec{x}||} \quad \text{and} \quad \cos(\alpha + \theta) = \frac{y_1}{||Q\vec{x}||} \quad \sin(\alpha + \theta) = \frac{y_2}{||Q\vec{x}||}.$$

Here's how to show that Q is a rotation through the angle θ.

1. Show that $||Q\vec{x}|| = ||\vec{x}||$.
   Consider $||Q\vec{x}||^2 = (Q\vec{x})^T Q\vec{x}$.

2. Use the trigonometric identity
   $$\cos(\alpha + \theta) = \cos(\alpha)\cos(\theta) - \sin(\alpha)\sin(\theta)$$
   and the identities above to show that

   $$y_1 = x_1 \cos(\theta) - x_2 \sin(\theta)$$

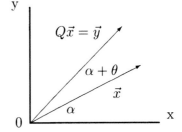

and

$$y_2 = x_1 \sin(\theta) + x_2 \cos(\theta).$$

This shows that the image $\vec{y} = Q\vec{x}$ is a vector with the same length as $\vec{x}$ and the vector $\vec{y}$ has been rotated through the angle θ.

Exercise 5.11 In Example(5.31) it was shown that the most general non-symmetric 2×2 real normal matrix is given by $A = \begin{bmatrix} a & b \\ -b & a \end{bmatrix}$.

1. Find the eigenvalues and the eigenvectors of A.

2. Find the unitary diagonalizer Q so that $Q^* A Q = \Lambda$. Compare with Example(5.30).

3. If $a = 0$, then, from Exercise(3.14), the matrix A is called skew-symmetric. It follows from part 2 that all 2×2 skew-symmetric matrices are diagonalizable.

4. Recall from Exercise(3.14) that an $n \times n$ real matrix A is called skew-symmetric if $A = -A^T$. Show any such matrix is normal. It follows that all $n \times n$ skew-symmetric matrices are diagonalizable.

Exercise 5.12 Let $A = \begin{bmatrix} 5 & -1 \\ 1 & 3 \end{bmatrix}$

1. Find the eigenvalue(s) of A.

2. What is the dim $\mathcal{N}(A - \lambda I)$? Is A diagonalizable?

3. Is the matrix A normal?

4. Find a matrix Q from Schur's Lemma so that $Q^T A Q = R$ where R is triangular.

Exercise 5.13 Let $A = \begin{bmatrix} 2 & i \\ i & 4 \end{bmatrix}$

1. Is A Hermitian (normal)?

2. Find the eigenvalues of A.

3. What is the dim $\mathcal{N}(A - \lambda I)$? Is A diagonalizable?

4. Find a matrix Q so that $Q^* A Q = R = \begin{bmatrix} \lambda & r_{12} \\ 0 & \lambda \end{bmatrix}$

Exercise 5.14 Let $A = \begin{bmatrix} 2 & 1+i \\ 1-i & 3 \end{bmatrix}$

1. Show that A is Hermitian.

2. Find the eigenvalues of A.

3. Find a matrix Q so that $Q^* A Q = \Lambda = \begin{bmatrix} 1 & 0 \\ 0 & 4 \end{bmatrix}$

Exercise 5.15 Let $A = \begin{bmatrix} 1 & 2 \\ 2 & 4 \end{bmatrix}$ and $P = \begin{bmatrix} 1 & 1 \\ -1 & 1 \end{bmatrix}$ so that

$$B = P^{-1} A P = \frac{1}{2} \begin{bmatrix} 1 & -3 \\ -3 & 9 \end{bmatrix}.$$

By inspection

$$\mathcal{C}_{P^{-1}AP} = \text{span} \left\{ \begin{bmatrix} 1 \\ -3 \end{bmatrix} \right\} \text{ and } \mathcal{C}_A = \text{span} \left\{ \begin{bmatrix} 1 \\ 2 \end{bmatrix} \right\}.$$

These column spaces are different but both are rank one. This is true in general. Let P and A be $n \times n$ with P invertible. Here's how to show that if $P^{-1} A P = B$, then rank$(A) = $ rank(B). This is the result used in Example(5.32) ($P^{-1} = Q^*$) to arrive at Theorem(5.33).

1. Make sure you can follow these steps. Assume that $\vec{b} \in \mathcal{C}_B$; then there exists an $\vec{x}$ so that $B\vec{x} = \vec{b}$. Since P is invertible, there exists a unique vector $\vec{y}$ satisfying $\vec{y} = P\vec{x}$ (namely $\vec{x} = P^{-1}\vec{y}$) so that

$$\vec{b} = B\vec{x} = P^{-1}AP\vec{x} = P^{-1}A\vec{y}.$$

This happens if and only if $A\vec{y} = \vec{z} = P\vec{b}$. A point $\vec{b} \in \mathcal{C}_B$ if and only if there is a point $\vec{z} = P\vec{b} \in \mathcal{C}_A$.

2. Here is another method to arrive at the same result. If $\vec{x} \in \mathcal{N}(B)$ then $\vec{0} = B\vec{x} = P^{-1}AP\vec{x}$ or $AP\vec{x} \equiv A\vec{y} = \vec{0}$. Hence, $\vec{x} \in \mathcal{N}(B)$ if and only if $\vec{y} = P\vec{x} \in \mathcal{N}(A)$. This shows that $\dim\mathcal{N}(A) = \dim\mathcal{N}(B)$. Now use the dimension theorem to see that $\operatorname{rank}(A) = \operatorname{rank}(B)$.

Exercise 5.16 Let A be a 4×4 matrix and denote its set of eigenvalues by $\sigma(A) = \{\lambda_1, \lambda_2, \lambda_3, \lambda_4\}$ Assume that λ_1 is a simple eigenvalue and $\lambda_2 = \lambda_3 = \lambda_4$ has algebraic multiplicity three. By Schur's lemma, there is an unitary Q so that

$$Q^*AQ = \begin{bmatrix} \lambda_1 & r_{12} & r_{13} & r_{14} \\ 0 & \lambda_2 & r_{23} & r_{24} \\ 0 & 0 & \lambda_3 & r_{34} \\ 0 & 0 & 0 & \lambda_4 \end{bmatrix} = \begin{bmatrix} \lambda_1 & r_{12} & r_{13} & r_{14} \\ 0 & \lambda_2 & r_{23} & r_{24} \\ 0 & 0 & \lambda_2 & r_{34} \\ 0 & 0 & 0 & \lambda_2 \end{bmatrix}.$$

It then follows that

$$Q^*(A - \lambda I)Q = \begin{bmatrix} \lambda_1 - \lambda & r_{12} & r_{13} & r_{14} \\ 0 & \lambda_2 - \lambda & r_{23} & r_{24} \\ 0 & 0 & \lambda_2 - \lambda & r_{34} \\ 0 & 0 & 0 & \lambda_2 - \lambda \end{bmatrix}.$$

1. Use the procedure discussed in Example(5.32) to find all possible values for the rank of the matrix $(A - \lambda_2 I)$. This is where Exercise(5.15) is used.

2. Find all possible values for the dimension of $\mathcal{N}(A - \lambda_2 I)$. Use the dimension theorem. Conclude that the geometric multiplicity of λ_2 is always less than or equal to its algebraic multiplicity and when equal the matrix is diagonalizable.

Exercise 5.17 Quadratic forms:

1. Find $\hat{q}(u_1, u_2)$ as in (5.48) for $q(x_1, x_2) = 2x_1^2 - 2x_1x_2 + 2x_2^2$. See part 1 of Exercise(5.1)

2. Find $\hat{q}(u_1, u_2)$ as in (5.48) for $q(x_1, x_2) = x_1^2 + 10x_1x_2 + x_2^2$. See part 2 of Exercise(5.1).

3. Find the matrix A for

$$q(x_1, x_2, x_3) = 20x_1^2 + 17x_2^2 + 17x_3^2 + 4x_1x_2 - 4x_1x_3 - 10x_2x_3.$$

The matrix $Q = \begin{bmatrix} 0 & \frac{2}{\sqrt{6}} & \frac{1}{\sqrt{3}} \\ \frac{1}{\sqrt{2}} & \frac{-1}{\sqrt{6}} & \frac{1}{\sqrt{3}} \\ \frac{1}{\sqrt{2}} & \frac{1}{\sqrt{6}} & \frac{-1}{\sqrt{3}} \end{bmatrix}$ from (5.52) diagonalizes the matrix A you just found. Given that the eigenvalues of A are $\sigma(A) = \{12, 18, 24\}$, find the quadric surface associated with $q(x_1, x_2, x_3) = \hat{q}(u_1, u_2, u_3) = \kappa = 1$. See the discussion in the lines following (5.51).

4. Repeat part 3 $q(x_1, x_2, x_3) = 8x_1^2 + 2x_2^2 + 2x_3^2 + 4x_1x_2 - 4x_1x_3 - 16x_2x_3$. The matrix Q in part 3 applies in the present case and $\sigma(A) = \{-6, 6, 12\}$

5. Repeat part 3 for $q(x_1, x_2, x_3) = 7x_1^2 + 7x_2^2 + 16x_3^2 + 2x_1x_2 - 16x_1x_3 - 16x_2x_3$. The matrix $Q = \begin{bmatrix} \frac{1}{\sqrt{3}} & \frac{1}{\sqrt{2}} & \frac{1}{\sqrt{6}} \\ \frac{1}{\sqrt{3}} & \frac{-1}{\sqrt{2}} & \frac{1}{\sqrt{6}} \\ \frac{1}{\sqrt{3}} & 0 & \frac{-2}{\sqrt{6}} \end{bmatrix}$ diagonalizes this matrix A and $\sigma(A) = \{24, 6, 0\}$.

Exercise 5.18 Min-Max Theorem The procedure to identify the graph of the quadratic forms in the last exercise has a different application.

1. Let $A = \begin{bmatrix} 3 & -1 \\ -1 & 3 \end{bmatrix}$ and for $\vec{x} = \begin{bmatrix} x_1 \\ x_2 \end{bmatrix}$ and define $q(\vec{x}) = \vec{x}^T A \vec{x}$. Evaluate $q(\vec{x})$ at the four points $\vec{x} = \vec{q}_1 = \frac{1}{\sqrt{2}} \begin{bmatrix} 1 \\ 1 \end{bmatrix}$, $\vec{x} = \vec{x}_1 = \frac{1}{\sqrt{5}} \begin{bmatrix} 2 \\ 1 \end{bmatrix}$, $\vec{x} = \vec{x}_2 = \begin{bmatrix} 1 \\ 0 \end{bmatrix}$, and $\vec{x} = \vec{q}_2 = \frac{1}{\sqrt{2}} \begin{bmatrix} -1 \\ 1 \end{bmatrix}$ to see that $q(\vec{q}_1) < q(\vec{x}_1) < q(\vec{x}_2) < q(\vec{q}_2)$.

2. Check that the eigenvalues of A are $\lambda_1 = 2$ and $\lambda_2 = 4$ with corresponding eigenvectors $\vec{q}_1$ and $\vec{q}_2$ in part 1 Hence, the orthogonal matrix $Q = \frac{1}{\sqrt{2}} \begin{bmatrix} 1 & -1 \\ 1 & 1 \end{bmatrix}$ diagonalizes the matrix A. Write the equation $Q^T A Q = \Lambda = \begin{bmatrix} \lambda_1 & 0 \\ 0 & \lambda_2 \end{bmatrix}$ in the form $A = Q\Lambda Q^T$ and set $\hat{q}(\vec{y}) = \vec{y}^T \Lambda \vec{y}$ where $\vec{y} = \begin{bmatrix} y_1 \\ y_2 \end{bmatrix} = Q^T \vec{x}$. Define the four vectors

$$\vec{y}_{q_1} = Q^T \vec{q}_1, \ \vec{y}_1 = Q^T \vec{x}_1, \ \vec{y}_2 = Q^T \vec{x}_2, \ \vec{y}_{q_2} = Q^T \vec{q}_2$$

where $\vec{q}_1, \vec{x}_1, \vec{x}_2$ and $\vec{q}_2$ are the vectors from part 1 Find $\hat{q}(\vec{y}_j)$ for $j = q_1, 1, 2, q_2$. Compare these values to the values found in part 1.

3. More generally, assume A is a symmetric $n \times n$ matrix, $Q^T A Q = \Lambda$ and the eigenvalues of A have been ordered $\lambda_1 \leq \lambda_2 \leq \cdots \lambda_n$. Define $\vec{y} = Q^T \vec{x}$ where $\vec{y}^T = [y_1, y_2, \ldots, y_n]$ and set $q(\vec{x}) = \vec{x}^T A \vec{x} = \vec{x}^T Q \Lambda Q^T \vec{x} = \vec{y}^T \Lambda \vec{y} = \sum_{j=1}^{n} \lambda_j |y_j|^2 = \hat{q}(\vec{y})$ Show that

$$\min_{||\vec{x}||=1} [q(\vec{x})] = \lambda_1 \quad \text{and} \quad \max_{||\vec{x}||=1} [q(\vec{x})] = \lambda_n$$

where min is the minimum (max is the maximum) over all unit vectors. Hints: It follows from Exercise(5.10) that if $||\vec{x}|| = 1$ and $\vec{x} = Q\vec{y}$ then $||\vec{y}|| = 1$. To find the minimum, fill in the details around the calculation

$$\hat{q}(\vec{y}) = \sum_{j=1}^{n} \lambda_j |y_j|^2 \geq \sum_{j=1}^{n} \lambda_1 |y_j|^2 = \lambda_1 \sum_{j=1}^{n} |y_j|^2 = \lambda_1 ||\vec{y}||^2 = \lambda_1.$$

To find the maximum, focus on λ_n in the last line.

Exercise 5.19 Let $a \neq 0$ and b be real numbers. The line l through the origin with slope b/a is given by the equation

$$l : ax_2 - bx_1 = -bx_1 + ax_2 = \begin{bmatrix} -b & a \end{bmatrix} \begin{bmatrix} x_1 \\ x_2 \end{bmatrix} = 0.$$

If $x_1 = a$ and $x_2 = b$ then $\begin{bmatrix} -b & a \end{bmatrix} \vec{x} = \begin{bmatrix} -b & a \end{bmatrix} \begin{bmatrix} a \\ b \end{bmatrix} = -ba + ab = 0$ implies the point $\vec{v} = \begin{bmatrix} a \\ b \end{bmatrix}$ is on the line l. Set $\vec{u} = \dfrac{\vec{v}}{||\vec{v}||}$ and define the 2×2 matrix $P = \vec{u}\vec{u}^T$.

1. The symmetry $P = P^T$ follows from part 2 of Theorem(3.7). Show that $P = P^2$. Any matrix P satisfying $P^2 = P$ is called a **projection matrix**. Here is the reason. Let $\vec{z} = \begin{bmatrix} z_1 \\ z_2 \end{bmatrix}$ and use Definition(1.11) to see that

$$\text{proj}_{\vec{u}}(\vec{z}) = (\vec{u} \cdot \vec{z})\vec{u} = \left(\vec{u}^T \vec{z}\right)\vec{u} = \vec{u}\left(\vec{u}^T \vec{z}\right) = \left(\vec{u}\vec{u}^T\right)\vec{z} = P\vec{z}$$

so that the action of the matrix P is to project $\vec{z}$ onto $\vec{u}$.

2. Find the unit vector $\vec{u}$, the matrix P and the projection $\vec{w} = P\vec{z}$ given that $\vec{v} = \begin{bmatrix} 2 \\ 1 \end{bmatrix}$ and $\vec{z} = \begin{bmatrix} 2 \\ 2 \end{bmatrix}$. In Figure 5.1 it does appear that $\vec{w} = P\vec{z}$ is longer than $\vec{v}$.

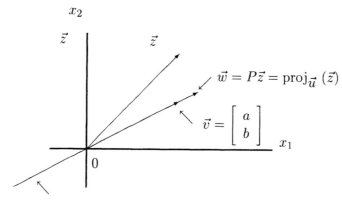

line $l : ay - bx = 0$

Figure 5.1

3. Repeat part 1 with $a = 0$. In this case the line l is the x_2 axis.

4. Since P is symmetric, Theorem(5.28) guarantees an orthogonal matrix Q satisfying
   $Q^T P Q = \Lambda = \begin{bmatrix} 1 & 0 \\ 0 & 0 \end{bmatrix}$. The last equality implies that $\sigma(P) = \{1, 0\}$. To see that
   $1 \in \sigma(P)$, finish the calculation $P\vec{u} = \left(\vec{u}\vec{u}^T \right) \vec{u}$. To see that $0 \in \sigma(P)$, finish the
   calculation $P \begin{bmatrix} b \\ a \end{bmatrix} = \left(\vec{u}\vec{u}^T \right) \begin{bmatrix} b \\ a \end{bmatrix}$. Recall the definition of $\vec{u}$. Conclude that the
   matrix $Q = \begin{bmatrix} \vec{u} & \dfrac{1}{||\vec{v}||} \begin{bmatrix} b \\ -a \end{bmatrix} \end{bmatrix} = \left(\dfrac{1}{||\vec{v}||} \right) \begin{bmatrix} a & b \\ b & -a \end{bmatrix}$.

5. More generally let $\vec{v}^T = [v_1 \ v_2 \ \cdots \ v_n] \in \mathcal{R}^n$ be a non-zero vector. Define $\vec{u} = \dfrac{1}{||\vec{v}||}\vec{v}$
   and the $n \times n$ matrix $P = \vec{u}\vec{u}^T$. Let $\vec{z} = [z_1 \ z_2 \ \cdots \ z_n] \in \mathcal{R}^n$. The equalities $P^2 = P$,
   $P\vec{z} = (\vec{u} \cdot \vec{z})\,\vec{u} = \mathrm{proj}_{\vec{z}}(\vec{u})$ and the symmetry $P^T = P$ all follows as done part 1 Hence
   there is an orthogonal Q so that $Q^T P Q = \Lambda$. Your work in part 4 can be repeated
   verbatim to see that if $\lambda = 1 \in \sigma(P)$. To see that $\lambda = 0 \in \sigma(P)$ write for a non-zero $\vec{y}$

$$P\vec{y} = \lambda\vec{y} \quad \text{so that} \quad P^2\vec{y} = \lambda P\vec{y} \quad \text{or} \quad P\vec{y} = \lambda P\vec{y} \quad \text{or} \quad (1 - \lambda)P\vec{y} = \vec{0}$$

and the last is zero if $\lambda = 1$ or $P\vec{y} = \vec{0}$. The latter statement implies that $\lambda = 0$ is
an eigenvalue of P. Assume that the first column of the matrix Q is the eigenvector
corresponding to the eigenvalue $\lambda = 1$ (from part 4 this column can be taken as $\vec{u}$).
Show that the diagonal matrix Λ is the $n \times n$ zero matrix with the exception of its
one-one entry which is the number one. Equivalently the geometric multiplicity of the
eigenvalue $\lambda = 1$ is one and the geometric multiplicity of the eigenvalue 0 is $n - 1$.

(Hint: In Exercise(4.13) use $A = \vec{u}$ and $P = \vec{u}^T$ to conclude that

$$\text{rank of } (P) = \text{rank of } \left(\vec{u}\vec{u}^T\right) \leq \text{rank of } (\vec{u}) = 1,$$

since the rank of any non-zero vector is one. Now apply the dimension theorem(4.22) to the matrix P to find the dimension of the null space of P).

Exercise 5.20 Let $\vec{z} = \begin{bmatrix} z_1 \\ z_2 \end{bmatrix}$, $\vec{v} = \begin{bmatrix} a \\ b \end{bmatrix}$, and define the unit vector $\vec{u} = \dfrac{1}{||\vec{v}||}\vec{v}$. Using the notation from Exercise(5.19) define the projection matrix $P = \vec{u}\vec{u}^T$ and $\vec{w} = P\vec{z}$.

1. Let $\vec{e} = \vec{z} - \vec{w}$. Show that $\vec{e} \cdot \vec{w} = 0$. You can use the calculation that was done in Definition(1.11) or proceed as follows: write $\vec{e} = (I - P)\vec{z}$ and $\vec{e} \cdot \vec{w} = (I - P)\vec{z} \cdot P\vec{z}$ and use the fact that $P^2 = P$.

Let $R(\vec{z})$ be the vector obtained by reflecting $\vec{z}$ across the line passing through $\vec{v}$. From part 1 the triangle with the sides $\vec{w}$, $\vec{e}$ and $\vec{z}$ is a right triangle. Geometrically (parallelogram rule for addition) the vector $R(\vec{z}) = \vec{w} + (-\vec{e})$. Here is how to find a matrix $\mathcal{R}$ so that $\mathcal{R}\vec{z} = R(z)$. Figure 5.2 shows that

$$
\begin{aligned}
R(\vec{z}) = \vec{w} + (-\vec{e}) &= P\vec{z} + (-\vec{e}) \\
&= P\vec{z} + (-\vec{z} + P\vec{z}) \\
&= -I\vec{z} + 2P\vec{z} \\
&= (-1)\,(I - 2P)\,\vec{z} \equiv -\mathcal{R}\vec{z}.
\end{aligned}
$$

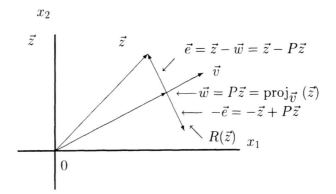

Figure 5.2

2. If $\vec{v} = \begin{bmatrix} 2 \\ 1 \end{bmatrix}$ then use P from part 2 of Exercise(5.19) to find the matrix $\mathcal{R}$. Let

   $\vec{z} = \begin{bmatrix} 2 \\ 2 \end{bmatrix}$ and show that $R(\vec{z}) = -\mathcal{R}\vec{z} = \dfrac{2}{5}\begin{bmatrix} 7 \\ 1 \end{bmatrix}$.

3. Let $\vec{v} = \begin{bmatrix} 3 \\ 2 \end{bmatrix}$, and $\vec{z} = \begin{bmatrix} 2 \\ 2 \end{bmatrix}$. Find the matrices P [see part 2 of Exercise(5.7)] and
   the vector $\vec{w}$. This looks like Figure 5.2 ($\vec{w}$ is shorter than $\vec{v}$). Find $\mathcal{R}$ and show that
   $R(\vec{z}) = -\mathcal{R}\vec{z} = \dfrac{2}{13}\begin{bmatrix} 17 \\ 7 \end{bmatrix}$.

4. The matrix $\mathcal{R} = I - 2P = I - 2\vec{u}\vec{u}^{\,T}$ where $\vec{u}$ is a given unit vector is called a
   reflection matrix. Show that $\mathcal{R}^T\mathcal{R} = I$. That is $\mathcal{R}$ is an orthogonal matrix.

5. As in part 5 of Exercise(5.19) let $\vec{v} = [v_1\ v_2\ \cdots\ v_n] \in \mathcal{R}^n$ be a non-zero vector. Define
   the unit vector $\vec{u} = \dfrac{\vec{v}}{||\vec{v}||}$ and the $n \times n$ matrix projection matrix $P = \vec{u}\vec{u}^{\,T}$. Show
   that $\mathcal{R} = I - 2P$ is an orthogonal matrix.

Exercise 5.21 Matrix Exponentials: Assume that the matrix $A = \begin{bmatrix} a_{11} & a_{12} \\ a_{21} & a_{22} \end{bmatrix}$ has
real eigenvalues $\lambda_1 < \lambda_2$ with corresponding independent eigenvectors $\vec{p}_1$ and $\vec{p}_2$. The
matrix $P = [\ \vec{p}_1\ \vec{p}_2]$ diagonalizes A, $P^{-1}AP = \Lambda = \begin{bmatrix} \lambda_1 & 0 \\ 0 & \lambda_2 \end{bmatrix}$ or $A = P\Lambda P^{-1}$. Let t be a
real number and define

$$e^{At} \equiv Pe^{\Lambda t}P^{-1} = P\begin{bmatrix} e^{\lambda_1 t} & 0 \\ 0 & e^{\lambda_2 t} \end{bmatrix}P^{-1}. \tag{5.55}$$

1. If $t = 0$ then $At = \begin{bmatrix} 0 & 0 \\ 0 & 0 \end{bmatrix} \equiv \mathcal{O}$, the 2×2 zero matrix. Show that $e^{\mathcal{O}} = \begin{bmatrix} 1 & 0 \\ 0 & 1 \end{bmatrix} = I$.
   The eigenvalues of $\mathcal{O}$ are $\lambda_1 = \lambda_2 = 0$. This is the matrix analogue of $e^0 = 1$.

2. Find e^{-At} and $e^{At}e^{-At}$. See part 7 of Exercise(5.6). (The latter is the matrix analogue
   of $e^a e^{-a} = e^0 = 1$).

3. The matrix e^{At} for $A = \begin{bmatrix} a & b \\ 1 & 0 \end{bmatrix}$ where it is assumed that $\lambda_+ \neq \lambda_-$ is found using
   part 3 of Exercise(5.3) which reads

$$A = P\Lambda\left\{P^{-1}\right\} = \begin{bmatrix} \lambda_+ & \lambda_- \\ 1 & 1 \end{bmatrix}\begin{bmatrix} \lambda_+ & 0 \\ 0 & \lambda_- \end{bmatrix}\left\{\left(\frac{1}{\lambda_+ - \lambda_-}\right)\begin{bmatrix} 1 & -\lambda_- \\ -1 & \lambda_+ \end{bmatrix}\right\}$$

so that (5.55) gives

$$e^{At} \equiv Pe^{\Lambda t}P^{-1} = P\begin{bmatrix} e^{\lambda_+ t} & 0 \\ 0 & e^{\lambda_- t} \end{bmatrix}P^{-1}.$$

4. If A is not diagonalizable, matters are a bit more complicated. To illustrate this situation, let $\lambda_+ = \lambda_- = \dfrac{a}{2} \equiv \lambda$ in part 1 of Exercise(5.4) reads

$$A = Q\,(R)\,Q^T = \frac{1}{\sqrt{\lambda^2 + 1}} \begin{bmatrix} \lambda & -1 \\ 1 & \lambda \end{bmatrix} \left(\begin{bmatrix} \lambda & -(\lambda^2 + 1) \\ 0 & \lambda \end{bmatrix} \right) \frac{1}{\sqrt{\lambda^2 + 1}} \begin{bmatrix} \lambda & 1 \\ -1 & \lambda \end{bmatrix}.$$

In this case (5.55) is replaced by

$$e^{At} \equiv Q e^{Rt} Q^T = Q \begin{bmatrix} e^{\lambda t} & -(\lambda^2 + 1)t e^{\lambda t} \\ 0 & e^{\lambda t} \end{bmatrix} Q^T. \tag{5.56}$$

Exercise 5.22 The method used in Exercises(5.3) can also be applied to the second-order constant coefficient linear differential equation

$$\frac{d^2 f(t)}{dt^2} = a \frac{df(t)}{dt} + b f(t), \quad t \geq 0. \tag{5.57}$$

Linear refers to the fact that the dependent variable $f(t)$ and its derivatives $\dfrac{d^2 f(t)}{dt^2}$ and $\dfrac{df(t)}{dt}$ appear to the first power. The second order means that the highest derivative of the dependent variable appearing in (5.57) is two. Constant coefficient means that a and b are numbers (they do not depend on t). If (5.57) is equipped with the initial conditions

$$f(0) = f_0 \quad f'(0) = f_1 \tag{5.58}$$

the problem (5.57) combined with (5.58) is called an **initial value problem**. This means find a function $f(t)$ which satisfies (5.57) on an interval containing zero and $f(t)$ satisfies (5.58). The following steps are the differential equation analogues to the difference equation steps in (5.3) through (5.4) of Example(5.1). Make the change of variable

$$\frac{df(t)}{dt} = u(t) \quad \text{and} \quad f(t) = v(t)$$

and rewrite the initial value problem in (5.57) and (5.58) as

$$\frac{du(t)}{dt} = \frac{d^2 f(t)}{dt^2} = au(t) + bv(t) \qquad u(0) = \frac{df(0)}{dt} = f_1$$

$$\frac{dv(t)}{dt} = \frac{df(t)}{dt} = u(t) \qquad v(0) = f(0) = f_0. \tag{5.59}$$

Set $\vec{w}(t) = \begin{bmatrix} u(t) \\ v(t) \end{bmatrix}$ and $\vec{w}'(t) = \begin{bmatrix} u'(t) \\ v'(t) \end{bmatrix}$ so the last display takes the form

$$\begin{bmatrix} u'(t) \\ v'(t) \end{bmatrix} = \begin{bmatrix} a & b \\ 1 & 0 \end{bmatrix} \begin{bmatrix} u(t) \\ v(t) \end{bmatrix} \quad \text{or in terms of } \vec{w}: \ \vec{w}'(t) = A\vec{w}(t). \tag{5.60}$$

Recall that the solution of the scalar problem $y'(t) = ay(t)$ satisfying $y(0) = y_0$ is given by $y(t) = e^{at}y_0$ (plug it in; it works). Forgetting the vector notation for a minute, the solution of (5.59) (think of the matrix A as a scalar) takes the form $\vec{w}(t) = e^{At}w(0)$ or written out

$$\vec{w}(t) = \begin{bmatrix} u(t) \\ v(t) \end{bmatrix} = e^{At}\vec{w}(0) = e^{At}\begin{bmatrix} u(0) \\ v(0) \end{bmatrix} = e^{At}\begin{bmatrix} f_1 \\ f_0 \end{bmatrix}. \tag{5.61}$$

This is the analogue of equation(5.5) for the difference equation in Example(5.1) where the matrix A^n in equation(5.5) here is replaced by e^{At}. Assume $\lambda_+ \neq \lambda_-$ and substitute the result in part 3 of Exercise(5.21) for e^{At} in (5.61), perform the matrix multiplications, and select the second component of the vector $\vec{w}(t)$ (since this component is $v(t) = f(t)$, the desired solution) to find

$$v(t) = f(t) = \left(\frac{1}{\lambda_+ - \lambda_-}\right)\left[e^{\lambda_+ t}\left(f_1 - \lambda_- f_0\right) + e^{\lambda_- t}\left(-f_1 + \lambda_+ f_0\right)\right]. \tag{5.62}$$

Notice that equation (5.61) does not depend on the nature of the eigenvalues of A. Hence, the case when $\lambda_+ = \lambda_- \equiv \lambda$ can be handled in the same manner as the previous case. That is, substitute the result stated in part 4 of Exercise(5.21) for e^{At} in (5.61), perform the matrix multiplication, and again select the second component $v(t)$ of the vector $\vec{w}(t)$ to find the desired solution

$$\begin{aligned} v(t) = f(t) &= \left(\frac{e^{\lambda t}}{\lambda^2 + 1}\right)\left\{\lambda f_1 + f_0 + (\lambda - (\lambda^2 + 1)t)(-f_1 + \lambda f_0)\right\} \\ &= e^{\lambda t}\left[f_0 + t\left(f_1 - \lambda f_0\right)\right]. \end{aligned} \tag{5.63}$$

5.15 Sample Tests

5.15.1 Sample Test 1

Name_____ Date_____

1. Given that

$$A\vec{p}_1 = \begin{bmatrix} -1 & 3+3i \\ 3-3i & 2 \end{bmatrix} \begin{bmatrix} 1+i \\ 2 \end{bmatrix} = 5 \begin{bmatrix} 1+i \\ 2 \end{bmatrix}$$

and $-4 \in \sigma(A)$.

(a) Find a second independent eigenvector, $\vec{p}_2$ for A.

(b) $\|\vec{p}_1\| =$

(c) $\|\vec{p}_2\| =$

(d) and the dot product $\vec{p}_1 \cdot \vec{p}_2 =$

(e) Write down an orthogonal diagonalizer for A.

2. Assume that A is 5×5 and $\sigma(A) = \{\lambda_1, \lambda_2, \lambda_3, \lambda_4, \lambda_5\}$. Mark each of the following either true T or false F.

   (a) __T or F__ : If A is invertible then A is diagonalizable.

   (b) __T or F__ : If A is diagonalizable then A is invertible.

   (c) __T or F__ : If $\lambda_j \neq \lambda_k$ for all $j \neq k$ then the matrix A is diagonalizable.

   (d) __T or F__ : If $\lambda_j \neq \lambda_k$ for all $j \neq k$ then the matrix A is invertible.

   (e) __T or F__ : If A is invertible then $\lambda_j \neq 0$ for $j = 1, 2, 3, 4, 5$.

3. Let $A = \begin{bmatrix} 2 & 1 \\ -1 & 4 \end{bmatrix}$.

   (a) Find the eigenvalues of A.

   (b) Find all of the independent eigenvectors for A.

   (c) The matrix A $\begin{cases} \text{is} \\ \text{is not} \end{cases}$ diagonalizable because

   _____.

4. The eigenvalues of the matrix $\mathcal{O} = \begin{bmatrix} 0 & 0 \\ 0 & 0 \end{bmatrix}$ are _____ and this matrix

   is orthogonally diagonalizable since $\mathcal{O}$ is _____ (word). The

   orthogonal matrix $\begin{bmatrix} \quad \end{bmatrix}$ (write one down) diagonalizes $\mathcal{O}$.

5. Let $A = \begin{bmatrix} 6 & -2 & -1 \\ -2 & 6 & -1 \\ -1 & -1 & 5 \end{bmatrix}$, $\vec{p}_1 = \begin{bmatrix} 1 \\ 1 \\ 1 \end{bmatrix}$ and $\vec{p}_2 = \begin{bmatrix} 1 \\ -1 \\ 0 \end{bmatrix}$.

(a) Since $A\vec{p}_1 = \begin{bmatrix} \\ \\ \\ \end{bmatrix}$, $\lambda_1 = $_____ is an eigenvalue of A.

(b) Since $A\vec{p}_2 = \begin{bmatrix} \\ \\ \\ \end{bmatrix}$ $\lambda_2 = $_____ is an eigenvalue of A.

(c) The characteristic equation for A is $\rho_A(\lambda) = -(\lambda - \lambda_2)(\lambda - 6)(\lambda - \lambda_1)$ so it follows that a third eigenvalue for A is _____.

(d) Find a third (independent) eigenvector for A.

6. Assume that $\left(P^{-1}AP = \Lambda = \begin{bmatrix} \lambda_1 & 0 & 0 \\ 0 & \lambda_2 & 0 \\ 0 & 0 & \lambda_3 \end{bmatrix} \right)$ for the 3×3 matrix A. That is assume that A is diagonalizable. In addition, assume that A is invertible. Show that the same is true for A^{-1}. Specifically, what is a matrix $\hat{P}$ which diagonalizes A^{-1}.

5.15.2 Sample Test 2

Name_____   Date_____

1. Given that if $A = \begin{bmatrix} 3 & -2 & 1 \\ 0 & 2 & 0 \\ 0 & 1 & 2 \end{bmatrix}$ then $\rho_A(\lambda) = (-1)(\lambda - 2)^2(\lambda - 3)$. Also, it is the case that

$$A \begin{bmatrix} 1 \\ 0 \\ 0 \end{bmatrix} = 3 \begin{bmatrix} 1 \\ 0 \\ 0 \end{bmatrix} \quad \text{and} \quad A \begin{bmatrix} 1 \\ 0 \\ -1 \end{bmatrix} = 2 \begin{bmatrix} 1 \\ 0 \\ -1 \end{bmatrix}.$$

(a) What is the spectrum of A?

(b) What is the algebraic multiplicity of each eigenvalue?

(c) What is the geometric multiplicity of each eigenvalue? Justify your answer.

(d) Is the matrix A diagonalizable? Explain your answer.

2. Mark each of the following either true T or false F. Let A be a real 4×4 matrix and denote its set of eigenvalues by $\sigma(A) = \{\lambda_1, \lambda_2, \lambda_3, \lambda_4\}$

(a) T or F: If $\lambda_j \neq 0$ for $j = 1, 2, 3$, and 4 then A is invertible.

(b) T or F: If A is diagonalizable then $\lambda_j \neq 0, j = 1, 2, 3, 4$.

(c) T or F: The eigenvalues of A^T are also $\{\lambda_1, \lambda_2, \lambda_3, \lambda_4\}$.

(d) T or F: Since $A\vec{0} = \vec{0}$ the zero vector, $\vec{0}$, is an eigenvector for A.

(e) T or F: If $\vec{p} \neq \vec{0}$ and $A\vec{p} = \vec{0}$ then $\lambda = 0$ is an eigenvalue of A.

(f) T or F: If $\lambda_1 = \lambda_2 = \lambda_3 \neq \lambda_4$ and $\dim(\mathcal{N}(A - \lambda_1 I)) = 3$ then A is diagonalizable.

(g) T or F: If the rank of A is four then A is diagonalizable.

(h) T or F: If the rank of A is two and A has four independent eigenvectors then A is diagonalizable.

(i) T or F: An invertible matrix is diagonalizable.

(j) T or F: A diagonalizable matrix is invertible.

3. Assume that the matrix A satisfies the equation

$$A = \begin{bmatrix} 1 & -1 & -1 \\ -1 & 1 & -1 \\ -1 & -1 & 1 \end{bmatrix} = P\Lambda P^{-1} = \begin{bmatrix} 1 & 0 & -2 \\ 1 & 1 & 1 \\ 1 & -1 & 1 \end{bmatrix} \begin{bmatrix} -1 & 0 & 0 \\ 0 & 2 & 0 \\ 0 & 0 & 2 \end{bmatrix} \left(\frac{1}{6} \begin{bmatrix} 2 & 2 & 2 \\ 0 & 3 & -3 \\ -2 & 1 & 1 \end{bmatrix} \right).$$

Label the eigenvalues of A by $\lambda_1 < \lambda_2 = \lambda_3$. That's a bit of a hint. Fill in the blanks.

(a) The Spectrum of A is $\sigma(A) = \Big\{ \underline{\hspace{2cm}} \Big\}$. The algebraic multiplicity of λ_1 is $\underline{\hspace{1.5cm}}$ and the algebraic multiplicity of λ_2 is $\underline{\hspace{1.5cm}}$. The geometric multiplicity of λ_1 is $\underline{\hspace{1.5cm}}$ and the geometric multiplicity of λ_2 is $\underline{\hspace{1.5cm}}$. The matrix A is called d $\underline{\hspace{3cm}}$.

(b) Is the matrix A orthogonally diagonalizable? If no, explain your answer. If yes, write down the orthogonal diagonalizer Q.

4. Let $A = \begin{bmatrix} -2 & 3 \\ 1 & 0 \end{bmatrix}$.

(a) Find the eigenvalues and eigenvectors of A (label them $\lambda_1 < \lambda_2$ and $\vec{p}_1$ and $\vec{p}_2$) .

(b) Define the matrix $P = [\vec{p}_1 \ \vec{p}_2]$. Find the matrix P^{-1}.

(c) Fill in the four entries in matrix $P^{-1}AP \equiv \Lambda = \begin{bmatrix} & \\ & \end{bmatrix}_{2\times 2}$

(d) **T or F:** $A = P\Lambda P^{-1}$.

(e) **T or F:** $A^2 = P\Lambda^2 P^{-1}$.

(f) **T or F:** $A^n = P\Lambda^n P^{-1}$ where n is a positive integer.

5. The Cooter quantities are defined by

$$c_{n+1} = -2c_n + 3c_{n-1}, \quad \text{with} \quad c_0 = 1 \quad \text{and} \quad c_1 = 2. \qquad (*)$$

Set $u_n = c_n$ and $v_n = c_{n-1}$ so that $u_1 = c_1 = 2$ and $v_1 = c_0 = 1$.

(a) Use equation (*) to write $u_{n+1} = c_{n+1}$ in terms of u_n and v_n.

(b) Write $v_{n+1} = c_n$ in terms the u_n.

(c) Use Parts (a) and (b) to find the matrix A in $\begin{bmatrix} u_{n+1} \\ v_{n+1} \end{bmatrix} = A \begin{bmatrix} u_n \\ v_n \end{bmatrix}$. Hint: The matrix in problem 4 on the previous page is the answer.

(d) Given that $\begin{bmatrix} u_{n+1} \\ v_{n+1} \end{bmatrix} = A^n \begin{bmatrix} u_1 \\ v_1 \end{bmatrix}$. Find the nth Cooter quantity. That is, find v_{n+1} which, by definition is c_n. The answer in Problem 4, Part(f), which is true, should be helpful when combined with Part (c) of Problem 4.

Chapter 6

Exercise Hints and Solutions

6.1 Exercise Set One

1.1 For $\vec{v} = \begin{bmatrix} 2 \\ 1 \end{bmatrix}$, $\vec{u} = \begin{bmatrix} -1 \\ 3 \end{bmatrix}$, $\vec{w} = \begin{bmatrix} 3 \\ -1 \end{bmatrix}$, $\vec{x} = \begin{bmatrix} 1 \\ 2 \\ 0 \end{bmatrix}$, $\vec{y} = \begin{bmatrix} 1 \\ 0 \\ -1 \end{bmatrix}$, $\vec{z} = \begin{bmatrix} 2 \\ 0 \\ 2 \end{bmatrix}$.

   (i) $||\vec{v}|| = \sqrt{5}$

   (ii) $||\vec{u}|| = \sqrt{10}$

   (iii) $||\vec{x}|| = \sqrt{5}$

   (iv) $\vec{v} \cdot \vec{u} = 1$

   (v) $\vec{w} \cdot \vec{u} = -6$

   (vi) $\vec{u} \cdot \vec{y}$ is undefined

   (vii) $\vec{v} + \vec{u} = \begin{bmatrix} 1 \\ 4 \end{bmatrix}$

   (viii) $\vec{u} + \vec{y}$ is undefined

   (ix) $\vec{y} + \vec{z} = [\, 3 \ 0 \ 1 \,]^T$

   (x) $\vec{v} \cdot \vec{y}$ is undefined

   (xi) $\vec{x} \cdot \vec{y} = 1$

   (xii) $\vec{y} \cdot \vec{z} = 0$

1.2 For $\vec{v} = \begin{bmatrix} 2 \\ 1 \end{bmatrix}$, $\vec{w} = \begin{bmatrix} -1 \\ 2 \end{bmatrix}$, and $\vec{u} = \begin{bmatrix} -1 \\ 3 \end{bmatrix}$,

   (i) $||\vec{v} + \vec{w}||^2 = ||[\, 1 \ 3 \,]||^2 = 10 = ||\vec{v}||^2 + ||\vec{w}||^2 = \sqrt{5}^2 + \sqrt{5}^2 = 10$

   (ii) $||\vec{v} - \vec{w}||^2 = ||[\, 3 \ -1 \,]||^2 = 10 = ||\vec{v}||^2 + ||\vec{w}||^2 = \sqrt{5}^2 + \sqrt{5}^2 = 10$.

   (iii) $\vec{v} \cdot \vec{w} = 0$

   (iv) $\mathrm{proj}_{\vec{v}}\,(\vec{w}) = 0$

   (v) $\mathrm{proj}_{\vec{w}}\,(\vec{u}) = \dfrac{7}{5}\begin{bmatrix} -1 \\ 2 \end{bmatrix}$

   (vi) $||\vec{v} + \vec{u}|| = ||[1 \ 4]|| = \sqrt{17} \approx 4.1 < ||\vec{v}|| + ||\vec{u}|| = \sqrt{5} + \sqrt{10} \approx 5.4$

   (vii) $||\vec{v} - \vec{u}|| = ||[3 \ -2]|| = \sqrt{13} \approx 3.6 < ||\vec{v}|| + ||\vec{u}|| = \sqrt{5} + \sqrt{10} \approx 5.4$

(viii) $\vec{v} \cdot \vec{u} = 1$

(ix) $\text{proj}_{\vec{v}} (\vec{u}) = \dfrac{1}{5} \begin{bmatrix} 2 \\ 1 \end{bmatrix}$

(x) $\text{proj}_{\vec{u}} (\vec{v}) = \dfrac{1}{10} \begin{bmatrix} -1 \\ 3 \end{bmatrix}$

1.3 Given $\vec{v} = \begin{bmatrix} 2 \\ 1 \\ 0 \end{bmatrix}$, $\vec{w} = \begin{bmatrix} -1 \\ 2 \\ 1 \end{bmatrix}$, and $\vec{u} = \begin{bmatrix} 1 \\ 1 \\ 1 \end{bmatrix}$.

(i) $||\vec{v} + \vec{w}||^2 = ||[\, 1 \ 3 \ 1 \,]||^2 = 11 = ||\vec{v}||^2 + ||\vec{w}||^2 = \sqrt{5}^2 + \sqrt{6}^2 = 11$

(ii) $||\vec{v} - \vec{w}||^2 = ||[\, 3 \ -1 \ -1 \,]||^2 = 11 = ||\vec{v}||^2 + ||\vec{w}||^2 = \sqrt{5}^2 + \sqrt{6}^2 = 11$

(iii) $\vec{v} \cdot \vec{w} = 0$

(iv) $\text{proj}_{\vec{v}} (\vec{w}) = 0.$

(v) $\text{proj}_{\vec{w}} (\vec{u}) = \dfrac{1}{3} \begin{bmatrix} -1 \\ 2 \\ 1 \end{bmatrix}.$

(vi) $||\vec{v} + \vec{u}|| = ||[\, 3 \ 2 \ 1 \,]|| = \sqrt{14} \approx 3.7 < ||\vec{v}|| + ||\vec{u}|| = \sqrt{5} + \sqrt{3} \approx 3.97$

(vii) $||\vec{v} - \vec{u}|| = ||[1 \ 0 \ -1]|| = \sqrt{2} \approx 1.4 < ||\vec{v}|| + ||\vec{u}|| = \sqrt{5} + \sqrt{3} \approx 3.97$

(viii) $\vec{v} \cdot \vec{u} = 3$

(ix) $\text{proj}_{\vec{v}} (\vec{u}) = \dfrac{3}{5} \begin{bmatrix} 2 \\ 1 \\ 0 \end{bmatrix}$

(x) $\text{proj}_{\vec{u}} (\vec{v}) = \begin{bmatrix} 1 \\ 1 \\ 1 \end{bmatrix}$

1.4 Part 1. The projection $\text{proj}_{\vec{v}} (\vec{u}) = \dfrac{-2}{5} \begin{bmatrix} -3 \\ 1 \end{bmatrix} = \dfrac{2}{5} \begin{bmatrix} 3 \\ -1 \end{bmatrix}$ which is a vector that lies along $-\vec{v}$. Part 2. The projection $\text{proj}_{\vec{u}} (\vec{v}) = \dfrac{-4}{8} \begin{bmatrix} 2 \\ 2 \end{bmatrix} = \begin{bmatrix} -1 \\ -1 \end{bmatrix}$ which is a vector that lies along $-\vec{u}$.

1.5 The vectors $\vec{v} = \begin{bmatrix} 6 \\ -4 \\ 2 \end{bmatrix}$ and $\vec{u} = \begin{bmatrix} 3 \\ -2 \\ 1 \end{bmatrix}$ have lengths $||\vec{v}|| = \sqrt{56} = \sqrt{4 \cdot 14} = 2\sqrt{14}$, and $||\vec{u}|| = \sqrt{14}$. Hence

$$||\vec{v}|| \, ||\vec{u}|| = \sqrt{56}\sqrt{14} = 2(\sqrt{14})^2 = 28$$

and $\vec{v} \cdot \vec{u} = 6(3) - 4(-2) + 2(1) = 28$ which gives (i). For (ii)

$$||\vec{v} + \vec{u}|| = ||[\ 9\ \ -6\ \ 3\ ]^T|| = \sqrt{81 + 36 + 9} = \sqrt{9(14)} = 3\sqrt{14}$$

and $||\vec{v}|| + ||\vec{u}|| = \sqrt{56} + \sqrt{14} = 2\sqrt{14} + \sqrt{14} = 3\sqrt{14}$

1.6 For $\vec{v} = \begin{bmatrix} -1 \\ 2 \end{bmatrix}$ and $\vec{u} = \begin{bmatrix} 2 \\ 1 \end{bmatrix}$ the lengths are $||\vec{v}|| = ||\vec{u}|| = \sqrt{5}$ so that $||\vec{v}||^2 +$

$||\vec{u}||^2 = 10$. The square of the lengths of the sum $\vec{v} + \vec{u} = \begin{bmatrix} 1 \\ 3 \end{bmatrix}$ and the difference

$\vec{v} - \vec{u} = \begin{bmatrix} -3 \\ 1 \end{bmatrix}$ are also 10. For the vectors $\vec{v} = \begin{bmatrix} -1 \\ 2 \\ 1 \end{bmatrix}$ and $\vec{u} = \begin{bmatrix} 1 \\ 1 \\ -1 \end{bmatrix}$ the lengths

are $||\vec{v}|| = \sqrt{6}$ and $||\vec{u}|| = \sqrt{3}$ so that $||\vec{v}||^2 + ||\vec{u}||^2 = 6 + 3 = 9$. The square of the

lengths of the sum $\vec{v} + \vec{u} = \begin{bmatrix} 0 \\ 3 \\ 0 \end{bmatrix}$ and the difference $\vec{v} - \vec{u} = \begin{bmatrix} -2 \\ 1 \\ 2 \end{bmatrix}$ are also 9.

1.7 Equating the first two components in $\vec{v} = \begin{bmatrix} 4 \\ 5 \\ -2 \end{bmatrix} = (\alpha)\begin{bmatrix} 1 \\ 1 \\ 0 \end{bmatrix} + (\beta)\begin{bmatrix} 1 \\ 1 \\ 1 \end{bmatrix} + (\gamma)\begin{bmatrix} 1 \\ 1 \\ -1 \end{bmatrix}$

gives $\alpha + \beta + \gamma = 4$ and $\alpha + \beta + \gamma = 5$. Subtract the first from the second to see $(\alpha + \beta + \gamma) - (\alpha + \beta + \gamma) = 0 = 4 - 5 = -1$ which is impossible.

1.8 For part 1, the area of a parallelogram with sides $\vec{v} = \begin{bmatrix} 3 \\ 1 \end{bmatrix}$ and $\vec{u} = \begin{bmatrix} 2 \\ 2 \end{bmatrix}$ from

the the formula $A_p = |2(3) - 2(1)| = 4$. Using $\vec{e} = \frac{1}{5}\begin{bmatrix} -2 \\ 6 \end{bmatrix}$ and $A_p = ||\vec{v}|| ||\vec{e}|| =$

$\sqrt{10}\sqrt{\frac{1}{25}\left((-2)^2 + 6^2\right)} = \sqrt{10}\sqrt{\frac{40}{25}} = \sqrt{10}\frac{\sqrt{4(10)}}{5} = \frac{2(10)}{5} = 4$.

For part 2, the area of a parallelogram with sides $\vec{v} = \begin{bmatrix} -3 \\ 1 \end{bmatrix}$ and $\vec{u} = \begin{bmatrix} 2 \\ 2 \end{bmatrix}$ from

the the formula $A_p = |2(-3) - 2(1)| = |-6 - 2| = 8$. Notice the absolute values.

What is the angle between $\vec{v}$ and $\vec{u}$? Using $\vec{e} = \begin{bmatrix} 2 \\ 2 \end{bmatrix} - \frac{2}{5}\begin{bmatrix} 3 \\ -1 \end{bmatrix} = \frac{4}{5}\begin{bmatrix} 1 \\ 3 \end{bmatrix}$ and

$A_p = ||\vec{v}|| ||\vec{e}|| = \sqrt{10}\sqrt{\frac{16}{25}\left(1^2 + 3^2\right)} = \sqrt{10}\left(\frac{4}{5}\sqrt{10}\right) = \frac{40}{5} = 8$.

6.1.1 Sample Quiz 1 Solutions

1. For $\vec{v} = \begin{bmatrix} -1 \\ 3 \end{bmatrix}$, $\vec{u} = \begin{bmatrix} 3 \\ 1 \end{bmatrix}$, $\vec{0} = \begin{bmatrix} 0 \\ 0 \end{bmatrix}$, and $\vec{z} = \begin{bmatrix} 2 \\ 1 \\ 1 \end{bmatrix}$ (a) $\vec{0} \cdot \vec{v} = 0$, (b) $\vec{v} +$

   $\begin{bmatrix} 1 \\ -3 \\ 0 \end{bmatrix}$ is undefined (different size summands), (c) $\vec{v} \cdot \vec{u} = (-1)(3) + (3)(1) = 0$, (d)

   $\mathrm{proj}_{\vec{v}}(\vec{u}) = \vec{0}$, (e) $||\vec{v}|| = \sqrt{10}$, (f) $||\vec{z}|| = \sqrt{6}$, (g) $||\vec{v} + \vec{u}||^2 = 2^2 + 4^2 = 20$, (h)

   $||\vec{v}||^2 + ||\vec{u}||^2 = 10 + 10 = 20$, (i) $\vec{0} \cdot \begin{bmatrix} 1 \\ -3 \\ 0 \end{bmatrix}$ is undefined (different size vectors), (j)

   $\mathrm{proj}_{\vec{u}}(\vec{v}) = \vec{0}$ and (k) $\mathrm{proj}_{\vec{z}}(\vec{w}) = \dfrac{-1}{6} \begin{bmatrix} 2 \\ 1 \\ 1 \end{bmatrix}$.

2. Require $\vec{x} \cdot \vec{v} = -x_1 + 3x_2 = 0$ and $\vec{x} \cdot \vec{u} = 3x_1 + x_2 = 0$. The first yields $x_1 = 3x_2$ which when substituted in the second gives $3(3x_2) + x_2 = 10x_2 = 0$. Hence $x_2 = 0$ and $x_1 = 0$.

3. Let $\vec{u} = \begin{bmatrix} 2 \\ 1 \end{bmatrix}$ and $\vec{v} = \begin{bmatrix} 4 \\ -3 \end{bmatrix}$ then (a) $||\vec{u}|| = \sqrt{5}$, (b) $||\vec{v}|| = \sqrt{25} = 5$ (c) the dot

   product $\vec{u} \cdot \vec{v} = (2)(4) + (1)(-3) = 5$ (d) $\mathrm{proj}_{\vec{u}}(\vec{v}) = \dfrac{5}{5}\vec{u} = \vec{u}$, (e) the angle between

   the vectors $\vec{u}$ and $\vec{u} - \vec{v} = \begin{bmatrix} -2 \\ 4 \end{bmatrix}$ is 90° since $= \vec{u} \cdot (\vec{u} - \vec{v}) = (2)(-2) + 1(4) = 0$ and

   (f) $\mathrm{proj}_{\vec{v}}(\vec{u}) = \dfrac{5}{25}\vec{v} = \dfrac{1}{5}\vec{v}$.

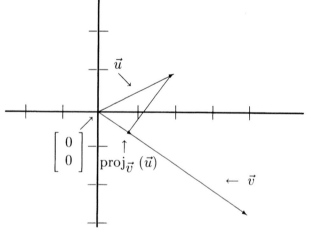

Figure 1

6.1.2 Sample Quiz 2 Solutions

1. For the vectors $\vec{u} = \begin{bmatrix} 3 \\ 3 \end{bmatrix}$ and $\vec{v} = \begin{bmatrix} 4 \\ 2 \end{bmatrix}$ (a) the vectors $\vec{u} - \vec{v}$ and $\vec{u} + \vec{v}$ are illustrated in Figure 1.2 in Example(1.4) (b) the cosine of the angle θ between the vectors $\vec{u}$ and $\vec{v}$ is given by

$$\vec{u} \cdot \vec{v} = 12 + 6 = 18 = ||\vec{u}|| ||\vec{v}|| \cos(\theta) = \sqrt{18}\sqrt{20}\cos(\theta)$$

so that $\cos(\theta) = \dfrac{18}{\sqrt{18}\sqrt{20}} = \dfrac{\sqrt{18}}{\sqrt{20}} = \dfrac{3}{\sqrt{10}}$ and (c) the number $\alpha = \dfrac{\vec{v} \cdot \vec{u}}{||\vec{v}||^2} = \dfrac{12 + 6}{18} = 1$ which is illustrated in Figure 1.5 of Example(1.12).

2. For $\vec{v} = \begin{bmatrix} -1 \\ 2 \end{bmatrix}$, $\vec{u} = \begin{bmatrix} 2 \\ 1 \end{bmatrix}$ and $\vec{0} = \begin{bmatrix} 0 \\ 0 \end{bmatrix}$ (a) $\vec{0} + \vec{v} = \vec{v}$, (b) $\vec{v} + \begin{bmatrix} 1 \\ -3 \\ 0 \end{bmatrix}$

is undefined (different size summands), (c) $\vec{v} \cdot \vec{v} = ||\vec{v}||^2 = 5$, (d) $||\vec{v}||^2 = 5$, (e) $||\vec{u}||^2 = 5$, (f) $||\vec{v} + \vec{u}||^2 = ||[\,1\ 3\,]^T||^2 = 10$, (g) $||\vec{v}||^2 + ||\vec{u}||^2 = 5 + 5 = 10$, (h) $||\vec{v} - \vec{u}||^2 = ||[\,-3\ 1\,]||^2 = 10$, (i) $\text{proj}_{\vec{u}}(\vec{v}) = \vec{0}$, (j) is undefined (different size vectors), if $\vec{w} = \begin{bmatrix} 2 \\ 2 \end{bmatrix}$ then (k) $\text{proj}_{\vec{w}}(\vec{v}) = \dfrac{2}{4}\begin{bmatrix} 2 \\ 2 \end{bmatrix} = \dfrac{1}{2}\vec{w}$ and (l) $\text{proj}_{\vec{w}}(\vec{u}) = \dfrac{6}{8}\begin{bmatrix} 2 \\ 2 \end{bmatrix} = \dfrac{3}{4}\vec{w}$.

3. The vector $\vec{x} = \begin{bmatrix} 5 \\ \alpha \\ \alpha \end{bmatrix}$ is orthogonal to $\vec{z} = \begin{bmatrix} -2 \\ 3 \\ 2 \end{bmatrix}$ if $\vec{x} \cdot \vec{z} = -10 + 3\alpha + 2\alpha = -10 + 5\alpha = 0$ so $\alpha = 2$.

6.2   Exercise Set Two

2.1 The unique solutions are

$$1.\ \vec{x} = \frac{1}{4}\begin{bmatrix} 7 \\ 5 \end{bmatrix} \quad 2.\ \vec{x} = \begin{bmatrix} 8 \\ -4 \\ 2 \end{bmatrix} \quad 3.\ \vec{x} = \frac{1}{3}\begin{bmatrix} 94 \\ -16 \\ -4 \end{bmatrix} \quad 4\text{ and }5.\ \vec{x} = \begin{bmatrix} 3 \\ -1 \end{bmatrix}$$

2.2 For each of parts 1 through 3 use Definition(2.10) in the row reduction

1. $\left[\ A\mid\vec{b}\ \right] = \begin{bmatrix} 2 & -2 & 3 \\ 1 & -1 & 2 \end{bmatrix} \sim \begin{bmatrix} 2 & -2 & 3 \\ 0 & 0 & 1/2 \end{bmatrix}.$

2. $\left[\ A\mid\vec{b}\ \right] = \begin{bmatrix} 1 & 2 & 3 & 6 \\ 2 & 5 & 4 & 4 \\ 1 & 3 & 1 & 3 \end{bmatrix} \sim \begin{bmatrix} 1 & 2 & 3 & 6 \\ 0 & 1 & -2 & -8 \\ 0 & 1 & -2 & -3 \end{bmatrix} \sim \begin{bmatrix} 1 & 2 & 3 & 6 \\ 0 & 1 & -2 & -8 \\ 0 & 0 & 0 & 5 \end{bmatrix}.$

3. $\begin{bmatrix} 1 & 1 & 2 \\ 1 & 2 & 1 \\ 2 & 4 & 3 \end{bmatrix} \sim \begin{bmatrix} 1 & 2 & 2 \\ 0 & 1 & -1 \\ 0 & 2 & -1 \end{bmatrix} \sim \begin{bmatrix} 1 & 2 & 2 \\ 0 & 1 & -1 \\ 0 & 0 & 1 \end{bmatrix}.$

2.3 The row reduction $\begin{bmatrix} 1 & 2 & 3 & 6 \\ 2 & 4 & 6 & b_2 \end{bmatrix} \sim \begin{bmatrix} 1 & 2 & 3 & 6 \\ 0 & 0 & 0 & b_2-6 \end{bmatrix}$ will yield a consistent system if $b_2 = 6$. Let both x_2 and x_3 be free variables so that the solutions are $x_1 = 6 - 2x_2 - 3x_3$. For any other choice of b_2 there is no solution.

2.4 Define $A = \begin{bmatrix} 2 & -2 \\ 1 & -1 \end{bmatrix}$ and use (2.27) to find

$$A\vec{x}_h = \begin{bmatrix} 2 & -2 \\ 1 & -1 \end{bmatrix}\left(x_2\begin{bmatrix} 1 \\ 1 \end{bmatrix}\right) = x_2\begin{bmatrix} 2 & -2 \\ 1 & -1 \end{bmatrix}\begin{bmatrix} 1 \\ 1 \end{bmatrix} = x_2\begin{bmatrix} 2-2 \\ 1-1 \end{bmatrix} = \begin{bmatrix} 0 \\ 0 \end{bmatrix}$$

and

$$A\vec{x}_p = \begin{bmatrix} 2 & -2 \\ 1 & -1 \end{bmatrix}\begin{bmatrix} 3/2 \\ 0 \end{bmatrix} = \begin{bmatrix} 2(3/2)-2(0) \\ 3/2-1(0) \end{bmatrix} = \begin{bmatrix} 3 \\ 3/2 \end{bmatrix}.$$

To see that $\vec{x}_p = \begin{bmatrix} 1/2 \\ -1 \end{bmatrix}$ is a particular solution substitute $x_2 = -1$ in the general solution $\vec{x} = x_2\begin{bmatrix} 1 \\ 1 \end{bmatrix} + \begin{bmatrix} 3/2 \\ 0 \end{bmatrix}$ or one can directly check

$$A\vec{x}_p = \begin{bmatrix} 2 & -2 \\ 1 & -1 \end{bmatrix}\begin{bmatrix} 1/2 \\ -1 \end{bmatrix} = \begin{bmatrix} 2(1/2)-2(0) \\ 1/2-1(-1) \end{bmatrix} = \begin{bmatrix} 3 \\ 3/2 \end{bmatrix}.$$

2.5 From the reduced row reduction $\begin{bmatrix} 1 & 2 & 3 & | & 6 \\ 2 & 5 & 4 & | & 4 \end{bmatrix} \sim \begin{bmatrix} 1 & 0 & 7 & | & 22 \\ 0 & 1 & -2 & | & -8 \end{bmatrix}$ the first and second row, when variables are restored, reads $x_1 = -7x_3 + 22$ and $x_2 = 2x_3 - 8$, respectively. Hence the reduced row form has carried out the back substitution which is in the display in the lines preceding the solution in (2.23).

2.6 Part 1 is a straightforward multiplication. For part 3 substitute , as indicated write $x_3 = \dfrac{x_2 + 8}{2}$ into

$$x_1 = -2x_2 - 3x_3 + 6 = -2x_2 - 3\left(\frac{x_2 + 8}{2}\right) + 6 = -\frac{7}{2}x_2 - 6$$

so the solution reads

$$\vec{x} = \begin{bmatrix} -(7/2)x_2 - 6 \\ x_2 \\ (1/2)x_2 + 4 \end{bmatrix} = x_2 \begin{bmatrix} -7/2 \\ 1 \\ 1/2 \end{bmatrix} + \begin{bmatrix} -6 \\ 0 \\ 4 \end{bmatrix}$$

which when evaluated at $x_2 = 2x_3 - 8$ gives

$$x_2 \begin{bmatrix} -7/2 \\ 1 \\ 1/2 \end{bmatrix} + \begin{bmatrix} -6 \\ 0 \\ 4 \end{bmatrix} = (2x_3 - 8)\begin{bmatrix} -7/2 \\ 1 \\ 1/2 \end{bmatrix} + \begin{bmatrix} -6 \\ 0 \\ 4 \end{bmatrix}$$

$$= x_3 \begin{bmatrix} -7 \\ 2 \\ 1 \end{bmatrix} + \begin{bmatrix} 28 \\ -8 \\ -4 \end{bmatrix} + \begin{bmatrix} -6 \\ 0 \\ 4 \end{bmatrix} = x_3 \begin{bmatrix} -7 \\ 2 \\ 1 \end{bmatrix} + \begin{bmatrix} 22 \\ -8 \\ 0 \end{bmatrix}$$

which is the solution found in (2.23) with x_3 as the free variable.

2.7 Row reduction of the augmented system

$$\begin{bmatrix} 1 & 1 & | & 2 \\ 1 & 2 & | & b_2 \\ 2 & a_{32} & | & b_3 \end{bmatrix} \sim \begin{bmatrix} 1 & 1 & | & 2 \\ 0 & 1 & | & b_2 - 2 \\ 0 & a_{32} - 2 & | & b_3 - 4 \end{bmatrix}.$$

If $b_2 = 3$ then the second row implies that $x_2 = 1$ which when substituted in the last line gives $a_{32} - 2 = b_3 - 4$ or $b_3 = a_{32} + 2$. The original third equation reads $2x_1 + a_{32}x_2 = a_{32} + 2$. The slope of the first equation is -1, the second is $-1/2$ and the third is $-2/a_{32}$ so select any a_{32} diffwerent then 2 or 4. If $b_2 = 2$ then $x_2 = 0$. The last row then shows $b_3 = 4$ for consistency no matter what the value of a_{32}.

2.8 Completing the row reduction gives

$$\begin{bmatrix} 1 & 2 & 3 & 4 & | & 1 \\ 0 & 0 & -2 & -3 & | & -2 \\ 0 & 0 & -4 & -6 & | & b_3 - 3 \end{bmatrix} \sim \begin{bmatrix} 1 & 2 & 3 & 4 & | & 1 \\ 0 & 0 & -2 & -3 & | & -2 \\ 0 & 0 & 0 & 0 & | & b_3 + 1 \end{bmatrix}$$

so that $b_3 = -1$ for consistency. The second row gives $x_3 = -(3/2)x_4 + 1$ and from the first row $x_1 = -2x_2 - 3(-(3/2)x_4 + 1) - 4x_4 + 1 = -2x_2 + (1/2)x_4 - 2$ which gives the solution listed in the problem. In the case $a_{32} = 7$

$$
\begin{bmatrix}
1 & 2 & 3 & 4 & \bigm| & 1 \\
0 & 0 & -2 & -3 & \bigm| & -2 \\
0 & 1 & -4 & -6 & \bigm| & b_3 - 3
\end{bmatrix}
\sim
\begin{bmatrix}
1 & 2 & 3 & 4 & \bigm| & 1 \\
0 & 1 & -4 & -6 & \bigm| & b_3 - 3 \\
0 & 0 & -2 & -3 & \bigm| & -2
\end{bmatrix}
$$

which is consistent for any value of b_3. To be specific, take $b_3 = -1$ as in part 1. The last equation gives $x_3 = -(3/2)x_4 + 1$,

$$
x_2 = 4x_3 + 6x_4 - 4 = 4(-(3/2)x_4 + 1) + 6x_4 - 4 = 0.
$$

and $x_1 = -2x_2 - 3x_3 - 4x_4 + 1 = -3(-(3/2)x_4 + 1) - 4x_4 + 1 = (1/2)x_4 - 2$ which is the solution listed in the problem.

2.9 Parts 1 and 2 are straightforward row reductions which lead to the matrix

$$
\hat{A} = \begin{bmatrix} 1/4 & 1/2 \\ -1/4 & 1/2 \end{bmatrix} = \frac{1}{4} \begin{bmatrix} 1 & 2 \\ -1 & 2 \end{bmatrix}.
$$

The calculation

$$
A\hat{A} = \begin{bmatrix} 2 & -2 \\ 1 & 1 \end{bmatrix} \begin{bmatrix} 1/4 & 1/2 \\ -1/4 & 1/2 \end{bmatrix} = \begin{bmatrix} 2(1/4) - 2(-1/4) & 2(1/2) - 2(1/2) \\ (1/4) - (1/4) & 1/2 + 1/2 \end{bmatrix} = \begin{bmatrix} 1 & 0 \\ 0 & 1 \end{bmatrix}
$$

shows $A\hat{A} = I$ and the calculation of $\hat{A}A$ is similar. The product $BI = \begin{bmatrix} b_{11} & b_{12} \\ b_{21} & b_{22} \end{bmatrix} \begin{bmatrix} 1 & 0 \\ 0 & 1 \end{bmatrix} = \begin{bmatrix} b_{11} & b_{12} \\ b_{21} & b_{22} \end{bmatrix}$ is straightforward.

6.2.1 Sample Quiz 1 Solutions

1. Answer each of the following for the system $\begin{cases} 2x_1 - 2x_2 = b_1 \\ x_1 + a_{22}x_2 = b_2 \end{cases}$. (a) If $a_{22} = 1$ then using the first equation gives $7/2 - 5/2 = 1 = b_1$ and from the second equation $7/4 + 5/4 = 12/4 = 3 = b_2$. (b) If $a_{22} = -1$ and $b_1 = 3$ then

$$\left[\begin{array}{cc|c} 2 & -2 & 3 \\ 1 & -1 & b_2 \end{array} \right] \sim \left[\begin{array}{cc|c} 2 & -2 & 3 \\ 0 & 0 & b_2 - 3/2 \end{array} \right]$$

so that the system is consistent if $b_2 = 3/2$ and then the first equation gives the solution $x_1 = x_2 + 3/2$. (c) The system is inconsistent for any choice of $b_2 \neq 3/2$.

2. Assume that A is 3×4 and the system $A\vec{x} = \vec{b} = \begin{bmatrix} b_1 \\ b_2 \\ b_3 \end{bmatrix}$ is row reduced as follows

$$[\,A \mid \vec{b}\,] \sim [\,U \mid \vec{b}\,] = \left[\begin{array}{cccc|c} 2 & 4 & 0 & -2 & b_1 \\ 0 & 0 & 1 & 2 & b_2 - 2b_1 \\ 0 & 0 & 0 & 0 & b_3 - b_2 - b_1 \end{array} \right]. \qquad (*)$$

(a) The matrix A has ___2___ pivots. If $\vec{b} = \begin{bmatrix} 2 \\ 2 \\ 3 \end{bmatrix}$ then augmented matrix $[\,A \mid \vec{b}\,]$

has ___3___ pivots. and if $\vec{b} = \begin{bmatrix} 1 \\ 2 \\ 3 \end{bmatrix}$ then $[\,A \mid \vec{b}\,]$ has ___2___ pivots. (b) If $\begin{bmatrix} 1 \\ 2 \\ 3 \end{bmatrix}$

then $b_2 - 2b_1 = 0$ so that $x_3 = -2x_4$ from the second row of $(*)$ and the first equation yields $x_1 = -2x_2 + x_4 + 1/2$ so the general solution is

$$\begin{bmatrix} x_1 \\ x_2 \\ x_3 \\ x_4 \end{bmatrix} = \begin{bmatrix} -2x_2 + x_4 + 1/2 \\ x_2 \\ -2x_4 \\ x_4 \end{bmatrix} = \left\{ x_2 \begin{bmatrix} -2 \\ 1 \\ 0 \\ 0 \end{bmatrix} + x_4 \begin{bmatrix} 1 \\ 0 \\ -2 \\ 1 \end{bmatrix} \right\} + \begin{bmatrix} 1/2 \\ 0 \\ 0 \\ 0 \end{bmatrix} = \{\vec{x}_h\} + \vec{x}_p.$$

6.2.2   Sample Quiz 2 Solutions

1. Consider the linear system $\begin{cases} 2x_1 - 2x_2 = 3 \\ -x_1 + x_2 = b_2 \end{cases}$ (*). (a) The augmented matrix for (*) with row reduction reads

$$\begin{bmatrix} 2 & -2 & | & 3 \\ -1 & 1 & | & b_2 \end{bmatrix} \sim \begin{bmatrix} 2 & -2 & | & 3 \\ 0 & 0 & | & b_2 + 3/2 \end{bmatrix}$$

(b) so if $b_2 \neq -3/2$ the linear system is inconsistent and (c) if $b_2 = -3/2$ the linear system is consistent (d) with the solution $x_1 = x_2 + 3/2$. (e) If $x_2 = -1$ the $x_1 = 1/2$ and finally (f) $-x_1 + x_2 = -1/2 - 1` = -3/2$.

2. Let $A = \begin{bmatrix} 1 & 2 & 3 & 4 \\ 2 & 4 & 4 & 5 \\ 3 & 6 & 5 & 6 \end{bmatrix}$. Assume that the linear system $A\vec{x} = \vec{b} = \begin{bmatrix} b_1 \\ b_2 \\ b_3 \end{bmatrix}$ has been **correctly** row reduced as follows

$$[\,A\mid\vec{b}\,] \sim [\,U\mid\vec{b}\,] = \begin{bmatrix} 1 & 2 & 3 & 4 & | & b_1 \\ 0 & 0 & -2 & -3 & | & b_2 - 2b_1 \\ 0 & 0 & 0 & 0 & | & b_3 - 2b_2 + b_1 \end{bmatrix}. \qquad (*)$$

(a) The matrix A has __2__ pivots. If $\vec{b} = \begin{bmatrix} 2 \\ 2 \\ 3 \end{bmatrix}$ then augmented matrix $[\,A\mid\vec{b}\,]$ has __3__ pivots. If $\vec{b} = \begin{bmatrix} 2 \\ 2 \\ 2 \end{bmatrix}$ then $[\,A\mid\vec{b}\,]$ has __2__ pivots. (b) If $\begin{bmatrix} 2 \\ 2 \\ 2 \end{bmatrix}$ then $b_2 - 2b_1 = -2$ so that $x_3 = -(3/2)x_4 + 1$ from the second row of (*) and the first equation yields

$$x_1 = -2x_2 - 3x_3 - 4x_4 + 2 = -2x_2 - 3(-(3/2)x_4 + 1) - 4x_4 + 2 = -2x_2 + 1/2x_4 - 1$$

so the general solution is

$$\begin{bmatrix} x_1 \\ x_2 \\ x_3 \\ x_4 \end{bmatrix} = \begin{bmatrix} -2x_2 + (1/2)x_4 - 1 \\ x_2 \\ -(3/2)x_4 + 1 \\ x_4 \end{bmatrix} = \left\{ x_2 \begin{bmatrix} -2 \\ 1 \\ 0 \\ 0 \end{bmatrix} + x_4 \begin{bmatrix} 1/2 \\ 0 \\ -3/2 \\ 1 \end{bmatrix} \right\} + \begin{bmatrix} -1 \\ 0 \\ 1 \\ 0 \end{bmatrix} = \{\vec{x}_h\} + \vec{x}_p.$$

6.3 Exercise Set Three

3.1 For $A = \begin{bmatrix} 2 & 0 & -1 \\ 1 & 2 & 2 \end{bmatrix}$, $B = \begin{bmatrix} 1 & -1 \\ 0 & 0 \\ 2 & 2 \end{bmatrix}$, $C = \begin{bmatrix} 0 & -2 & 0 \\ -2 & 4 & 0 \\ 0 & 0 & 0 \end{bmatrix}$ and $\mathcal{O} = \begin{bmatrix} 0 & 0 & 0 \\ 0 & 0 & 0 \end{bmatrix}$.

Additions

(i) $A + B$ is undefined

(ii) $A + B^T = \begin{bmatrix} 3 & 0 & 1 \\ 0 & 2 & 4 \end{bmatrix}$

(iii) $A + C$ is undefined

(iv) $A + \mathcal{O} = A$

(v) $B + \mathcal{O}$ is undefined

(vi) $A^T + B = \begin{bmatrix} 3 & 0 \\ 0 & 2 \\ 1 & 4 \end{bmatrix}$

(vii) $\mathcal{O} + B^T = B^T$

(viii) $B + C$ is undefined

(ix) $A^T + B^T$ is undefined

Multiplications

(i) $AB = \begin{bmatrix} 0 & -4 \\ 5 & 3 \end{bmatrix}$

(ii) $BA = \begin{bmatrix} 1 & -2 & -3 \\ 0 & 0 & 0 \\ 5 & 4 & 2 \end{bmatrix}$

(iii) $CB = \begin{bmatrix} 0 & 0 \\ -2 & 2 \\ 0 & 0 \end{bmatrix}$

(iv) $A\mathcal{O}$ is undefined

(v) $\mathcal{O}A$ is undefined

(vi) BC is undefined

(vii) $C^T B^T$ is undefined

(viii) $B^T C^T = \begin{bmatrix} 0 & -2 & 0 \\ 0 & 2 & 0 \end{bmatrix}$

(ix) $(CB)^T = B^T C^T$

3.2 For part 1, write

$$\Lambda A = \begin{bmatrix} \lambda_1 & 0 \\ 0 & \lambda_2 \end{bmatrix} \begin{bmatrix} a_{11} & a_{12} \\ a_{21} & a_{22} \end{bmatrix} = \begin{bmatrix} \lambda_1 a_{11} & \lambda_1 a_{12} \\ \lambda_2 a_{21} & \lambda_2 a_{22} \end{bmatrix} = \begin{bmatrix} \lambda_1 \vec{a_{1*}}^T \\ \lambda_2 \vec{a_{2*}}^T \end{bmatrix} = \Lambda A_r$$

For part 2, a similar calculation can be made or, as in part 3,

$$(\Lambda A_r)^T = (A_r)^T \Lambda^T = A_c \Lambda$$

since $\Lambda^T = \Lambda$ and $A_r^T = A_c$ (the rows of the transpose of A_r are the columns of the transpose, A_c).

3.3 The two products

$$A_4 A_4^T = \begin{bmatrix} 1 & 1 \\ 1 & 2 \\ 2 & 0 \end{bmatrix} \begin{bmatrix} 1 & 1 & 2 \\ 1 & 2 & 0 \end{bmatrix} = \begin{bmatrix} 2 & 3 & 2 \\ 3 & 5 & 2 \\ 2 & 2 & 4 \end{bmatrix} \text{ and } A_4^T A_4 = \begin{bmatrix} 1 & 1 & 2 \\ 1 & 2 & 0 \end{bmatrix} \begin{bmatrix} 1 & 1 \\ 1 & 2 \\ 2 & 0 \end{bmatrix} = \begin{bmatrix} 6 & 3 \\ 3 & 5 \end{bmatrix}$$

are symmetric. For part 3, $W^T = (BB^T)^T = (B^T)^T B^T = BB^T$ from parts 1 and 3 of Theorem(3.7).

3.4 For part 1, the products are straightforward multiplications

$$AB = \begin{bmatrix} 1 & 0 \\ 0 & 0 \end{bmatrix}\begin{bmatrix} 0 & 0 \\ 1 & 2 \end{bmatrix} = \begin{bmatrix} 0 & 0 \\ 0 & 0 \end{bmatrix} \neq \begin{bmatrix} 0 & 0 \\ 1 & 0 \end{bmatrix} = BA.$$

Part 2 gives the argument that neither A nor B is invertible. Part 3 is a simple calculation.

3.5 For the first product

$$AB = \begin{bmatrix} 3 & 2 \\ 0 & 1 \end{bmatrix}\begin{bmatrix} 1 & 5 \\ 5 & 1 \end{bmatrix} = \begin{bmatrix} 13 & 17 \\ 5 & 1 \end{bmatrix} \neq \begin{bmatrix} 3 & 7 \\ 15 & 11 \end{bmatrix} = \begin{bmatrix} 1 & 5 \\ 5 & 1 \end{bmatrix}\begin{bmatrix} 3 & 2 \\ 0 & 1 \end{bmatrix} = BA.$$

and for the second product

$$BC = \begin{bmatrix} 1 & 5 \\ 5 & 1 \end{bmatrix}\begin{bmatrix} 2 & -1 \\ -1 & 2 \end{bmatrix} = \begin{bmatrix} -3 & 9 \\ 9 & -3 \end{bmatrix} = \begin{bmatrix} 2 & -1 \\ -1 & 2 \end{bmatrix}\begin{bmatrix} 1 & 5 \\ 5 & 1 \end{bmatrix} = CB$$

so that

$$(A \pm B)^2 = A^2 \pm AB \pm BA + B^2 \quad \text{and} \quad (B \pm C)^2 = B^2 \pm 2BC + C^2.$$

3.6 Parts 5, 6, 7and 8 all have zero determinants, so there is no matrix inverse for these examples. For parts 1, 2 and 3 the inverses are:

1. If $A = \begin{bmatrix} 1 & 2 \\ 2 & 1 \end{bmatrix}$ then $A^{-1} = \dfrac{1}{3}\begin{bmatrix} -1 & 2 \\ 2 & -1 \end{bmatrix}$

2. If $A = \begin{bmatrix} 1 & 1 \\ 1 & 2 \end{bmatrix}$ then $A^{-1} = \begin{bmatrix} 2 & -1 \\ -1 & 1 \end{bmatrix}$

3. If $A = \begin{bmatrix} 2 & -1 & 3 \\ 4 & 0 & 2 \\ 0 & -1 & 3 \end{bmatrix}$ then $A^{-1} = \dfrac{1}{4}\begin{bmatrix} 1 & 0 & -1 \\ -6 & 3 & 4 \\ -2 & 1 & 2 \end{bmatrix}.$

4. If $A = \begin{bmatrix} 0 & -1 & 3 & 1 \\ 4 & 0 & 2 & 2 \\ 0 & -1 & 2 & 0 \\ 1 & 0 & 1 & 0 \end{bmatrix}$ then $A^{-1} = \dfrac{1}{2}\begin{bmatrix} -2 & 1 & 2 & 0 \\ 4 & -2 & -8 & 8 \\ 2 & -1 & -2 & 4 \\ 2 & 1 & -2 & -4 \end{bmatrix}$

3.7 Using row reductions or the adjoint formula in (3.21) the inverses of

$$T_2 = \begin{bmatrix} 2 & -1 \\ -1 & 2 \end{bmatrix}, \quad T_3 = \begin{bmatrix} 2 & -1 & 0 \\ -1 & 2 & -1 \\ 0 & -1 & 2 \end{bmatrix}, \quad \text{and} \quad T_4 = \begin{bmatrix} 2 & -1 & 0 & 0 \\ -1 & 2 & -1 & 0 \\ 0 & -1 & 2 & -1 \\ 0 & 0 & -1 & 2 \end{bmatrix}.$$

are

$$T_2^{-1} = \frac{1}{3}\begin{bmatrix} 2 & 1 \\ 1 & 2 \end{bmatrix}, \quad T_3^{-1} = \frac{1}{4}\begin{bmatrix} 3 & 2 & 1 \\ 2 & 4 & 2 \\ 1 & 2 & 3 \end{bmatrix}, \quad \text{and} \quad T_4^{-1} = \frac{1}{5}\begin{bmatrix} 4 & 3 & 2 & 1 \\ 3 & 6 & 4 & 2 \\ 2 & 4 & 6 & 3 \\ 1 & 2 & 3 & 4 \end{bmatrix}.$$

The three determinants $|T_2| = 3$, $|T_3| = 4$ and $|T_4| = 5$ are simple applications of the Laplace expansions.

Expand the determinant around row one to see

$$|T_n| = \begin{vmatrix} 2 & -1 & 0 & 0 & \cdots & 0 \\ -1 & 2 & -1 & 0 & \vdots & 0 \\ 0 & -1 & 2 & -1 & \vdots & 0 \\ \vdots & \ddots & 0 & \ddots & \ddots & \vdots \\ 0 & 0 & \ddots & & 2 & -1 \\ 0 & 0 & \cdots & & -1 & 2 \end{vmatrix}$$

$$= 2\begin{vmatrix} 2 & -1 & 0 & \cdots & 0 \\ -1 & 2 & -1 & \vdots & 0 \\ \vdots & \ddots & \ddots & \ddots & \vdots \\ 0 & 0 & \ddots & 2 & -1 \\ 0 & 0 & \cdots & -1 & 2 \end{vmatrix} + \begin{vmatrix} -1 & -1 & 0 & \cdots & 0 \\ 0 & 2 & -1 & \vdots & 0 \\ \vdots & \ddots & \ddots & \ddots & \vdots \\ 0 & 0 & \ddots & 2 & -1 \\ 0 & 0 & \cdots & -1 & 2 \end{vmatrix}.$$

The first determinant is $\det(T_{n-1})$ and the second determinant (after expanding around column one) is $\det(T_{n-2})$ so that $|T_n| = 2|T_{n-1}| - |T_{n-2}|$. Assume that it has been shown that $|T_{j-1}| = j$ for $j \le n$ (the inductive step). The formula shows that

$$\begin{aligned} |T_n| &= 2|T_{n-1}| - |T_{n-2}| \\ &= 2n - (n-1) = n+1 \end{aligned}$$

where the second equality uses the inductive step $|T_{n-1}| = n$ and $|T_{n-2}| = n - 1$.

3.8 is a straightforward substitution using (3.18).

3.9 is also a straightforward substitution using (3.18).

3.10 This is simply verifying the adjoint formula in (3.21) when $n = 3$. The inverse of

$$A = \begin{bmatrix} 1 & 2 & 3 \\ 2 & 5 & 4 \\ 1 & 3 & 2 \end{bmatrix} \quad \text{is} \quad A^{-1} = \begin{bmatrix} -2 & 5 & -7 \\ 0 & -1 & 2 \\ 1 & -1 & 1 \end{bmatrix}.$$

3.11 Apply row reductions to

$$[\,A \mid \vec{b}\,] = \begin{bmatrix} 1 & -2 & 2 & 3 \\ -2 & 1 & 2 & 0 \\ 2 & 2 & 1 & -3 \end{bmatrix} \sim \begin{bmatrix} 1 & -2 & 2 & 3 \\ 0 & -3 & 6 & 6 \\ 0 & 6 & -3 & -9 \end{bmatrix} \sim \begin{bmatrix} 1 & -2 & 2 & 3 \\ 0 & -3 & 6 & 6 \\ 0 & 0 & 9 & 3 \end{bmatrix}$$

so that $x_3 = \dfrac{3}{9} = \dfrac{1}{3}$, $x_2 = \dfrac{-4}{3}$ and $x_1 = \dfrac{-1}{3}$. Part 2 continues the above row reduction

to reduced echelon form. The inverse of A is $A^{-1} = \dfrac{1}{27} \begin{bmatrix} 3 & -6 & 6 \\ -6 & 3 & 6 \\ 6 & 6 & 3 \end{bmatrix}$ and $A^{-1}\vec{b}$ is

the previous result.

3.12 Part 1 is simply checking definitions. For example expand U repeatedly around column one to find $\det(U) = u_{11}u_{22}\cdots u_{nn}$. U is invertible if $u_{ii} \neq 0$ for all $i = 1, 2, \ldots n$. Part 2 is verifying the statement for the upper triangular matrix U. For part 3, use the fact that $u_{ij} = 0$ if $i > j$ in the formula for A^{-1} in Exercise(3.10) to see that this inverse is upper triangular. To see part 4, use the hint given in the problem to write

$$L^{-1} = (U^T)^{-1} = (U^{-1})^T \text{ and find } L^{-1} = \begin{bmatrix} 1 & 0 & 0 \\ -1 & 1 & 0 \\ 1 & -1 & 1 \end{bmatrix} \text{ from part 2.}$$

3.13 For part 1 expand A around the zero row using (3.19) or the zero column using (3.20). For part 2 , apply part 1 of Theorem(3.20) to the two equal rows with the scalar $= -1$. For the column statement, use the previous sentence on A^T. For part 3, apply part 1 of Theorem(3.20) to the proportional rows with scalar equal to the negative of the proportionality constant. For the column statement, use the previous sentence on A^T. For part 4 assume that A is not invertible then Theorem(3.26) guarantees that $\det(A) = 0$. Part 5 of Theorem(3.20) gives $\det(AB) = \det(A)\det(B) = 0$, so that, by Theorem(3.26), AB is not invertible.

3.14 In part 1 use $j = 3$ to get

$$\det(A) = \begin{vmatrix} 1 & 2 & 0 & 2 \\ -1 & 1 & 0 & 2 \\ 0 & 1 & 2 & 1 \\ 1 & -1 & 0 & -2 \end{vmatrix} = 2 \begin{vmatrix} 1 & 2 & 2 \\ -1 & 1 & 2 \\ 1 & -1 & -2 \end{vmatrix}$$

$$= 2 \begin{vmatrix} 1 & 2 & 2 \\ 0 & 3 & 4 \\ 0 & -3 & -4 \end{vmatrix} = 2(-12 + 12) = 0.$$

Assuming you also used $i = 1$ in (3.19), do you see why this is preferable? In part 2, $\det(A) = 5$ since rows one and two of the matrix in Example (3.21) have been interchanged. For part 3

$$|A| = \begin{vmatrix} 1 & 2 & 0 & 4 \\ 0 & 1 & 2 & 3 \\ 3 & 2 & 0 & 1 \\ 1 & 1 & 2 & 1 \end{vmatrix} \sim \begin{vmatrix} 1 & 2 & 0 & 4 \\ 0 & 1 & 2 & 3 \\ 0 & -4 & 0 & -11 \\ 0 & -1 & 2 & -3 \end{vmatrix} = \begin{vmatrix} 1 & 2 & 3 \\ -4 & 0 & -11 \\ -1 & 2 & -3 \end{vmatrix} = \begin{vmatrix} 1 & 2 & 3 \\ 0 & 8 & 1 \\ 0 & 4 & 0 \end{vmatrix} = -4.$$

and $|\hat{A}| = \begin{vmatrix} 1 & 2 & 0 & 4 \\ 3 & 2 & 0 & 1 \\ 0 & 2 & 4 & 6 \\ 1 & 1 & 2 & 1 \end{vmatrix} = (-2)|A| = 8$ since row three of $\hat{A}$ is 2 times row two of A

and $\hat{A}$ is obtained from A by interchanging rows two and three of A. For Part 4 one finds the row reduction

$$A = \begin{vmatrix} 1 & 2 & 3 & 4 \\ 2 & 3 & 4 & 5 \\ 3 & 4 & a_{33} & 6 \\ 4 & 5 & 6 & a_{44} \end{vmatrix} \sim \begin{vmatrix} 1 & 2 & 3 & 4 \\ 0 & -1 & -2 & -3 \\ 0 & -2 & a_{33}-9 & -6 \\ 0 & -3 & -6 & a_{44}-16 \end{vmatrix}$$

$$\sim \begin{vmatrix} 1 & 2 & 3 & 4 \\ 0 & -1 & -2 & -3 \\ 0 & 0 & a_{33}-5 & 0 \\ 0 & 0 & 0 & a_{44}-7 \end{vmatrix} = (-1)(a_{33}-5)(a_{44}-7)$$

so that if $a_{33} = 5$ the matrix is never invertible (a zero third row) and if $a_{33} = 6$ then $|A| = (-1)(a_{44} - 7) = 0$ if $a_{44} = 7$. Part 5 provides an alternative definition of a determinant.

3.15 Expand the determinant around column three

$$\det(A) = \begin{vmatrix} 1 & 2 & 0 & 2 \\ -1 & 1 & 0 & 2 \\ 0 & 1 & 2 & 1 \\ 1 & -1 & 0 & -3 \end{vmatrix} = 2\begin{vmatrix} 1 & 2 & 2 \\ -1 & 1 & 2 \\ 1 & -1 & -3 \end{vmatrix}$$

$$= 2\begin{vmatrix} 1 & 2 & 2 \\ 0 & 3 & 4 \\ 0 & -3 & -5 \end{vmatrix} = 2(-15 + 12) = -6.$$

The inverse of A is $A^{-1} = \dfrac{1}{6}\begin{bmatrix} 2 & -8 & 0 & -4 \\ 2 & 10 & 0 & 8 \\ -1 & -2 & 3 & -1 \\ 0 & -6 & 0 & -6 \end{bmatrix}$ and the row reductions in part 2

is, in general, a simpler procedure to find A^{-1} then is the adjoint formula in (3.21).

3.16 For the matrix $A_1^T = \begin{bmatrix} 0 & -1 \\ 1 & 0 \end{bmatrix}^T = \begin{bmatrix} 0 & 1 \\ -1 & 0 \end{bmatrix} = -A_1$. and $\det(A_1) = 1$. For the

$$\text{matrix } A^T = \begin{bmatrix} 0 & -1 & 2 \\ 1 & 0 & -3 \\ -2 & 3 & 0 \end{bmatrix}^T = \begin{bmatrix} 0 & -1 & 2 \\ 1 & 0 & -3 \\ -2 & 3 & 0 \end{bmatrix} = -A. \text{ To find the determinant}$$

$$\det(A) = \begin{vmatrix} 0 & 1 & -2 \\ -1 & 0 & 3 \\ 2 & -3 & 0 \end{vmatrix} = \begin{vmatrix} 0 & 1 & -2 \\ -1 & 0 & 3 \\ 0 & -3 & 6 \end{vmatrix} = -(-1)\begin{vmatrix} 1 & -2 \\ -3 & 6 \end{vmatrix} = 6 - 6 = 0.$$

For part 3, from part 4 of Theorem(3.20)

$$\det(A) = \det(A^T) = \det(-A) = (-1)^3\det(A)$$

where the last equality uses the second sentence of part 2 of Theorem(3.20). The last display gives $\det(A) = -\det(A)$ or $\det(A) = 0$.

For part 4, write $A = [a_{ij}]$ and the relation $A^T = -A$ applied to the diagonal elements gives $a_{ii} = -a_{ii}$ or $a_{ii} = 0$. For part 5, repeat the last display with 3 replaced by n and $(-1)^n = -1$ if n is odd.

3.17 For part 1 require

$$0 = \det(A - \lambda I) = \begin{bmatrix} 8 - \lambda & -5 \\ 10 & -7 - \lambda \end{bmatrix} = (8-\lambda)(-7-\lambda)+50 = \lambda^2-\lambda-6 = (\lambda+2)(\lambda-3)$$

so that $\lambda_1 = -2$ and $\lambda_2 = 3$. Parts 2 and 3 are matrix multiplications. For part 4,

$$0 = \det(A - \lambda I) = \begin{bmatrix} 1 - \lambda & 2 \\ 2 & 1 - \lambda \end{bmatrix} = (1 - \lambda)^2 - 4 = \lambda^2 - 2\lambda - 3 = (\lambda + 1)(\lambda - 3)$$

so that $\lambda_1 = -1$ and $\lambda_2 = 3$. In this case the vectors are $\vec{p}_1 = \begin{bmatrix} 1 \\ -1 \end{bmatrix}$ for $\lambda_1 = -1$ and $\vec{p}_2 = \begin{bmatrix} 1 \\ 1 \end{bmatrix}$ for $\lambda_2 = 3$. The dot product $\vec{p}_1 \cdot \vec{p}_2 = (1)(1) + (1)(-1) = 0$ so $\vec{p}_1 \perp \vec{p}_2$.

Define $P = \begin{bmatrix} 1 & 1 \\ -1 & 1 \end{bmatrix}$ and calculate

$$P^{-1}AP = \frac{1}{2}\begin{bmatrix} 1 & -1 \\ 1 & 1 \end{bmatrix}\begin{bmatrix} 1 & 2 \\ 2 & 1 \end{bmatrix}\begin{bmatrix} 1 & 1 \\ -1 & 1 \end{bmatrix} = \begin{bmatrix} -1 & 0 \\ 0 & 3 \end{bmatrix}.$$

For part 5

$$0 = \det(A - \lambda I) = \begin{bmatrix} 2 - \lambda & -1 \\ 4 & 6 - \lambda \end{bmatrix} = (2 - \lambda)(6 - \lambda) + 4 = \lambda^2 - 8\lambda + 16 = (\lambda - 4)^2$$

so that $\lambda_1 = \lambda_2 = 4$ and there is only one vector $\vec{p}_2 = \begin{bmatrix} 1 \\ -2 \end{bmatrix}$ satisfying $A\vec{p}_1 = 4\vec{p}_1$.

3.18 part 1 is the multiplication

$$Q^T Q = \frac{1}{\sqrt{2}} \begin{bmatrix} 1 & 1 \\ 1 & -1 \end{bmatrix} \frac{1}{\sqrt{2}} \begin{bmatrix} 1 & 1 \\ 1 & -1 \end{bmatrix}$$

$$= \frac{1}{2} \begin{bmatrix} 1 & 1 \\ 1 & -1 \end{bmatrix} \begin{bmatrix} 1 & 1 \\ 1 & -1 \end{bmatrix} = \frac{1}{2} \begin{bmatrix} 2 & 0 \\ 0 & 2 \end{bmatrix} = \begin{bmatrix} 1 & 0 \\ 0 & 1 \end{bmatrix}.$$

Part 2 is similar

$$Q^T Q = \begin{bmatrix} \cos(\theta) & \sin(\theta) \\ -\sin(\theta) & \cos(\theta) \end{bmatrix} \begin{bmatrix} \cos(\theta) & -\sin(\theta) \\ \sin(\theta) & \cos(\theta) \end{bmatrix}$$

$$= \begin{bmatrix} \cos^2(\theta) + \sin^2(\theta) & -\cos(\theta)\sin(\theta) + \sin(\theta)\cos(\theta) \\ -\sin(\theta)\cos(\theta) + \cos(\theta)\sin(\theta) & \sin^2(\theta) + \cos^2(\theta) \end{bmatrix} = \begin{bmatrix} 1 & 0 \\ 0 & 1 \end{bmatrix}$$

since $\cos^2(\theta) + \sin^2(\theta) = 1$. If $\theta = \dfrac{\pi}{4}$ this is the matrix in part 1. Part 3 is a simple verification.

6.3.1 Sample Test 1 Solutions

1. For the given problem the sum (a) $\begin{bmatrix} 1 & 2 \\ 2 & 3 \end{bmatrix} + \begin{bmatrix} 0 & 0 & 0 \\ 0 & 0 & 0 \end{bmatrix}$ is undefined and the sum (b)

$$\begin{bmatrix} 1 & 2 & 0 \\ 2 & 3 & 0 \end{bmatrix} + \begin{bmatrix} 2 & 0 & 0 \\ 0 & 3 & 0 \end{bmatrix} = \begin{bmatrix} 3 & 2 & 0 \\ 2 & 6 & 0 \end{bmatrix}. \text{ The product (c) } \begin{bmatrix} 2 & 0 & 0 \\ 0 & 3 & 0 \end{bmatrix} \begin{bmatrix} 1 & 2 & 0 \\ 2 & 3 & 0 \\ 0 & 0 & 0 \end{bmatrix} =$$

$\begin{bmatrix} 2 & 4 & 0 \\ 6 & 9 & 0 \end{bmatrix}$ and the product (d) $\begin{bmatrix} 1 & 2 & 0 \\ 2 & 3 & 0 \\ 0 & 0 & 0 \end{bmatrix} \begin{bmatrix} 2 & 0 & 0 \\ 0 & 3 & 0 \end{bmatrix}$ is undefined. (e) The in-

verse of $\begin{bmatrix} 2 & 2 \\ 1 & 3 \end{bmatrix} = \frac{1}{4} \begin{bmatrix} 3 & -2 \\ -1 & 2 \end{bmatrix}$. The matrix (f) $\begin{bmatrix} 2 & 2 & 0 \\ 1 & 3 & 0 \end{bmatrix}$ has no inverse. The

product (g) $\begin{bmatrix} 1 & 0 \\ 1 & 0 \end{bmatrix} \begin{bmatrix} 0 & 0 \\ 1 & 1 \end{bmatrix} = \begin{bmatrix} 0 & 0 \\ 0 & 0 \end{bmatrix}$ and (h) $J^2 = \begin{bmatrix} 0 & 1 \\ 1 & 0 \end{bmatrix}^2 = \begin{bmatrix} 1 & 0 \\ 0 & 1 \end{bmatrix}$ so that $J^{-1} =$

J. The product (i) $N^2 = \begin{bmatrix} 0 & 1 & 0 \\ 0 & 0 & 1 \\ 0 & 0 & 0 \end{bmatrix}^2 = \begin{bmatrix} 0 & 1 & 0 \\ 0 & 0 & 1 \\ 0 & 0 & 0 \end{bmatrix} \begin{bmatrix} 0 & 1 & 0 \\ 0 & 0 & 1 \\ 0 & 0 & 0 \end{bmatrix} = \begin{bmatrix} 0 & 0 & 1 \\ 0 & 0 & 0 \\ 0 & 0 & 0 \end{bmatrix}$

and (j) $N^3 = NN^2 = \begin{bmatrix} 0 & 1 & 0 \\ 0 & 0 & 1 \\ 0 & 0 & 0 \end{bmatrix} N^2 = \begin{bmatrix} 0 & 0 & 0 \\ 0 & 0 & 0 \\ 0 & 0 & 0 \end{bmatrix}$.

2. Suppose the matrix B is $p \times q$. Assume that the product ABC is defined and it's size is $m \times n$. (a) The size of A is $\underline{m \times p}$. (b) The size of C is $\underline{q \times n}$. (c) The size of AB is $m \times q$. (d) The size of BC is $\underline{p \times n}$. (e) The size of $(ABC)^T$ is $\underline{n \times m}$.

3. The determinant

$$\begin{vmatrix} 1 & 2 & 0 & 4 \\ 0 & 1 & 2 & 0 \\ 1 & 1 & 3 & 0 \\ 1 & 0 & 2 & 2 \end{vmatrix} = \begin{vmatrix} 1 & 2 & 0 & 4 \\ 0 & 1 & 2 & 0 \\ 0 & -1 & 3 & -4 \\ 0 & -2 & 2 & -2 \end{vmatrix} = \begin{vmatrix} 1 & 2 & 0 \\ -1 & 3 & -4 \\ -2 & 2 & -2 \end{vmatrix}$$

$$= \begin{vmatrix} 1 & 2 & 0 \\ 0 & 5 & -4 \\ 0 & 6 & -2 \end{vmatrix} = -10 + 24 = 14.$$

4. Let $A = \begin{bmatrix} 1 & 1 & 2 & 1 \\ 2 & 0 & 2 & -4 \\ 0 & 1 & -1 & -1 \\ 0 & 1 & 0 & 1 \end{bmatrix}$. (a) The product $\begin{bmatrix} 1 & 1 & 2 & 1 \\ 2 & 0 & 2 & -4 \\ 0 & 1 & -1 & -1 \\ 0 & 1 & 0 & 1 \end{bmatrix} \begin{bmatrix} 4 \\ -1 \\ -2 \\ 1 \end{bmatrix} = \begin{bmatrix} 0 \\ 0 \\ 0 \\ 0 \end{bmatrix}$.

(b) The matrix A **does not** have an inverse. (c) The determinant of A **is zero**.

5. For the matrix $A = \begin{bmatrix} 1 & 0 & 1 \\ 1 & 1 & \alpha \\ 0 & 1 & 1 \end{bmatrix}$, (a) the $\det(A) = 1 - \alpha + 1 = 2 - \alpha = 0$ if $\alpha = 2$

and (b) $\det(A) = 1$ if $\alpha = 1$. (c) Using Gauss-Jordan reduction

$$[\, A \mid I \,] = \begin{bmatrix} 1 & 0 & 1 & 1 & 0 & 0 \\ 1 & 1 & 1 & 0 & 1 & 0 \\ 0 & 1 & 1 & 0 & 0 & 1 \end{bmatrix} \sim \begin{bmatrix} 1 & 0 & 1 & 1 & 0 & 0 \\ 0 & 1 & 0 & -1 & 1 & 0 \\ 0 & 1 & 1 & 0 & 0 & 1 \end{bmatrix}$$

$$\sim \begin{bmatrix} 1 & 0 & 1 & 1 & 0 & 0 \\ 0 & 1 & 0 & -1 & 1 & 0 \\ 0 & 0 & 1 & 1 & -1 & 1 \end{bmatrix}$$

$$\sim \begin{bmatrix} 1 & 0 & 0 & 0 & 1 & -1 \\ 0 & 1 & 0 & -1 & 1 & 0 \\ 0 & 0 & 1 & 1 & -1 & 1 \end{bmatrix}$$

gives $A^{-1} = \begin{bmatrix} 0 & 1 & -1 \\ -1 & 1 & 0 \\ 1 & -1 & 1 \end{bmatrix}$ and (d) the unique solution to the linear system

$$\begin{bmatrix} 1 & 0 & 1 \\ 1 & 1 & 1 \\ 0 & 1 & 1 \end{bmatrix} \begin{bmatrix} x_1 \\ x_2 \\ x_3 \end{bmatrix} = \begin{bmatrix} 1 \\ 2 \\ 3 \end{bmatrix} \text{ is } \vec{x} = A^{-1} \begin{bmatrix} 1 \\ 2 \\ 3 \end{bmatrix} = \begin{bmatrix} 0 & 1 & -1 \\ -1 & 1 & 0 \\ 1 & -1 & 1 \end{bmatrix} \begin{bmatrix} 1 \\ 2 \\ 3 \end{bmatrix} = \begin{bmatrix} -1 \\ 1 \\ 2 \end{bmatrix}.$$

6.3.2   Sample Test 2 Solutions

1. For the matrices

$$A = \begin{bmatrix} 3 & 0 \\ 1 & 2 \end{bmatrix} \quad B = \begin{bmatrix} -3 & 0 \\ 2 & 3 \end{bmatrix}, \quad \mathcal{O} = \begin{bmatrix} 0 & 0 & 0 \\ 0 & 0 & 0 \end{bmatrix} \quad C = \begin{bmatrix} 3 & 0 \\ 1 & 2 \\ 0 & 0 \end{bmatrix}, D = \begin{bmatrix} 1 & 2 & 0 \\ 2 & 3 & 0 \\ 0 & 0 & 0 \end{bmatrix}$$

The sum (a) $A + B = \begin{bmatrix} 0 & 0 \\ 3 & 5 \end{bmatrix}$ and (b) $B^T + C$ is undefined. The product (c)

$DC = \begin{bmatrix} 4 & 4 \\ 7 & 6 \\ 0 & 0 \end{bmatrix}$ and (d) $\mathcal{O}C = \begin{bmatrix} 0 & 0 \\ 0 & 0 \end{bmatrix}$. The inverse (e) $A^{-1} = \dfrac{1}{6} \begin{bmatrix} 2 & 0 \\ -1 & 3 \end{bmatrix}$. The

product (f) $AB = \begin{bmatrix} -9 & 0 \\ 1 & 6 \end{bmatrix}$ and the sum (g) $\mathcal{O} + C =$ is undefined. Use (c) to find

the transpose (h) $C^T D^T = \begin{bmatrix} 4 & 7 & 0 \\ 4 & 6 & 0 \end{bmatrix}$. Both (i) $D\mathcal{O}$ and (j) are undefined.

2. Let A and B be the same as in #1. (a) The determinants are: $\det(A) \underline{\ = 6\ }$, (b) $\det(B) \underline{\ = -9\ }$, (c) $\det(AB) \underline{\ = -54\ }$, (d) $\det(BA) \underline{\ = -54\ }$, (e) $\det(A + B) \underline{\ = 0\ }$

3. To guarantee the matrix is not invertible require

$$0 = |A| = \begin{vmatrix} 1 & 2 & 3 & 4 \\ 2 & 3 & 4 & 5 \\ 3 & 4 & 6 & 6 \\ 4 & 5 & 6 & a_{44} \end{vmatrix} = \begin{vmatrix} 1 & 2 & 3 & 4 \\ 0 & -1 & -2 & -3 \\ 0 & -2 & -3 & -6 \\ 0 & -3 & -6 & a_{44} - 16 \end{vmatrix} = \begin{vmatrix} -1 & -2 & -3 \\ -2 & -3 & -6 \\ -3 & -6 & a_{44} - 16 \end{vmatrix} = \begin{vmatrix} -1 & -2 & -3 \\ 0 & 1 & 0 \\ 0 & 0 & a_{44} - 7 \end{vmatrix}$$

so $a_{44} = 7$.

4. Consider the system $A \begin{bmatrix} x_1 \\ x_2 \\ x_3 \end{bmatrix} = \vec{b} = \begin{bmatrix} 1 \\ 0 \\ 1 \end{bmatrix}$ where $A = \begin{bmatrix} 1 & 1 & 0 \\ 0 & 1 & 3 \\ 2 & 3 & 4 \end{bmatrix}$. (a) Using

Gauss-Jordan reduction

$$[\,A \mid I\,] \sim \begin{bmatrix} 1 & 1 & 0 & 1 & 0 & 0 \\ 0 & 1 & 3 & 0 & 1 & 0 \\ 2 & 3 & 4 & 0 & 0 & 1 \end{bmatrix} \sim \begin{bmatrix} 1 & 1 & 0 & 1 & 0 & 0 \\ 0 & 1 & 3 & 0 & 1 & 0 \\ 0 & 1 & 4 & -2 & 0 & 1 \end{bmatrix}$$

$$\sim \begin{bmatrix} 1 & 1 & 0 & 1 & 0 & 0 \\ 0 & 1 & 3 & 0 & 1 & 0 \\ 0 & 0 & 1 & -2 & -1 & 1 \end{bmatrix}$$

$$\sim \begin{bmatrix} 1 & 1 & 0 & 1 & 0 & 0 \\ 0 & 1 & 0 & 6 & 4 & -3 \\ 0 & 0 & 1 & -2 & -1 & 1 \end{bmatrix}$$

$$\sim \begin{bmatrix} 1 & 0 & 0 & -5 & -4 & 3 \\ 0 & 1 & 0 & 6 & 4 & -3 \\ 0 & 0 & 1 & -2 & -1 & 1 \end{bmatrix}$$

shows $A^{-1} = \begin{bmatrix} -5 & -4 & 3 \\ 6 & 4 & -3 \\ -2 & -1 & 1 \end{bmatrix}$ and hence the unique solution to the linear system is

(b) $\vec{x} = A^{-1}\vec{b} = \begin{bmatrix} -5 & -4 & 3 \\ 6 & 4 & -3 \\ -2 & -1 & 1 \end{bmatrix} \begin{bmatrix} 1 \\ 0 \\ 1 \end{bmatrix} = \begin{bmatrix} -2 \\ 3 \\ -1 \end{bmatrix}$.

5. Assume that A, B are invertible $n \times n$ matrices and set $C = A + B$. Answer each of the following T (true) or F (false). (a) The statement $\det(C) = \det(A) + \det(B)$ is **False**. (b) The matrix C is invertible is **False**. (c) $\det(AB) = \det(A)\det(B)$ is **True**. (d) $(AB)^{-1} = A^{-1}B^{-1}$ is **False**. (e) The problem $A\vec{x} = \vec{b}$ has a unique solution for all $\vec{b} \in \mathcal{R}^3$ is **True**.

6. For $A = \begin{bmatrix} 1 & 2 \\ 2 & 1 \end{bmatrix}$. (a) Require

$$\det(B) = \det(A - \lambda I) = \det\left(\begin{bmatrix} 1-\lambda & 2 \\ 2 & 1-\lambda \end{bmatrix}\right) = (1-\lambda)^2 - 4 = (\lambda+1)(\lambda-3) = 0$$

so that $\lambda_1 = -1$ and $\lambda_2 = 3$. (b) A $\vec{p}_1$ satisfying $(A - \lambda_1 I)\vec{p}_1 = \begin{bmatrix} 2 & 2 \\ 2 & 2 \end{bmatrix} \vec{p}_1 = \begin{bmatrix} 0 \\ 0 \end{bmatrix}$

is $\vec{p}_1 = \begin{bmatrix} 1 \\ -1 \end{bmatrix}$. A $\vec{p}_2$ satisfying $(A - \lambda_2 I)\vec{p}_2 = \begin{bmatrix} -2 & 2 \\ 2 & -2 \end{bmatrix} \vec{p}_2 = \begin{bmatrix} 0 \\ 0 \end{bmatrix}$ is $\vec{p}_2 = \begin{bmatrix} 1 \\ 1 \end{bmatrix}$.

6.4   Exercise Set Four

4.1 The sets in parts 1 3, 5 and 6 are vector spaces. Spanning sets are

$$\mathcal{V} = \text{span}\left\{ \begin{bmatrix} 1 \\ -1 \end{bmatrix} \right\} \quad \text{for part 1} \quad \mathcal{V} = \text{span}\left\{ \begin{bmatrix} 1 \\ -1 \\ 0 \end{bmatrix}, \begin{bmatrix} 0 \\ 0 \\ 1 \end{bmatrix} \right\} \text{for part 3}$$

$$\mathcal{V} = \text{span}\left\{ \begin{bmatrix} 1 \\ 1 \\ 0 \end{bmatrix}, \begin{bmatrix} 0 \\ 1 \\ 1 \end{bmatrix} \right\} \text{for part 3 and } \mathcal{V} = \text{span}\left\{ \begin{bmatrix} 1 & 0 \\ 0 & -1 \end{bmatrix}, \begin{bmatrix} 0 & 1 \\ 0 & 0 \end{bmatrix}, \begin{bmatrix} 0 & 0 \\ 1 & 0 \end{bmatrix} \right\}.$$

The sets in parts 2, 4 and 7 are not vector spaces. For example, the zero vector $\begin{bmatrix} 0 \\ 0 \end{bmatrix}$,

$\begin{bmatrix} 0 \\ 0 \\ 0 \end{bmatrix}$ and $\begin{bmatrix} 0 & 0 \\ 0 & 0 \end{bmatrix}$ is not in $\mathcal{V}$ for part 2, 4 and 7, respectively.

4.2 Using $\alpha = \gamma + 2\delta$ and $\beta = 2\gamma + 3\delta$ calculate

$$-\alpha + 2\beta = -(\gamma + 2\delta) + 2(2\gamma + 3\delta) = -\gamma + 4\gamma - 2\delta + 6\delta = 3\gamma + 4\delta$$

so that the third equation is also satisfied.

4.3 Row reduction gives

$$A = \begin{bmatrix} 1 & 2 & 3 \\ 2 & 5 & 4 \\ 1 & 3 & a_{33} \end{bmatrix} \sim \begin{bmatrix} 1 & 2 & 3 \\ 0 & 1 & -2 \\ 0 & 1 & a_{33} - 3 \end{bmatrix} \sim \begin{bmatrix} 1 & 2 & 3 \\ 0 & 1 & -2 \\ 0 & 0 & a_{33} - 1 \end{bmatrix}$$

so, if $a_{33} = 2$, A has three pivots so that the columns of A are independent and form a basis for $\mathcal{C}_A$ so that dim $\mathcal{C}_A = 3$. $A\vec{x} = \vec{b}$ is always solvable since $\mathcal{R}^3 = \mathcal{C}_A$. For part 4, if $a_{33} = 2$, the first two columns are a basis for $\mathcal{C}_A$ or from (4.9) $\vec{b} \in \mathcal{C}_A$ iff $b_3 - b_2 + b_1 = 0$. So select $\vec{b} = \begin{bmatrix} 1 \\ 1 \\ 2 \end{bmatrix} \notin \mathcal{C}_A$.

4.4 Part 1 is a matrix multiplication. For part 2, find $\gamma = 7\alpha - 2\beta$ and then

$$A\begin{bmatrix} \alpha \\ \beta \\ 7\alpha - 2\beta \end{bmatrix} = \begin{bmatrix} 1 & 2 & 3 \\ 2 & 5 & 4 \\ 1 & 3 & 1 \end{bmatrix} \begin{bmatrix} \alpha \\ \beta \\ 7\alpha - 2\beta \end{bmatrix} = \begin{bmatrix} 22\alpha - 4\beta \\ 30\alpha - 3\beta \\ 8\alpha + \beta \end{bmatrix} = \begin{bmatrix} 6 \\ 4 \\ -2 \end{bmatrix}$$

Solve the first two equations to find $\alpha = \dfrac{-1}{27}$ and $\beta = \dfrac{-46}{27}$. Check that $8\alpha + \beta = -2$ and then $\gamma = 7\alpha - 2\beta = \dfrac{85}{27}$.

4.5 Row reduction gives

$$[A \mid \vec{b}\,] = \begin{bmatrix} 1 & 2 & 3 & b_1 \\ 2 & 5 & 4 & b_2 \end{bmatrix} \sim \begin{bmatrix} 1 & 2 & 3 & b_1 \\ 0 & 1 & -2 & b_2 - 2b_1 \end{bmatrix}$$

and back substitution gives $x_2 = 2x_3 + b_2 - 2b_1$ (x_3 is free)

$$\begin{aligned} x_1 &= -2x_2 - 3x_3 + b_1 \\ &= -2(2x_3 + b_2 - 2b_1) - 3x_3 + b_1 = -7x_3 - 2b_2 + 5b_1. \end{aligned}$$

Writing $\vec{x}$ as a vector gives part 1. Parts 2 and 3 are verifications. There is no restriction on the components of $\vec{b}$ so dim $\mathcal{C}_A = 2$. The $\alpha_j, j = 1, 2, 3$ are $\alpha_1 = -7, \alpha_2 = 2$ and $\alpha_3 = 1$ are the components of the vector in $\mathcal{N}(A)$.

4.6 Part 1 is as follows

$$[A \mid \vec{b}\,] = \begin{bmatrix} 1 & 2 & 3 & 4 & b_1 \\ 2 & 4 & 4 & 5 & b_2 \\ 3 & 6 & 5 & 7 & b_3 \end{bmatrix} \sim \begin{bmatrix} 1 & 2 & 3 & 4 & b_1 \\ 0 & 0 & -2 & -3 & b_2 - 2b_1 \\ 0 & 0 & -4 & -5 & b_3 - 3b_1 \end{bmatrix}$$

$$\sim \begin{bmatrix} 1 & 2 & 3 & 4 & b_1 \\ 0 & 0 & -2 & -3 & b_2 - 2b_1 \\ 0 & 0 & 0 & 1 & b_3 - 2b_2 + b_1 \end{bmatrix}$$

so the rank of A is three which implies that dim $\mathcal{C}_A = 3$ by the dimension theorem. Part 2 is found by applying back substitution to the above row reduction. To find a spanning set for $\mathcal{C}_B$ do the row reduction

$$\begin{bmatrix} 1 & 2 & 3 & y_1 \\ 2 & 4 & 6 & y_2 \\ 3 & 4 & 5 & y_3 \\ 4 & 5 & 7 & y_4 \end{bmatrix} \sim \begin{bmatrix} 1 & 2 & 3 & y_1 \\ 0 & 0 & 0 & y_2 - 2y_1 \\ 0 & -2 & -4 & y_3 - 3y_1 \\ 0 & -3 & -5 & y_4 - 4y_1 \end{bmatrix} \sim \begin{bmatrix} 1 & 2 & 3 & y_1 \\ 0 & 0 & 0 & y_2 - 2y_1 \\ 0 & -2 & -4 & y_3 - 3y_1 \\ 0 & 0 & 1 & y_4 - (3/2)y_3 + (1/2y_1) \end{bmatrix}$$

to see that $\vec{y} \in \mathcal{C}_B$ if $y_2 - 2y_1 = 0$ and y_3 and y_4 are unrestricted so

$$\vec{y} = \begin{bmatrix} y_1 \\ 2y_1 \\ y_3 \\ y_4 \end{bmatrix} = y_1 \begin{bmatrix} 1 \\ 2 \\ 0 \\ 0 \end{bmatrix} + y_3 \begin{bmatrix} 0 \\ 0 \\ 1 \\ 0 \end{bmatrix} + y_4 \begin{bmatrix} 0 \\ 0 \\ 0 \\ 1 \end{bmatrix} = \text{span} \left\{ \begin{bmatrix} 1 \\ 2 \\ 0 \\ 0 \end{bmatrix}, \begin{bmatrix} 0 \\ 0 \\ 1 \\ 0 \end{bmatrix}, \begin{bmatrix} 0 \\ 0 \\ 0 \\ 1 \end{bmatrix} \right\} = \mathcal{C}_B,$$

which completes part 3. To see that $\mathcal{N}(B) = \{\vec{0}\}$ set $\vec{y} = \vec{0}$ in the previous row reduction to see that the only solution to $B\vec{n} = \vec{y} = \vec{0}$ is $\vec{n} = \begin{bmatrix} 0 \\ 0 \\ 0 \end{bmatrix}$. Now let

$$\vec{n} = \begin{bmatrix} n_1 \\ n_2 \\ n_3 \\ n_4 \end{bmatrix} \in \mathcal{C}_B^{\perp} \text{ and require } \vec{n} \text{ to be orthogonal to each base vector defining } \mathcal{C}_B.$$

That is,

$$\vec{n}^T \begin{bmatrix} 1 \\ 2 \\ 0 \\ 0 \end{bmatrix} = n_1 + 2n_2 = 0, \ \vec{n}^T \begin{bmatrix} 0 \\ 0 \\ 1 \\ 0 \end{bmatrix} = n_3 = 0 \text{ and } \vec{n}^T \begin{bmatrix} 0 \\ 0 \\ 0 \\ 1 \end{bmatrix} = n_4 = 0.$$

This gives the vector whose span is $\mathcal{N}(A)$ found in part 2.

4.7 Write the equation

$$\alpha \begin{bmatrix} 1 \\ 0 \\ -1 \end{bmatrix} + \beta \begin{bmatrix} 0 \\ 1 \\ 2 \end{bmatrix} = \gamma \begin{bmatrix} 1 \\ 2 \\ 3 \end{bmatrix} + \delta \begin{bmatrix} 3 \\ 4 \\ 5 \end{bmatrix}$$

to see that $\alpha = \gamma + 3\delta$ and $\beta = 2\gamma + 4\delta$ and then check that $-\alpha + 2\beta = 3\gamma + 5\delta$. For part 2 write the equation

$$\alpha \begin{bmatrix} 1 \\ 2 \\ 0 \\ -1/2 \end{bmatrix} + \beta \begin{bmatrix} 0 \\ 0 \\ 1 \\ 3/2 \end{bmatrix} = \gamma \begin{bmatrix} 1 \\ 2 \\ 3 \\ 4 \end{bmatrix} + \delta \begin{bmatrix} 0 \\ 0 \\ -2 \\ -3 \end{bmatrix}$$

to see that $\alpha = \gamma$ (first component) and $\beta = 3\gamma - 2\delta$ (second component) and check each of the equalities $2\alpha = 2\gamma$ (second component) and $-1/2\alpha + 3/2\beta = 4\gamma - 3\delta$ (fourth component). The other basis representations can be established in the same manner.

4.8 Part 1 consists of the two calculations

$$\vec{x}_r \cdot \begin{bmatrix} -2 \\ 1 \\ 0 \\ 0 \end{bmatrix} = -2\alpha + \beta = 0 \text{ which implies } \beta = 2\alpha$$

and

$$\vec{x}_r \cdot \begin{bmatrix} 1/2 \\ 0 \\ -3/2 \\ 1 \end{bmatrix} = (1/2)\alpha - (3/2)\gamma + \delta = 0 \text{ which implies} \delta = (-1/2)\alpha + (3/2)\gamma$$

which gives part 1. The remainder of the problem are verifications.

4.9 The vectors $\vec{v}_1 = \begin{bmatrix} 1 \\ 0 \\ 1 \\ 2 \end{bmatrix}, \vec{v}_2 = \begin{bmatrix} 1 \\ 1 \\ 1 \\ 2 \end{bmatrix}, \vec{v}_3 = \begin{bmatrix} 1 \\ 1 \\ 0 \\ 1 \end{bmatrix}$ are the span of $\mathcal{C}_A$ and $\vec{w}_1 =$

$\begin{bmatrix} 1 \\ -1 \\ 1 \\ -1 \\ 0 \end{bmatrix}$ and $\vec{w}_2 = \begin{bmatrix} 1 \\ -2 \\ 1 \\ 0 \\ 1 \end{bmatrix}$ are the span of $\mathcal{N}_A$ and both sets are independent, the

size of the matrix A is $\underline{4 \times 5}$ and the dimension of $\mathcal{C}_A$ is $\underline{3}$. Theorem(4.20) then guarantees that the dimension of R_A is $\underline{3}$. Hence the dimension theorem implies that the dimension of $\mathcal{N}(A^T)$ is $\underline{4 - 3 = 1}$ and that the dimension of $\mathcal{N}(A)$ is $\underline{5 - 3 = 2}$. Assume that $\vec{b} \in \mathcal{C}_A$ and $\vec{x}$ satisfies $A\vec{x} = \vec{b}$. The number of free variables in $\vec{x}_h$ is the dimension of the $\mathcal{N}(A) = 2$. You cannot conclude that $\vec{x}_p \in R_A$. Any element of the null space of A added to x_p is a "new" particular solution. See Exercise(4.8). There are non-zero solutions of $A^T \vec{w} = \vec{0}$ since $\underline{\dim \mathcal{N}(A^T) = 1}$.

4.10 From the row reduction

$$[A \mid \vec{b}] = \begin{bmatrix} 1 & 1 & 1 & 1 & 0 & b_1 \\ 0 & 1 & 1 & 0 & 1 & b_2 \\ 1 & 1 & 0 & 0 & 1 & b_3 \\ 2 & 2 & 1 & 1 & 1 & b_4 \end{bmatrix} \sim \begin{bmatrix} 1 & 1 & 1 & 1 & 0 & b_1 \\ 0 & 1 & 1 & 0 & 1 & b_2 \\ 0 & 0 & -1 & -1 & 1 & b_3 - b_1 \\ 0 & 0 & 0 & 0 & 0 & b_4 - b_1 - b_3 \end{bmatrix}$$

and the lines following (4.27) a basis $\mathcal{C}_A$ is $\{\vec{v}_1 \ \vec{v}_2 \ \vec{v}_3\}$ (the first three columns of A). Use $b_4 - b_1 - b_3 = 0$ in

$$\vec{b} = \begin{bmatrix} b_1 \\ b_2 \\ b_3 \\ b_4 \end{bmatrix} = \begin{bmatrix} b_1 \\ b_2 \\ b_3 \\ b_1 + b_3 \end{bmatrix} = b_1 \begin{bmatrix} 1 \\ 0 \\ 0 \\ 1 \end{bmatrix} + b_2 \begin{bmatrix} 0 \\ 1 \\ 0 \\ 0 \end{bmatrix} + b_3 \begin{bmatrix} 0 \\ 0 \\ 1 \\ 1 \end{bmatrix}$$

and conclude that

$$\mathcal{C}_A = \text{span}\,\{\vec{v}_1 \ \vec{v}_2 \ \vec{v}_3\} = \text{span}\left\{ \begin{bmatrix} 1 \\ 0 \\ 0 \\ 1 \end{bmatrix}, \begin{bmatrix} 0 \\ 1 \\ 0 \\ 0 \end{bmatrix}, \begin{bmatrix} 0 \\ 0 \\ 1 \\ 1 \end{bmatrix} \right\} \equiv \text{span}\,\{\vec{c}_1 \ \vec{c}_2 \ \vec{c}_3\}.$$

To find $\mathcal{N}(A^T) = \text{span}\,\{\eta\}$ where $\eta \cdot \vec{c}_j = 0\, j = 1, 2, 3$. This gives $\eta = [\, 1 \ 0 \ 1 \ -1\,]^T$. For part 2 use back substitution in the row reduced form above. There are two free variables and $\vec{x}_p \notin R_A$.

4.11 For part 1, $\mathcal{V}^\perp = \text{span}\left\{ \begin{bmatrix} 1 \\ -1 \end{bmatrix} \right\}$ and solve

$$\vec{x} = \begin{bmatrix} x_1 \\ x_2 \end{bmatrix} = \alpha \begin{bmatrix} 1 \\ 1 \end{bmatrix} + \beta \begin{bmatrix} 1 \\ -1 \end{bmatrix} = \begin{bmatrix} 1 & 1 \\ 1 & -1 \end{bmatrix} \begin{bmatrix} \alpha \\ \beta \end{bmatrix}$$

to find $\alpha = \dfrac{(x_1 + x_2)}{2}$ and $\beta = \dfrac{(x_1 - x_2)}{2}$.

For part 2, $\mathcal{W}^\perp = \text{span} \left\{ \begin{bmatrix} 1 \\ -2 \\ 1 \end{bmatrix} \right\}$ and write a general $\vec{x} \in \mathcal{R}^3$ as a linear combination

of the basis for $\mathcal{W}$ and $\mathcal{W}^\perp$

$$\begin{bmatrix} x_1 \\ x_2 \\ x_3 \end{bmatrix} = \left\{ \alpha \begin{bmatrix} 1 \\ 1 \\ 1 \end{bmatrix} + \beta \begin{bmatrix} 1 \\ 0 \\ -1 \end{bmatrix} \right\} + \gamma \begin{bmatrix} 1 \\ -2 \\ 1 \end{bmatrix} = \begin{bmatrix} 1 & 1 & 1 \\ 1 & 0 & -2 \\ 1 & -1 & 1 \end{bmatrix} \begin{bmatrix} \alpha \\ \beta \\ \gamma \end{bmatrix}$$

Solve the above, say by inverting the matrix,

$$\begin{bmatrix} \alpha \\ \beta \\ \gamma \end{bmatrix} = \begin{bmatrix} 1/3 & 1/3 & 1/3 \\ 1/2 & 0 & -1/2 \\ 1/6 & -1/3 & 1/6 \end{bmatrix} \begin{bmatrix} x_1 \\ x_2 \\ x_3 \end{bmatrix} = \begin{bmatrix} \dfrac{x_1 + x_2 + x_3}{3} \\ \dfrac{x_1 - x_3}{2} \\ \dfrac{x_1 - 2x_2 + x_3}{6} \end{bmatrix}.$$

Alternatively, take the dot product

$$\begin{bmatrix} 1 \\ 1 \\ 1 \end{bmatrix} \cdot \begin{bmatrix} x_1 \\ x_2 \\ x_3 \end{bmatrix} = x_1 + x_2 + x_3$$

$$= \begin{bmatrix} 1 \\ 1 \\ 1 \end{bmatrix} \cdot \left(\left\{ \alpha \begin{bmatrix} 1 \\ 1 \\ 1 \end{bmatrix} + \beta \begin{bmatrix} 1 \\ 0 \\ -1 \end{bmatrix} \right\} + \gamma \begin{bmatrix} 1 \\ -2 \\ 1 \end{bmatrix} \right)$$

$$= 3\alpha$$

by orthogonality. Replace $[\, 1 \ 1 \ 1 \,]^T$ by $[\, 1 \ 0 \ -1 \,]^T$ and then $[\, 1 \ -2 \ 1 \,]^T$ to find β and γ, respectively.

4.12 For part 1 assume $\vec{u} \in \mathcal{V}^\perp$ and $\vec{\hat{u}} \in \mathcal{V}^\perp$. This means that $\vec{v} \cdot \vec{u} = \vec{v} \cdot \vec{\hat{u}} = 0$ for every $\vec{v} \in \mathcal{V}$. Hence $\vec{v} \cdot \left(\alpha \vec{u} + \beta \vec{\hat{u}} \right) = \alpha(\vec{v} \cdot \vec{u}) + \beta(\vec{v} \cdot \vec{\hat{u}}) = 0$ so $\alpha \vec{u} + \beta \vec{\hat{u}} \in \mathcal{V}^\perp$. Hence $\mathcal{V}^\perp$ is a subspace. For part 2, $\vec{0} \in \mathcal{V}^\perp$ since $\vec{0}$ is orthogonal to every vector by the declaration in Definition(1.9). For part 3 the orthogonal complement of $\mathcal{V} = \left\{ \vec{0} \right\}$ is $\mathcal{R}^n$.

4.13 The matrix $AP = \begin{bmatrix} 2 & 3 & 4 \\ 2 & 3 & 4 \end{bmatrix} \sim \begin{bmatrix} 2 & 3 & 4 \\ 0 & 0 & 0 \end{bmatrix}$ so the column space of AP is spanned by the first column of AP (there is only one pivot in the row reduced form, see lines following (4.27)). Hence $\mathcal{C}_{AP} = \text{span} \left\{ \begin{bmatrix} 1 \\ 1 \end{bmatrix} \right\}$. Since the rank of A is two it follows that $\mathcal{C}_A$ is all of $\mathcal{R}^2$ so that $\mathcal{C}_A = \text{span} \left\{ \begin{bmatrix} 1 \\ 0 \end{bmatrix}, \begin{bmatrix} 0 \\ 1 \end{bmatrix} \right\} = R^2$. This illustrates that

$\text{rank}(AP) \le \text{rank}(A)$. The matrix $A\hat{P} = \begin{bmatrix} 2 & 3 & 4 \\ 2 & 3 & 5 \end{bmatrix} \sim \begin{bmatrix} 2 & 3 & 4 \\ 0 & 0 & 1 \end{bmatrix}$ has rank two so, in this case, $\text{rank}(A\hat{P}) = \text{rank}(A)$.

4.14 The matrix product $QB = \begin{bmatrix} 1 & 1 & 1 \\ 2 & 1 & 2 \\ 3 & 1 & 3 \end{bmatrix} \begin{bmatrix} 1 & 0 \\ 1 & 1 \\ 0 & 1 \end{bmatrix} = \begin{bmatrix} 2 & 2 \\ 3 & 3 \\ 4 & 4 \end{bmatrix}$ so $\mathcal{C}_{QB} = \text{span} \left\{ \begin{bmatrix} 2 \\ 3 \\ 4 \end{bmatrix} \right\}$

and therefore the rank $\mathcal{C}_{QB} = 1$. The two columns of B are independent so that the rank $\mathcal{C}_{QB} = 1$. To see there are not scalars α and β satisfying

$$\begin{bmatrix} 2 \\ 3 \\ 4 \end{bmatrix} = \alpha \begin{bmatrix} 1 \\ 1 \\ 0 \end{bmatrix} + \beta \begin{bmatrix} 0 \\ 1 \\ 1 \end{bmatrix}$$

the first component requires $\alpha = 2$ and third component requires $\beta = 4$. The middle component reads $\alpha + \beta = 3$ but the two values of α and β give $\alpha + \beta = 6$. Hence, the vector on the left is not in the span of the vectors on the right. For part 2,

$$\hat{Q}B = \begin{bmatrix} 1 & 1 & 1 \\ 2 & 1 & 2 \\ 3 & 1 & 4 \end{bmatrix} \begin{bmatrix} 1 & 0 \\ 1 & 1 \\ 0 & 1 \end{bmatrix} = \begin{bmatrix} 2 & 2 \\ 3 & 3 \\ 4 & 5 \end{bmatrix} \text{ has rank two.}$$

4.15 For part 1, check that $\mathcal{N}(A) = \text{span} \left\{ \begin{bmatrix} 1 \\ -1 \\ 1 \end{bmatrix} \right\} = \mathcal{N}(A^T A)$. Part 2 $\mathcal{N}(B) =$

$\text{span} \left\{ \begin{bmatrix} 0 \\ 0 \end{bmatrix} \right\} = \mathcal{N}(B^T b)$.

4.16 To check that $\vec{v}_1 = \vec{w}_1$ is perpendicular to $\vec{v}_2 = \vec{w}_2 - \left(\dfrac{\vec{w}_2 \cdot \vec{v}_1}{||\vec{v}_1||^2} \right) \vec{v}_1$ see the calculation done in Definition(1.11). To see that $\vec{v}_3 = \vec{w}_3 - \left(\dfrac{\vec{w}_3 \cdot \vec{v}_1}{||\vec{v}_1||^2} \right) \vec{v}_1 - \left(\dfrac{\vec{w}_3 \cdot \vec{v}_2}{||\vec{v}_2||^2} \right) \vec{v}_2$ is orthogonal to $\vec{v}_1$ calculate

$$\begin{aligned} \vec{v}_1 \cdot \vec{v}_3 &= \vec{v}_1 \cdot \vec{w}_3 - \left(\frac{\vec{w}_3 \cdot \vec{v}_1}{||\vec{v}_1||^2} \right) (\vec{v}_1 \cdot \vec{v}_1) - \left(\frac{\vec{w}_3 \cdot \vec{v}_2}{||\vec{v}_2||^2} \right) (\vec{v}_1 \cdot \vec{v}_2) \\ &= \vec{v}_1 \cdot \vec{w}_3 - \left(\frac{\vec{w}_3 \cdot \vec{v}_1}{||\vec{v}_1||^2} \right) (\vec{v}_1 \cdot \vec{v}_1) \quad \text{since } \vec{v}_1 \cdot \vec{v}_2 = 0 \\ &= \vec{v}_1 \cdot \vec{w}_3 - \vec{w}_3 \cdot \vec{v}_1 \quad \text{since } ||\vec{v}_1||^2 = \vec{v}_1 \cdot \vec{v}_1 \\ &= 0 \quad \text{since } \vec{v}_1 \cdot \vec{w}_3 = \vec{w}_3 \cdot \vec{v}_1. \end{aligned}$$

The calculation $\vec{v}_2 \cdot \vec{v}_3 = 0$ is almost identical. Parts 2, 3 and 4 are for your information.

Substituting $\vec{w}_1$ and $\vec{w}_2$ into (4.47) to find the two orthogonal vectors $\vec{v}_1 = \begin{bmatrix} 0 \\ 1 \\ 1 \end{bmatrix}$ and

$\vec{v}_2 = \dfrac{1}{2} \begin{bmatrix} 2 \\ -1 \\ 1 \end{bmatrix}$. Let $\vec{w} = \begin{bmatrix} 2 \\ 3 \\ 1 \end{bmatrix}$ in the formula $\vec{w} = \mathrm{proj}_{\mathcal{V}_2}(\vec{w}) + (\vec{w} - \mathrm{proj}_{\mathcal{V}_2}(\vec{w}))$ to see that this is the same as the vector in (4.41) from Example(4.27).

4.17 For (4.50), the unique solution to $(A^T A)\vec{x} = \begin{bmatrix} 2 & 1 \\ 1 & 2 \end{bmatrix} \vec{x} = A^T \vec{b} = \begin{bmatrix} 4 \\ 3 \end{bmatrix}$ is

$$\vec{x}_{ls} = (A^T A)^{-1}(A^T \vec{b}) = \begin{bmatrix} 2 & -1 \\ -1 & 2 \end{bmatrix} \begin{bmatrix} 4 \\ 3 \end{bmatrix} = \frac{1}{3} \begin{bmatrix} 5 \\ 2 \end{bmatrix}.$$

For part 2 the vector $A\vec{x}_{ls} = \dfrac{5}{3} \begin{bmatrix} 0 \\ 1 \\ 1 \end{bmatrix} + \dfrac{2}{3} \begin{bmatrix} 1 \\ 0 \\ 1 \end{bmatrix} = \dfrac{1}{3} \begin{bmatrix} 2 \\ 5 \\ 7 \end{bmatrix} = \mathrm{proj}_{\mathcal{C}_A}(\vec{b})$ from part 4

of Exercise(4.16). Consistency is verified by the row reduction

$$[\, A \mid \mathrm{proj}_{\mathcal{C}_A}(\vec{b}) \,] = \begin{bmatrix} 0 & 1 & 2/3 \\ 1 & 0 & 5/3 \\ 1 & 1 & 7/3 \end{bmatrix} \sim \begin{bmatrix} 1 & 1 & 7/3 \\ 1 & 0 & 5/3 \\ 0 & 1 & 2/3 \end{bmatrix}$$

$$\sim \begin{bmatrix} 1 & 1 & 7/3 \\ 0 & -1 & -2/3 \\ 0 & 1 & 2/3 \end{bmatrix} \sim \begin{bmatrix} 1 & 1 & 7/3 \\ 0 & -1 & -2/3 \\ 0 & 0 & 0 \end{bmatrix}.$$

For part 3, the reason for each step is listed on the right

$$\begin{aligned} \vec{c}_A \cdot \vec{r}_{ls} &= (A\vec{x} - A\vec{x}_{ls})^T \cdot (A\vec{x}_{ls} - \vec{b}) && \text{definition of these vectors} \\ &= (\vec{x} - \vec{x}_{ls})^T A^T (A\vec{x}_{ls} - \vec{b}) && \text{Theorem(3.7)} \\ &= (\vec{x} - \vec{x}_{ls})^T (A^T A\vec{x}_{ls} - A^T \vec{b}) = 0 && A^T A\vec{x}_{ls} = A^T \vec{b}. \end{aligned}$$

The normal equations for part 4 reads

$$\begin{bmatrix} 3 & 6 \\ 6 & 14 \end{bmatrix} \vec{x}_{ls} = \begin{bmatrix} 9 \\ 22 \end{bmatrix} \quad \text{whose solution reads } \vec{x}_{ls} = \begin{bmatrix} -1 \\ 2 \end{bmatrix}$$

In this case it is also the traditional which can be verified by the row reduction

$$\begin{bmatrix} 1 & 1 & 1 \\ 1 & 2 & 3 \\ 1 & 3 & 5 \end{bmatrix} \sim \begin{bmatrix} 1 & 1 & 1 \\ 0 & 1 & 2 \\ 0 & 2 & 4 \end{bmatrix} \sim \begin{bmatrix} 1 & 1 & 1 \\ 0 & 1 & 2 \\ 0 & 0 & 0 \end{bmatrix}.$$

If $\vec{b} \in \mathcal{C}_A$ then $\mathrm{proj}_{\mathcal{C}_A}(\vec{b}) = \vec{b} \in \mathcal{C}_A$. The solution in part 5 is

$$\vec{x}_{ls} = (A^T A)^{-1}(A^T \vec{b}) = \frac{1}{6} \begin{bmatrix} 14 & -6 \\ -6 & 3 \end{bmatrix} \begin{bmatrix} 7 \\ 18 \end{bmatrix} = \begin{bmatrix} -5/3 \\ 2 \end{bmatrix}.$$

The vector $A\vec{x}_{ls} - \vec{b} = -\dfrac{5}{3}\begin{bmatrix} 1 \\ 1 \\ 1 \end{bmatrix} + 2\begin{bmatrix} 1 \\ 2 \\ 3 \end{bmatrix} - \begin{bmatrix} 0 \\ 3 \\ 4 \end{bmatrix} = \begin{bmatrix} 1/3 \\ -2/3 \\ 1/3 \end{bmatrix}$

$$||\vec{r}_{ls}||^2 = ||A\vec{x}_{ls} - \vec{b}||^2 = (1/3)^2 + (2/3)^2 + (1/3)^2 = \frac{4}{9}.$$

Using $y = 2x - \dfrac{5}{3}$ one finds $d_1 = -1/3$ $d_2 = 2/3$ and $d_3 = -1/3$. Hence, $d_1^2 + d_2^2 + d_3^2 = ||\vec{r}_{ls}||^2$. For part 6 the normal equations reads

$$A^T A\vec{x} = \begin{bmatrix} 3 & 3 \\ 3 & 3 \end{bmatrix}\begin{bmatrix} 9 \\ 9 \end{bmatrix} \quad \text{whose solutions are } x_{ls}(x_2) = \begin{bmatrix} 3 - x_2 \\ x_2 \end{bmatrix}$$

where x_2 is a free variable. The solution $x_{ls}(3/2) = \begin{bmatrix} 3/2 \\ 3/2 \end{bmatrix} = \dfrac{3}{2}\begin{bmatrix} 1 \\ 1 \end{bmatrix} \in R_A$ since

$\mathcal{N}(A) = \text{span}\left\{ \begin{bmatrix} 1 \\ -1 \end{bmatrix} \right\}$ and the dot product $[\,1 \;\; 1\,]\begin{bmatrix} 1 \\ -1 \end{bmatrix} = 0.$

6.4.1   Sample Test 1 Solutions

1. For the matrix $A = \begin{bmatrix} 1 & 2 & 0 & 3 \\ 2 & 1 & 1 & 1 \\ 1 & -1 & 1 & -2 \end{bmatrix}$ the $\mathcal{C}_A = \text{span} \left\{ \begin{bmatrix} 1 \\ 0 \\ -1 \end{bmatrix}, \begin{bmatrix} 0 \\ 1 \\ 1 \end{bmatrix} \right\}$.

The vector $\vec{b} = \begin{bmatrix} 1 \\ 1 \\ 1 \end{bmatrix}$ is not in $\mathcal{C}_A$ since the linear combination $\begin{bmatrix} 1 \\ 1 \\ 1 \end{bmatrix} = a \begin{bmatrix} 1 \\ 0 \\ -1 \end{bmatrix} +$

$b \begin{bmatrix} 0 \\ 1 \\ 1 \end{bmatrix}$ implies that $a = b = 1$ but then the last component reads $1 = -a + b = -1 +$

$1 = 0$, a contradiction. (b) The vector $\vec{b} = \begin{bmatrix} 2 \\ 1 \\ -1 \end{bmatrix}$ is in $\mathcal{C}_A$ since $\begin{bmatrix} 2 \\ 1 \\ -1 \end{bmatrix} = a \begin{bmatrix} 1 \\ 0 \\ -1 \end{bmatrix} +$

$b \begin{bmatrix} 0 \\ 1 \\ 1 \end{bmatrix}$ is satisfied with $a = 2$ and $b = 1$. (c) The vector $\vec{\eta} = \begin{bmatrix} a \\ b \\ c \end{bmatrix} \in \mathcal{N}(A^T)$ if

$\vec{\eta} \cdot \begin{bmatrix} 1 \\ 0 \\ -1 \end{bmatrix} = a - c = 0$ and $\vec{\eta} \cdot \begin{bmatrix} 0 \\ 1 \\ 1 \end{bmatrix} = b + c = 0$. Hence $\mathcal{N}(A^T) = \text{span} \left\{ \begin{bmatrix} 1 \\ -1 \\ 1 \end{bmatrix} \right\}$.

2. An arbitrary vector in $\mathcal{R}^3$ defined by $\mathcal{H} = \text{span} \left\{ \begin{bmatrix} a \\ a+b \\ b \end{bmatrix} \in \mathcal{R}^3, a, b \in \mathcal{R} \right\}$ can be

written as $\begin{bmatrix} a \\ a+b \\ b \end{bmatrix} = a \begin{bmatrix} 1 \\ 1 \\ 0 \end{bmatrix} + b \begin{bmatrix} 0 \\ 1 \\ 1 \end{bmatrix}$ so that $\vec{v}_1 = \begin{bmatrix} 1 \\ 1 \\ 0 \end{bmatrix}$ and $\vec{v}_2 = \begin{bmatrix} 0 \\ 1 \\ 1 \end{bmatrix}$ form

a basis for $\mathcal{H}$. This is given. To find an orthonormal set of vectors, (b) set $\vec{q}_1 =$

$\dfrac{\vec{v}_1}{||\vec{v}_1||} = \dfrac{1}{\sqrt{2}} \begin{bmatrix} 1 \\ 1 \\ 0 \end{bmatrix}$. To find a vector orthogonal to $\vec{v}_1$, use the Gram-Schmidt (see

Exercise(4.16) or simply use Definition(1.11)) to write $\vec{w} = \vec{v}_2 - (\text{proj}_{\vec{v}_1} \vec{v}_2)\vec{v}_1 = \vec{v}_2 - \dfrac{1}{2}\vec{v}_1$

which is a vector in $\mathcal{H}$ (it is a linear combination of $\vec{v}_1$ and $\vec{v}_2$). Moreover, $\vec{v}_1$ and $\vec{w}$

are orthogonal since $\vec{v}_1 \cdot \vec{w} = \vec{v}_1 \cdot \vec{v}_2 - \dfrac{1}{2}\vec{v}_1 \cdot \vec{v}_1 = \vec{v}_1 \cdot \vec{v}_2 - \dfrac{1}{2}||\vec{v}_1||^2 = 1 - \dfrac{1}{2}2 = 0$. Define

$\vec{q}_2 = \dfrac{\vec{w}}{||\vec{w}||}$ so the set $\{\vec{q}_1, \vec{q}_2\}$ is an orthonormal set of vectors which span $\mathcal{H}$.

3. Since the matrix A is a 3×4 the dimension theorem gives $4 = \dim \mathcal{N}(A) + \dim R_A$ and $3 = \dim \mathcal{N}(A)^T + \dim \mathcal{C}_A$. (a) so if the dimension of the $\mathcal{N}(A) = 2$, then the dimension of $R_A = 2$ is **True** and (b) if the dimension of the $\mathcal{N}(A) = 2$, then the dimension of $R_A = 1$ is **False**. (c) If the dimension of the $\mathcal{N}(A) = 1$, then the problem $A\vec{x} = \vec{b}$ is solvable is **True** since the dimension of $\mathcal{C}_A$ is three and the dimension of $\mathcal{N}(A)^T = 0$ (Fredholm Alternative). (d) If $\dim N(A^T) = 1$ then the rank of A is 2 is **True**. The rank of A could be 4 is **False**.

4. Let the A be the 2×3 matrix $A = \begin{bmatrix} 1 & 3 & 5 \\ 2 & 6 & 10 \end{bmatrix}$ Use the row reduction $\begin{bmatrix} 1 & 3 & 5 \\ 2 & 6 & 10 \end{bmatrix} \sim$

$\begin{bmatrix} 1 & 3 & 5 \\ 0 & 0 & 0 \end{bmatrix}$ to find $x_1 = -3x_2 - 5x_3$. Hence, the homogeneous solution is given

by $\vec{x} = \begin{bmatrix} x_1 \\ x_2 \\ x_3 \end{bmatrix} = \begin{bmatrix} -3x_2 - 5x_3 \\ x_2 \\ x_3 \end{bmatrix} = x_2 \begin{bmatrix} -3 \\ 1 \\ 0 \end{bmatrix} + x_3 \begin{bmatrix} -5 \\ 0 \\ 1 \end{bmatrix}$. It follows that

$\mathcal{N}(A) = \text{span} \left\{ \begin{bmatrix} -3 \\ 1 \\ 0 \end{bmatrix}, \begin{bmatrix} -5 \\ 0 \\ 1 \end{bmatrix} \right\}$. For the row space of A take either of the rows

of A (the rows are linearly dependent) so that $R_A = \text{span} \left\{ \begin{bmatrix} 1 \\ 3 \\ 5 \end{bmatrix} \right\}$. (b) Using the

row reduction in (a) the column space $\mathcal{C}_A = \text{span} \left\{ \begin{bmatrix} 1 \\ 2 \end{bmatrix} \right\}$ and, since $\mathcal{N}(A^T) \perp \mathcal{C}_A$,

it follows $\mathcal{N}(A^T) = \text{span} \left\{ \begin{bmatrix} -2 \\ 1 \end{bmatrix} \right\}$.

6.4.2 Sample Test 2 Solutions

1. An arbitray vector in $V = \left\{ \begin{bmatrix} x_1 \\ x_2 \\ x_3 \end{bmatrix} : x_1 + x_2 = 0, x_3 \in \mathcal{R} \right\}$ can be written $\begin{bmatrix} x_1 \\ x_2 \\ x_3 \end{bmatrix} =$

$\begin{bmatrix} -x_2 \\ x_2 \\ x_3 \end{bmatrix} = x_2 \begin{bmatrix} -1 \\ 1 \\ 0 \end{bmatrix} + x_3 \begin{bmatrix} 0 \\ 0 \\ 1 \end{bmatrix}$ so the set $\left\{ \begin{bmatrix} -1 \\ 1 \\ 0 \end{bmatrix}, \begin{bmatrix} 0 \\ 0 \\ 1 \end{bmatrix} \right\}$ is a basis for V.

2. Suppose that A is a matrix and that

$$\mathcal{C}_A = \text{span}\{\vec{v}_1, \vec{v}_2\} \text{ and } \mathcal{N}(A) = \text{span}\{\vec{w}_1, \vec{w}_2\}.$$

where $\vec{v}_1 = \begin{bmatrix} 1 \\ 2 \\ 1 \end{bmatrix}$, $\vec{v}_2 = \begin{bmatrix} 2 \\ 1 \\ -1 \end{bmatrix} \in \mathcal{R}^3$ and $\vec{w}_1 = \begin{bmatrix} -2 \\ 1 \\ 3 \\ 0 \end{bmatrix}$, $\vec{w}_2 = \begin{bmatrix} 1 \\ -5 \\ 0 \\ 3 \end{bmatrix} \in \mathcal{R}^4$. (a)

The size of the matrix A is __3 × 4__. (b) The dimension of $\mathcal{N}(A)$ is __2__. (c) The rank of the matrix A is __2__. (d) The dimension of $\mathcal{C}_A$ is __2__. (e) The problem $A\vec{x} = \vec{b}$ is solvable for all $\vec{b} \in \mathcal{R}^3$ is __False__ since (f) the dimension of $\mathcal{N}(A^T)$ is __1__. (g) The rank of the matrix A^T is __2__. (h) The dimension of $\mathcal{C}_{A^T} = R_A$ is __2__. There are **nonzero** solutions of $A^T \vec{w} = \vec{0}$ is __True__.

3. Consider the problem $A\vec{x} = \begin{bmatrix} 1 & 2 & 3 \\ 2 & 5 & 4 \end{bmatrix} \begin{bmatrix} x_1 \\ x_2 \\ x_3 \end{bmatrix} = \begin{bmatrix} b_1 \\ b_2 \end{bmatrix}$. (a) The row reduction

$\begin{bmatrix} 1 & 2 & 3 & | & b_1 \\ 2 & 5 & 4 & | & b_2 \end{bmatrix} \sim \begin{bmatrix} 1 & 2 & 3 & | & b_1 \\ 0 & 1 & -2 & | & b_2 - 2b_1 \end{bmatrix}$ $A\vec{x} = \vec{b}$ gives $x_2 = 2x_3 + b_2 - 2b_1$ and

$x_1 = -2x_2 - 3x_3 + b_1 = -2(2x_3 + b_2 - 2b_1) - 3x_3 + b_1 - 7x_3 + 5b_1 - 2b_2$. Hence

$\vec{x} = \{\vec{x}_h\} + \vec{x}_p = \left\{ x_3 \begin{bmatrix} -7 \\ 2 \\ 1 \end{bmatrix} \right\} + \begin{bmatrix} 5b_1 - 2b_2 \\ b_2 - 2b_1 \\ 0 \end{bmatrix}$. (b) A basis for $\mathcal{N}(A)$ is given by

$\text{span}\left\{ \begin{bmatrix} -7 \\ 2 \\ 1 \end{bmatrix} \right\}$. (c) A basis for $\mathcal{C}_A$ is $\text{span}\left\{ \begin{bmatrix} 1 \\ 0 \end{bmatrix}, \begin{bmatrix} 0 \\ 1 \end{bmatrix} \right\}$. Any basis for R^2 is fine

since $R^2 = \mathcal{C}_A$. A basis for $\mathcal{C}_{A^T} = R_A = \text{span}\left\{ \begin{bmatrix} 1 \\ 2 \\ 3 \end{bmatrix}, \begin{bmatrix} 2 \\ 5 \\ 4 \end{bmatrix} \right\}$ (the two rows of A).

4. The set of vectors in $S = \left\{ \begin{bmatrix} 1 \\ 2 \end{bmatrix}, \begin{bmatrix} 2 \\ 5 \end{bmatrix}, \begin{bmatrix} 3 \\ 4 \end{bmatrix} \right\}$ is a linearly dependent set since

$(-7) \begin{bmatrix} 1 \\ 2 \end{bmatrix} + (2) \begin{bmatrix} 2 \\ 5 \end{bmatrix} + (1) \begin{bmatrix} 3 \\ 4 \end{bmatrix} = \begin{bmatrix} 0 \\ 0 \end{bmatrix}$.

5. The matrix $A = \begin{bmatrix} 1 & 2 & 0 & 3 \\ 2 & 1 & 1 & 1 \\ 1 & -1 & 1 & -2 \end{bmatrix}$ has the row echelon form

$$[\,A\,] = \begin{bmatrix} 1 & 2 & 0 & 3 \\ 2 & 1 & 1 & 1 \\ 1 & -1 & 1 & -2 \end{bmatrix} \sim \begin{bmatrix} 1 & 2 & 0 & 3 \\ 0 & -3 & 1 & -5 \\ 0 & 0 & 0 & 0 \end{bmatrix}$$

so (a) the matrix A has __2__ pivots so the rank of A is __2__. It follows that the dimension of $\mathcal{C}_A$ is __2__ and the dimension of $\mathcal{C}_{A^T} = R_A$ is __2__. (b) It follows from work in class (discussion following equation (4.27)) that $\mathcal{C}_A = \text{span} \left\{ \begin{bmatrix} 1 \\ 2 \\ 1 \end{bmatrix}, \begin{bmatrix} 2 \\ 1 \\ -1 \end{bmatrix} \right\}$

(the columns of A corresponding to the pivot columns). This is given. Let $\vec{\eta} = \begin{bmatrix} a \\ b \\ c \end{bmatrix} \in$

$\mathcal{N}(A^T)$. Using $\vec{\eta} \cdot \vec{v} = 0$ for every $\vec{v} \in \mathcal{C}_A$ leads to $\eta \cdot \begin{bmatrix} 1 \\ 2 \\ 1 \end{bmatrix} = a + 2b + c = 0$ and

$\eta \cdot \begin{bmatrix} 2 \\ 1 \\ -1 \end{bmatrix} = 2a + b - c = 0$. Solve these two equations to find the basis for the

$\mathcal{N}(A^T) = \text{span} \left\{ \begin{bmatrix} 1 \\ -1 \\ 1 \end{bmatrix} \right\}$.

6.5   Exercise Set Five

5.1 The matrix $P = \begin{bmatrix} 1 & 1 \\ 1 & -1 \end{bmatrix}$ diagonalizes each of parts 1 and 2,

$$P^{-1}AP = \frac{1}{2}\begin{bmatrix} 1 & 1 \\ 1 & -1 \end{bmatrix} A \begin{bmatrix} 1 & 1 \\ 1 & -1 \end{bmatrix} = \Lambda = \begin{bmatrix} 1 & 0 \\ 0 & 3 \end{bmatrix} \text{ and } \begin{bmatrix} 6 & 0 \\ 0 & -4 \end{bmatrix}$$

respectively. For part 3

$$P^{-1}AP = \frac{1}{2i}\begin{bmatrix} 1 & -i \\ 1 & i \end{bmatrix} \begin{bmatrix} 0 & 1 \\ -1 & 0 \end{bmatrix} \begin{bmatrix} i & i \\ -1 & 1 \end{bmatrix} = \Lambda = \begin{bmatrix} -i & 0 \\ 0 & i \end{bmatrix}$$

For part 4,

$$P^{-1}AP = \begin{bmatrix} 1 & 1 \\ -1 & -2 \end{bmatrix} \begin{bmatrix} 2 & -2 \\ 1 & 5 \end{bmatrix} \begin{bmatrix} 2 & 1 \\ -1 & -1 \end{bmatrix} = \Lambda = \begin{bmatrix} 3 & 0 \\ 0 & 4 \end{bmatrix}$$

For part 5 the algebraic multiplicity of the eigenvalue $\lambda = 4$ is two and the geometric multiplicity is one. Hence, according to Theorem(5.33), this matrix is not diagonalizable. Finally, replace P in parts 1 and 2 with $Q = \dfrac{1}{\sqrt{2}}\begin{bmatrix} 1 & 1 \\ 1 & -1 \end{bmatrix}$ and

$Q = \dfrac{1}{\sqrt{2}}\begin{bmatrix} i & i \\ -1 & 1 \end{bmatrix}$ for part 3 There is no Q for part 4 (eigenvectors are not orthogonal) or part 5 (not enough eigenvectors).

5.2 The matrix $P = \begin{bmatrix} 1 & 2 & 0 \\ 1 & -1 & -1 \\ 1 & -1 & 1 \end{bmatrix}$ diagonalizes both parts 1 and 2 and

$$P^{-1}AP = \frac{1}{6}\begin{bmatrix} 2 & 2 & 2 \\ 2 & -1 & -1 \\ 0 & -3 & 3 \end{bmatrix} A \begin{bmatrix} 1 & 2 & 0 \\ 1 & -1 & -1 \\ 1 & -1 & 1 \end{bmatrix} = \Lambda = \begin{bmatrix} -1 & 0 & 0 \\ 0 & 2 & 0 \\ 0 & 0 & 2 \end{bmatrix}, \begin{bmatrix} 0 & 0 & 0 \\ 0 & 3 & 0 \\ 0 & 0 & 3 \end{bmatrix}$$

respectively. For part 3

$$P^{-1}AP = \begin{bmatrix} -1 & -1 & 1 \\ 0 & -1 & 1 \\ 1 & 1 & 0 \end{bmatrix} \begin{bmatrix} 1 & -1 & 1 \\ 2 & 4 & -1 \\ 2 & 2 & 1 \end{bmatrix} \begin{bmatrix} -1 & 1 & 0 \\ 1 & -1 & 1 \\ 1 & 0 & 1 \end{bmatrix} = \Lambda = \begin{bmatrix} 1 & 0 & 0 \\ 0 & 2 & 0 \\ 0 & 0 & 3 \end{bmatrix}.$$

For part 4 the eigenvalue $\lambda = 3$ the algebraic multiplicity is three and the geometric multiplicity is one. Hence, according to Theorem(5.33) this matrix is not diagonalizable. Finally, replace P in parts 1 and 2 with $Q = \begin{bmatrix} 1/\sqrt{3} & 2/\sqrt{6} & 0 \\ 1/\sqrt{3} & -1/\sqrt{6} & -1/\sqrt{2} \\ 1/\sqrt{3} & -1/\sqrt{6} & 1/\sqrt{2} \end{bmatrix}$.

There is no Q for part 3 (eigenvectors are not orthogonal) or part 4 (not enough eigenvectors).

5.3 The change of variable in (5.3) immediately leads to the matrix $A = \begin{bmatrix} a & b \\ 1 & 0 \end{bmatrix}$. For part 2 use the quadratic formula on

$$\det{(A - \lambda I))} = \det{\left(\begin{bmatrix} a - \lambda & b \\ 1 & -\lambda \end{bmatrix} \right)} = (a - \lambda)(-\lambda) - b = \lambda^2 - a\lambda - b = 0$$

to find the eigenvalues $\lambda_{\pm} = \dfrac{a \pm \sqrt{a^2 + 4b}}{2}$ from which $\lambda_+ \pm \lambda_- = \begin{cases} a \\ \sqrt{a^2 + b^2} \end{cases}$

follows by addition and subtraction and the product is

$$\lambda_+ \lambda_- = \frac{\left(a + \sqrt{a^2 + 4b} \right) \left(a - \sqrt{a^2 + 4b} \right)}{4} = \frac{\left(a^2 - [\sqrt{a^2 + 4b}]^2 \right)}{4} = \frac{-4b}{4} = -b.$$

For part 3 the calculation

$$(A - \lambda_+ I))\, \vec{p}_+ = \begin{bmatrix} \lambda_- & b \\ 1 & -\lambda_+ \end{bmatrix} \begin{bmatrix} \lambda_+ \\ 1 \end{bmatrix} = \begin{bmatrix} \lambda_- \lambda_+ + b \\ \lambda_+ - \lambda_+ \end{bmatrix} = \begin{bmatrix} 0 \\ 0 \end{bmatrix}$$

uses the arithmetic from part 2 This shows $\vec{p}_+ = \begin{bmatrix} \lambda_+ \\ 1 \end{bmatrix}$ is an eigenvector for λ_+.

Showing $\vec{p}_- = \begin{bmatrix} \lambda_- \\ 1 \end{bmatrix}$ is an eigenvector for λ_- is similar. Part 4 follows using the remainder of part 3 and using a product similar to that in (5.7).

5.4 Since $\lambda = \dfrac{a}{2}$ is the only eigenvalue it follows that $a^2 + 4b = 0$ so that $b = \dfrac{-a^2}{4} = -\lambda^2$ so the matrix

$$A = \begin{bmatrix} a & b \\ 1 & 0 \end{bmatrix} = \begin{bmatrix} 2\lambda & -\lambda^2 \\ 1 & 0 \end{bmatrix}.$$

By direct calculation

$$\begin{aligned}
\vec{p}^{\,T} A \vec{q} &= \frac{1}{\sqrt{\lambda^2 + 1}}[\,\lambda \;\; 1\,] \begin{bmatrix} 2\lambda & -\lambda^2 \\ 1 & 0 \end{bmatrix} \left(\frac{1}{\sqrt{\lambda^2 + 1}} \begin{bmatrix} -1 \\ \lambda \end{bmatrix} \right) \\
&= \frac{1}{\lambda^2 + 1}[\,\lambda \;\; 1\,] \begin{bmatrix} -2\lambda - \lambda^3 \\ -1 \end{bmatrix} = \frac{1}{\lambda^2 + 1}\left(-2\lambda^2 - \lambda^4 - 1 \right) \\
&= \frac{-(\lambda^4 + 2\lambda^2 + 1)}{\lambda^2 + 1} = -\frac{(\lambda^2 + 1)^2}{\lambda^2 + 1} = -(\lambda^2 + 1)
\end{aligned}$$

A similar calculation gives $\vec{q}^{\,T} A \vec{q} = \dfrac{a}{2} = \lambda$. For part 2 take the second component of (5.7) (with Q replacing P) to find the formula for α_n. For part 3 substitute $\alpha_0 = 1$, $\alpha_1 = 2$ and $\lambda = 1$ to find $\alpha_n = n + 1$. The recursion relation for $|T_n|$ in (3.4) is the same as the recursion for the α_n in part 3. For part 4 substitute $\alpha_0 = 1$, $\alpha_1 = \dfrac{3}{2}$ and $\lambda = \dfrac{3}{2}$ to find $\alpha_n = \left(\dfrac{3}{2} \right)^n$.

5.5 The eigenvalues of the matrix $A = \begin{bmatrix} 1 & 1 \\ 1 & 0 \end{bmatrix}$ are given by $\lambda_{\pm} = \dfrac{1 \pm \sqrt{5}}{2}$. Since A has two distinct eigenvalues there are two independent eigenvectors for A given by

$$\vec{p}_+ = \begin{bmatrix} \dfrac{1 + \sqrt{5}}{2} \\ 1 \end{bmatrix} \text{ and } \vec{p}_- = \begin{bmatrix} \dfrac{1 - \sqrt{5}}{2} \\ 1 \end{bmatrix}.$$

The matrix $P = [\ \vec{p}_+ \ \vec{p}_- \ ]$ whose inverse is $P^{-1} = \dfrac{1}{\sqrt{5}} \begin{bmatrix} 1 & \dfrac{1 - \sqrt{5}}{2} \\ -1 & \dfrac{1 + \sqrt{5}}{2} \end{bmatrix}$. Using

$$P^{-1}AP = \Lambda = \begin{bmatrix} \dfrac{1 + \sqrt{5}}{2} & 0 \\ 0 & \dfrac{1 - \sqrt{5}}{2} \end{bmatrix}$$

in the form $A = P\Lambda P^{-1}$ gives

$$\vec{z}_{n+1} = \begin{bmatrix} u_{n+1} \\ v_{n+1} \end{bmatrix} = \begin{bmatrix} f_{n+1} \\ f_n \end{bmatrix} = A^n \vec{z}_1 = \left(P\Lambda P^{-1} \right)^n \begin{bmatrix} f_1 \\ f_0 \end{bmatrix}$$

$$= P\Lambda^n P^{-1} \begin{bmatrix} 1 \\ 0 \end{bmatrix} = P \begin{bmatrix} \left(\dfrac{1 + \sqrt{5}}{2} \right)^n & 0 \\ 0 & \left(\dfrac{1 - \sqrt{5}}{2} \right)^n \end{bmatrix} P^{-1} \begin{bmatrix} 1 \\ 0 \end{bmatrix}$$

where formula (5.6) is used in the second to last equality. Perform the multiplication on the right hand side of the last equation and the second component of the resulting vector gives the nth **Fibonacci number**

$$f_n = \frac{1}{\sqrt{5}} \left(\left[\frac{1 + \sqrt{5}}{2} \right]^n - \left[\frac{1 - \sqrt{5}}{2} \right]^n \right).$$

5.6 For part 1 note that the columns of P_A are different from the columns of P_B, and since these columns are the eigenvectors of A and B, respectively, the matrices have different eigenvectors. Use the hint in part 2 to see that

$$P = P_A P_B^{-1} = \begin{bmatrix} 2 & 1 \\ -1 & -1 \end{bmatrix} \begin{bmatrix} 0 & 1 \\ 1 & -4 \end{bmatrix} = \begin{bmatrix} 1 & -2 \\ -1 & 3 \end{bmatrix}.$$

For part 3 recall that $\rho_A(\lambda) = \det(A - \lambda I)$. Now since the determinant of a product is the product of determinants and $\det(P^{-1}P) = 1$, it follows that

$$\begin{aligned} \rho_A(\lambda) &= \det(A - \lambda I) = \det \left(P^{-1}(A - \lambda I)P \right) \\ &= \det \left(P^{-1}AP - \lambda I \right) = \det \left(B - \lambda I \right) = \rho_B(\lambda). \end{aligned}$$

Finally, one cannot conclude that $\vec{v}$ is an eigenvector for the matrix B. Here is why. Write $\lambda\vec{v} = A\vec{v} = PBP^{-1}\vec{v}$ so if one sets $\vec{w} = P^{-1}\vec{v}$ the previous statement reads $\lambda P^{-1}\vec{v} = \lambda\vec{w} = B\vec{w}$ so that $\vec{w} = P^{-1}\vec{v}$ is an eigenvector for the matrix B. part 4 is a matrix multiplication. For parts 5 and 6

$$
\begin{aligned}
A_1 A_2 &= \left(P\Lambda_1 P^{-1}\right)\left(P\Lambda_2 P^{-1}\right) = P\Lambda_1\left(P^{-1}P\right)\Lambda_2 P^{-1} \\
&= P\Lambda_1\Lambda_2 P^{-1} = P\Lambda_2\Lambda_1 P^{-1} \quad \text{diagonal matrices commute: } \Lambda_1\Lambda_2 = \Lambda_2\Lambda_1 \\
&= P\Lambda_2\left(P^{-1}P\right)\Lambda_1 P^{-1} = \left(P\Lambda_2 P^{-1}\right)\left(P\Lambda_1 P^{-1}\right) = A_2 A_1
\end{aligned}
$$

so the matrices A_1 and A_2 commute.

5.7 The matrix $A(\alpha) = \begin{bmatrix} 1 & 0 & 0 \\ \alpha & 1 & 0 \\ 0 & 1 & 1 \end{bmatrix}$ is lower triangular, so the eigenvalues of $A(\alpha)$ are

its diagonal entries [part 4 of Theorem(5.5)]. From $[A(\alpha) - I] = \begin{bmatrix} 0 & 0 & 0 \\ \alpha & 0 & 0 \\ 0 & 1 & 0 \end{bmatrix}$, it

follows that the rank$[A(0) - I] = 1$ so that the dim$[\mathcal{N}(A(0) - I)]$ is two [dimension

theorem(4.22)]. Two independent eigenvectors for $A(0)$ are $\begin{bmatrix} 1 \\ 0 \\ 0 \end{bmatrix}$ and $\begin{bmatrix} 0 \\ 0 \\ 1 \end{bmatrix}$ Simi-

larly, the rank$[A(1) - I] = 2$ so that the dim$[\mathcal{N}(A(0) - I)]$ is one. The one eigenvector

for $A(1)$ is $\begin{bmatrix} 0 \\ 0 \\ 1 \end{bmatrix}$. If the number one in the last two sentences is replaced by any

non-zero α, the sentences remain true. By Theorem(5.34) there is no α, so that the matrix $A(\alpha)$ is diagonalizable.

5.8 Evaluate $(A - 3I)$ at $\lambda_3 = 3$ to find

$$
(A - 3I)\vec{p}_3 = \begin{bmatrix} -1 & 1 & 0 \\ 0 & -1 & 0 \\ \beta & -2 & 0 \end{bmatrix}\begin{bmatrix} 0 \\ 0 \\ 1 \end{bmatrix} = \begin{bmatrix} 0 \\ 0 \\ 0 \end{bmatrix}
$$

which shows that $\vec{p}_3$ is an eigenvector for $\lambda_3 = 3$. The rank of $A - 2I$ is two, no matter what the value of the parameter β. Hence for any value of β the dimension theorem gives dim$\mathcal{N}(A - 2I) = 3 - \text{rank}(A - 2I) = 3 - 2 = 1$. Since the geometric multiplicity of $\lambda_1 = 2$ is less then its algebraic multiplicity the matrix is never diagonalizable. An

eigenvector for $\lambda_1 = 2$ is $\begin{bmatrix} 1 \\ 0 \\ -\beta \end{bmatrix}$.

5.9 Expand $\rho_A(\lambda) = |A - \lambda I| = \begin{bmatrix} 2 - \lambda & 1 & 0 & 0 \\ 0 & 3 - \lambda & 0 & 0 \\ \beta & -2 & 3 - \lambda & 0 \\ 0 & 1 & 0 & 3 - \lambda \end{bmatrix}$ around the last column to see that $\rho_A(\lambda) = (2-\lambda)(3-\lambda)^3$. To find $\vec{p}_1$ in part 2 a few row operations gives

$$(A - 2I) = \begin{bmatrix} 0 & 1 & 0 & 0 \\ 0 & 1 & 0 & 0 \\ \beta & -2 & 1 & 0 \\ 0 & 1 & 0 & 1 \end{bmatrix} \sim \begin{bmatrix} \beta & 0 & 1 & 0 \\ 0 & 1 & 0 & 0 \\ 0 & 0 & 0 & 1 \\ 0 & 0 & 0 & 0 \end{bmatrix}$$

from which $\vec{p}_1$ follows. For part 3 the

$$\text{rank of}(A - 3I) = \begin{bmatrix} -1 & 1 & 0 & 0 \\ 0 & 0 & 0 & 0 \\ \beta & -2 & 0 & 0 \\ 0 & 1 & 0 & 0 \end{bmatrix} \sim \begin{bmatrix} -1 & 0 & 0 & 0 \\ 0 & 1 & 0 & 0 \\ 0 & 0 & 0 & 0 \\ 0 & 0 & 0 & 0 \end{bmatrix}$$

is two for any value of β. A basis for $\mathcal{N}(A - 3I)$ is $\vec{e}_3$ and $\vec{e}_4$ [see Example(5.11)], so that A is never diagonalizable. For part 5

$$\text{rank of}(A - 3I) = \begin{bmatrix} 0 & 1 & 0 & 0 \\ 0 & 0 & 0 & 0 \\ \beta & -2 & 0 & 0 \\ 0 & 1 & 0 & 0 \end{bmatrix} \sim \begin{bmatrix} \beta & -2 & 0 & 0 \\ 0 & 1 & 0 & 0 \\ 0 & 0 & 0 & 0 \\ 0 & 0 & 0 & 0 \end{bmatrix}$$

is 2 ($\beta \neq 0$) or 1 ($\beta = 0$) so that A is never diagonalizable.

5.10 To see part 1 $||Q\vec{x}||^2 = (Q\vec{x})^T Q\vec{x} = \vec{x}^T Q^T Q\vec{x} = \vec{x}^T \vec{x} = ||\vec{x}||^2$ since $Q^T Q = I$. The remaining parts of the problem are substitutions. For example,

$$\begin{aligned} y_1 &= ||Q\vec{x}|| \cos(\alpha + \theta) = ||\vec{x}|| \cos(\alpha + \theta) \quad \text{since } ||Q\vec{x}|| = ||\vec{x}|| \\ &= (||\vec{x}|| \cos(\alpha)) \cos(\theta) - (||\vec{x}|| \sin(\alpha)) \sin(\theta) \\ &= x_1 \cos(\theta) - x_2 \sin(\theta). \end{aligned}$$

5.11 The eigenvalues are found from

$$\begin{aligned} \det (A - \lambda I)) &= \left(\begin{bmatrix} a & b \\ -b & a \end{bmatrix} - \lambda \begin{bmatrix} 1 & 0 \\ 0 & 1 \end{bmatrix} \right) \\ &= \det \left(\begin{bmatrix} a - \lambda & b \\ -b & a - \lambda \end{bmatrix} \right) = \lambda^2 - 2a\lambda + a^2 + b^2 = 0. \end{aligned}$$

Using the quadratic formula gives

$$\lambda_{\pm} = \frac{-(-2a) \pm \sqrt{(-2a)^2 - 4(a^2 + b^2)}}{2} = \frac{2a \pm \sqrt{-4b^2}}{2} = a \pm bi$$

A unit eigenvector for A corresponding to $\lambda_+ = a + bi$ is $\vec{q}_+ = \dfrac{1}{\sqrt{2}} \begin{bmatrix} i \\ -1 \end{bmatrix}$ and one

corresponding to $\lambda_- = a - bi$ is $\vec{q}_- = \dfrac{1}{\sqrt{2}} \begin{bmatrix} i \\ 1 \end{bmatrix}$. The matrix $Q = \dfrac{1}{\sqrt{2}} \begin{bmatrix} i & i \\ -1 & 1 \end{bmatrix}$ is a

unitary diagonalizer of A so that $Q^*AQ = \Lambda$. To see part 3 write

$$AA^T = A(-A) = -A^2 = (-A)A = A^T A,$$

so that A is normal.

5.12 The matrix $A = \begin{bmatrix} 5 & -1 \\ 1 & 3 \end{bmatrix}$ is not normal, since

$$AA^T = \begin{bmatrix} 26 & 2 \\ 2 & 10 \end{bmatrix} \neq \begin{bmatrix} 26 & -2 \\ -2 & 10 \end{bmatrix} = A^T A.$$

The eigenvalue $\lambda = 4$ of A has algebraic multiplicity two and a unit eigenvector is $\vec{q}_1 = \dfrac{1}{\sqrt{2}} \begin{bmatrix} 1 \\ 1 \end{bmatrix}$. The vector $\vec{q}_2 = \dfrac{1}{\sqrt{2}} \begin{bmatrix} 1 \\ -1 \end{bmatrix}$ is a unit vector orthogonal to $\vec{q}_1$. The matrix $Q = [\, \vec{q}_1 \ \vec{q}_2 \,] = \dfrac{1}{\sqrt{2}} \begin{bmatrix} 1 & 1 \\ 1 & -1 \end{bmatrix}$ and $R = \begin{bmatrix} 4 & 2 \\ 0 & 4 \end{bmatrix}$ satisfy $Q^T A Q = R$.

5.13 The matrix A is not Hermitian, since $A^* = \begin{bmatrix} 2 & -i \\ -i & 4 \end{bmatrix} \neq A$. The eigenvalues of $A = \begin{bmatrix} 2 & i \\ i & 4 \end{bmatrix}$ are found from

$$\begin{aligned} \det(A - \lambda I)) &= \left(\begin{bmatrix} 2 & i \\ i & 4 \end{bmatrix} - \lambda \begin{bmatrix} 1 & 0 \\ 0 & 1 \end{bmatrix} \right) \\ &= \det \left(\begin{bmatrix} 2 - \lambda & 1 + i \\ 1 - i & 3 - \lambda \end{bmatrix} \right) \\ &= \lambda^2 - 6\lambda + 9 = (\lambda - 3)^2. \end{aligned}$$

so that $\lambda_1 = \lambda_2 = 3$ is the eigenvalue of A with algebraic multiplicity two. Since

$$\mathrm{rank}\,(A - \lambda_1 I) = \mathrm{rank}(A - 3I) = \mathrm{rank}\left(\begin{bmatrix} -1 & i \\ i & 1 \end{bmatrix} \right) = \mathrm{rank}\left(\begin{bmatrix} -1 & i \\ 0 & 0 \end{bmatrix} \right) = 1$$

there is only one eigenvector for A. A unit eigenvector for A corresponding to $\lambda_1 = 3$ is $\vec{q}_1 = \dfrac{1}{\sqrt{2}} \begin{bmatrix} i \\ 1 \end{bmatrix}$. A unit vector orthogonal to $\vec{q}_1$ is $\vec{q}_2 = \dfrac{1}{\sqrt{2}} \begin{bmatrix} i \\ -1 \end{bmatrix}$ and the matrix $Q = [\, \vec{q}_1 \ \vec{q}_2 \,] = \dfrac{1}{\sqrt{2}} \begin{bmatrix} i & i \\ 1 & -1 \end{bmatrix}$ and $R = \begin{bmatrix} 3 & -2 \\ 0 & 3 \end{bmatrix}$ satisfy $Q^* A Q = R$.

5.14 The eigenvalues are found from

$$\begin{aligned} \det(A - \lambda I)) &= \left(\begin{bmatrix} 2 & 1 + i \\ 1 - i & 3 \end{bmatrix} - \lambda \begin{bmatrix} 1 & 0 \\ 0 & 1 \end{bmatrix} \right) \\ &= \det \left(\begin{bmatrix} 2 - \lambda & 1 + i \\ 1 - i & 3 - \lambda \end{bmatrix} \right) \\ &= \lambda^2 - 5\lambda + 4 = (\lambda - 1)(\lambda - 4) \end{aligned}$$

so that $\lambda_1 = 1$ and $\lambda_2 = 4$ are the eigenvalues of A. Unit eigenvectors for A are

$$\vec{q_1} = \frac{1}{\sqrt{3}} \begin{bmatrix} 1+i \\ -1 \end{bmatrix} \text{ and } \vec{q_2} = \frac{1}{\sqrt{3}} \begin{bmatrix} 1 \\ 1-i \end{bmatrix}$$

corresponding to λ_1 and λ_2 respectively. Hence,

$$Q^*AQ = \frac{1}{\sqrt{3}} \begin{bmatrix} 1-i & -1 \\ 1 & 1+i \end{bmatrix} \begin{bmatrix} 2 & 1+i \\ 1-i & 3 \end{bmatrix} \frac{1}{\sqrt{3}} \begin{bmatrix} 1+i & 1 \\ -1 & 1-i \end{bmatrix} = \begin{bmatrix} 1 & 0 \\ 0 & 4 \end{bmatrix}.$$

5.15 This exercise is worked out in the statement of the problem. It gives a reason to believe Theorem(5.33).

5.16 From the given information

$$Q^*(A - \lambda I)Q = \begin{bmatrix} \lambda_1 - \lambda & r_{12} & r_{13} & r_{14} \\ 0 & \lambda_2 - \lambda & r_{23} & r_{24} \\ 0 & 0 & \lambda_2 - \lambda & r_{34} \\ 0 & 0 & 0 & \lambda_2 - \lambda \end{bmatrix}$$

$$= \begin{bmatrix} \lambda_1 - \lambda_2 & r_{12} & r_{13} & r_{14} \\ 0 & 0 & r_{23} & r_{24} \\ 0 & 0 & 0 & r_{34} \\ 0 & 0 & 0 & 0 \end{bmatrix}.$$

This is (5.44) with $a = 3$, $n = 4$, so $\gamma = n - a = 1$. Hence the

$$\text{rank}(A - \lambda_2 I) = \begin{cases} 1, & \text{if } r_{23} = r_{24} = r_{34} = 0 \\ 2, & \text{if } r_{34} = 0 \text{ and } r_{24} \text{ or } r_{34} \neq 0 \\ 3, & \text{if } r_{23} \neq 0 \text{ and } r_{34} \neq 0 \end{cases},$$

so by the dimension theorem

$$\begin{aligned} \dim \mathcal{N}(A - \lambda_2 I) &= 4 - \text{rank}(A - \lambda_2 I) \\ &= \begin{cases} 3, & \text{if } r_{23} = r_{24} = r_{34} = 0 \\ 2, & \text{if } r_{34} = 0 \text{ and } r_{24} \text{ or } r_{34} \neq 0 \\ 1, & \text{if } r_{23} \neq 0 \text{ and } r_{34} \neq 0 \end{cases}. \end{aligned}$$

In all cases the algebraic multiplicity of λ_2 is $a = 3 \geq g = \dim \mathcal{N}(A - \lambda_2 I)$ the geometric multiplicity of λ_2.

5.17 The graph of $q(x_1, x_2) = 2x_1^2 - 2x_1x_2 + 2x_2^2$ is an ellipse since the eigenvalues of $A = \begin{bmatrix} 2 & -1 \\ -1 & 2 \end{bmatrix}$ are both positive $\sigma(A) = \{1, 3\}$. The graph the graph of $q(x_1, x_2) = x_1^2 - 10x_1x_2 + x_2^2$ is a hyperbola since the eigenvalues of $A = \begin{bmatrix} 1 & 5 \\ 5 & 1 \end{bmatrix}$ are opposite in sign $\sigma(A) = \{-4, 6\}$. The matrices for the quadratic forms are

$$A = \begin{bmatrix} 20 & 2 & -2 \\ 2 & 17 & -5 \\ -2 & -5 & 17 \end{bmatrix}, \begin{bmatrix} 8 & 2 & -2 \\ 2 & 2 & -8 \\ -2 & -8 & 2 \end{bmatrix}, \begin{bmatrix} 7 & 1 & -8 \\ 1 & 7 & -8 \\ -8 & -8 & 16 \end{bmatrix}$$

for parts 3, 4 and 5, respectively. The surfaces are an ellipsoid, (part 3) a hyperboloid (one sheet) (part 4) and an elliptic cylinder (part 5).

5.18 The function $q(\vec{x}) = \vec{x}^T A \vec{x} = 3x_1^2 - 2x_1 x_2 + 3x_2^2 = 2, \, 11/5, \, 3, \, 4$ at $\vec{x} = \vec{q}_1, \vec{x}_1, \vec{x}_2, \vec{q}_2$, respectively which is part 1 The four vectors

$$\vec{y}_{q_1} = Q^T \vec{q}_1 = \begin{bmatrix} 1 \\ 0 \end{bmatrix}, \, \vec{y}_1 = Q^T \vec{x}_1 = \frac{1}{\sqrt{10}} \begin{bmatrix} 3 \\ -1 \end{bmatrix},$$

and

$$\vec{y}_2 = Q^T \vec{x}_2 = \frac{1}{\sqrt{2}} \begin{bmatrix} 1 \\ -1 \end{bmatrix}, \, \vec{y}_{q_2} = Q^T \vec{q}_2 = \begin{bmatrix} 0 \\ 1 \end{bmatrix}$$

and from $\hat{q}(\vec{y}) = \lambda_1 |y_1|^2 + \lambda_2 |y_2|^2 = 2, \, 11/5, \, 3, \, 4$ which is part 2 For part 3 write $\sum_{j=1}^{n} \lambda_j |y_j|^2 \geq \lambda_1 \sum_{j=1}^{n} |y_j|^2$ since $\lambda_j \geq \lambda_1$ and $\sum_{j=1}^{n} |y_j|^2 = 1$ since $\|\vec{y}\| = 1$. To find the maximum, write $\sum_{j=1}^{n} \lambda_j |y_j|^2 \leq \lambda_n \sum_{j=1}^{n} |y_j|^2$ since $\lambda_j \leq \lambda_n$ and once again $\|\vec{y}\| = 1$.

5.19 For part 1. $P^2 = \left(\vec{u} \vec{u}^T \right) \left(\vec{u} \vec{u}^T \right) = \vec{u} \left(\vec{u}^T \vec{u} \right) \vec{u}^T = \vec{u} \|\vec{u}\|^2 \vec{u}^T = \vec{u} \vec{u}^T = P$ since $\|\vec{u}\|^2$

For part 2 the unit vector $\vec{u} = \frac{\vec{v}}{\|\vec{v}\|} = \frac{1}{\sqrt{5}} \begin{bmatrix} 2 \\ 1 \end{bmatrix}$ so that $P = \vec{u} \vec{u}^T = \frac{1}{5} \begin{bmatrix} 4 & 2 \\ 2 & 1 \end{bmatrix}$ and therefore

$$\vec{w} = P\vec{z} = \frac{1}{5} \begin{bmatrix} 4 & 2 \\ 2 & 1 \end{bmatrix} \begin{bmatrix} 2 \\ 2 \end{bmatrix} = \begin{bmatrix} 12/5 \\ 6/5 \end{bmatrix} = \frac{6}{5} \begin{bmatrix} 2 \\ 1 \end{bmatrix}.$$

For part 3, set $a = 0$ then $\vec{u} = \frac{1}{|b|} \begin{bmatrix} 0 \\ b \end{bmatrix}$ so that matrix $P = \vec{u} \vec{u}^T = \frac{1}{|b|^2} \begin{bmatrix} 0 & 0 \\ 0 & b^2 \end{bmatrix} = \begin{bmatrix} 0 & 0 \\ 0 & 1 \end{bmatrix}$ and $P\vec{z} = P \begin{bmatrix} z_1 \\ z_2 \end{bmatrix} = \begin{bmatrix} 0 \\ z_2 \end{bmatrix}$. Further, the projection reads

$$(\vec{u} \cdot \vec{z})\vec{u} = \left(\frac{1}{|b|} \begin{bmatrix} 0 \\ b \end{bmatrix} \cdot \begin{bmatrix} z_1 \\ z_2 \end{bmatrix} \right) \frac{1}{|b|} \begin{bmatrix} 0 \\ b \end{bmatrix} = \left(\frac{bz_2}{|b|} \right) \frac{1}{|b|} \begin{bmatrix} 0 \\ b \end{bmatrix} = \begin{bmatrix} 0 \\ \frac{b^2 z_2}{|b|^2} \end{bmatrix} = \begin{bmatrix} 0 \\ z_2 \end{bmatrix}$$

so that $P\vec{z} = (\vec{u} \cdot \vec{z})\vec{u}$. To see part 4 write

$$P\vec{u} = \left(\vec{u} \vec{u}^T \right) \vec{u} = \vec{u} \left(\vec{u}^T \vec{u} \right) = \left(\vec{u}^T \vec{u} \right) \vec{u} = 1\vec{u}$$

since $\vec{u}$ is a unit vector. This shows that 1 is an eigenvalue for P. Use the definition $P = \vec{u}\vec{u}^{\,T}$ to find the matrix $P = \left(\dfrac{1}{||\vec{v}||^2}\right)\begin{bmatrix} a^2 & ab \\ ab & b^2 \end{bmatrix}$ and then make the calculation

$$P\left(\frac{1}{||\vec{v}||^2}\right)\begin{bmatrix} b \\ -a \end{bmatrix} = \begin{bmatrix} 0 \\ 0 \end{bmatrix}$$

which shows that $\lambda = 0$ is an eigenvalue. Since $\vec{q}_1 = \vec{u}$ and $\vec{q}_2 = \left(\dfrac{1}{||\vec{v}||^2}\right)\begin{bmatrix} b \\ -a \end{bmatrix}$ are unit eigenvectors corresponding to $\lambda = 1$ and $\lambda = 0$, respectively the matrix $Q = [\vec{q}_1 \ \vec{q}_2]$ orthogonally diagonalizes the matrix P.

For part 5 use the fact that the unit vector $\vec{u} = \dfrac{\vec{v}}{||\vec{v}||}$ satisfies

$$\text{rank of } (P) = \text{rank of }\left(\vec{u}\vec{u}^{\,T}\right) \le \text{rank of }(\vec{u}) = 1$$

since $\vec{u}$ is non-zero [this is a direct application of Exercise(4.13)]. This is where the assumption that $\vec{v}$ is a non-zero vector comes into play. The only matrix with zero rank is the zero matrix. Since the rank of P is one, the dimension theorem(4.22) gives $n = \dim(\mathcal{N})(P) + \text{rank of }(P) = \dim(\mathcal{N})(P) + 1$ or $\dim(\mathcal{N})(P) = n - 1$. Hence, the diagonal matrix Λ has one it its one-one position and zeros elsewhere.

5.20 Use $\vec{e} = \vec{z} - \vec{w} = \vec{z} - P\vec{z} = (I - P)\vec{z}$ so that

$$\begin{aligned}
\vec{e}\cdot\vec{w} &= (I - P)\vec{z}\cdot P\vec{z} = ((I - P)\vec{z})^T P\vec{z}, \quad \text{dot product definition} \\
&= \vec{z}^{\,T}(I - P)^T P\vec{z} = \vec{z}^{\,T}(I - P)P\vec{z}, \quad \text{the matrix } I - P \text{ is symmetric} \\
&= \vec{z}^{\,T}(P - P^2)\vec{z} = 0, \quad \text{the matrix } P \text{ is a projection.}
\end{aligned}$$

For part 2 use $Q = \dfrac{1}{5}\begin{bmatrix} -3 & -4 \\ -4 & 3 \end{bmatrix}$ to find $\mathcal{R}(\vec{z})$. For part 3 $P = \dfrac{1}{13}\begin{bmatrix} 9 & 6 \\ 6 & 4 \end{bmatrix}$ and

$\vec{w} = P\vec{z} = \dfrac{1}{13}\begin{bmatrix} 9 & 6 \\ 6 & 4 \end{bmatrix}\begin{bmatrix} 2 \\ 2 \end{bmatrix} = \dfrac{1}{13}\begin{bmatrix} 30 \\ 20 \end{bmatrix}$ and $Q = I - 2P = \dfrac{1}{13}\begin{bmatrix} -5 & -12 \\ -12 & 5 \end{bmatrix}$ so that

$$\mathcal{R}(\vec{z}) = -Q\vec{z} = \frac{1}{13}\begin{bmatrix} 5 & 12 \\ 12 & -5 \end{bmatrix}\begin{bmatrix} 2 \\ 2 \end{bmatrix} = \frac{2}{13}\begin{bmatrix} 17 \\ 7 \end{bmatrix}.$$

For part 4 calculate the matrix

$$Q^T Q = (I - 2P)^T(I - 2P) = (I - 2P)(I - 2P) = I - 4P + 4P^2 = I$$

where $P^T = P$ and $P^2 = P$ has been used. This calculation also works for part 5.

5.21 For part 1 the matrix $At = \begin{bmatrix} 0 & 0 \\ 0 & 0 \end{bmatrix} \equiv \mathcal{O}$ is the 2×2 zero matrix. The eigenvalues of $\mathcal{O}$ are $\lambda_1 = \lambda_2 = 0$ and using any invertible matrix P in formula (5.55) yields:

$$e^{\mathcal{O}} = P \begin{bmatrix} e^0 & 0 \\ 0 & e^0 \end{bmatrix} P^{-1} = P \begin{bmatrix} 1 & 0 \\ 0 & 1 \end{bmatrix} P^{-1} = I.$$ For part 2, use part 7 of Exercise(5.6) to replace λ_1 with $-\lambda_1$ and λ_2 with $-\lambda_2$ (P also diagonalizes $-A$) in (5.55) so that

$$
\begin{aligned}
e^{At}e^{-At} &= \left(P \begin{bmatrix} e^{\lambda_1} & 0 \\ 0 & e^{\lambda_2} \end{bmatrix} P^{-1} \right) \left(P \begin{bmatrix} e^{-\lambda_1} & 0 \\ 0 & e^{-\lambda_2} \end{bmatrix} P^{-1} \right) \\
&= P \begin{bmatrix} e^{\lambda_1} & 0 \\ 0 & e^{\lambda_2} \end{bmatrix} \left(P^{-1} P \right) \begin{bmatrix} e^{-\lambda_1} & 0 \\ 0 & e^{-\lambda_2} \end{bmatrix} P^{-1} \\
&= P \begin{bmatrix} e^{\lambda_1 - \lambda_1} & 0 \\ 0 & e^{\lambda_2 - \lambda_2} \end{bmatrix} P^{-1} = P \begin{bmatrix} 1 & 0 \\ 0 & 1 \end{bmatrix} P^{-1} = I.
\end{aligned}
$$

parts 3 and 4 represent two specific cases of use for (5.55).

5.22 The matrix multiplication

$$\vec{w}(t) = \begin{bmatrix} u(t) \\ v(t) \end{bmatrix} = P \begin{bmatrix} e^{\lambda_- t} & 0 \\ 0 & e^{\lambda_+ t} \end{bmatrix} P^{-1} \begin{bmatrix} f_1 \\ f_0 \end{bmatrix}$$

where $\lambda_+ \neq \lambda_-$ and P are from Exercise(5.3) lead directly to (5.62). Similarly, the multiplication

$$\vec{w}(t) = \begin{bmatrix} u(t) \\ v(t) \end{bmatrix} = Q \begin{bmatrix} e^{\lambda t} & -(\lambda^2 + 1)te^{\lambda t} \\ 0 & e^{\lambda t} \end{bmatrix} Q^T \begin{bmatrix} f_1 \\ f_0 \end{bmatrix}$$

where $\lambda_+ = \lambda_- = \lambda$ and Q are from Exercise(5.4) lead directly to (5.63)

6.5.1 Sample Test 1 Solutions

1. The equation $A\vec{p}_1 = \begin{bmatrix} -1 & 3+3i \\ 3-3i & 2 \end{bmatrix} \begin{bmatrix} 1+i \\ 2 \end{bmatrix} = 5 \begin{bmatrix} 1+i \\ 2 \end{bmatrix}$ implies $5 \in \sigma(A)$ and

   $\begin{bmatrix} 1+i \\ 2 \end{bmatrix}$ is a corresponding eigenvector. (a) Since it is given that $-4 \in \sigma(A)$, solve

   $(A+4I)\vec{p}_2 = \begin{bmatrix} 3 & 3+3i \\ 3-3i & 6 \end{bmatrix} = \begin{bmatrix} 0 \\ 0 \end{bmatrix}$ for $\vec{p}_2 = \begin{bmatrix} 1+i \\ -1 \end{bmatrix}$ for a second independent

   eigenvector. (b) The length squared is $||\vec{p}_1||^2 = \sqrt{\vec{p}_1^* \vec{p}_1} = [\,1-i \;\; 2\,] \begin{bmatrix} 1+i \\ 2 \end{bmatrix} = 2+4 =$

   6 so $||\vec{p}_1|| = \sqrt{6}$. (c) In a similar calculation, $||\vec{p}_2||^2 = \sqrt{\vec{p}_2^* \vec{p}_2} = [\,1-i \;\; -1\,] \begin{bmatrix} 1-i \\ -1 \end{bmatrix} =$

   3. (d) The dot product $\vec{p}_1 \cdot \vec{p}_2 = \vec{p}_1^* \vec{p}_2 = [\,1-i \;\; 2\,] \begin{bmatrix} 1+i \\ -1 \end{bmatrix} 2-2 = 0$. (e) An orthogonal

   diagonalizer for A is defined by the matrix $Q = \begin{bmatrix} \dfrac{\vec{p}_1}{||\vec{p}_1||} & \dfrac{\vec{p}_1}{||\vec{p}_1||} \end{bmatrix}$.

2. Assume that A is 5×5 and $\sigma(A) = \{\lambda_1, \lambda_2, \lambda_3, \lambda_4, \lambda_5\}$. (a) If A is invertible then A is diagonalizable is **False** and (b) if A is diagonalizable then A is invertible is also **False**. (c) If $\lambda_j \neq \lambda_k$ for all $j \neq k$ then the matrix A is diagonalizable is **True**. (d) If $\lambda_j \neq \lambda_k$ for all $j \neq k$ then the matrix A is invertible is **False**. and (e) if A is invertible then $\lambda_j \neq 0$ for $j = 1, 2, 3, 4, 5$ is **True**.

3. Since (a) $\det[A - \lambda I] = \begin{vmatrix} 2-\lambda & 1 \\ -1 & 4-\lambda \end{vmatrix} = (2-\lambda)(4-\lambda)+1 = \lambda^2 - 6\lambda + 9 = (\lambda-3)^2 = 0$,

   the eigenvalue(s) of A is $\lambda_1 = \lambda_2 = 3$. (b) The only eigenvector for A is found by

   solving $[A - 3I]\vec{p}_1 = \begin{bmatrix} -1 & 1 \\ -1 & 1 \end{bmatrix} \vec{p}_1 = \vec{0}$ so $\vec{p}_1 = \begin{bmatrix} 1 \\ 1 \end{bmatrix}$. (c) Since the the rank of the

   matrix $[A-3I]$ is one, the dimension theorem implies that $\dim \mathcal{N}(A-3I) = 1$ so there is not a second independent eigenvector. Hence the matrix A **is not** diagonalizable

4. The eigenvalues of the matrix $\mathcal{O} = \begin{bmatrix} 0 & 0 \\ 0 & 0 \end{bmatrix}$ are $\lambda_1 = \lambda_2 = 0$ and this matrix

   is orthogonally diagonalizable since $\mathcal{O}$ is **<u>symmetric</u>**. The orthogonal matrix $\begin{bmatrix} 1 & 0 \\ 0 & 1 \end{bmatrix}$

   (one can write down any orthogonal matrix here) diagonalizes $\mathcal{O}$.

5. (a) Since $A\vec{p}_1 = \begin{bmatrix} 6 & -2 & -1 \\ -2 & 6 & -1 \\ -1 & -1 & 5 \end{bmatrix} \begin{bmatrix} 1 \\ 1 \\ 1 \end{bmatrix} = \begin{bmatrix} 3 \\ 3 \\ 3 \end{bmatrix} = 3 \begin{bmatrix} 1 \\ 1 \\ 1 \end{bmatrix}$ the number $\lambda_1 = 3$ is

   an eigenvalue of A and (b) $A\vec{p}_2 = \begin{bmatrix} 6 & -2 & -1 \\ -2 & 6 & -1 \\ -1 & -1 & 5 \end{bmatrix} \begin{bmatrix} 1 \\ -1 \\ 0 \end{bmatrix} = \begin{bmatrix} 8 \\ -8 \\ 0 \end{bmatrix} = 8 \begin{bmatrix} 1 \\ -1 \\ 0 \end{bmatrix}$

shows that $\lambda_2 = 8$ is an eigenvalue of A. (c) The characteristic equation for A is $\rho_A(\lambda) = -(\lambda - \lambda_2)(\lambda - 6)(\lambda - \lambda_1)$ so it follows that a third eigenvalue for A is $\lambda_3 = 6$. (d) A third (independent) eigenvector for A is found from $[A - 6I] = \begin{bmatrix} 0 & -2 & -1 \\ -2 & 0 & -1 \\ -1 & -1 & -1 \end{bmatrix} = \begin{bmatrix} 0 \\ 0 \\ 0 \end{bmatrix}$ is given by $\vec{p}_3 = \begin{bmatrix} 1 \\ 1 \\ -2 \end{bmatrix}$.

6. Since A is invertible, no $\lambda_j, j = 1, 2$ and 3 is zero. Take the inverse of the equation $P^{-1}AP = \Lambda = \begin{bmatrix} \lambda_1 & 0 & 0 \\ 0 & \lambda_2 & 0 \\ 0 & 0 & \lambda_3 \end{bmatrix}$ to find $(P^{-1}AP)^{-1} = \Lambda^{-1} = \begin{bmatrix} 1/\lambda_1 & 0 & 0 \\ 0 & 1/\lambda_2 & 0 \\ 0 & 0 & 1/\lambda_3 \end{bmatrix}$.

Using part 4 of Theorem(3.12) to write $(P^{-1}AP)^{-1} = P^{-1}A^{-1}(P^{-1})^{-1} = P^{-1}A^{-1}P$. Hence $P = \hat{P}$ is also the diagonalizer of A^{-1}. It is equaivalent to multiply both sides of the equation $A\vec{p}_j = \lambda_j \vec{p}_j$ for $j = 1, 2, 3$ by A^{-1} and $1/\lambda_j$ to find $(1/\lambda_j)\vec{p}_j = A^{-1}\vec{p}_j$ which shows that the $\vec{p}_j$ are the eigenvectors for A^{-1} with corresponing eigenvalue $1/\lambda_j$.

6.5.2   Sample Test 2 Solutions

1. (a) Since $A = \begin{bmatrix} 3 & -2 & 1 \\ 0 & 2 & 0 \\ 0 & 1 & 2 \end{bmatrix}$ then $\rho_A(\lambda) = (-1)(\lambda - 2)^2(\lambda - 3)$, it follows that $\sigma(A) = \{2, 2, 3\}$. (b) The algebraic multiplicity of $\lambda = 2$ is **two** and the algebraic multiplicity $\lambda = 3$ is **one**. The geometric multiplicity of $\lambda = 3$ is **one** since the eigenvalue is simple. Since the rank of $[A - 2I] = \begin{bmatrix} 1 & -2 & 1 \\ 0 & 0 & 0 \\ 0 & 1 & 0 \end{bmatrix}$ is two it follows (the dimension theorem) $\dim \mathcal{N}(A - 2I) = 3 - 2 = 1$ so the geometric multiplicity of $\lambda = 2$ is **one**. Since this is less then its algebraic multiplicity the matrix is A not diagonalizable.

2. Let A be a real 4×4 matrix and denote its set of eigenvalues by $\sigma(A) = \{\lambda_1, \lambda_2, \lambda_3, \lambda_4\}$ (a) If $\lambda_j \neq 0$ for $j = 1, 2, 3$, and 4 then A is invertible is **True** and (b) if A is diagonalizable then $\lambda_j \neq 0, j = 1, 2, 3, 4$ is **False**. (c) The eigenvalues of A^T are also $\{\lambda_1, \lambda_2, \lambda_3, \lambda_4\}$ is **True**. (d) Since $A\vec{0} = \vec{0}$ the zero vector, $\vec{0}$, is an eigenvector for A is **False**. (e) If $\vec{p} \neq \vec{0}$ and $A\vec{p} = \vec{0}$ then $\lambda = 0$ is an eigenvalue of A is **True**. (f) If $\lambda_1 = \lambda_2 = \lambda_3 \neq \lambda_4$ and $\dim(\mathcal{N}(A - \lambda_1 I)) = 3$ then A is diagonalizable is **True**. (g) If the rank of A is four then A is diagonalizable is **False**. (h) If the rank of A is two and A has four independent eigenvectors then A is diagonalizable is **True**. (i) An invertible matrix is diagonalizable is **False** (j) A diagonalizable matrix is invertible is **False**.

3. The given information

$$A = \begin{bmatrix} 1 & -1 & -1 \\ -1 & 1 & -1 \\ -1 & -1 & 1 \end{bmatrix} = P\Lambda P^{-1}$$

$$= \begin{bmatrix} 1 & 0 & -2 \\ 1 & 1 & 1 \\ 1 & -1 & 1 \end{bmatrix} \begin{bmatrix} -1 & 0 & 0 \\ 0 & 2 & 0 \\ 0 & 0 & 2 \end{bmatrix} \left(\frac{1}{6} \begin{bmatrix} 2 & 2 & 2 \\ 0 & 3 & -3 \\ -2 & 1 & 1 \end{bmatrix} \right).$$

and label the eigenvalues of A by $\lambda_1 < \lambda_2 = \lambda_3$ show that (a) the Spectrum of A is $\sigma(A) = \left\{ \lambda_1 = -1, \lambda_2 = \lambda_3 = 2 \right\}$. The algebraic multiplicity of λ_1 is is **one** and the algebraic multiplicity of λ_2 is **two**. The geometric multiplicity of λ_1 is **one** and the geometric multiplicity of λ_2 is **two**. The matrix A is called **diagonalizable** the

matrix $Q = \left[\frac{1}{\sqrt{3}} \begin{bmatrix} 1 \\ 1 \\ 1 \end{bmatrix} \frac{1}{\sqrt{2}} \begin{bmatrix} 0 \\ 1 \\ -1 \end{bmatrix} \frac{1}{\sqrt{6}} \begin{bmatrix} -2 \\ 1 \\ 1 \end{bmatrix} \right]$ **is an orthogonal diagonalizable**

for A.

4. The eigenvalues for $A = \begin{bmatrix} -2 & 3 \\ 1 & 0 \end{bmatrix}$ are found from

$$\det(A - \lambda I) = \det\left(\begin{bmatrix} -2-\lambda & 3 \\ 1 & -\lambda \end{bmatrix}\right) = (-2-\lambda)(-\lambda) - 3 = \lambda^2 + 2\lambda - 3$$

$$= (\lambda + 3)(\lambda - 1) = 0$$

so that $\lambda_1 = -3$ and $\lambda_2 = 1$. Solving $(A - \lambda_j I)\vec{p}_j = \vec{0}, j = 1,2$ yields $\vec{p}_1 = \begin{bmatrix} 3 \\ -1 \end{bmatrix}$

and $\vec{p}_2 = \begin{bmatrix} 1 \\ 1 \end{bmatrix}$ so $P = \begin{bmatrix} 3 & 1 \\ -1 & 1 \end{bmatrix}$ and $P^{-1} = \frac{1}{4}\begin{bmatrix} 1 & -1 \\ 1 & 3 \end{bmatrix}$ and $P^{-1}AP \equiv \Lambda = $

$\begin{bmatrix} -3 & 0 \\ 0 & 1 \end{bmatrix}$. Each of $A = P\Lambda P^{-1}$, $A^2 = P\Lambda^2 P^{-1}$. and $A^n = P\Lambda^n P^{-1}$ are **True**.

5. Set $u_n = c_n$ and $v_n = c_{n-1}$ so that $u_1 = c_1 = 2$ and $v_1 = c_0 = 1$ in the Cooter quantities

$$c_{n+1} = -2c_n + 3c_{n-1}, \quad \text{with} \quad c_0 = 1 \quad \text{and} \quad c_1 = 2.$$

to find $u_{n+1} = c_{n+1} = -2u_n + 3v_n$ and $v_{n+1} = c_n = v_n$ so that

$$\begin{bmatrix} u_{n+1} \\ v_{n+1} \end{bmatrix} = \begin{bmatrix} -2 & 3 \\ 1 & 0 \end{bmatrix}\begin{bmatrix} u_n \\ v_n \end{bmatrix} = A\begin{bmatrix} u_n \\ v_n \end{bmatrix} = A^n\begin{bmatrix} u_1 \\ v_1 \end{bmatrix} = P\Lambda^n P^{-1}\begin{bmatrix} u_1 \\ v_1 \end{bmatrix}.$$

Use the result from problem #4, to find $v_{n+1} = c_n = \dfrac{5 - (-3)^n}{4}$.

Index